Ed Berghorn

60 — 24
$14.87

60 24
$ 9.37

7.50

BUCKLING STRENGTH OF METAL STRUCTURES

ENGINEERING SOCIETIES MONOGRAPHS

Bakhmeteff: *Hydraulics of Open Channels*
Bleich: *Buckling Strength of Metal Structures*
Crandall: *Engineering Analysis*
Elevatorski: *Hydraulic Energy Dissipators*
Leontovich: *Frames and Arches*
Nadai: *Theory of Flow and Fracture of Solids*
Timoshenko and Gere: *Theory of Elastic Stability*
Timoshenko and Goodier: *Theory of Elasticity*
Timoshenko and Woinowsky-Krieger: *Theory of Plates and Shells*

Five national engineering societies, the American Society of Civil Engineers, the American Institute of Mining, Metallurgical, and Petroleum Engineers, the American Society of Mechanical Engineers, the American Institute of Electrical Engineers, and the American Institute of Chemical Engineers, have an arrangement with the McGraw-Hill Book Company, Inc., for the production of a series of selected books adjudged to possess usefulness for engineers and industry.

The purposes of this arrangement are: to provide monographs of high technical quality within the field of engineering; to rescue from obscurity important technical manuscripts which might not be published commercially because of too limited sale without special introduction; to develop manuscripts to fill gaps in existing literature; to collect into one volume scattered information of especial timeliness on a given subject.

The societies assume no responsibility for any statements made in these books. Each book before publication has, however, been examined by one or more representatives of the societies competent to express an opinion on the merits of the manuscript.

Ralph H. Phelps, CHAIRMAN
Engineering Societies Library
New York

ENGINEERING SOCIETIES MONOGRAPHS COMMITTEE

A. S. C. E.

Howard T. Critchlow
H. Alden Foster

A. I. M. E.

Nathaniel Arbiter
John F. Elliott

A. S. M. E.

Calvin S. Cronan
Raymond D. Mindlin

A. I. E. E.

F. Malcolm Farmer
Royal W. Sorensen

A. I. Ch. E.

Joseph F. Skelly
Charles E. Reed

BUCKLING STRENGTH

OF

METAL STRUCTURES

By

FRIEDRICH BLEICH

Late Consulting Engineer

With the Collaboration of

Commander Lyle B. Ramsey, USN

Edited by

Hans H. Bleich

Associate Professor of Civil
Engineering, Columbia University

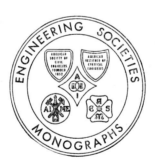

McGRAW-HILL BOOK COMPANY

NEW YORK   TORONTO   LONDON

1952

FOREWORD

For many years naval architects and engineers, who have worked on ship design, have urgently needed dependable data on the behavior of fabricated steel structure under compression loading. To obtain pertinent information and assemble it in a single publication, the Bureau of Ships, through the David Taylor Model Basin, and Frankland and Lienhard, Consulting Engineers of New York, has sponsored this excellent work by Dr. Friedrich Bleich. Dr. Bleich, with the cooperation of the Column Research Council, has assembled all available data on this subject, has appraised it and selected the most useful and applicable methods of analysis for inclusion in this book, and has supplemented this work by suggestions and recommendations of members of the staff of the David Taylor Model Basin and the Bureau of Ships to provide this up-to-date treatise on the buckling strength of metal structures. To make this work available to all who may have need for it, the Bureau of Ships of the Navy Department releases this work for publication in cooperation with the Engineering Foundation, the Column Research Council, and the Engineering Societies Monographs Committee.

C. O. KELL
Rear Admiral, USN
Commanding Officer and Director
David Taylor Model Basin

EDITOR'S PREFACE

The present volume is the outcome of a survey of the literature on the subject made by the author. It is, however, not simply a compilation of results from all sources. After critical evaluation which eliminated obsolete or erroneous theories, the author attempted to select the most useful and practically applicable methods and weld them into a unit suitable for presentation. Alternative approaches to the solution of important problems were naturally considered, but for the multitude of minor problems it was at times necessary to select but one among a number of methods of equal merit, and the book does not, therefore, claim completeness. The choice between alternative methods was of necessity influenced by the purely pedagogic advantage of using similar approaches in the solution of several problems.

In reviewing the many research papers in the literature the author frequently found that many investigations had not been carried far enough to be useful for actual design in engineering offices, mainly for one or both of the following reasons: (1) The results were too complicated for practical use, and tables or graphs showing results were not prepared, or could not be prepared because of the large number of variables. (2) All too often theoretical papers considered only the cases of stability in the elastic range, and results were therefore not applicable in the inelastic range, which with advances and improvements in methods of analysis and with the increasing use of high-strength alloys is becoming of increasing importance in structural and naval construction.

The author considered it to be one of his principal tasks to rectify this situation wherever it occurred by simplifying available theories to make them practically useful, by providing numerous tables or approximate formulas, and, particularly, by extending theories of elastic buckling into the inelastic range. To achieve this end much original work by the author was required, which is being presented for the first time in this volume.

The presentation throughout concentrates on problems frequently encountered in the design of engineering and naval structures, and tables and approximate formulas have been devised in a form suitable for use in design offices; they are generally applicable not only to steel but also to light alloys, making the volume also of interest to aeronautical engineers. The book, however, does not treat many of the special problems which are due to the lightweight construction necessary in air frames, because such special problems have been considered outside the scope of this work. Also, in certain questions aeronautical engineering philosophy differs from that of structural engineers or naval architects; in such cases the latter's viewpoint was adopted.

The volume is intended for classroom or self-study by advanced students and research workers, and also for use by practicing engineers engaged in actual design of engineering structures or ships' hulls.

The editor takes this opportunity to thank all those who have assisted in various ways in the preparation of this volume. Particularly, he wishes to acknowledge the decisive part which the late Dr. D. F. Windenburg had in initiating and planning the work leading to this volume, to thank Mr. F. H. Frankland for his assistance in proofreading and his many efforts in furthering the book in all its stages, and to thank Dr. William R. Osgood for his constructive criticisms and valuable advice on many questions. The editor is also very grateful for the many suggestions received from members of the Column Research Council who reviewed the original reports on which this book is based.

HANS H. BLEICH

NEW YORK, N.Y.
September, 1951

CONTENTS

CHAPTER III
BUCKLING OF CENTRALLY LOADED COLUMNS BY TORSION AND FLEXURE

CHAPTER IV
LATERAL BUCKLING OF BEAMS

CHAPTER V
BUILT-UP COLUMNS AND COLUMNS OF VARIABLE STIFFNESS

CHAPTER VI
THE STABILITY OF FRAMEWORKS

CHAPTER VII

THE EFFECTIVE LENGTH OF COMPRESSION MEMBERS IN TRUSSES AND THE STABILITY OF RIGID-FRAME STRUCTURES

CHAPTER VIII

STABILITY OF AXIALLY COMPRESSED BARS ELASTICALLY SUPPORTED AT SPECIFIC POINTS

CHAPTER IX

LOCAL BUCKLING OF PLATE ELEMENTS OF COLUMNS

Chapter x
Rectangular Plates with Longitudinal Stiffeners

Chapter xi
Stability of Web Plates of Girders

Chapter xii
Special Problems in the Design of Ship Plating

CHAPTER I

BUCKLING OF CENTRALLY OR ECCENTRICALLY LOADED COLUMNS

1. Introduction

No other field in the study of strength of materials has such a varied history as the theory of the buckling strength of compression members in metal structures. Even today, in spite of the numerous investigations of past decades, research in this specialized field has by no means reached finality. Since the beginning of this century substantial progress has been made in solving theoretically many complex problems, but a majority of these theoretical solutions still remain to be verified by experimental research so that they may be included among our assured scientific assets.

The causes of the difficulties encountered in research on the problem of buckling are due partly to the peculiarities of the problem itself and partly to the peculiarities of the material from which metal structures are made. Structural design normally is concerned with the determination of stresses based upon the tacit assumption that stable equilibrium exists between internal and external forces. That is to say, the equilibrium is such that, within certain limits, any slight change of the loading condition does not produce disproportionate increase of the stresses or elastic distortions of the system. Hence, adherence to a certain stress—the allowable stress—determines the degree of safety of the structure. The buckling problem presents an entirely new aspect—the investigation of the potential unstable equilibrium between the external loading and the internal response of the structure. An added complication is the fact that the buckling phenomenon in general is controlled by the entire complex stress-strain relationship of the material under consideration, resulting in many difficulties in the field of theoretical as well as experimental research.

In judging column strength it is not a question of avoiding a certain stress in the structure or in one of its members by an adequate margin, but of preventing the occurrence of a peculiar condition of unstable equilibrium. This condition is characterized by disproportionately large increases, indeterminate as to magnitude, to which deformations and stresses are subject at slight increases in load.   In this more or less sudden breakdown of the internal resistance lies the characteristic feature of the buckling phenomenon, regardless of whether at the instant of failure the elastic limit is exceeded or not.   Hence the problem of buckling of metal structures must be conceived as a problem of stability.   The chief cause of the errors and unsuccessful attempts of investigators during the nineteenth century was the lack of appreciation of this fact; they tried in vain to determine column strength by consideration of flexural stresses in a condition of stable equilibrium.   This view retarded the solution of the problem of column strength, although Euler,[1] who was the first to occupy himself with the column problem, pointed to the real nature of the problem and to the right path to its theoretical solution.   Euler's conclusions were confirmed and extended by Lagrange (1770), who presented an improved analysis.

The failure of Euler's formula in the case of short and medium-length columns was the primary cause of its almost complete abandonment, together with the reasoning by which it was derived.   It was not recognized clearly enough that the observed discrepancies had their origin in the fact that the elastic limit was exceeded before the occurrence of buckling.   This fact naturally was not taken into account by Euler's theory in its original form.

In the third chapter of his book "Columns," Salmon[2] gives a lively account of the confusion which, during the nineteenth century, governed all attempts to reconcile Euler's theory with the facts observed in column tests.

It was the Belgian investigator E. Lamarle who, as early as 1845, had established the elastic limit as the limit of validity of Euler's formula. However, he, too, had no clear insight into the behavior of columns stressed beyond the elastic limit before buckling.   We quote Salmon:

"He [Lamarle] showed that if the ideal column bends, the material in the most highly stressed fibre would immediately pass the elastic limit.   Euler's limit load may therefore be looked upon not only as the load corresponding to the first deflection, but as the failure load to the specimen.   Further, if the elastic limit load is less than the Euler load the ideal column will fail by direct compression rather than by bending.   This condition determines the value of l/r below which Euler's formula is not applicable."

It was not until 1889 that Considère in France and Engesser in Germany, independently of each other, proclaimed the unlimited validity of

[1] Euler, Leonhard, "De curvis elasticis," Lausanne and Geneva, 1744.   The Euler formula was derived in a later paper, Sur la force de colonnes, published 1759 in the Mémoires de l'Académie de Berlin.

[2] Salmon, E. H., "Columns," Oxford Technical Publications, London, 1921.

Euler's formula, though in generalized form.[1] Engesser[2] published his complete double-modulus theory in 1895. His theoretical studies, however, received scant notice until Kármán[3] performed a series of very careful tests designed to show that Engesser's assumptions were correct. The importance of the work of Engesser and Kármán lies primarily in the fact that a general solution of the column problem, considered as a stability problem, was achieved in a rational manner, taking into account the elastic and plastic properties of the material from which the column is made. Moreover, Engesser's theory and Kármán's tests supplied the fundamentals for a theoretical treatment of all kinds of problems in the field of buckling.

It is obvious that a numerical determination of certain empirical values is necessary for the practical application of the results of the above-mentioned theoretical investigations. These numerical data may be represented by a column formula derived from careful tests on centrally loaded columns or from the compressive stress-strain diagram of the material. By starting, therefore, with the theoretical reasoning of Engesser and Kármán, and by using a column formula (or a table or diagram based on such a formula) as the proper expression of those empirical values which characterize the material, it is now possible, with a prospect of success, to discuss and solve theoretically even difficult problems in the entire elastic and inelastic range of buckling. In this sense Considère's and Engesser's conception and Kármán's experimental studies may be considered milestones in the long history of the buckling problem.

Theoretically, every elastic system, under certain loading conditions, may pass into an unstable state of equilibrium. However, the fact that the modulus of elasticity of metal structures is large compared with the elastic limit of the material renders it probable that only when considerable elastic deformation can occur before the elastic limit is reached will structural members become unstable in the elastic range. This will be the case where at least one or two dimensions of the compression member are relatively small in comparison with the third one, as, for instance, with slender columns, or thin plates or shells. But owing to the rapid decrease of the modulus of elasticity upon passing the elastic limit, the entire range of systems which may become unstable under conventional loading conditions is greatly extended. The partial breakdown of the

---

[1] Considère, A., Resistance des pièces comprimées, *Congrès international de procedés de construction*, 1889. Engesser, F., *Zeitschrift für Architektur und Ingenieurwesen*, 1889, p. 455.

[2] Engesser, F., *Schweizerische Bauzeitung*, Vol. 26, p. 24, 1895.

[3] v. Kármán, T., Die Knickfestigkeit gerader Stäbe, *Physikalische Zeitschrift*, Vol. 9, p. 136, 1908; and Untersuchungen über Knickfestigkeit, *Mitteilungen über Forschungsarbeiten auf dem Gebiete des Ingenieurwesens*, No. 81, Berlin, 1910.

internal structure of the material, after passing the elastic limit, accel-
erates the inception of the critical state of buckling. This fact explains
the controlling position which problems of stability occupy in the design
of metal structures.

After these brief introductory and historical remarks, the essence and
nature of the buckling phenomenon will be demonstrated in the following
article by means of the basic problem, the elastic buckling of straight
slender columns. In Arts. 3 to 6 the phenomenon of instability of
columns which fail beyond the elastic limit will be discussed.

2. Elastic Buckling of Straight Columns

Consider a perfectly elastic slender column of constant cross section,
originally perfectly straight, acted upon by a longitudinal force P applied
along the centroidal axis of the member (Fig. 1). Let
there be also a transverse load which, acting alone, would
produce the moment m_x at the point x. The total bending moment at x will be

$$M_x = Py + m_x$$

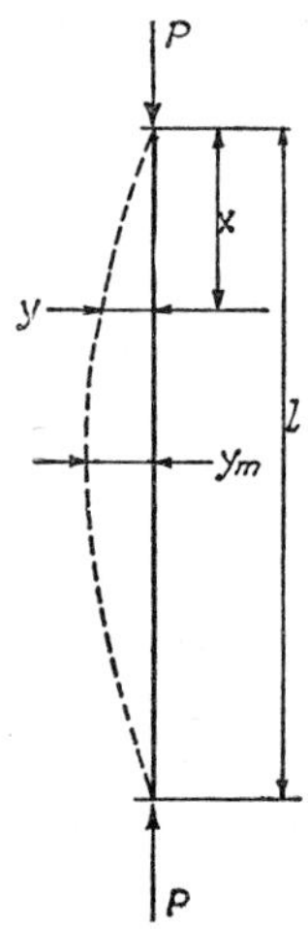

Let the plane of bending coincide with the plane of the
minimum moment of inertia I of the cross sections of the
column. Under the assumption of small deflections y,
the differential equation of the elastic curve of the deflected column is

$$EI \frac{d^2y}{dx^2} + Py + m_x = 0 \qquad (1)$$

We now consider a case in which the column is simply
supported (free to rotate at the ends) and m_x is caused
by a small concentrated transverse load Q acting at the
middle of the column. Noting $m_x = Qx/2$ and $\alpha = \sqrt{P/EI}$, the
expression

$$y = \frac{m_x}{P} \left(\frac{\sin \alpha x}{\alpha x \cos \dfrac{\alpha l}{2}} - 1 \right) \qquad (2)$$

Fig. 1

is a solution of Eq. (1), valid for the upper half of the bar, $0 \leq x \leq l/2$.
Equation (2) will satisfy the differential equation (1) as long as the disturbing moment m_x is other than zero. For small values of P, the factor
$\cos (\alpha l/2)$, in Eq. (2) is only slightly different from unity, but as P (and
consequently α) increases, the value of the fraction in Eq. (2) will likewise
increase, growing in magnitude very rapidly when $\alpha l/2$ approaches
$\pi/2$. Thus y will increase gradually, until, when αl approaches π, it
increases beyond limit. The column has already buckled. From

$\alpha l = l \sqrt{P/EI} = \pi$ follows Euler's formula for the upper limit P_E of the buckling load:

$$P_E = \frac{\pi^2 EI}{l^2} \tag{3}$$

The smaller the moment m_x, the closer is the load P under which the column fails to the Euler load P_E.

Now let us consider the case where the disturbing moment vanishes. When $m_x = 0$, Eq. (1) reduces to a homogeneous differential equation having the solution $y = 0$ for any arbitrary value of P. The column remains straight. Beside this trivial solution of the homogeneous differential equation there exists a system of so-called characteristic solutions

$$y = C \sin n \frac{\pi x}{l} \tag{4}$$

pertaining to the characteristic values of $P = n^2 \pi^2 EI / l^2$, where n is an integer and C an arbitrary constant. Of these solutions, only the smallest one with $n = 1$, furnishing $P = P_E$, and the solution $P = 0$ have any significance, since the configuration of the column corresponding to other values of n can exist only under certain artificial circumstances, which need not be considered. In the absence of a disturbing moment the column remains straight at any value of $P < P_E$; when $P = P_E$, it bends in a sine curve of indeterminate amplitude C. Thus the Euler load P_E may be defined as the smallest load which can keep the column in slightly bent shape.

Summing up, we may therefore state that a centrally loaded, perfectly straight column will behave as follows:

If the column carries an axial load P smaller than the critical load P_E, it will remain straight. If a disturbing moment m_x is added, it will deflect and the magnitude of this deflection is given by Eq. (2). If the moment m_x ceases to act, the column will resume its straight position. External and internal forces are in stable equilibrium. In the absence of a transverse load, a deflected state, a sine curve of indeterminate amplitude, is possible if P becomes equal to P_E, but the slightest disturbing moment will suffice to cause an indefinitely large deflection of the column, which will not return to its original condition when the disturbing moment is removed. The case is one of unstable equilibrium between the internal and external forces. The critical load P_E thus characterizes a point of instability in the behavior of the column.

These remarkable findings, however, are partially the result of a mathematical fiction, since the differential equation (1), from which the foregoing conclusions were drawn, describes the behavior of a deflected column only approximately. Starting the investigation with the true equation for the elastic curve,

$$\frac{EI}{\rho} = -M_x$$

where ρ represents the radius of curvature of the distorted axis of the column, the value y_m for the deflection at the middle of the column with vanishing transverse load takes the more accurate form

$$y_m = \frac{2l}{\pi} \sqrt{\frac{P_E}{P}} \left(\sqrt{\frac{P}{P_E}} - 1 \right) \tag{5}$$

P and P_E having the same meaning as in the foregoing.[1]

As long as $P < P_E$, y_m will be imaginary; there will be no real deflection, and the column remains straight. Even when $P = P_E$, we obtain $y_m = 0$, and the column undergoes no distortion. Only when $P > P_E$ does there occur a finite deflection determinate as to magnitude. However, as may be easily computed, a very slight increase of P beyond P_E will be sufficient to cause an appreciable deflection. Although P_E may be only slightly exceeded, deflections occur which are dangerous to the existence of the column.

For example, if we let $P/P_E = 1.001$, it follows that $y_m = 0.0142l$. For a column, say, of $l/r = 120$ and $c/r = 2$ (where c is the distance of the extreme fiber from the axis of the column), the maximum fiber stress will be $\sigma = 3.41 P_E/A$ (A is the area of the cross section). Accordingly, an increase over the critical load P_E of $1/1,000$ of its value will be sufficient to raise the extreme fiber stress to 3.41 times the buckling stress P_E/A, a stress which mild steel is unable to withstand. Therefore, the column will fail somewhat earlier.

Likewise it can be shown that, when $P = P_E$, a sufficiently small disturbing moment can still be carried; when $P = P_E$, the column is merely very sensitive to disturbances, reacting to them with finite but very large deflections.

Practically speaking, therefore, the result of a more accurate study is the same as that obtained in the foregoing. After Euler's buckling load has been reached, the behavior of the column becomes uncertain, and extremely small excesses of this load or very slight disturbances will cause failure. The more accurate analysis shows only that between P_E and the actual load which produces a certain finite deflection there is a narrow zone of transition, through the existence of which any unnatural discontinuity in the behavior of the column near the buckling limit is avoided. In the formulas initially derived, this transitional zone, owing to the neglect of certain terms of higher order in the basic equation, shrinks to a

[1] Grashof, F., Theorie der Elasticität und Festigkeit, 2d ed., p. 168, Berlin, 1878.

point of discontinuity. We are concerned only with determining the critical load P_E at which the behavior of the column changes more or less suddenly. More precisely, we wish to establish the conditions for the inception of buckling but are not concerned with the action of buckling itself. In order to simplify the analysis we employ the fiction of a column which fails abruptly. Thus, we may base the investigation on the linear differential equation

$$EI \frac{d^2y}{dx^2} + Py = 0 \tag{6}$$

which is exact for the limiting case of infinitesimally small deflections y. This fact explains why Eq. (6) and the refined equation

$$\frac{EI}{\rho} + Py = 0$$

yield the same value P_E for the buckling load.

The above reasoning leads to a criterion of instability (buckling) which may be expressed in the following way: Upon reaching the critical load P_E there are two equilibrium positions possible, the straight form and a deflected form infinitesimally near to it, both under the same axial load P_E. We are speaking of a "bifurcation of the equilibrium position" and consider such a bifurcation as the criterion of instability.

Transforming Eq. (3) by dividing by the cross-sectional area and replacing the moment of inertia I by Ar^2, r denoting the radius of gyration, this equation may be written in the form

$$\frac{P_E}{A} = \frac{\pi^2 E}{(l/r)^2} \tag{7}$$

where l/r is the slenderness ratio.

Euler's formula (3) and therefore Eq. (7) have been derived under the tacit assumption that the modulus of elasticity E is invariable. Accordingly, Eq. (7) is valid only when the modulus E does not change its value before buckling occurs; i.e., Eq. (7) is valid only as long as P_E/A remains below the elastic limit. This condition restricts the applicability of Eq. (7) to the so-called elastic range of buckling and confines the validity of this equation to a slenderness ratio l/r above a certain limiting value which depends on the properties of the material of the column. It is nearly incomprehensible that a century had to elapse, from Euler to Lamarle, before this fundamental fact was conceived.

So far we have considered only columns simply supported at each end. A column with elastically restrained or fixed ends exhibits essentially the same behavior, so that it is permissible to extend the foregoing conclusions to the more general cases. We may write Eq. (7) in a generalized form, using the symbol σ_c (critical stress) for P_c/A (P_c is the critical load or buckling load):

$$\sigma_c = \frac{\pi^2 E}{(kl/r)^2} \tag{8}$$

wherein the dimensionless factor k indicates the effect of the end conditions upon the critical load. kl is referred to as the "effective length" or "free length."

In the subsequent discussion the case $k = 1$ will be referred to as the fundamental case of buckling and the associated critical stress σ_c will be denoted σ_E.

The value of the buckling load P_E determined from Euler's formula (3) naturally can never be reached in actual conditions, since no absolutely straight column exists and since no loads are ever applied exactly along the centroidal axis in the manner assumed by the theory. Nevertheless, in careful tests on small specimens, eliminating disturbing moments as far as possible, investigators have found the observed buckling loads so close to the theoretical loads P_E that the experimental error actually shrinks into insignificance.

3. Inelastic Buckling of Straight Columns

The considerations outlined in the preceding article were based on the assumption that the critical stress, *i.e.*, the compressive stress uniformly distributed over the cross section, would still be below the elastic limit at the instant when equilibrium becomes unstable. This, however, is true only of slender columns. In shorter columns the elastic limit is exceeded before inception of buckling, and the modulus of elasticity E, hitherto constant, becomes a function of the critical stress $\sigma_c = P_c/A$.

Considère and Engesser were the first to realize the possibility of utilizing Euler's formula for the inelastic zone of buckling by introducing a variable modulus of elasticity. Engesser[1] presented his tangent-modulus theory in 1889, at about the same time as Considère[2] predicted, in a lecture before an international congress in Paris, that column strength in the case of inelastic buckling may be determined by a generalized Euler formula, $\pi^2 \bar{E} I/l^2$, in which the variable modulus $\bar{E}$ lies between Young's modulus and the tangent-modulus. While Considère did not present any theory to determine the actual value of $\bar{E}$, he already recognized that, as an axially loaded column stressed beyond the proportional limit starts to bend, the stresses on the concave side increase according to the law of the compressive stress-strain curve whereas the stresses on

---

[1] Engesser, F., *Zeitschrift für Architektur und Ingenieurwesen*, 1889, p. 455.

[2] Considère, A., Resistance des pièces comprimées, *Congrès international des procédés de construction*, Vol. 3, p. 371, Paris, 1891.

the convex side decrease proportionally to the strain.[1] Engesser later acknowledged Considère's concept and in 1895 gave an improved solution of the column problem in the inelastic range of buckling, the double-modulus theory.[2]

No further progress was made until 1908, when Kármán[3] took up the question of column action in the inelastic range. He presented Engesser's theory anew, basing it on results of tests made by Meyer,[4] who proved that the principles of the conventional theory of bending (assumptions 2 and 3 in Art. 4) also remain valid after the bending stresses exceed the proportional limit. In 1910 Kármán gave the theory real life by a series of careful experiments on small specimens of rectangular cross section.

It is of interest to mention that Southwell, apparently without knowledge of Engesser's and Kármán's work, presented in 1912 the double-modulus theory in his paper "The Strength of Struts."[5]

The double-modulus theory since then has been accepted as the true theory of column action in the inelastic range. However, in more recent time some doubt has been raised as to the correctness of the double-modulus concept. Data from tests made on specimens of various shapes of cross section indicate that the actual buckling loads lie between the values computed from Engesser's tangent-modulus theory and the values predicted by the double-modulus theory, usually closer to the tangent-modulus load. In a recently published paper, Shanley[6] discusses the necessity of revising the double-modulus theory and advances an improved concept which finally leads to a just appreciation of Engesser's original tangent-modulus theory.

In the following, the double-modulus theory and Engesser's earlier tangent-modulus theory will be presented and the significance of both concepts for the actual correlation of the stress-strain curve with the critical column load will be discussed in the light of Shanley's improved theory.

4. The Double-modulus Theory of Inelastic Buckling[7]

We shall now attempt to follow, as in the analysis of the perfectly elastic column, the process of bending as equilibrium becomes unstable at stresses beyond the proportional limit. To do this we make the following assumptions:

[1] Osgood, W. R., The Double-modulus Theory of Column Action, *Civil Eng.*, Vol. 5, p. 173, 1935.

[2] Engesser, *op. cit.* on p. 3.

[3] Kármán, *op. cit.* on p. 3.

[4] *Zeitschrift des Vereines deutscher Ingenieure*, Vol. 52, 1908.

[5] Southwell, R. V., The Strength of Struts, *Engineering*, Vol. 94, p. 249, 1912.

[6] Shanley, F. R., Inelastic Column Theory, *Jour. Aeronaut. Sci.*, 1947, p. 261.

[7] Referred to sometimes as the reduced-modulus theory.

1. The displacements are very small in comparison to the cross-sectional dimensions of the column.
2. Plane cross sections remain plane and normal to the center line after bending.
3. The relationship between stress and strain in any longitudinal fiber is given by the stress-strain diagram of the material.
4. The plane of bending is a plane of symmetry of the column section.

Consider now a short column compressed by an axially applied load P so that $\sigma = P/A$ exceeds the proportional limit. Then let the load be further increased until the column reaches the condition of unstable equilibrium similar to the condition of unstable equilibrium of the perfectly elastic column discussed previously. In this condition let the column be deflected slightly. In every cross section there will be an axis n-n perpendicular to the plane of

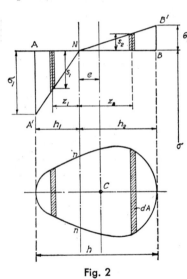

Fig. 2

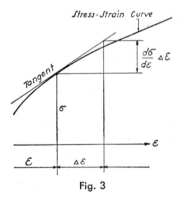

Fig. 3

bending, in which the cross-sectional stress σ developed prior to deflection remains unchanged (Fig. 2). On one side of the line n-n the longitudinal compressive stresses will be increased by bending, the rate of increase being proportional to $\dfrac{d\sigma}{d\epsilon} = E_t$ as can be inferred from Fig. 3. E_t is the tangent-modulus of the stress-strain curve of the material at the stress σ. On the other side there will be a reduction of longitudinal stresses due to the superimposed bending stresses in connection with the strain reversal, and since this reversal relieves only the elastic portion of the strain, the law of proportionality of stress and strain with the constant modulus E remains in effect. The stress diagram on the convex side is bounded by the line NA' (Fig. 2) having a different slope from that of the line NB'.

Using the symbols shown in Fig. 2, equilibrium between the internal stresses and the external load P requires

$$\int_0^{h_1} s_1 \, dA - \int_0^{h_2} s_2 \, dA = 0 \tag{9a}$$

and

$$\int_0^{h_1} s_1(z_1 + e) \, dA + \int_0^{h_2} s_2(z_2 - e) \, dA = Py \tag{9b}$$

The deflection y is taken with respect to the centroidal axis of the column. From Fig. 2 we readily infer

$$s_1 = \frac{\sigma_1}{h_1} z_1, \quad \text{and} \quad s_2 = \frac{\sigma_2}{h_2} z_2$$

From Fig. 4, which pictures the relative rotation of two cross sections infinitesimally close to each other, it is evident that $\Delta \, dx = h_1 \, d\varphi$, and

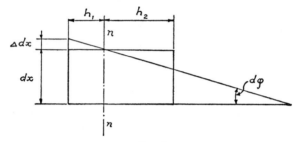

Fig. 4

since $\Delta \, dx = \dfrac{\sigma_1 \, dx}{E}$, we have $\dfrac{d\varphi}{dx} = \dfrac{\sigma_1}{Eh_1}$ and likewise $\dfrac{d\varphi}{dx} = \dfrac{\sigma_2}{E_t h_2}$. Since for small deformations $\dfrac{d\varphi}{dx} = \dfrac{d^2y}{dx^2}$, we finally obtain

$$\sigma_1 = Eh_1 \frac{d^2y}{dx^2} \quad \text{and} \quad \sigma_2 = E_t h_2 \frac{d^2y}{dx^2}$$

Therefore condition (9a) becomes

$$E \frac{d^2y}{dx^2} \int_0^{h_1} z_1 \, dA - E_t \frac{d^2y}{dx^2} \int_0^{h_2} z_2 \, dA = 0$$

or

$$ES_1 - E_t S_2 = 0 \tag{10}$$

where S_1 and S_2 denote the statical moments of the cross-sectional areas to the left and right of the axis n-n, about this axis. This equation and the relation $h_1 + h_2 = h$ determine the position of the axis n-n.

The second condition [(9b)] yields the equation

$$\frac{d^2y}{dx^2}\left(E\int_0^{h_1} z_1^2\, dA + E_t\int_0^{h_2} z_2^2\, dA\right)$$
$$+ e\frac{d^2y}{dx^2}\left(E\int_0^{h_1} z_1\, dA - E_t\int_0^{h_2} z_2\, dA\right) = Py$$

In view of Eq. (10) the second expression vanishes, and we obtain

$$\frac{d^2y}{dx^2}(EI_1 + E_tI_2) = Py$$

where I_1 and I_2 represent the moments of inertia of the cross-sectional areas separated by the line n-n, with reference to this line as axis. Introducing

$$\bar{E}I = EI_1 + E_tI_2 \tag{11}$$

we finally obtain

$$\bar{E}I\frac{d^2y}{dx^2} + Py = 0 \tag{12}$$

wherein

$$\bar{E} = E\frac{I_1}{I} + E_t\frac{I_2}{I} \tag{13}$$

I is the moment of inertia of the cross-sectional area about the axis through the center of gravity C (Fig. 2).

Equation (12) represents the differential equation of the center line in the state of unstable equilibrium. $\bar{E}$ is called the "effective modulus" or "reduced modulus." Its value depends upon the shape of the cross section and the properties of the material. For any given cross section, $\bar{E}$ can be determined by means of Eqs. (10) and (13) from the stress-strain curve as a function of the critical stress $\sigma = P/A$.

The differential equation (12) has the same form as the differential equation (6) for the elastic curve of a perfectly elastic column, in the state of unstable equilibrium, where $\bar{E}$ as well as E is independent of the abscissa x. We have established the important fact that the differential equation for the deflected center line in the state of unstable equilibrium [Eq. (12)] is valid in the elastic as well as in the inelastic range. In the inelastic range $\bar{E}$ is variable and depends on $\sigma = P/A$, while in the elastic range $\bar{E}$ becomes equal to E.

Furthermore, when the axially loaded simply supported column is considered, the solution

$$y = C \sin n\frac{\pi x}{l}$$

will again apply, as in Art. 2, in the absence of a disturbing moment.

This solution, however, is valid only when

$$P = n^2\pi^2 \frac{\bar{E}I}{l^2}$$

With $n = 1$ we arrive at the equation for the smallest buckling load, P_r, according to the reduced-modulus theory:

$$P_r = \pi^2 \frac{\bar{E}I}{l^2} \tag{14}$$

This is a generalized form of Euler's formula.

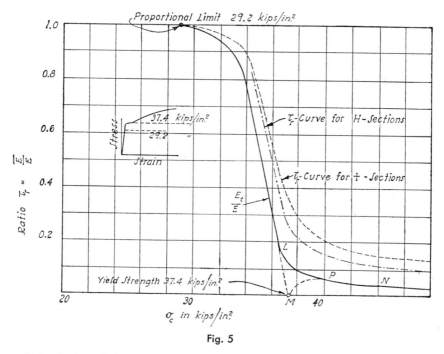

Fig. 5

Introducing for convenience the ratio $\tau_r = \bar{E}/E$, the fundamental equations assume the form

$$EI\tau_r \frac{d^2y}{dx^2} + Py = 0 \tag{15}$$

$$\tau_r = \frac{I_1}{I} + \frac{E_t}{E}\frac{I_2}{I} \tag{16}$$

$$\sigma_r = \frac{P_r}{A} = \frac{\pi^2 E\tau_r}{(l/r)^2} \tag{17}$$

The effect of the shape of the cross section upon τ_r and thus upon the ultimate strength σ_r is shown for a particular material in Fig. 5. For two widely different forms of cross section, τ_r and the ratio E_t/E are plotted against $\sigma_r = P_r/A$. The figure shows the stress-strain curve for a steel with an elastic limit of 29.2 kips/in.^{2} and with a yield point of 37.4 kips/in.^{2} and the τ_r-curves derived for $+$ and H-sections, the latter curve applying for the case of buckling in the plane of the web. The differences between the curves begin to be appreciable in the vicinity of the yield point.[1] The influence of the shape of the cross section increases with increasing σ_r, i.e., with decreasing slenderness ratio.

It is significant that in the case of cross sections having only one axis of symmetry, which lies in the plane of buckling, the value of τ_r varies with the direction of buckling. For a T-section, for instance, τ_r will be smaller for buckling toward the flange than for buckling in the opposite direction. Accordingly, the column will buckle in the direction from mid-depth toward the center of gravity of the section when the load is centered with sufficient accuracy. The reason for this behavior is that two different conditions of equilibrium of the deflected column are possible, according to whether the axis n-n of average stress lies to the right or the left of the center of gravity of the cross section.

5. The Tangent-modulus Theory of Inelastic Buckling

Engesser's original theory of buckling beyond the elastic limit was based on the assumption that, at a certain critical stress $\sigma_t = P_t/A$, an unstable deflected equilibrium configuration is possible and that the deformation is controlled simply by the tangent-modulus $E_t = \dfrac{d\sigma}{d\epsilon}$, which corresponds to the critical stress σ_t. He assumed therefore that no strain reversal takes place on the convex side of the bent column when it passes from the straight form to the adjacent deflected configuration. The recognition that this assumption is not justified led to the early abandonment of Engesser's theory. However, this theory has now regained usefulness. Let us consider all possible deflected states of equilibrium of initially straight columns under axial load P; depending on the loading history of the column, whether strain reversal has taken place or not, we must apply the double-modulus or the tangent-modulus theory. In the same way as for elastic buckling, where no deflected state is possible if $P \leq P_E$, we can conclude that no deflected state is possible for $P \leq P_r$ if strain reversal took place and likewise for $P \leq P_t$ if there was no strain reversal. We will find below that $P_t < P_r$, and consequently the tangent-modulus load P_t, is the maximum load under which an initially

---

[1] The actual E_t/E-curve in the neighborhood of the yield point as derived from the stress-strain diagram follows L-M-P. This part of the E_t/E-diagram was replaced by the continuous curve L-P-N. An explanation will be given in Art. 7.

the strain associated with P_t. In Fig. 8 $\Delta\epsilon/\epsilon_t$ is plotted against
[...] assumed $\tau = E_t/E = 0.75$. On the concave side of the column
[...] compressive strain increases rapidly after the tangent-modulus load
[...]eeded, while on the convex side the strain starts to decrease rather
[...]. Equations (22) and (23) have been derived for an extremely
[...]ified column type, and therefore Fig. 8 gives but a rough picture of
[...]ehavior of an actual column. It may be readily conceived that in a
[...]olumn the additional strain $\Delta\epsilon_1$, due to bending, increases far more
[...]ly, since distortions of all elements of the column contribute to the
[...]ction. Furthermore, the rapid increase of the compressive strain,
[...]ired to satisfy the condition of equilibrium between the load P and

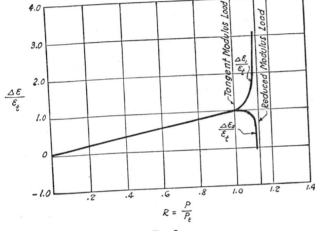

Fig. 8

the internal stresses, will cause an appreciable reduction of E_t. The
implication from this reasoning is that in the majority of actual cases the
critical load at which the column loses its usefulness will exceed the
tangent-modulus load P_t by only a small amount.

The significance of Shanley's work was acknowledged by Kármán[1] in a
comment on Shanley's paper. Since this comment elucidates in an excellent manner the entire question the following sentences may be quoted
from it:

"Both Engesser's and my own analysis of the problem were based on
the assumption that the equilibrium of the straight column becomes
unstable when there are equilibrium positions infinitesimally near to the
straight equilibrium position under the same axial load. The correct
answer to this question is given by replacing, in Euler's equation, Young's
modulus by the so-called reduced modulus. Mr. Shanley's analysis

[1] *Jour. Aeronaut. Sci.*, 1947, pp. 267–268.

straight column will necessarily remain straight. This fact is the starting
point for Shanley's theory, which will be considered in the next article.

Under the assumption that the value of the tangent-modulus E_t applies
over the entire cross section, the differential equation of the deflected
center line takes the form

$$E_t I \frac{d^2y}{dx^2} + Py = 0$$

and upon introducing

$$\tau = \frac{E_t}{E} \tag{18}$$

we may write

$$EI\tau \frac{d^2y}{dx^2} + Py = 0 \tag{19}$$

The buckling load P_t therefore is defined by

$$\sigma_t = \frac{P_t}{A} = \frac{\pi^2 E\tau}{(l/r)^2} \tag{20}$$

Since in Eq. (11) $I_1 + I_2 > I$ (I_1 and I_2 refer to the axis n-n outside
the center of gravity), and since $E > E_t$, we conclude that $\tau = E_t/E$ is
smaller than the value of τ_r derived from Eq. (16). The tangent-modulus
theory, therefore, leads to lower values of the buckling strength than the
double-modulus theory. In the tangent-modulus theory, τ, and consequently P_t, are not affected by the shape of the column section and depend
only on the elastic-plastic properties of the material.

Introducing the values of the coefficient τ_r for H-sections shown in
Fig. 5 and of the corresponding values of the stress σ_r into Eq. (17) and
solving for l/r leads to a series of l/r-values corresponding to these values
of the stress σ_r. The result of this computation is represented by curve
A in Fig. 6, where σ_r is plotted versus the slenderness ratio l/r. In the
elastic zone of buckling the Euler hyperbola represents the relationship
between σ_r and l/r. In the same way curve B has been determined by
using the E_t/E-curve of Fig. 5 and Eq. (20) of the tangent-modulus
theory. The deviation of the two curves is rather slight in the range of
$l/r = 60$ to 90 but increases markedly for slenderness ratios below
$l/r = 40$. Stress-slenderness diagrams as shown in Fig. 6 will be referred
to as column curves.

Formulas (17) and (20) may also be generalized in order to include the
effect of restraints at the ends of the column; similar to Eq. (8), these
formulas may be written in the generalized form

$$\sigma_c = \frac{\pi^2 E\tau}{(kl/r)^2} \tag{21}$$

where kl indicates the free length of the compression member.

The following is important to note: Within the elastic range $\tau = 1$, buckling strength decreases in proportion to the square of kl/r. Slender columns, accordingly, are very sensitive to variations in the factor k. In the inelastic range $\tau < 1$, the increasing effect of a diminishing factor k on the buckling load is partially offset by the influence of the very rapid decrease of τ with decreasing kl/r. The result is a considerably slower increase of the strength of the shorter columns with decreasing k. A glance at Fig. 6 confirms this reasoning. In the range $l/r = 40$ to 90 the column curve is nearly parallel to the axis of abscissas. Accordingly, elastic restraint of the ends of the column expressed by an appropriate

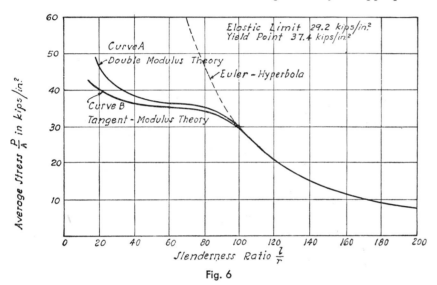

Fig. 6

factor k is of great influence on buckling strength in the elastic range and of relatively slight influence in the inelastic range.

6. Shanley's Theory of Inelastic Column Action

The puzzling fact that the apparently accurate reduced-modulus theory leads to buckling loads which, in many cases, proved greater than those observed in careful tests has been explained by F. R. Shanley[1] in a recent paper. He deserves the credit for having called attention to a questionable assumption tacitly implied in the double-modulus theory. This theory assumes that the column remains straight until the critical load P_r is reached, being based upon the same concept as used in the derivation of the Euler load in the theory of the perfectly elastic column. The theory does not take into account the possibility that, upon reaching the tangent-modulus load P_t, i.e., the maximum load for which the column

[1] Shanley, *op. cit.* on p. 9.

must be straight, bending of the column n with increasing axial load. Shanley showed case. There is a continuous spectrum of possi which correspond to values of P between the and the double-modulus load P_r. The deflect load P, has a definite value and increases from changes from P_t to P_r.

Shanley demonstrates analytically the colum range by means of a simplified column type rep hinged column in which an elastic-plastic hinge sisting of two small longitudinal elements connect legs, whereas the legs of the column are assumed infinitely rigid (Fig. 7). Assuming that such a col starts to bend as soon as the tangent-modulus load P exceeded, Shanley considers the effect of an increa load $P > P_t$ by investigating the interrelation betwe $P - P_t$ and the deflection d at mid-height of the colum He finally arrives at the following relationship betwee the load P and deflection d:

$$P = P_t\left(1 + \cfrac{1}{\cfrac{b}{2d} + \cfrac{1+\tau}{1-\tau}}\right) \qquad (22)$$

where b is the width of the column and $\tau = E_t/E$. τ is assumed to remain constant at the value which corresponds to P_t.

The fact must be stressed that the bent configuration under the load P is, at least theoretically, a stable one and is analogous to the stable deflected configuration given by the refined theory of a perfectly elastic column when the Euler load P_E is somewhat exceeded. The possibili deflected configurations may exist after passing the tangent-m was not recognized until Shanley called attention to this fac

The equations expressing the variation of strain in the tv elements as a function of the ratio $R = P/P_t$ are according t

$$\text{Concave side:} \qquad \frac{\Delta\epsilon_1}{\epsilon_t} = \cfrac{2\left(\cfrac{1}{\tau} - R\right)}{\cfrac{1-\tau}{R-1} - (1+\tau)}$$

$$\text{Convex side:} \qquad \frac{\Delta\epsilon_2}{\epsilon_t} = \cfrac{2(R-1)}{\cfrac{1-\tau}{R-1} - (1+\tau)}$$

ϵ_t is
R for
the co
is exce
slowly
simpl
the b
real
rapid
defle
requ

represents a generalization of the question. His procedure can be formulated as follows: What is the smallest value of the axial load at which bifurcation of the equilibrium positions can occur, regardless of whether or not the transition to the bent position requires an increase of the axial load? The answer to this question is that the first equilibrium bifurcation from the straight equilibrium configuration occurs at a load given by the Euler formula when Young's modulus is replaced by the tangent-modulus. In fact, one can construct sequences of equilibrium positions starting from any load between the two limiting values corresponding to the tangent and the reduced moduli.

"My original analysis, and also Engesser's, is a generalization of the reasoning used in the theory of elastic buckling. Why does this not cover all possible equilibrium positions in the inelastic case? Obviously, it is not because of the nonlinearity of the stress-strain relation in the inelastic range but because of the nonreversible character of the process. There are infinite values of the permanent strain which may correspond to the same stress, corresponding to different history of the loading and unloading procedure. Hence, the definition of the stability limit must be revised for nonreversible processes. This necessity was intuitively recognized by Mr. Shanley, which is, I believe, a great merit of his paper."

Summing up, it may be said: The tangent-modulus load does not accurately define the actual buckling load, the load which the column can carry without too large a deflection, but it can be considered as a lower limit of the buckling load, a limit which for most of the metals used in structural engineering lies only slightly below the critical column load. *The tangent-modulus load therefore may be considered as the critical load, and we are justified in basing column formulas on Engesser's original equation, i.e., Eq. (20) of the preceding article.* Equation (19) represents the generalized fundamental differential equation for the study of the condition of instability of columnlike compression members and of all metal structures which contain such members.

Typical examples of test data are shown in Figs. 9 and 10 confirming the conclusions drawn from Shanley's theory of column action.[1] Figure 9 shows the results of tests on solid round rods of aluminum alloy. Figure 10 gives the data concerning tests with a mild steel rod. Both groups of tests indicate reasonably good agreement of the observed data with the tangent-modulus theory.

Figure 11 represents data from tests made on H-shaped specimens of

[1] Templin, R. L., R. G. Sturm, E. C. Hartmann, and M. Holt, Column Strength of Various Aluminum Alloys, *Aluminum Research Labs., Tech. Paper* 1, Aluminum Company of America, Pittsburgh, 1938.

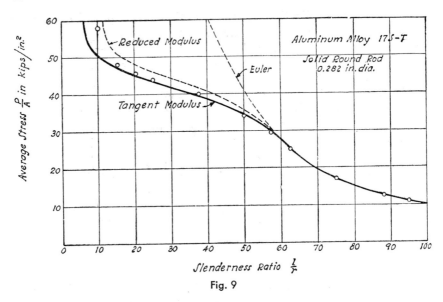

Fig. 9

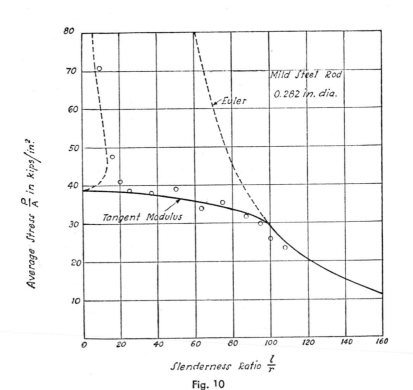

Fig. 10

extruded aluminum alloy.[1]　　Again, this figure shows far better agreement of the plotted test results with the tangent-modulus curve than with the reduced-modulus curve.

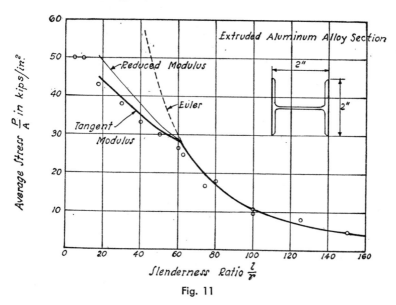

Fig. 11

7. The Column Curve

The shape of the stress-strain curve greatly affects the column curve which defines the interrelation between critical stress and slenderness ratio.

Figure 12a represents the stress-strain curve for a material having no sharply defined yield strength, as, for instance, the aluminum alloys and high-strength steel.　The related column curve assumes a form as illustrated by Fig. 12b.

Structural steel with a sharply defined yield strength and a relatively short zone of yielding (Fig. 12c) shows a column curve similar to that in Fig. 12d.　The involved shape of this curve needs some explanation. When σ approaches the yield strength σ_y, the tangent modulus E_t reduces steadily until it becomes zero when the yield point is reached.　Since $l/r = 0$ corresponds to $E_t = 0$, the column curve embracing the portion O to Y of the stress-strain diagram is represented by the curve L-σ_p-M in Fig. 12d.　If the column were supported against bending when σ passes the zone of yielding and then further axially loaded so that σ extends into the strain-hardening region, critical stresses above the yield point may

[1] Osgood, William R., and Marshall Holt, The Column Strength of Two Extruded Aluminum-alloy H-sections, *NACA Tech. Rept.* 656, 1939.

be obtained which would result in the branch M-P-N of the column curve. This branch corresponds to the portion of the stress-strain diagram above the yield point. Now it is quite possible that, in cases where the horizontal portion of the stress-strain curve is short, the tendency of the column to become unstable at the yield point might be overcome without lateral support, so that strain hardening may take place. In this case the column curve would follow the line σ_p-P-N. Indeed, care-

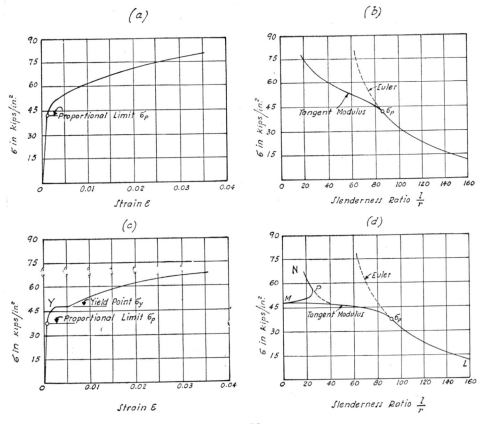

Fig. 12

fully loaded specimens of structural steel below $l/r = 30$ frequently show a buckling strength P/A far above the yield strength. The explanation may be that, owing to variations in the homogeneity of the material, yielding does not occur simultaneously over the entire cross section and that in one region strain hardening already has taken place while in other regions yielding begins. In this way it is possible that bending, which should start at the yield point, is more or less delayed and buckling takes place at average stresses above the yield-point stress. However, such high values for the critical stress of very short columns could be observed only in very careful tests on small specimens and cannot be relied upon in design of columns. It is therefore advisable to consider the column curve L-σ_p-M as the real column curve for structural steel. The yield point therefore is to be considered as the upper limit of the average stress at which a short column of structural steel with sharply defined yield point will fail.

In the preceding articles the theoretical aspect of the problem of column strength considered as a stability problem has been discussed and the criterion of failure analyzed. In the elastic range the Euler load and in the inelastic range the tangent-modulus load have been established as the limiting values of the carrying capacity up to which a column can be loaded without dangerous deflection. Thus the fundamental relationship between buckling load and slenderness ratio over the entire range of buckling can be derived in a rational way for any structural metal provided a complete compressive stress-strain diagram of the material is available. This relationship, represented graphically by the column curve, valid for an idealized column of solid cross section of any shape, should be regarded as the sole rational basis from which design formulas for axially loaded columns may be developed.

Article 18 will discuss further the principles upon which the development of buckling formulas for practical design are to be based and the difficulties in establishing such formulas arising out of the irregularities in the elastic-plastic behavior of the material and the complex conditions to which compression members in metal structure are subjected.

8. Effect of Shear Stresses on Buckling Loads

In the mathematical derivation of the buckling load we have so far not made allowance for the effect of the shearing stresses in the deflected column when it passes from its stable to its unstable equilibrium position. This effect, as will be shown hereafter, is very small and negligible for columns of solid cross section discussed in this chapter.

The shearing force Q in a column acted upon by the bending moment $M = Py$ is given by

$$Q = \frac{dM}{dx} = P\frac{dy}{dx}$$

This force produces an additional deflection Δy, and according to elastic theory the change in slope of the deflection curve y is

$$\frac{d\,\Delta y}{dx} = \frac{Q\beta}{GA}$$

where G is the modulus of rigidity and β a factor which depends on the shape of the column cross section. β is 1.2 for rectangular cross sections and becomes approximately 2 for an H-section bent in the plane of the web.   The change in curvature due to the effect of the shearing force is

$$\frac{d^2\,\Delta y}{dx^2} = \frac{\beta}{GA}\frac{dQ}{dx} = \frac{P\beta}{GA}\frac{d^2y}{dx^2}$$

The total curvature of the deflection curve due to bending moment and shearing force becomes therefore

$$\frac{d^2y}{dx^2} = -\frac{Py}{E_t I} + \frac{P\beta}{G_t A}\frac{d^2y}{dx^2}$$

where the tangent-modulus E_t and the tangent-modulus of rigidity G_t have been introduced to render the equation valid for the entire range of buckling.   On rearranging this equation it assumes the form

$$\frac{d^2y}{dx^2} + \frac{Py}{(1 - \beta P/G_t A)E_t I} = 0 \tag{24}$$

Using the abbreviation $\alpha^2 = \dfrac{P}{(1 - \beta P/G_t A)E_t I}$ we may write

$$\frac{d^2y}{dx^2} + \alpha^2 y = 0$$

Applying the same reasoning as in the preceding discussions, we find that the critical load again is defined by the condition $\alpha l = \pi$, from which

$$P = \frac{\pi^2 E_t I}{l^2}\left(1 - \frac{\beta P}{G_t A}\right)$$

can be derived.   Solving for P leads to the following expression for the critical load P_c':

$$P_c' = \frac{\pi^2 E_t I}{l^2}\frac{1}{1 + \dfrac{\beta}{G_t A}\dfrac{\pi^2 E_t I}{l^2}}$$

Assuming that the ratio E_t/G_t remains constant and equal to $v = E/G$ this equation becomes

$$P_c' = \pi^2 E_t I \frac{1}{\left[1 + \pi^2\beta v\left(\dfrac{r}{l}\right)^2\right]l^2} = \frac{\pi^2 E_t I}{(kl)^2} \tag{25}$$

The factor k, given by

$$k = \sqrt{1 + \pi^2\beta v\left(\frac{r}{l}\right)^2} \tag{26}$$

depends upon the slenderness ratio l/r.   Since $k > 1$, P_c' is smaller than the critical load P_c computed for the same slenderness ratio but neglecting the effect of the shearing forces.

Poisson's ratio ν for metals varies between $\frac{1}{3}$ and $\frac{1}{4}$, and therefore $v = 2(1 + \nu)$ lies between $\frac{8}{3}$ and $\frac{5}{2}$. We choose the ratio $v = \frac{8}{3}$, which is more unfavorable in the present instance, and using $\beta = 2$ for an H-section, we obtain for various values of l/r:

l/r	20	30	40	50	100	150
k	1.063	1.028	1.016	1.010	1.003	1.002
P_c'/P_c	0.995	0.997	0.998	0.998	0.997	0.998

The last line was computed by using the column curve of Fig. 12d for structural steel. For very short columns k departs appreciably from unity; nevertheless the ratio P_c'/P_c is very close to 1, since a change in the factor k, as was pointed out in Art. 5, has only a minor effect upon the critical load for small values of l/r. The decrease in strength for all practical slenderness ratios is consequently extremely slight for columns of solid cross section and need not be considered in practical applications.

9. Eccentrically and Laterally Loaded Columns. Historical Development

In order to avoid any confusion about the problems to which the methods discussed in this chapter are applicable, it is desirable to define clearly the type of loading assumed in this and the following articles. We consider as eccentrically or laterally loaded columns explicitly those columns where the plane of the moment of eccentricity, or the plane of the lateral forces, is identical with the plane of actual buckling. When buckling occurs in a plane perpendicular to the plane of the before-mentioned bending moments, we are speaking of "lateral buckling." The latter problem will be treated in Chap. IV.

In a brief account of the development of the theory of eccentrically loaded columns, Ostenfeld[1] must be mentioned, who, half a century ago, made an attempt to derive design formulas for centrally and eccentrically loaded columns. His method was based upon the concept that the critical column load is defined as the loading which first produces external fiber stresses equal to the yield strength.

The first to consider the determination of the buckling load of eccentrically loaded columns as a stability problem was Kármán,[2] who gave, in connection with his investigations on centrally loaded columns, a complete and exact analysis of this rather involved problem. He called attention to the sensitiveness of short and medium-length columns to

[1] Ostenfeld, A., Exzentrische und zentrische Knickfestigkeit, *Zeitschrift des Vereines deutscher Ingenieure*, Vol. 94, p. 1462, 1898.

[2] *Loc. cit.* on p. 3.

even very slight eccentricities of the imposed load, which reduce the carrying capacity of straight columns considerably. Roš and Brunner published in 1926 a simplified stability theory of eccentrically loaded columns and proved the theoretical results by a number of tests. Roš[1] and Brunner assumed that the deflected center line of the column can be represented by the half wave of a sine curve but based the computation of the critical load upon the actual stress-strain diagram.

Westergaard and Osgood[2] presented in 1928 a paper in which the behavior of eccentrically loaded columns and initially curved columns were discussed analytically. The method is based upon the same equations as were used by Kármán but assumes the deflected center line of eccentrically loaded compression members to be part of a cosine curve, thereby simplifying Kármán's method without impairing the practical accuracy of the results.

Starting from Kármán's exact concept, Chwalla,[3] in a series of papers between 1928 and 1937, investigated in a very elaborate manner the stability of eccentrically loaded columns and presented the results of his studies for various shapes of column cross sections in tables and diagrams. Chwalla based all his computations on one and the same stress-strain diagram adopted as typical for structural steel. The significance of his laborious work is that the numerous tables and diagrams brought insight into the behavior of eccentrically loaded columns as influenced by shape of the column cross section, slenderness ratio, and eccentricity and that his exact results can serve as a measure for the accuracy of approximate methods.

A very valuable contribution to the solution of the problem was offered by Ježek,[4] who gave an analytical solution for steel columns based upon a simplified stress-strain curve consisting of two straight lines and showed that the results agree rather well with the values obtained from the real stress-strain relation. The underlying concept of Ježek's theory proves useful in devising analytical expressions from which, in a rather simple manner, diagrams, tables, or design formulas for all kinds of material having a sharply defined yield strength can be derived.

A different approach to the complex problem of eccentrically loaded

[1] Roš, M., Die Bemessung zentrisch und exzentrisch gedrückter Stäbe auf Knickung, Rept. 2d Internat. Cong. Bridge and Structural Eng., Vienna, 1928.

[2] Westergaard, H. M., and W. R. Osgood, Strength of Steel Columns, Trans. ASME, Vols. 49, 50, APM-50-9, p. 65, 1928.

[3] Chwalla, E., Die Stabilität zentrisch und exzentrisch gedrückter Stäbe aus Baustahl, Sitzungsberichte der Akademie de Wissenschaften in Wien, Abt. IIa, p. 469, 1928. Further references are listed at the end of the chapter.

[4] Ježek, K., Die Tragfähigkeit des exzentrisch beanspruchten und des querbelasteten Druckstabes aus einem ideal plastischen Material, Sitzungsberichte der Akademie der Wissenschaften in Wien, Abt. IIa, Vol. 143, 1934.

straight column will necessarily remain straight. This fact is the starting point for Shanley's theory, which will be considered in the next article.

Under the assumption that the value of the tangent-modulus E_t applies over the entire cross section, the differential equation of the deflected center line takes the form

$$E_t I \frac{d^2 y}{dx^2} + P y = 0$$

and upon introducing

$$\tau = \frac{E_t}{E} \tag{18}$$

we may write

$$E I \tau \frac{d^2 y}{dx^2} + P y = 0 \tag{19}$$

The buckling load P_t therefore is defined by

$$\sigma_t = \frac{P_t}{A} = \frac{\pi^2 E \tau}{(l/r)^2} \tag{20}$$

Since in Eq. (11) $I_1 + I_2 > I$ (I_1 and I_2 refer to the axis n-n outside the center of gravity), and since $E > E_t$, we conclude that $\tau = E_t/E$ is smaller than the value of τ_r derived from Eq. (16). The tangent-modulus theory, therefore, leads to lower values of the buckling strength than the double-modulus theory. In the tangent-modulus theory, τ, and consequently P_t, are not affected by the shape of the column section and depend only on the elastic-plastic properties of the material.

Introducing the values of the coefficient τ_r for H-sections shown in Fig. 5 and of the corresponding values of the stress σ_r into Eq. (17) and solving for l/r leads to a series of l/r-values corresponding to these values of the stress σ_r. The result of this computation is represented by curve A in Fig. 6, where σ_r is plotted versus the slenderness ratio l/r. In the elastic zone of buckling the Euler hyperbola represents the relationship between σ_r and l/r. In the same way curve B has been determined by using the E_t/E-curve of Fig. 5 and Eq. (20) of the tangent-modulus theory. The deviation of the two curves is rather slight in the range of $l/r = 60$ to 90 but increases markedly for slenderness ratios below $l/r = 40$. Stress-slenderness diagrams as shown in Fig. 6 will be referred to as column curves.

Formulas (17) and (20) may also be generalized in order to include the effect of restraints at the ends of the column; similar to Eq. (8), these formulas may be written in the generalized form

$$\sigma_c = \frac{\pi^2 E \tau}{(kl/r)^2} \tag{21}$$

where kl indicates the free length of the compression member.

The following is important to note: Within the elastic range $\tau = 1$, buckling strength decreases in proportion to the square of kl/r. Slender columns, accordingly, are very sensitive to variations in the factor k. In the inelastic range $\tau < 1$, the increasing effect of a diminishing factor k on the buckling load is partially offset by the influence of the very rapid decrease of τ with decreasing kl/r. The result is a considerably slower increase of the strength of the shorter columns with decreasing k. A glance at Fig. 6 confirms this reasoning. In the range $l/r = 40$ to 90 the column curve is nearly parallel to the axis of abscissas. Accordingly, elastic restraint of the ends of the column expressed by an appropriate

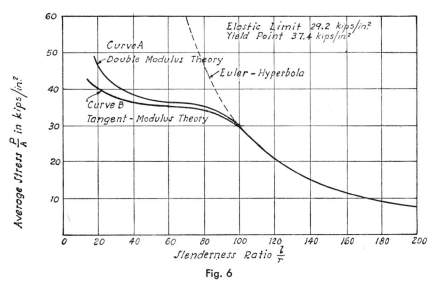

Fig. 6

factor k is of great influence on buckling strength in the elastic range and of relatively slight influence in the inelastic range.

6. Shanley's Theory of Inelastic Column Action

The puzzling fact that the apparently accurate reduced-modulus theory leads to buckling loads which, in many cases, proved greater than those observed in careful tests has been explained by F. R. Shanley[1] in a recent paper. He deserves the credit for having called attention to a questionable assumption tacitly implied in the double-modulus theory. This theory assumes that the column remains straight until the critical load P_r is reached, being based upon the same concept as used in the derivation of the Euler load in the theory of the perfectly elastic column. The theory does not take into account the possibility that, upon reaching the tangent-modulus load P_t, i.e., the maximum load for which the column

[1] Shanley, *op. cit.* on p. 9.

must be straight, bending of the column may proceed simultaneously with increasing axial load. Shanley showed that such is actually the case. There is a continuous spectrum of possible deflected configurations which correspond to values of P between the tangent-modulus load P_t and the double-modulus load P_r. The deflection y, connected with the load P, has a definite value and increases from zero to infinity when P changes from P_t to P_r.

Shanley demonstrates analytically the column action in the inelastic range by means of a simplified column type representing a two-legged hinged column in which an elastic-plastic hinge con-sisting of two small longitudinal elements connects the legs, whereas the legs of the column are assumed to be infinitely rigid (Fig. 7). Assuming that such a column starts to bend as soon as the tangent-modulus load P_t is exceeded, Shanley considers the effect of an increased load $P > P_t$ by investigating the interrelation between $P - P_t$ and the deflection d at mid-height of the column. He finally arrives at the following relationship between the load P and deflection d:

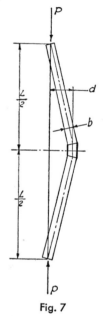

Fig. 7

$$P = P_t\left(1 + \cfrac{1}{\cfrac{b}{2d} + \cfrac{1 + \tau}{1 - \tau}}\right) \qquad (22)$$

where b is the width of the column and $\tau = E_t/E$. τ is assumed to remain constant at the value which corre-sponds to P_t.

The fact must be stressed that the bent configuration under the load P is, at least theoretically, a stable one and is analogous to the stable deflected configuration given by the refined theory of a perfectly elastic column when the Euler load P_E is somewhat exceeded. The possibility that such deflected configurations may exist after passing the tangent-modulus load was not recognized until Shanley called attention to this fact.

The equations expressing the variation of strain in the two column elements as a function of the ratio $R = P/P_t$ are according to Shanley

$$
\left.
\begin{aligned}
\text{Concave side:} \quad \frac{\Delta\epsilon_1}{\epsilon_t} &= \frac{2\left(\dfrac{1}{\tau} - R\right)}{\dfrac{1 - \tau}{R - 1} - (1 + \tau)} \\[2em]
\text{Convex side:} \quad \frac{\Delta\epsilon_2}{\epsilon_t} &= \frac{2\,(R - 1)}{\dfrac{1 - \tau}{R - 1} - (1 + \tau)}
\end{aligned}
\right\} \qquad (23)
$$

ϵ_t is the strain associated with P_t. In Fig. 8 $\Delta\epsilon/\epsilon_t$ is plotted against R for an assumed $\tau = E_t/E = 0.75$. On the concave side of the column the compressive strain increases rapidly after the tangent-modulus load is exceeded, while on the convex side the strain starts to decrease rather slowly. Equations (22) and (23) have been derived for an extremely simplified column type, and therefore Fig. 8 gives but a rough picture of the behavior of an actual column. It may be readily conceived that in a real column the additional strain $\Delta\epsilon_1$, due to bending, increases far more rapidly, since distortions of all elements of the column contribute to the deflection. Furthermore, the rapid increase of the compressive strain, required to satisfy the condition of equilibrium between the load P and

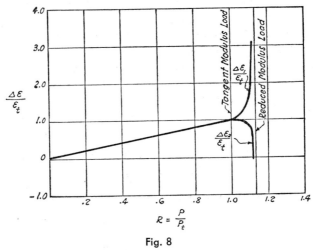

Fig. 8

the internal stresses, will cause an appreciable reduction of E_t. The implication from this reasoning is that in the majority of actual cases the critical load at which the column loses its usefulness will exceed the tangent-modulus load P_t by only a small amount.

The significance of Shanley's work was acknowledged by Kármán[1] in a comment on Shanley's paper. Since this comment elucidates in an excellent manner the entire question the following sentences may be quoted from it:

"Both Engesser's and my own analysis of the problem were based on the assumption that the equilibrium of the straight column becomes unstable when there are equilibrium positions infinitesimally near to the straight equilibrium position under the same axial load. The correct answer to this question is given by replacing, in Euler's equation, Young's modulus by the so-called reduced modulus. Mr. Shanley's analysis

[1] *Jour. Aeronaut. Sci.*, 1947, pp. 267–268.

represents a generalization of the question. His procedure can be formulated as follows: What is the smallest value of the axial load at which bifurcation of the equilibrium positions can occur, regardless of whether or not the transition to the bent position requires an increase of the axial load? The answer to this question is that the first equilibrium bifurcation from the straight equilibrium configuration occurs at a load given by the Euler formula when Young's modulus is replaced by the tangent-modulus. In fact, one can construct sequences of equilibrium positions starting from any load between the two limiting values corresponding to the tangent and the reduced moduli.

"My original analysis, and also Engesser's, is a generalization of the reasoning used in the theory of elastic buckling. Why does this not cover all possible equilibrium positions in the inelastic case? Obviously, it is not because of the nonlinearity of the stress-strain relation in the inelastic range but because of the nonreversible character of the process. There are infinite values of the permanent strain which may correspond to the same stress, corresponding to different history of the loading and unloading procedure. Hence, the definition of the stability limit must be revised for nonreversible processes. This necessity was intuitively recognized by Mr. Shanley, which is, I believe, a great merit of his paper."

Summing up, it may be said: The tangent-modulus load does not accurately define the actual buckling load, the load which the column can carry without too large a deflection, but it can be considered as a lower limit of the buckling load, a limit which for most of the metals used in structural engineering lies only slightly below the critical column load. *The tangent-modulus load therefore may be considered as the critical load, and we are justified in basing column formulas on Engesser's original equation, i.e., Eq. (20) of the preceding article.* Equation (19) represents the generalized fundamental differential equation for the study of the condition of instability of columnlike compression members and of all metal structures which contain such members.

Typical examples of test data are shown in Figs. 9 and 10 confirming the conclusions drawn from Shanley's theory of column action.[1] Figure 9 shows the results of tests on solid round rods of aluminum alloy. Figure 10 gives the data concerning tests with a mild steel rod. Both groups of tests indicate reasonably good agreement of the observed data with the tangent-modulus theory.

Figure 11 represents data from tests made on H-shaped specimens of

[1] Templin, R. L., R. G. Sturm, E. C. Hartmann, and M. Holt, Column Strength of Various Aluminum Alloys, *Aluminum Research Labs.*, *Tech. Paper* 1, Aluminum Company of America, Pittsburgh, 1938.

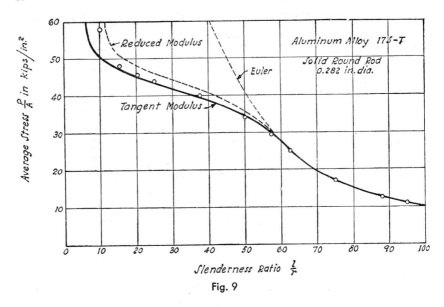

Fig. 9

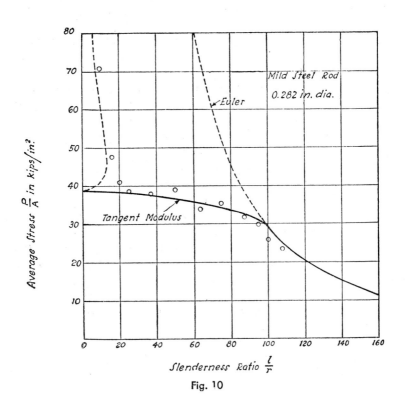

Fig. 10

extruded aluminum alloy.[1]   Again, this figure shows far better agreement
of the plotted test results with the tangent-modulus curve than with the
reduced-modulus curve.

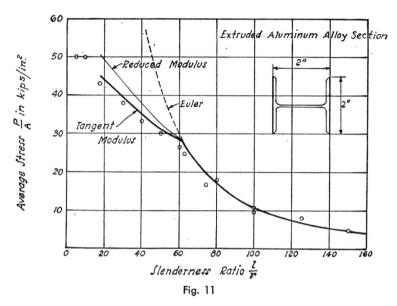

Fig. 11

7. The Column Curve

The shape of the stress-strain curve greatly affects the column curve
which defines the interrelation between critical stress and slenderness
ratio.

Figure 12a represents the stress-strain curve for a material having no
sharply defined yield strength, as, for instance, the aluminum alloys and
high-strength steel.   The related column curve assumes a form as illustrated by Fig. 12b.

Structural steel with a sharply defined yield strength and a relatively
short zone of yielding (Fig. 12c) shows a column curve similar to that in
Fig. 12d.   The involved shape of this curve needs some explanation.
When σ approaches the yield strength σ_y, the tangent modulus E_t reduces
steadily until it becomes zero when the yield point is reached.   Since
$l/r = 0$ corresponds to $E_t = 0$, the column curve embracing the portion
O to Y of the stress-strain diagram is represented by the curve L-σ_p-M
in Fig. 12d.   If the column were supported against bending when σ passes
the zone of yielding and then further axially loaded so that σ extends into
the strain-hardening region, critical stresses above the yield point may

---

[1] Osgood, William R., and Marshall Holt, The Column Strength of Two Extruded
Aluminum-alloy H-sections, *NACA Tech. Rept.* 656, 1939.

be obtained which would result in the branch *M-P-N* of the column curve. This branch corresponds to the portion of the stress-strain diagram above the yield point. Now it is quite possible that, in cases where the horizontal portion of the stress-strain curve is short, the tendency of the column to become unstable at the yield point might be overcome without lateral support, so that strain hardening may take place. In this case the column curve would follow the line σ_p-*P-N*. Indeed, care-

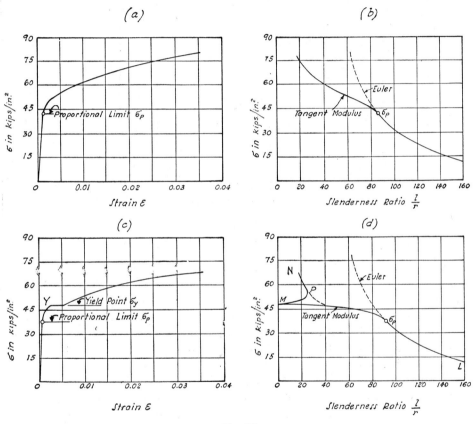

Fig. 12

fully loaded specimens of structural steel below $l/r = 30$ frequently show a buckling strength P/A far above the yield strength. The explanation may be that, owing to variations in the homogeneity of the material, yielding does not occur simultaneously over the entire cross section and that in one region strain hardening already has taken place while in other regions yielding begins. In this way it is possible that bending, which should start at the yield point, is more or less delayed and buckling takes place at average stresses above the yield-point stress. However, such high values for the critical stress of very short columns could be observed only in very careful tests on small specimens and cannot be relied upon in design of columns. It is therefore advisable to consider the column curve L-σ_p-M as the real column curve for structural steel. The yield point therefore is to be considered as the upper limit of the average stress at which a short column of structural steel with sharply defined yield point will fail.

In the preceding articles the theoretical aspect of the problem of column strength considered as a stability problem has been discussed and the criterion of failure analyzed. In the elastic range the Euler load and in the inelastic range the tangent-modulus load have been established as the limiting values of the carrying capacity up to which a column can be loaded without dangerous deflection. Thus the fundamental relationship between buckling load and slenderness ratio over the entire range of buckling can be derived in a rational way for any structural metal provided a complete compressive stress-strain diagram of the material is available. This relationship, represented graphically by the column curve, valid for an idealized column of solid cross section of any shape, should be regarded as the sole rational basis from which design formulas for axially loaded columns may be developed.

Article 18 will discuss further the principles upon which the development of buckling formulas for practical design are to be based and the difficulties in establishing such formulas arising out of the irregularities in the elastic-plastic behavior of the material and the complex conditions to which compression members in metal structure are subjected.

8. Effect of Shear Stresses on Buckling Loads

In the mathematical derivation of the buckling load we have so far not made allowance for the effect of the shearing stresses in the deflected column when it passes from its stable to its unstable equilibrium position. This effect, as will be shown hereafter, is very small and negligible for columns of solid cross section discussed in this chapter.

The shearing force Q in a column acted upon by the bending moment $M = Py$ is given by

$$Q = \frac{dM}{dx} = P\frac{dy}{dx}$$

This force produces an additional deflection Δy, and according to elastic theory the change in slope of the deflection curve y is

$$\frac{d\,\Delta y}{dx} = \frac{Q\beta}{GA}$$

where G is the modulus of rigidity and β a factor which depends on the shape of the column cross section. β is 1.2 for rectangular cross sections and becomes approximately 2 for an H-section bent in the plane of the web.   The change in curvature due to the effect of the shearing force is

$$\frac{d^2\,\Delta y}{dx^2} = \frac{\beta}{GA}\frac{dQ}{dx} = \frac{P\beta}{GA}\frac{d^2y}{dx^2}$$

The total curvature of the deflection curve due to bending moment and shearing force becomes therefore

$$\frac{d^2y}{dx^2} = -\frac{Py}{E_t I} + \frac{P\beta}{G_t A}\frac{d^2y}{dx^2}$$

where the tangent-modulus E_t and the tangent-modulus of rigidity G_t have been introduced to render the equation valid for the entire range of buckling.   On rearranging this equation it assumes the form

$$\frac{d^2y}{dx^2} + \frac{Py}{(1 - \beta P/G_t A)E_t I} = 0 \tag{24}$$

Using the abbreviation $\alpha^2 = \dfrac{P}{(1 - \beta P/G_t A)E_t I}$ we may write

$$\frac{d^2y}{dx^2} + \alpha^2 y = 0$$

Applying the same reasoning as in the preceding discussions, we find that the critical load again is defined by the condition $\alpha l = \pi$, from which

$$P = \frac{\pi^2 E_t I}{l^2}\left(1 - \frac{\beta P}{G_t A}\right)$$

can be derived.   Solving for P leads to the following expression for the critical load P_c':

$$P_c' = \frac{\pi^2 E_t I}{l^2}\,\frac{1}{1 + \dfrac{\beta}{G_t A}\dfrac{\pi^2 E_t I}{l^2}}$$

Assuming that the ratio E_t/G_t remains constant and equal to $v = E/G$ this equation becomes

$$P_c' = \pi^2 E_t I\,\frac{1}{\left[1 + \pi^2 \beta v \left(\dfrac{r}{l}\right)^2\right] l^2} = \frac{\pi^2 E_t I}{(kl)^2} \tag{25}$$

The factor k, given by

$$k = \sqrt{1 + \pi^2 \beta v \left(\frac{r}{l}\right)^2} \tag{26}$$

depends upon the slenderness ratio l/r.   Since $k > 1$, P_c' is smaller than the critical load P_c computed for the same slenderness ratio but neglecting the effect of the shearing forces.

Poisson's ratio ν for metals varies between $\frac{1}{3}$ and $\frac{1}{4}$, and therefore $v = 2(1 + \nu)$ lies between $\frac{8}{3}$ and $\frac{5}{2}$. We choose the ratio $v = \frac{8}{3}$, which is more unfavorable in the present instance, and using $\beta = 2$ for an H-section, we obtain for various values of l/r:

l/r	20	30	40	50	100	150
k	1.063	1.028	1.016	1.010	1.003	1.002
P_c'/P_c	0.995	0.997	0.998	0.998	0.997	0.998

The last line was computed by using the column curve of Fig. 12d for structural steel. For very short columns k departs appreciably from unity; nevertheless the ratio P_c'/P_c is very close to 1, since a change in the factor k, as was pointed out in Art. 5, has only a minor effect upon the critical load for small values of l/r. The decrease in strength for all practical slenderness ratios is consequently extremely slight for columns of solid cross section and need not be considered in practical applications.

9. Eccentrically and Laterally Loaded Columns. Historical Development

In order to avoid any confusion about the problems to which the methods discussed in this chapter are applicable, it is desirable to define clearly the type of loading assumed in this and the following articles. We consider as eccentrically or laterally loaded columns explicitly those columns where the plane of the moment of eccentricity, or the plane of the lateral forces, is identical with the plane of actual buckling. When buckling occurs in a plane perpendicular to the plane of the before-mentioned bending moments, we are speaking of "lateral buckling." The latter problem will be treated in Chap. IV.

In a brief account of the development of the theory of eccentrically loaded columns, Ostenfeld[1] must be mentioned, who, half a century ago, made an attempt to derive design formulas for centrally and eccentrically loaded columns. His method was based upon the concept that the critical column load is defined as the loading which first produces external fiber stresses equal to the yield strength.

The first to consider the determination of the buckling load of eccentrically loaded columns as a stability problem was Kármán,[2] who gave, in connection with his investigations on centrally loaded columns, a complete and exact analysis of this rather involved problem. He called attention to the sensitiveness of short and medium-length columns to

---

[1] Ostenfeld, A., Exzentrische und zentrische Knickfestigkeit, *Zeitschrift des Vereines deutscher Ingenieure*, Vol. 94, p. 1462, 1898.

[2] *Loc. cit.* on p. 3.

even very slight eccentricities of the imposed load, which reduce the carrying capacity of straight columns considerably. Roš and Brunner published in 1926 a simplified stability theory of eccentrically loaded columns and proved the theoretical results by a number of tests. Roš[1] and Brunner assumed that the deflected center line of the column can be represented by the half wave of a sine curve but based the computation of the critical load upon the actual stress-strain diagram.

Westergaard and Osgood[2] presented in 1928 a paper in which the behavior of eccentrically loaded columns and initially curved columns were discussed analytically. The method is based upon the same equations as were used by Kármán but assumes the deflected center line of eccentrically loaded compression members to be part of a cosine curve, thereby simplifying Kármán's method without impairing the practical accuracy of the results.

Starting from Kármán's exact concept, Chwalla,[3] in a series of papers between 1928 and 1937, investigated in a very elaborate manner the stability of eccentrically loaded columns and presented the results of his studies for various shapes of column cross sections in tables and diagrams. Chwalla based all his computations on one and the same stress-strain diagram adopted as typical for structural steel. The significance of his laborious work is that the numerous tables and diagrams brought insight into the behavior of eccentrically loaded columns as influenced by shape of the column cross section, slenderness ratio, and eccentricity and that his exact results can serve as a measure for the accuracy of approximate methods.

A very valuable contribution to the solution of the problem was offered by Ježek,[4] who gave an analytical solution for steel columns based upon a simplified stress-strain curve consisting of two straight lines and showed that the results agree rather well with the values obtained from the real stress-strain relation. The underlying concept of Ježek's theory proves useful in devising analytical expressions from which, in a rather simple manner, diagrams, tables, or design formulas for all kinds of material having a sharply defined yield strength can be derived.

A different approach to the complex problem of eccentrically loaded

[1] Roš, M., Die Bemessung zentrisch und exzentrisch gedrückter Stäbe auf Knickung, *Rept. 2d Internat. Cong. Bridge and Structural Eng.*, Vienna, 1928.

[2] Westergaard, H. M., and W. R. Osgood, Strength of Steel Columns, *Trans. ASME*, Vols. 49, 50, APM-50-9, p. 65, 1928.

[3] Chwalla, E., Die Stabilität zentrisch und exzentrisch gedrückter Stäbe aus Baustahl, *Sitzungsberichte der Akademie de Wissenschaften in Wien*, Abt. IIa, p. 469, 1928. Further references are listed at the end of the chapter.

[4] Ježek, K., Die Tragfähigkeit des exzentrisch beanspruchten und des querbelasteten Druckstabes aus einem ideal plastischen Material, *Sitzungsberichte der Akademie der Wissenschaften in Wien*, Abt. IIa, Vol. 143, 1934.

columns, starting from the secant formula, was made by Young.[1] He considers, as Ostenfeld and others did, the failure load as the load which produces the beginning of yielding in the highest stressed fiber. For structural steel having 36 kips/in.[2] yield strength, he develops column curves for various values of the eccentricity, and he treated initially curved columns by the same method.

In the following Arts. 10 and 11 a brief account will be given of the nature of the stability problem of eccentrically loaded columns, of the theory developed by Kármán and Chwalla, and of the simplified method presented by Westergaard and Osgood. Articles 12 and 13 will deal with Ježek's method of approach and the utilization of the analytical results attained from this theory for practical design. The secant-formula concept will be critically discussed in Art. 15.

10. Eccentrically Loaded Columns of Rectangular Cross Section. The Method of Kármán and Chwalla

The theory is based upon the same assumptions as made in the preceding articles discussing the stability of columns axially loaded beyond the proportional limit. An initially straight column of rectangular cross section of width b and depth h is loaded by the compressive load P acting on the lever arm e in the plane of the cross-sectional axis 1-1 (Fig. 13a). Since bending and direct stresses occur simultaneously from the beginning and grow together with increasing load P, no strain reversal is presumed to occur on the convex side of the deflected column at the instant at which the critical load is reached. When P increases until the proportional limit is exceeded in the entire cross section, or at least in the highest stressed portion of the section, the distribution of stress (Fig. 13b) will follow the stress-strain diagram. In every cross section there will be a σ_0-axis along which σ equals the average stress $\sigma_0 = P/A$, indicated by point O in Fig. 13b. It is convenient to split the stress σ in two parts, $\sigma = \sigma_0 + \sigma_b$, where σ_b denotes the stresses due to bending (shaded areas in Fig. 13b). The conditions of equilibrium then assume the form

$$b \int_{h_1}^{h_2} \sigma_b \, dz = 0 \quad \text{and} \quad b \int_{h_1}^{h_2} \sigma_b z \, dz = P(e + y) \tag{27}$$

where the deflection y refers to the centroidal axis of the column. The reference axis for the moment of the bending stresses σ_b may be chosen arbitrarily, since these stresses form a couple, and axis O was used to obtain the second Eq. (27).

[1] Young, D. H., Rational Design of Steel Columns, *Trans. ASCE*, Vol. 101, p. 422, 1936.

We introduce the following notations:

z = the distance of a fiber from the σ_0-axis of the cross section

σ_1 and σ_2 = the minimum and the maximum longitudinal stresses, respectively, at the external fibers

ϵ_0 = the compressive strain corresponding to the average stress σ_0

ϵ_1 and ϵ_2 = the minimum and maximum compressive strains, respectively, corresponding to the stresses σ_1 and σ_2

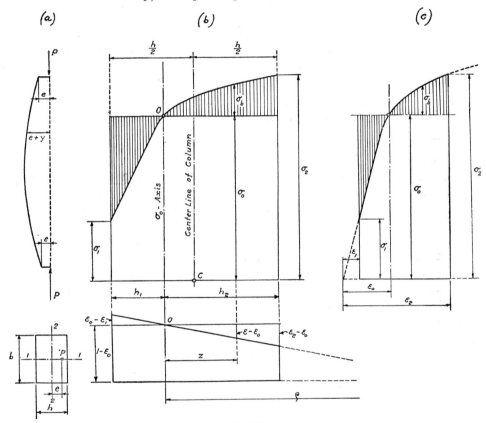

Fig. 13

Considering the relative rotation of two cross sections a distance unity apart, we may write with reference to Fig. 13b

$$\epsilon - \epsilon_0 = \frac{z}{\rho} \tag{28}$$

and

$$\epsilon_2 - \epsilon_1 = \frac{h}{\rho} \tag{29}$$

ρ is the radius of curvature of the bent column at the cross section under consideration. Eliminating ρ from these two equations leads to

$$\epsilon - \epsilon_0 = \frac{z}{h} (\epsilon_2 - \epsilon_1) \qquad (30)$$

from which by differentiation with respect to z

$$d\epsilon = \frac{\epsilon_2 - \epsilon_1}{h} dz \qquad (31)$$

follows. Introducing (30) and (31) into the relations (27) gives

$$\frac{bh}{\epsilon_2 - \epsilon_1} \int_{\epsilon_1}^{\epsilon_2} \sigma_b \, d\epsilon = 0 \qquad (32)$$

$$\frac{bh^2}{(\epsilon_2 - \epsilon_1)^2} \int_{\epsilon_1}^{\epsilon_2} \sigma_b (\epsilon - \epsilon_0) \, d\epsilon = P(e + y) \qquad (33)$$

In these equations σ_b should be considered a function of ϵ represented by the portion of the stress-strain curve which lies between ϵ_1 and ϵ_2 (Fig. 13c).

For a given average stress $\sigma_0 = P/A$ and a given maximum compressive strain ϵ_2 on the concave side of the column Eq. (32) yields the minimum compressive strain ϵ_1.* In this way a set of various distributions of stress pertaining to the same axial load P can be determined. Such a set represents possible distributions of stress which may exist at the various cross sections of the bent column. Each of these stress areas, defined by σ_0 and $\epsilon_2 - \epsilon_1$, determines through Eq. (29) a certain value of the radius of curvature ρ. On the other hand, after determining

$$\frac{1}{(\epsilon_2 - \epsilon_1)^2} \int_{\epsilon_1}^{\epsilon_2} \sigma_b (\epsilon - \epsilon_0) \, d\epsilon$$

from the stress-strain diagram, a corresponding value of y can be obtained from Eq. (33). We obtain in this manner a set of correlated values ρ and y which define a function $\rho = F(y)$. Since for a small deflection $\frac{1}{\rho} = \frac{d^2y}{dx^2}$, a relationship

$$\frac{d^2y}{dx^2} = F(y) \qquad (34)$$

can be established. $F(y)$ may be defined numericaliy by a table or graphically in the form of a diagram. Differential equation (34) defines y, the shape of the deflected center line, for any value of $\sigma_0 = P/A$, eccentricity e, and length l of the column.

---

* Equation (32) expresses the condition that the two shaded areas in Fig. 13c must be equal.

We shall not concern ourselves with the highly involved procedure of solving Eq. (34). It may be noted only that as a result of various graphical integrations the length l of the column (or the slenderness ratio l/r) can be presented as a function of σ_0 and e. From these curves another group of curves can be derived finally showing for given values l/r and e the relationship between the average stress σ_0 and the deflection y_m at mid-height of a column.

Such a (σ_0, y_m)-curve, typical for the behavior of an eccentrically loaded column of elastic-plastic material, is shown in Fig. 14. A parallel to the y_m-axis at the distance σ_0 intersects the curve at two points. This indicates that two configurations of equilibrium are possible, both per-

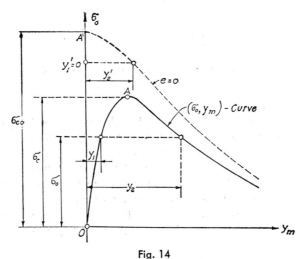

Fig. 14

taining to the same load $P = A\sigma_0$. The first configuration, corresponding to the deflection $y_m = y_1$, is stable because an increase of σ_0 is required to increase the deflection. After the load P is removed, the column returns toward its originally straight form but retains a slightly bent shape owing to the residual plastic strain in those fibers where the proportional limit was exceeded. The second configuration associated with the deflection $y_m = y_2$ is an unstable configuration, since a further increase of y_m involves a diminishing of σ_0. The maximum value of σ_0, given by the ordinate σ_c of the highest point A of the curve, indicates, therefore, the transition from stable to unstable equilibrium. Accordingly, $P_c = A\sigma_c$ defines the failure load of the eccentrically loaded column. It becomes clear from this reasoning that failure of an eccentrically loaded column of structural metal is not a consequence of reaching a certain critical fiber stress but is due to the fact that, at a certain critical load, stable equilibrium is no longer possible between the internal and external bending moment. All attempts to approach the column problem under consideration as a stress problem must fail because in such attempts the principal nature of the problem is completely misunderstood.

It is worthy of note that the (σ_0, y_m)-curve shows the same characteristics, *i.e.*, an ascending and a descending branch with a definite apex

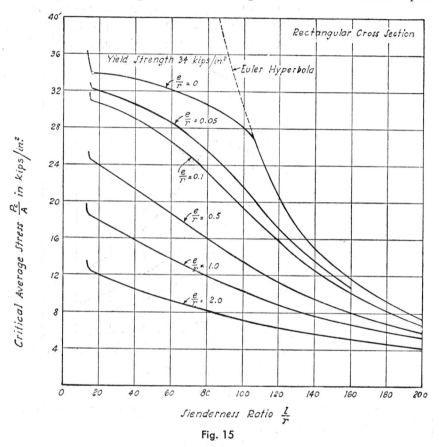

Fig. 15

which defines the buckling load, if σ_c lies below the proportional limit.   It must be kept in mind that the particular properties of the material as expressed by the shape of the stress-strain diagram control the equilibrium between external forces and internal stresses; such an equilibrium condition determines the critical load, whether σ_c lies below or above the proportional limit.

Chwalla succeeded, by means of a special arrangement of his tests on eccentrically loaded small specimens of rectangular cross section, in measuring the deflection y_m after passing the buckling load.   The shape of the observed (σ_0, y_m)-curve was in surprisingly good accord with the shape predicted by the theory.[1] The importance of these experiments is that they may be considered strong evidence supporting Kármán's conception of the problem as a stability problem.

In the limiting case of the centrally loaded column, $e = 0$, the (σ_0, y_m)-curve assumes the form indicated by the dashed curve in Fig. 14. The apex A' determines the Euler load or the tangent-modulus load of the axially loaded column. Below this load there are also two different equilibrium configurations possible: the straight and stable form

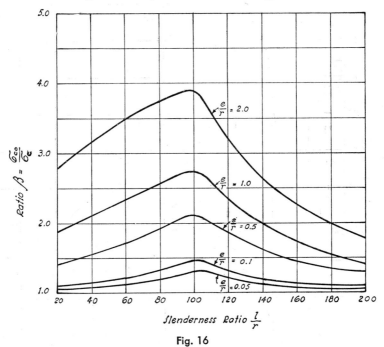

Fig. 16

$y_m = y_1' = 0$ and the bent but unstable configuration which corresponds to the deflection $y_m = y_2'$.

A group of (σ_0, y_m)-curves, calculated for various values of the slenderness ratio l/r and eccentricity e, finally constitute the basis for a tabulation of the critical average stress $\sigma_c = P_c/A$ as a function of l/r and e. In Fig. 15 the critical average stress $\sigma_c = P_c/A$ is plotted versus the slenderness ratio l/r for various values of the ratio e/r. In this way a group of column curves are obtained which show clearly the considerable effect of load eccentricity upon the carrying capacity of the column. The curves in Fig. 15 were computed for columns with rectangular cross

[1] Chwalla, E., Über die experimentelle Untersuchung des Tragverhaltens gedrückter Stäbe aus Baustahl, *Der Stahlbau*, Vol. 7, p. 17, 1934.

section of structural steel having a proportional limit $\sigma_p = 27$ kips/in.^{2} and a yield point $\sigma_y = 34$ kips/in.^{2} The effect of an eccentricity is very considerable for short and medium-long columns but diminishes in the region of elastic buckling with increasing l/r. Inspection of Fig. 16, where the ratio $\beta = \sigma_{c0}/\sigma_c$ (σ_{c0} being the critical average stress of the axially loaded column) is plotted against l/r, shows this behavior very clearly.

11. The Method of Westergaard and Osgood

The analysis in the previous article can be considerably simplified by assuming a suitable shape of the deflected column axis. This has been done by Westergaard and Osgood,[1] who assumed that the center line can be represented by a portion of a cosine curve with a half wavelength L_j^s (Fig. 17). The authors start from the basic equations used above [Eqs. (29), (30), (32), and (33)] and proceed in the following way:

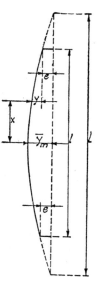

Fig. 17

Introducing the radius of gyration of the rectangular cross section, $r = h/\sqrt{12}$, and using the abbreviations

$$R = \int_{\epsilon_1}^{\epsilon_2} \sigma_b(\epsilon - \epsilon_0)\, d\epsilon \qquad \text{and} \qquad S = \frac{\sqrt{12}\, R}{\sigma_0(\epsilon_2 - \epsilon_1)^2}$$

Eq. (33) assumes the form

$$\frac{e + y}{r} = S \tag{35}$$

The numerical work proceeds in the same manner as described above, by computing a set of distributions of stress from the stress-strain diagram, in this way obtaining sets of correlated values of σ_0, $\epsilon_2 - \epsilon_1$, R, and S.

The shape of the deflected center line is then assumed

$$e + y = \bar{y}_m \cos ax \tag{36}$$

where $\bar{y}_m = e + y_m$ and $a = \pi/L$, (Fig. 17). From this equation

$$\frac{1}{\rho} = -\frac{d^2y}{dx^2} = \bar{y}_m\, a^2 \cos ax$$

is derived. Hence Eq. (29) assumes the form

$$\frac{\epsilon_2 - \epsilon_1}{r\sqrt{12}} = \bar{y}_m a^2 \cos ax \tag{37}$$

[1] Westergaard and Osgood, *loc. cit.* on p. 26.

Next, considering a column of given length l loaded with a given load P, the problem can be solved by finding the corresponding maximum eccentricity e at which stable equilibrium is possible. Equation (36) gives, with $x = l/2$,

$$e = \bar{y}_m \cos \frac{al}{2} \tag{38}$$

The condition $\dfrac{de}{d\bar{y}_m}$ defines this maximum. Observing that a is a function of $\bar{y}_m$, having a derivative $a' = \dfrac{da}{d\bar{y}_m}$, we obtain

$$\frac{\bar{y}_m a'}{a} = \frac{1}{(al/2)\,\tan\,(al/2)} \tag{39}$$

Equations (35) to (39) solve the problem. For a given value of σ_0 a series of values $\bar{y}_m$ and π/L may be found corresponding to a series of strain differences $\epsilon_2 - \epsilon_1$. Upon determining a' graphically from the curve $a = f(\bar{y}_m)$ and computing $\bar{y}_m a'/a$, the ratio $e/\bar{y}_m$ and the quantity al can be evaluated graphically with the aid of Eqs. (38) and (39) and the values of e and l can be determined.

In another part of the paper Westergaard and Osgood investigated the effect of initial crookedness upon the ultimate strength of axially loaded columns. Assuming the initial center line to be a smooth, flat curve and assuming the additional deflection y due to the load P to be the half wave of length L of a cosine curve, the authors arrived finally at a set of column curves for various ratios e/r where e expresses the initial deflection at mid-height of the column. In order to check the accuracy of the assumed cosine curve the computation was repeated by expressing y by a two-term Fourier series. It was found from these comparative computations that the assumption of a simple cosine curve furnishes results which deviate only slightly from the more accurate solution. The simpler investigation gives values which lie on the safe side.

12. Approximate Solution of the Stability Problem

The serious difficulties encountered in the preceding treatment of the problem of instability of eccentrically loaded columns, which have their origin in the complicated shape of the stress-strain curve, naturally lead to the idea of arriving at an analytical solution of the problem by basing it upon a simplified stress-strain relationship. The aim is to develop sufficiently simple equations which may define the relation between the slenderness ratio l/r and the critical average stress σ_c.

This idea was taken up by Ježek, who based his investigation upon the stress-strain diagram of an ideal, elastic-plastic material. The modulus of elasticity E is assumed constant up to the yield point; from here on it is $E = 0$ (Fig. 18a).   The yield point is assumed to be the same in tension and in compression.   The column curve is then built up from the Euler hyperbola and from a straight line at the distance σ_y from the l/r-axis (Fig. 18b).   For comparison the column curve for structural steel is indicated by a dashed line.   The idealized relationship between stress and strain renders it now feasible to obtain an analytical solution for the stability problem of eccentrically and laterally loaded columns.

Ježek[1] gave in his first publication on the subject an exact solution of the stability problem starting from the above-described simplified stress-strain curve.   In two later papers[2] he presented an approximate

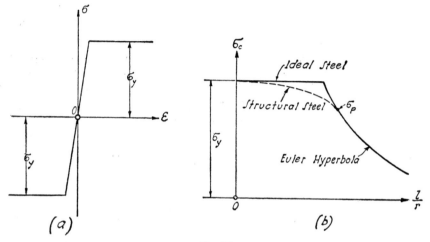

Fig. 18

method and showed that, for all practical purposes, this method gives satisfactory results.   The axis of the deflected column is assumed to be the half wave of a sine curve.   This is a rather crude approximation, but the nature of most buckling problems is such that an error in the assumed shape of the deflection curve does not substantially affect the outcome of the analysis.   On the other hand this simplification of the deflection curve offers the advantage of leading to a general method which is valid for eccentrically as well as laterally loaded or initially curved compression members.   An outline of this approximate theory is given in the following paragraphs.

Consider a simply supported straight column of rectangular cross section axially loaded by the force P and under the action of a bending

[1] Ježek, *loc. cit.* on p. 26.

[2] Ježek, K., Näherungsberechnung der Tragkraft exzentrisch gedrückter Stahlstäbe, *Der Stahlbau*, Vol. 8, p. 89, 1935; Die Tragfähigkeit axial gedrückter und auf Biegung beanspruchter Stahlstäbe, *Der Stahlbau*, Vol. 9, p. 12, 1936.   A further reference is listed at the end of the chapter.

moment m_x, varying over the length l of the column as shown by the moment diagram in Fig. 19.   The moment curve m_x is assumed to be symmetrical.   At the cross section x the total bending moment will be

$$M_x = m_x + Py$$

Under the assumption that the centroidal axis of the column takes the form

$$y = y_m \sin \frac{\pi x}{l}$$

the curvature at mid-height of the column may be expressed by

$$\frac{1}{\rho_m} = - \left[\frac{d^2 y}{dx^2}\right]_{x=\frac{l}{2}} = \frac{\pi^2}{l^2} y_m \qquad (40)$$

By equating expression (40) and the expression for the curvature derived from the distribution of stress in the cross section at $x = l/2$, a relation

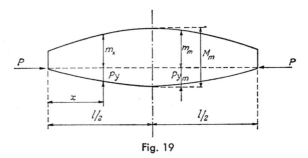

Fig. 19

is obtained between the deflection y_m and the average stress $\sigma_0 = P/A$, which relation, however, takes the distribution of stress at the mid-section only into consideration.   At this section there are two different distributions of stress possible, indicated in Figs. 20a and 20b.

Case I (Fig. 20a): The yield point is reached on the concave side of the bent column, while the tensile stresses on the convex side still remain in the elastic range.   The region of yielding is assumed to extend a distance e_1 into the cross section.

Case II (Fig. 20b): The yield strength is reached at both sides of the cross section, and it is assumed that yielding extends distances e_2 and d_2, respectively, into the cross section.

Case I will be investigated first.   The conditions of equilibrium between internal and external forces at the cross section at mid-height of the column are

$$b \int_{h_1}^{h_2} \sigma \, dz = P \qquad \text{and} \qquad b \int_{h_1}^{h_2} \sigma z \, dz = M_m$$

where z denotes the fiber distance from the σ_0-axis. Since the variable stress σ is defined by the straight lines in Fig. 20a, the integrals above are readily computed. Thus, these two equations lead to two relations which determine the distances e_1 and d_1. By introducing the average

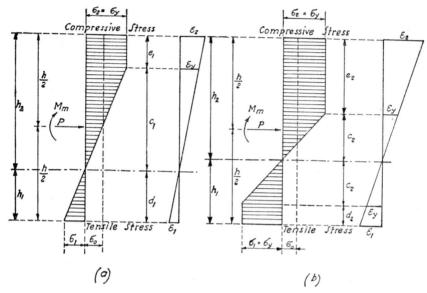

Fig. 20

stress $\sigma_0 = P/A$, and observing that $e_1 + c_1 + d_1 = h$, the following two equations are obtained:

$$\frac{e_1}{h} = \frac{3M_m}{(\sigma_y - \sigma_0)bh^2} - \frac{1}{2} \quad \text{and} \quad \frac{c_1}{h} = \frac{9\left(\sigma_y - \sigma_0 - \dfrac{2M_m}{bh^2}\right)^2}{8(\sigma_y - \sigma_0)^3} \cdot \sigma_y \quad (41)$$

From Fig. 20a follows

$$\frac{\epsilon_2 - \epsilon_1}{h} = \frac{\epsilon_y}{c_1} = \frac{\sigma_y}{Ec_1}$$

and because of $(\epsilon_2 - \epsilon_1)/h = 1/\rho_m$ [Eq. (29) on page 28] we have

$$\frac{1}{\rho_m} = \frac{\sigma_y}{Ec_1}$$

Introducing the value of c_1 from the second expression (41) gives the curvature $1/\rho_m$ at the cross section under consideration:

$$\frac{1}{\rho_m} = \frac{2\sigma_0\left(\dfrac{\sigma_y}{\sigma_0} - 1\right)^3 h}{9E\left[\dfrac{h}{2}\left(\dfrac{\sigma_y}{\sigma_0} - 1\right) - \dfrac{M_m}{P}\right]^2} \quad (42)$$

Combination of Eqs. (40) and (42) finally leads to a relation between y_m and σ_0, namely,

$$9Ey_m \left[\frac{h}{2} \left(\frac{\sigma_y}{\sigma_0} - 1 \right) - y_m - \frac{m_m}{P} \right]^2 - 2\sigma_0 h \left(\frac{\sigma_y}{\sigma_0} - 1 \right)^3 \frac{l^2}{\pi^2} = 0 \quad (43)$$

where M_m was replaced by $m_m + Py$.

Equation (43) is the analytical expression for the (y_m, σ_0)-curves which can be drawn for various values of the parameter m_m/P. These curves are of the same nature as the (y_m, σ_0)-curves discussed in the preceding Arts. 10 and 11. The apex of each curve, defined by $\frac{d\sigma_0}{dy_m} = 0$, determines the critical value of the average stress σ_0, which leads to a second-degree equation in the variable y_m:

$$3y_m{}^2 - 4y_m \left[\frac{h}{2} \left(\frac{\sigma_y}{\sigma_0} - 1 \right) - \frac{m_m}{P} \right] + \left[\frac{h}{2} \left(\frac{\sigma_y}{\sigma_0} - 1 \right) - \frac{m_m}{P} \right]^2 = 0$$

from which the critical value of y_m, corresponding to the critical value of σ_0, may be derived:

$$y_m = \frac{1}{3} \left[\frac{h}{2} \left(\frac{\sigma_y}{\sigma_0} - 1 \right) - \frac{m_m}{P} \right] \quad (44)$$

Introducing (44) into (43) finally furnishes the following Eq. (45), representing a relation between the critical average stress $\sigma_0 = \sigma_c$ and the slenderness ratio l/r for any given value of the parameter m_m/P:

$$\sigma_c = \frac{\pi^2 E}{(l/r)^2} \left(\frac{\frac{\sigma_y}{\sigma_c} - 1 - \frac{2m_m}{Ph}}{\frac{\sigma_y}{\sigma_c} - 1} \right)^3 \quad (45)$$

Case II: The procedure is the same as before. The conditions of equilibrium define the distances c_2, e_2, and d_2 in Fig. 20b:

$$\left. \begin{aligned} \frac{c_2}{h} &= \sqrt{\frac{3}{4} \left(1 - \frac{\sigma_0{}^2}{\sigma_y{}^2} \right)} - \frac{3M_m}{bh^2 \sigma_y} \\ \frac{e_2}{h} &= \frac{1}{2} \left(1 + \frac{\sigma_0}{\sigma_y} \right) - \sqrt{\frac{3}{4} \left(1 - \frac{\sigma_0{}^2}{\sigma_y{}^2} \right)} - \frac{3M_m}{bh^2 \sigma_y} \\ \frac{d_2}{h} &= \frac{1}{2} \left(1 - \frac{\sigma_0}{\sigma_y} \right) - \sqrt{\frac{3}{4} \left(1 - \frac{\sigma_0{}^2}{\sigma_y{}^2} \right)} - \frac{3M_m}{bh^2 \sigma_y} \end{aligned} \right\} \quad (46)$$

From Fig. 20b we find in the same manner as before, by using Eq. (29),

$$\frac{1}{\rho_m} = \frac{\sigma_y}{Ec_2}$$

and replacing c_2 by means of the first Eq. (46) we obtain

$$\frac{1}{\rho_m} = \sqrt{\frac{\sigma_y^3/3hE^2\sigma_0}{\frac{h\sigma_y}{4\sigma_0}\left(1 - \frac{\sigma_0^2}{\sigma_y^2}\right) - \frac{M_m}{P}}} \tag{47}$$

Equating the right sides of (40) and (47) we arrive at

$$y_m \sqrt{\frac{h\sigma_y}{4\sigma_0}\left(1 - \frac{\sigma_0^2}{\sigma_y^2}\right)} - y_m - \frac{m_m}{P} - \frac{l^2}{\pi^2}\sqrt{\frac{\sigma_y^3}{3hE^2\sigma_0}} = 0 \tag{48}$$

representing the (y_m,σ_0)-curves. The condition $\dfrac{d\sigma_0}{dy_m} = 0$ gives the value of y_m which is associated with the critical average stress σ_0:

$$y_m = \frac{h\sigma_y}{6\sigma_0}\left(1 - \frac{\sigma_0^2}{\sigma_y^2}\right) - \frac{2m_m}{3P} \tag{49}$$

Substituting y_m from Eq. (49) into (48) finally leads to the relation between the critical average stress $\sigma_0 = \sigma_c$ and the slenderness ratio l/r for any given value of m_m/P:

$$\sigma_c = \frac{\left[\dfrac{(l/r)^2}{\pi^2 E}\right]^2 \sigma_y^3}{\left(\dfrac{\sigma_y}{\sigma_c} - \dfrac{\sigma_c}{\sigma_y} - \dfrac{4m_m}{Ph}\right)^3} \tag{50}$$

The two Eqs (45) and (50) permit the direct computation of the critical slenderness ratio l/r, which corresponds to given values of the "equivalent eccentricity" $e = m_m/P$, and of the critical average stress σ_c. It is convenient to express h by the core radius $s = h/6$ of the rectangular section in order to facilitate the application of these two formulas for cross sections other than rectangular. Upon introducing the eccentricity ratio

$$\kappa = \frac{e}{s} = \frac{m_m}{Ps} \tag{51}$$

into Eqs. (45) and (50), we solve for l/r and obtain

$$\left(\frac{l}{r}\right)^2 = \frac{\pi^2 E}{\sigma_c}\left[\frac{3\left(\dfrac{\sigma_y}{\sigma_c} - 1\right) - \kappa}{3\left(\dfrac{\sigma_y}{\sigma_c} - 1\right)}\right]^3 \tag{52}$$

valid for

$$\left(\frac{l}{r}\right)^2 - \frac{\pi^2 E\kappa^3}{9\sigma_y(3 - \kappa)} > 0 \qquad \text{(Stress distribution, Case I)}$$

and

$$\left(\frac{l}{r}\right)^2 = \frac{\pi^2 E}{\sigma_y} \sqrt{\frac{\sigma_c}{\sigma_y}\left(\frac{\sigma_y}{\sigma_c} - \frac{\sigma_c}{\sigma_y} - \frac{2}{3}\kappa\right)^3} \tag{53}$$

valid for

$$\left(\frac{l}{r}\right)^2 - \frac{\pi^2 E \kappa^3}{9\sigma_y(3 - \kappa)} < 0 \qquad \text{(Stress distribution, Case II)}$$

For large eccentricities $\kappa \geq 3$, the stress distribution will be according to Case II, and Eq. (53) is applicable.

Ježek's algebraic formulas do not give the critical stress $\sigma_c = P_c/A$ explicitly as a function of l/r. For a given material it is necessary to compute first a table which shows l/r at suitable intervals as function of σ_c and κ. Then it is easy to develop column curves or to compute tables which give, for varying values of the eccentricity ratio κ, the critical average stress σ_c as a function of the slenderness ratio. The column curves essentially have the same shape as the curves which are derived from the exact theory, samples of which are shown in Fig. 15. Table 1 shows the σ_c-values in tabulated form. This table was computed by Ježek from Eqs. (52) and (53) for structural steel having a yield strength $\sigma_y = 2400$ kg/cm^2 (27 kips/in.^{2}).

TABLE 1. Critical Stresses $\sigma_c = P_c/A$, in kips/in.^{2}, for Eccentrically Loaded Columns of Structural Steel

$(\sigma_y = 34$ kips/in.$^2)$

l/r	Eccentricity ratio $\kappa = e/s$													
	0	0.10	0.175	0.25	0.50	0.75	1.00	1.25	1.50	1.75	2.00	2.50	3.00	3.50	4.00
20	34.0	32.4	31.3	30.3	27.3	24.9	22.9	21.3	19.8	18.3	17.1	14.9	13.4	11.9	10.8
30	34.0	32.1	30.9	29.7	26.3	23.9	21.9	20.2	18.8	17.5	16.3	14.3	12.8	11.4	10.4
40	34.0	31.7	30.3	29.0	25.3	22.8	20.8	19.0	17.7	16.5	15.5	13.6	12.1	10.9	9.9
50	34.0	31.3	29.6	28.0	24.3	21.6	19.6	18.0	16.6	15.6	14.6	12.9	11.5	10.4	9.4
60	34.0	30.6	28.7	26.9	23.0	20.3	18.4	16.9	15.6	14.6	13.8	12.1	10.9	9.8	9.0
70	34.0	29.4	27.6	25.8	21.6	19.0	17.2	15.8	14.6	13.6	12.9	11.4	10.3	9.3	8.5
80	34.0	28.0	26.0	24.0	20.2	17.8	16.1	14.8	13.6	12.8	12.1	10.7	9.7	8.8	8.1
90	34.0	26.0	24.0	22.0	18.6	16.5	14.9	13.7	12.7	12.0	11.2	10.1	9.1	8.4	7.7
100	29.6	23.5	21.8	20.2	17.1	15.2	13.8	12.7	11.8	11.1	10.4	9.4	8.5	7.8	7.3
110	24.5	20.8	19.5	18.2	15.5	13.9	12.7	11.7	10.9	10.2	9.7	8.8	8.0	7.4	6.8
120	20.6	18.2	17.2	16.2	14.2	12.6	11.7	10.8	10.1	9.5	9.0	8.2	7.5	7.0	6.4
130	17.5	16.0	15.2	14.5	12.8	11.5	10.7	10.0	9.4	8.8	8.4	7.7	7.1	6.5	6.1
140	15.1	14.1	13.5	13.0	11.5	10.5	9.8	9.2	8.7	8.2	7.8	7.2	6.7	6.1	5.7
150	13.1	12.4	12.0	11.5	10.4	9.7	9.0	8.4	8.0	7.6	7.2	6.7	6.3	5.7	5.4
160	11.6	11.1	10.7	10.4	9.4	8.8	8.2	7.8	7.4	7.1	6.7	6.3	5.8	5.4	5.1

At this point it is necessary to explain the degree of approximation involved in the use of the idealized stress-strain diagram. The deviation between the values of the critical stresses σ_c computed from the approximate theory and the values determined from the real stress-strain curve of structural steel becomes appreciable for small values of κ and reaches a maximum when κ approaches zero but decreases rapidly when the eccentricity ratio increases. The part of each column curve below point A in Fig. 21 shows the greatest deviation from the exact curves, which is due to the fact that the difference between the real and ideal stress-strain diagram in that region is greatest. A simple way to improve the σ_c-values by a correction in this region will be shown in the next article.

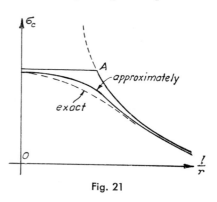

When such a correction is made, the maximum error involved in the analytical results of the approximate method shrinks to an amount which is of the magnitude of the unavoidable fluctuations of the yield strength in any steel structure. Therefore, the analytical results of the approximate theory discussed, which permits comparatively quick

Fig. 21

calculation of column curves for any material with a sharply defined yield point, may be considered a suitable basis for a method of design for eccentrically loaded compression members.

13. Method of Designing Eccentrically Loaded Columns

In the following, the concept of a practical method of designing eccentrically or laterally loaded columns and initially curved columns will be outlined. For this purpose we introduce the ratio

$$\beta = \frac{\sigma_{c0}}{\sigma_c} \tag{54}$$

already used in the foregoing article, into the column design. σ_{c0} is the critical stress for $\kappa = 0$. Assuming that the factor β, computed from the approximate theory, depicts with sufficient practical accuracy the ratio between σ_{c0}, the critical stress of the axially loaded column, and σ_c, the critical stress of the eccentrically loaded column, we may express the latter by

$$\sigma_c = \frac{\sigma_{c0}}{\beta} \tag{55}$$

where σ_{c0} now is understood to be the critical average stress of the centrally loaded column derived from an actual column curve. Dividing both sides of Eq. (55) by the safety factor, we obtain a relationship between the working stresses:

$$F' = \frac{F}{\beta} \tag{56}$$

where F is the working stress for a centrally loaded column while F' is the working stress for the eccentrically or laterally loaded column. It should be stressed that Eq. (56) yields the allowable average stress $F' = P/A$,

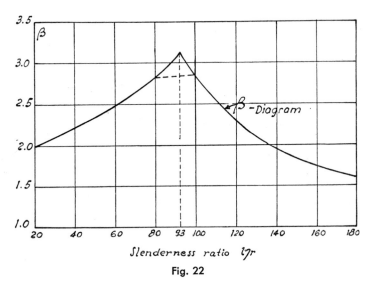

Fig. 22

not the maximum fiber stress. The β-values can be computed easily by dividing the first column in Table 1 ($\kappa = 0$) by the other columns.

The nature of the β-curves may be seen from Fig. 22, where, for $\kappa = 2$, β is plotted against l/r. The β-curve shows a sharp discontinuity at $l/r = 93$ which is due to the discontinuity of the column curve for $\kappa = 0$. Cutting off the apex by a straight line between $l/r = 80$ and 100, we eliminate the effect of this unnatural discontinuity and arrive at a form of the β-curve which agrees rather well with curves derived from the exact theory.

In order to facilitate the application of the β-concept in practical design it is convenient to replace the family of β-curves for the various eccentricity values by simple algebraic formulas, which depict the curves with reasonable accuracy. The author suggests the use of such formulas because they permit computation of β quickly without the complex procedure of twofold interpolation. The following formulas were developed

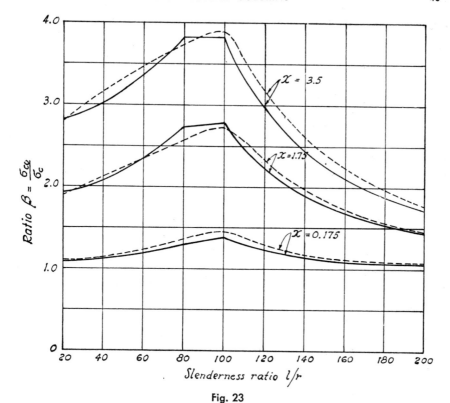

Fig. 23

for mild steel ($\sigma_y = 34$ and 40 kips/in.^{2}) and for high-tensile carbon steel ($\sigma_y = 50$ kips/in.^{2}).

Structural Steel ($\sigma_y = 34$ kips/in.^{2}):

$$\left.\begin{array}{ll} \text{For } \dfrac{l}{r} = 20 \text{ to } 80: & \beta = \left(1 + \dfrac{\kappa}{2}\right) + \dfrac{\sqrt{\kappa}}{10{,}000}\left(\dfrac{l}{r}\right)^2 \\[3mm] \text{For } \dfrac{l}{r} = 100 \text{ to } 200: & \beta = 1 + \dfrac{12{,}200\sqrt[3]{\kappa^2}}{(l/r)^2} \end{array}\right\} \quad (57)$$

For values $80 < l/r < 100$ interpolate linearly between β_{80} and β_{100}.

Structural Steel ($\sigma_y = 40$ kips/in.^{2}):

$$\left.\begin{array}{ll} \text{For } \dfrac{l}{r} = 20 \text{ to } 75: & \beta = \left(1 + \dfrac{\kappa}{2}\right) + \dfrac{\sqrt{\kappa}}{9{,}000}\left(\dfrac{l}{r}\right)^2 \\[3mm] \text{For } \dfrac{l}{r} = 95 \text{ to } 200: & \beta = 1 + \dfrac{10{,}600\sqrt[3]{\kappa^2}}{(l/r)^2} \end{array}\right\} \quad (58)$$

For values $75 < l/r < 95$ interpolate linearly between β_{75} and β_{95}.

High-tensile Carbon Steel $(\sigma_y = 50 \text{ kips/in.}^2)$:

$$\left. \begin{array}{ll} \text{For } \dfrac{l}{r} = 20 \text{ to } 70: & \beta = \left(1 + \dfrac{\kappa}{2}\right) + \dfrac{\sqrt{\kappa}}{7{,}000}\left(\dfrac{l}{r}\right)^2 \\[3mm] \text{For } \dfrac{l}{r} = 90 \text{ to } 200: & \beta = 1 + \dfrac{8{,}400 \sqrt[3]{\kappa^2}}{(l/r)^2} \end{array} \right\} \qquad (59)$$

For values $70 < l/r < 90$ interpolate linearly between β_{70} and β_{90}.

The expressions (57) to (59) render it possible to compute β directly from given values of κ and l/r. The critical stress and the allowable stress of the eccentrically loaded column can then be obtained from Eqs. (55) and (56).

Figure 23 shows three β-curves computed from the Eqs. (57) for $\kappa = 0.175$, 1.75, and 3.50. The dashed lines indicate, for comparison, the exact β-values taken from Fig. 16.[1] The deviation between the two groups of curves diminishes with decreasing value of κ.

14. Influence of the Cross-sectional Shape upon Column Strength

So far we have discussed columns of rectangular cross section, and the question arises whether Eqs. (57) to (59) may be applied to cross-sectional shapes commonly used in steel structures. Careful analytical studies and comparative calculations made by Chwalla,[2] Ježek,[3] and Fritsche[4] indicate that the column strength is considerably influenced by the particular shape of the cross section. As a rule, cross sections having the material concentrated near the center of gravity (*i.e.*, + sections) possess greater strength, for a given l/r, than those where the material is located some distance from the center of gravity (H-sections for buckling in plane of the web). The rectangular section lies between these extremes. Hence, it is necessary to allow for the form of the cross section, at least approximately. This can be done by multiplying the equivalent eccentricity κ by a factor μ which depends upon the geometric form of the cross section and using the value $\mu\kappa$ instead of κ when applying formulas (57) to (59).

Table 2 gives average values of the multiplier μ for various cross sections condensed from the investigations of Chwalla and Fritsche. The values of μ in Table 2 must be considered as crude approximations only,

[1] The eccentricity ratios in Fig. 16, $e/r = 0.1$, 1.0, and 2.0, correspond almost exactly with the ratios $\kappa = e/s$ given above.

[2] Chwalla, E., Der Einfluss der Querschnittsform auf das Tragvermögen aussermittig gedrückter Baustahlstäbe, *Der Stahlbau*, Vol. 8, p. 193, 1935.

[3] Ježek, K., Die Festigkeit aussermittig gedrückter Stahlstäbe beliebiger Querschnittsform, *Der Bauingenieur*, Vol. 17, p. 306, 1936.

[4] Fritsche, J., Näherungsverfahren zur Berechnung der Tragfähigkeit aussermittig gedrückter Stäbe aus Baustahl, *Der Stahlbau*, Vol. 8, p. 137, 1935.

since the effect of the cross-sectional form upon the buckling strength of eccentrically loaded columns is by no means sufficiently cleared up.

TABLE 2

Shape of cross section		μ
		0.75
		0.80
		1.0
		1.3

15. The Secant Formula

Many attempts have been made to treat the problem of eccentrically loaded columns as a stress problem by defining the failure load of the column as the load which produces the beginning of yielding in the fibers subject to maximum compression. Under the assumption that the modulus of elasticity remains constant up to the yield point, the deflection of the center line is given by the equation

$$ y = \left(\frac{\cos \alpha \left(\frac{l}{2} - x \right)}{\cos \frac{\alpha l}{2}} - 1 \right) e \quad \text{and} \quad \alpha = \sqrt{\frac{P}{EI}} $$

where e is the eccentricity of the load P. y_m denoting the deflection at $x = l/2$, the maximum fiber stress at mid-length of the column is

$$ \sigma = \frac{P}{A} + \frac{P(y_m + e)}{I} c \tag{60} $$

where c is the distance of the extreme fibers from the centroidal axis. Introducing

$$ y_m = \left(\frac{1}{\cos \frac{\alpha l}{2}} - 1 \right) e $$

into Eq. (60), and replacing I by Ar^2, we arrive at the so-called secant formula

$$\sigma = \frac{P}{A}\left(1 + \frac{ec}{r^2}\sec\frac{l}{2r}\sqrt{\frac{P}{EA}}\right) \tag{61}$$

The carrying capacity P_c of the column is defined as the load producing the yield stress $\sigma = \sigma_y$, computed by Eq. (61). The critical average stress in the column is $\sigma_c = P_c/A$, and the allowable column load P_c/n, where n is the safety factor.

The interrelation between the critical load given by Eq. (61) and the actual buckling load is readily seen when we again consider the (σ_0, y_m)-curve as derived, for instance, by the method discussed in Art. 12. In Fig. 24 point B corresponds to the value of P/A at which the yield point

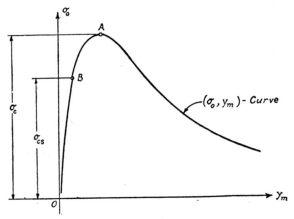

Fig. 24

is reached in the fibers of maximum stress of the bent column. Therefore, the ordinate σ_{cs} of point B indicates the critical value of P_c/A as given by the secant formula, while the real magnitude of the critical stress is defined by the highest point A of the (σ_0, y_m)-curve. The deviation between the two values σ_{cs} and σ_c will vary widely with the shape of the cross section, the slenderness ratio l/r, and the eccentricity ratio ec/r^2. The difference is considerable when buckling takes place in such manner that the narrow edges of outstanding flanges are subjected to maximum compressive stress. It is comparatively small when the maximum stress occurs over the entire width of the flange of H-columns. For short columns and for certain cross-sectional shapes the difference may amount to 30 to 40% of the actual buckling load (see Fig. 26).

The high regard in which the engineering profession has held and still holds the secant formula has its origin in the fact that, for small values of the eccentricity, this formula leads to a column curve for axially loaded columns which complies fairly well with values of P/A derived from column tests, provided that an "equivalent eccentricity" e in Eq. (61) is suitably but arbitrarily selected to agree with these tests. This may be considered a happy coincidence but does not raise the secant-formula concept to the rank of a rational theory for buckling problems. The determination of the failure load is based upon an arbitrarily chosen criterion which does not bear any relation to the fundamental aspect of the problem as a stability problem.

This explains the wide deviation, found in many cases, between the predictions of theories based on the secant-formula concept and the actual buckling load.

16. Tests on Eccentrically Loaded Columns

As mentioned in Art. 9, Roš and Brunner have made a series of tests to check their method of calculation. The specimens investigated were I-beams NP22 and NP32 (standard beams of $8\frac{5}{8}$ and $12\frac{5}{8}$ in. depth), for eccentricities $\kappa = 0, 1$, and 3. The plane of loading was perpendicular to the web; thus buckling could, in all cases, be expected in the plane of loading. The analysis was based upon a stress-strain diagram obtained from tension tests showing the following characteristics: $\sigma_p = 25$ kips/in.[2] and $\sigma_y = 38$ kips/in.[2] The column curves calculated from Eqs. (58) and the test results are shown in Fig. 25. The observed values of σ_c agree with the calculated curves to a reasonable degree.

Grüning[1] reported on another series of tests. Five tests were made on columns of I-,][-, and + -sections having slenderness ratios between 52 and 75. The eccentricity ratio in one test was $\kappa = 0.38$, in the other cases $\kappa = 1$. Good agreement was found between the observed column strength and the values of σ_c calculated from the Kármán-Chwalla theory, taking into account the actual shapes of the cross sections.

Recently conducted tests on 93 H-shaped columns constitute a remarkable contribution to the experimental study of the problem of eccentrically loaded columns.[2] The tests were made with knife-edge supports on 3-in. I 5.7-lb sections with various slenderness ratios between 26 and 126 and eccentricity ratios $\kappa = 0, 0.5, 1, 1.5, 2, 3, 5, 7$. The same test program was carried out in both the weak and strong directions. Since the columns which were loaded eccentrically in the plane of the web usually failed by lateral torsional buckling, we consider in the following discussion only those tests where the moment of eccentricity lies in a plane perpendicular to the web.

The results of 18 tests with eccentricities $\kappa = 0$ and 1 are presented

---

[1] Grüning, G., *Der Stahlbau*, Vol. 8, p. 17, 1936.

[2] Johnston, B. G., and L. Cheney, Steel Columns of Rolled Wide Flange Section, *Committee on Tech. Research, Am. Inst. Steel Construction, Progress Rept.* 2, 1942.

in Fig. 26.   The results of tests on axially loaded specimens ($\kappa = 0$) were used to draw a smooth column curve (curve A in Fig. 26) fitted to the observed (σ_c, l/r)-values.   Curve A represents the values of σ_{c0} in Eq. (55).   By applying the β-concept discussed above, curve B was computed for $\kappa = 1$ from the equation σ_{c0}/β, applying Eq. (58) for the determination

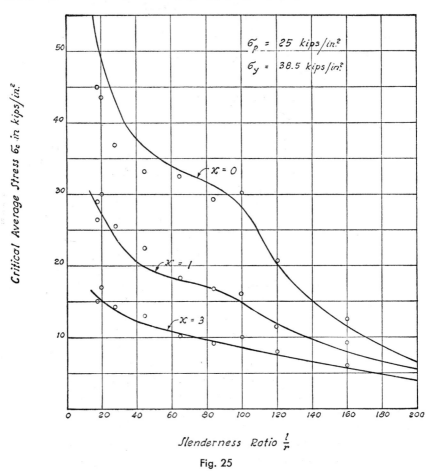

Fig. 25

of β.   The multiplier μ was assumed 0.75.   When the unavoidable variations in the material are taken into account, curve B, based on the rational concept of Art. 13, may be considered in fairly good agreement with the observed data.   For comparison, the column curve for $\kappa = 1$ computed from the secant formula is also shown in Fig. 26.   Figure 27 represents column curves computed for $\kappa = 2$ and $\kappa = 3$ from the basic column curve A of Fig. 26, as well as observed values of σ_c for $\kappa = 2$ and 3.   The test points lie rather close to the σ_c-curves.

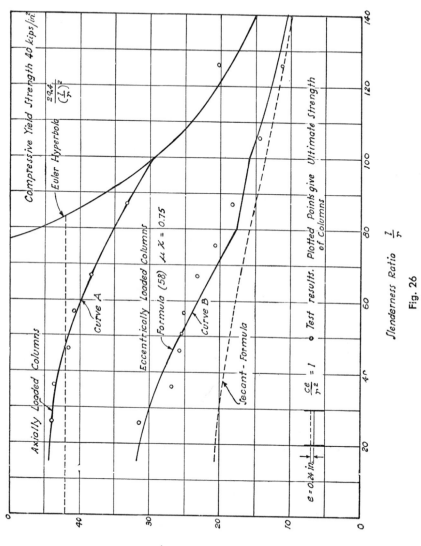

Fig. 26

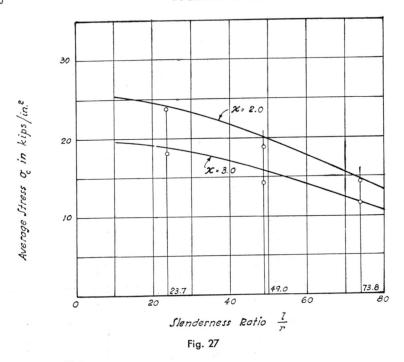

Fig. 27

17. Future Development of Theory of Eccentrically Loaded Columns

Review of the theory of eccentrically or laterally loaded compression members outlined in this chapter indicates that a rational solution of this problem, considered as a stability problem, has been achieved. However, the labor involved in the numerical calculations based upon the exact theory makes its practical use nearly impossible. Therefore, special emphasis has been laid upon the presentation of an approximate method based on an idealized stress-strain diagram which leads to algebraic relations between critical average stress, slenderness ratio, and eccentricity, from which simple design formulas can be derived. The application of this method is restricted to material which shows a sharply defined yield point. Comparison of the results of the approximate method with results obtained from the exact theory and with the results of tests proves that the idealizing simplification which underlies the approximate theory is justified and that this theory is fundamentally sound.

However, the theory of eccentric buckling developed in this chapter deals only with simply supported columns. Actual columns usually are framed into the adjacent members of the structure and may be regarded as columns having elastically restrained ends. There are only a few studies by Chwalla,[1] who investigated the effect of end restraints upon the failure load of eccentrically loaded columns.[2] From Chwalla's computations the inference can be drawn that end restraints reduce materially the effect of the moment of eccentricity upon the buckling load. Such behavior is easily understood by realizing that an appreciable portion of the acting moment of eccentricity may be directly transferred to the adjacent constraining members. The amount of the transferred moment increases with increasing degree of constraint. Further investigation in this field is desirable, since it would clear up the behavior of eccentrically loaded compression members under conditions encountered in actual metal structures. Ježek's approximate theory may offer an opportunity to study systematically the effect of elastic restraint of the column ends without too much labor. An elaborate study of eccentrically loaded columns with end restraints must be considered as the first step in an investigation of the behavior of columns as part of a rigid frame or in estimating the effect of secondary stresses in trusses upon the buckling strength of its compression members. This study will presumably prove that the effect upon buckling strength of an initial eccentricity of the axial load or an initial curvature of the column is considerably overestimated in view of the end conditions which prevail in conventional metal structures.

18. The Column as Part of a Structure. Principles of Column Design

Columns as used in metal structures may differ widely from the idealized columns considered so far in this chapter. There is a multiplicity of factors that affect the ultimate strength of columns which are integral parts of engineering structures:

1. Effect on column action of continuity conditions in framed structures.
2. Effect of eccentricity of axial load.
3. Effect of bending moments transmitted to the ends of columns from adjoining structural members, due to the rigid-frame action of the structure.

It is assumed in the following discussion that accidental imperfections, such as nonhomogeneity of the material, deviation from the assumed geometric form (initial crookedness), unintentional eccentricities of the axial load due to the unavoidable imperfection of shop and erection work, are taken care of by a proper choice of the factor of safety.

Each of the above-enumerated factors varies over a wide range and

[1] Chwalla, E., Aussermittig gedrückte Baustahlstäbe mit elastisch eingespannten Enden und verschieden grossen Angriffshebeln, *Die Bautechnik*, Vol. 10, 1937.
[2] See Chap. VI, Art. 62.

combines with the others in each individual case in a particular manner
The determination of the actual carrying capacity of a compression member as part of a structure therefore requires in each case: (1) establishment
of the effective length of the column, allowing for continuity conditions
at the ends which depend on the stiffness of the adjoining members and
the loads they carry; (2) the evaluation of any potential eccentricity
effect due to bending moments from frame action or due to the eccentric
transfer of the compressive load from adjacent members of the structure.

Fortunately, in many practical cases it is possible to judge the effect
upon column action of the factors mentioned above by rational methods
and to condense the results of the analysis to simple design rules, formulas,
or numerical tables for use in practical design. In this chapter we have
already considered the basic problems of the eccentricity effect. Later
chapters will be devoted to the presentation of theoretical investigations
and laboratory studies concerning column action in trusses and rigid
frames. These theories may serve as starting points from which simplified methods of design can be derived.

It was pointed out above that each compression member in a metal
structure represents an individual case which must be designed according
to its particular loading and end conditions, the design being based upon
the rationally derived, ideal column curve discussed in Art. 7. In such
a concept of column design the ideal column curve represents the graphical
(or tabulated) expression of the effect of the elastic-plastic properties of
the material on the column strength and nothing else. There is no logical
reason to incorporate in the column formula any of the accidental factors
affecting the buckling strength such as accidental eccentricities or initial
crookedness. These uncertainties are best taken care of by the factor of
safety. It must be borne in mind that the column problem proper, as
discussed before, represents only a small portion of the entire group of
buckling problems in structural design. It is not only logical, but also a
matter of convenience, to base the design in all cases of instability upon
one and the same column curve. Accordingly, this fundamental characteristic which controls the behavior of any structural element under
compression should not be obscured by any particular factor which may
have importance for one type of structural members but is of no significance for another.

Inspecting the relationship between the critical stress σ_c and the slenderness ratio l/r of an ideal column of structural steel, illustrated by the
curve in Fig. 28, it is readily seen that the shape of the curve is controlled
essentially by three parameters: the modulus of elasticity E, which defines
the Euler hyperbola, and the proportional limit σ_p and yield point σ_y,
determining the end points A and B of the curve for the inelastic range.
The curve AB derived from the tangent-modulus concept can con-

veniently be replaced for practical use in column design by the quadratic parabola

$$\sigma_c = \sigma_y - \frac{\sigma_y - \sigma_p}{(l'/r)^2}\left(\frac{l}{r}\right)^2 \tag{62}$$

The coefficient of the second term is defined by the two characteristics of the material, σ_p and σ_y, and by the slenderness ratio l'/r which cor-

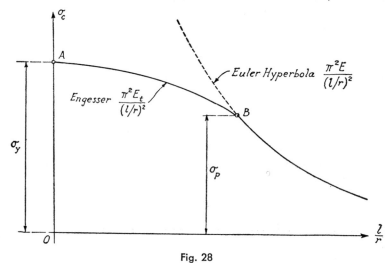

Fig. 28

responds to the critical stress $\sigma_c = \sigma_p$. This slenderness ratio l'/r is

$$\left(\frac{l'}{r}\right)^2 = \frac{\pi^2 E}{\sigma_p}$$

Introduction of this value into Eq. (62) leads to the formula

$$\sigma_c = \sigma_y - \frac{\sigma_p(\sigma_{yf} - \sigma_p)}{\pi^2 E}\left(\frac{l}{r}\right)^2 \tag{63}$$

Thus for any given material with a distinctly marked yield zone the basic column formula can be easily established when the three characteristics of the material, E, σ_p, and σ_y, are known. For use in practical design the values of the ultimate average stress σ_c, given by the column formula (63), may be divided by the factor of safety n. Then the values of σ_c/n can be considered as the safe working stresses of the ideal column and can be applied to the column design based upon the actual working load.

As will be seen in subsequent chapters, the ratio $\tau = E_t/E$ plays an important role in the analysis of the various buckling problems, and it is convenient to have available a simple analytical expression for τ which fits the above suggested analytical column formula. Such an expression is readily derived.

We write equation (62) in the condensed form

$$\sigma_c = a - b \left(\frac{l}{r}\right)^2$$

where a and b are constants depending upon the characteristics σ_p and σ_y. On the other hand σ_c can also be expressed by Eq. (20):

$$\sigma_c = \frac{\pi^2 E \tau}{(l/r)^2}$$

Eliminating $(l/r)^2$ from these two equations we arrive at an expression for τ:

$$\tau = \frac{\sigma_c(a - \sigma_c)}{\pi^2 E b}$$

showing it as a function of the critical average stress $\sigma_c = P_c/A$. Replacing a by σ_y and $\pi^2 E b$ by $\sigma_p(\sigma_y - \sigma_p)$ we finally arrive at the formula

$$\tau = \frac{(\sigma_y - \sigma_c)\sigma_c}{(\sigma_y - \sigma_p)\sigma_p} \tag{64}$$

For routine calculation it is convenient to provide a table of the τ-values computed from Eq. (64). A sample of such a table is given as Table 3, computed for structural steel with an assumed proportional limit $\sigma_p = 25$ kips/in.^{2} and a yield strength $\sigma_y = 33$ kips/in.^{2}

Basing column design upon these rational column formulas, attention must be directed to the fact that the characteristics of the material supplied under the usual specifications may vary within a certain range. Consequently, possible minimum values of σ_y and σ_p must be introduced into the column formula, taking into account the frequency of their occurrence; the selection of minimum values of the characteristics of the material properties is to be based upon probability considerations, assuming that extraordinary deviations from the standard values which occur comparatively seldom are covered by a special margin in the factor of safety.

19. The Factor of Safety

The principles upon which the choice of the factor of safety in design of compression members is based are essentially the same as in the case of tension members. The purpose of the factor of safety is to provide a reasonable margin for all indeterminable factors, including a certain allowance for the imperfection of the analytical methods applied to the determination of stresses. Whenever a factor of safety is employed, it must be clear to which condition it refers; as far as tensile stresses are concerned, the factor of safety in present-day practice will indicate safety against the yield point and, in cases where alternating stresses occur, against the fatigue strength of the material. For structural members under compression the factor of safety naturally should refer to the buckling strength of the members. However, in judging the safety of compression members a more cautious viewpoint must be adopted, since occurrence of instability in a member may lead to failure of the entire structure, while yielding of a tension member does not necessarily imperil

TABLE 3. Ratio $\tau = E_t/E$ for Structural Steel

σ_c	τ	σ_c	τ	σ_c	τ	σ_c	τ
25.0	1.000	27.0	0.810	29.0	0.580	31.0	0.310
25.2	0.983	27.2	0.789	29.2	0.555	31.2	0.281
25.4	0.965	27.4	0.767	29.4	0.529	31.4	0.251
25.6	0.947	27.6	0.745	29.6	0.503	31.6	0.221
25.8	0.929	27.8	0.723	29.8	0.477	31.8	0.1908
26.0	0.910	28.0	0.700	30.0	0.450	32.0	0.1600
26.2	0.891	28.2	0.677	30.2	0.423	32.2	0.1288
26.4	0.871	28.4	0.652	30.4	0.395	32.4	0.0972
26.6	0.851	28.6	0.629	30.6	0.367	32.6	0.0652
26.8	0.831	28.8	0.605	30.8	0.339	32.8	0.0328
						33.0	0

the life of the structure, but only produces excessive deflections. It also must be kept in mind that in establishing the factor of safety for compression members further allowance must be made to cover special effects (eccentricity) which play a minor role in tension members but may affect the buckling strength of columns considerably.

The question also arises whether the factor of safety should be assumed constant throughout the whole range of slenderness ratios or should vary for short and slender columns. The considerations which determine the factor of safety fall into two groups: Unintentional variation of the loading condition, inefficiency of design methods, deviation of the cross-sectional areas of the members from the assumed values, etc., apply to all parts of a structure and therefore affect short and slender columns equally, while accidental imperfections, deviation of actual properties of material from the assumed standard, inaccurate estimate of the degree of fixity at the ends, effect of secondary stresses, etc., are factors which are closely related to the column problem and may have different weights depending on whether a short or slender column is concerned.

The effect of unintentional eccentricity of axial load and also the effect of deviation of the column axis from the straight line are considerable for short and medium-length columns. Variation in characteristics of the material, especially of the yield point, influences column strength in the inelastic range appreciably, whereas slender columns remain unaffected by these variations, as their carrying capacity depends upon the modulus of elasticity, which varies but slightly from its standard value. On the other hand, an error in estimating the free length of a column is of great effect on the calculated strength within the elastic range and of relatively slight influence in the inelastic range.

In view of these facts no good reason seems to exist for designing short columns with a factor of safety lower than that applied in the case of slender columns. Considering further all the uncertainties in the entire reasoning connected with the determination of the factor of safety, it appears advisable to rely upon an invariable value of this factor applying over the entire range of practical slenderness ratios.

Additional References

References to Arts. 1 to 8

Basquin, O. H., Tangent Modulus and the Strength of Steel Columns in Tests, *Natl. Bur. Standards (U.S.), Technol. Paper* 263, 1924.

v. Mises, R., Ausbiegung eines auf Knicken beanspruchten Stabes, *Zeitschrift für angewandte Mathematik und Mechanik*, Vol. 4, p. 435, 1924.

Zimmermann, H., Der Begriff der Knickgrenze, *Zeitschrift des Vereines deutscher Ingenieure*, Vol. 70, p. 221, 1926.

Domke, O., Die Ausbiegung eines Druckstabes bei Überschreitung der Knicklast, *Die Bautechnik*, Vol. 4, p. 747, 1926.

Gehler, W., Die Spannungs-Dehnungslinie im plastischen Druckbereich und die Knickspannungslinie, *Proc. 2d Intern. Cong. Applied Mechanics*, 1926, Zürich, 1927, p. 364.

Lundquist, E. E., A Method of Estimating the Critical Buckling Load for Structural Members, *NACA, Tech. Note* 717, 1939.

Wolford, D. S., Significance of the Secant- and Tangent-Moduli of Elasticity in Structural Design, *Jour. Aeronaut. Sci.*, Vol. 10, p. 169, 1943.

Van den Broek, J. A., Evaluation of Aeroplane Metals, *Eng. Jour.*, Vol. 28, p. 424, 1945.

Van den Broek, J. A., Column Formula for Material of Variable Modulus, *Eng. Jour.*, Vol. 28, p. 772, 1945.

Jones, J., Stability of 9 × 4 Steel Angle, *Civil Eng.*, Vol. 15, p. 377, 1945.

Van den Broek, J. A., Euler's Classic Paper "On the Strength of Columns," *Jour. Phys.*, Vol. 15, p. 309, 1947. The author discusses briefly the history of the theory of bending and Euler's contribution to this problem. The paper contains a translation of Secs. I to XVIII of Euler's paper of 1759 dealing with the derivation of $P = \pi^2 EI/l^2$ and showing Euler's clear insight into the buckling problem.

Ryder, F. L., Column Behavior, *Trans. ASCE*, Vol. 113, p. 40, 1948.

Lin, Tung-Hua, Inelastic Column Buckling, *Jour. Aeronaut Sci.*, Vol. 17, p. 159, 1950.

Duberg, J. E., and T. W. Wilder, Column Behavior in the Plastic Stress Range, *Jour. Aeronaut. Sci.*, Vol. 17, p. 323, 1950.

Pearson, C. E., Bifurcation Criterion and Plastic Buckling of Plates and Columns, *Jour. Aeronaut Sci.*, Vol. 17, p. 417, 1950.

Cicala, P., Column Buckling in the Elastroplastic Range, *Jour. Aeronaut. Sci.*, Vol. 17, p. 508, 1950.

References to Arts. 9 to 15

Greene, T. W., Strength of Steel Tubing under Combined Column and Transverse Loading, Including Tests of Columns and Beams, *Natl. Bur. Standards (U.S.)*, *Technol. Paper* 258, Vol. 18, 1924.

Lee, J. G., Tests on Duralumin Columns for Aircraft Construction, *NACA Tech. Note* 208, 1924.

Osgood, W. R., Eccentric Loads on Column, *Eng. News-Record*, Vol. 101, p. 30, 1928.

Tuckerman, L. B., S. N. Petrenko, and J. D. Johnson, Strength of Tubing under combined Axial and Transverse Load, *NACA Tech. Note* 307, 1929.

Young, D. H., Stresses in Eccentrically Loaded Steel Columns, *Pubs. Intern. Assoc. Bridge and Structural Eng.*, Vol. 1, p. 507, 1932.

Hartmann, F., Der einseitige (excentrische) Druck bei Stäben aus Baustahl, *Zeitschrift des Österreichischen Ingenieur- und Architektenvereines*, Vol. 85, p. 65, 1933.

Young, D. H., Rational Design of Steel Columns, *Trans. ASCE*, Vol. 98, p. 1376, 1933.

Chwalla, E., Theory des aussermittig gedrückten Stabes aus Baustahl, *Der Stahlbau*, Vol. 7, p. 161, 1934.

Chwalla, E., Das Tragvermögen gedrückter Baustahlstäbe mit krummer Achse und zusätzlicher Querbelastung, *Der Stahlbau*, Vol. 8, p. 34, 1935.

Ratzersdorfer, J., "Die Knickfestigkeit von Stäben und Stabwerken," Julius Springer, Vienna, 1936.

Hartmann, F., "Knickung Kippung Beulung," Franz Deuticke, Leipzig and Vienna, 1937.

Ježek, K., "Die Festigkeit von Druckstäben aus Stahl," Julius Springer, Vienna, 1937.

Schleussner, A., "Strenge Theorie der Knickung und Biegung," B. G. Teubner, Leipzig and Berlin, 1937.

Kollbrunner, C. F., Zentrischer und exzentrischer Druck von an beiden Enden gelenkig gelagerten Rechteckstäben aus Avional M und Baustahl, *Der Stahlbau*, Vol. 11, p. 25, 1938. The author compares the results obtained from the theories of Roš and Brunner, Hartmann, and Chwalla for various eccentricities of the axial load with test results (170 tests). The critical stresses computed from the theories of Roš and Brunner and of Hartmann deviate a maximum of 5% from Chwalla's values. The tests made with eccentricities of 0, 0.25, 1, 3, 6 core radius showed good agreement with the result obtained from Chwalla's theory. The majority of the test points lie somewhat below the computed Chwalla curves.

Gottlieb, R., T. M. Thompson, and E. C. Witt, Combined Beam Column Stresses of Aluminum Alloy Channel Sections, *NACA Tech. Note* 726, 1939.

Gemer, W., Vorschlag und Kritik einer Bemessungsformel bei aussermittig beanspruchten Knickstäben, *Der Stahlbau*, Vol. 13, p. 57, 1940.

Kármán, T., L. G. Dunn, and H. S. Tsien, The Influence of Curvature on the Buckling Characteristics of Structures, *Jour. Aeronaut. Sci.*, Vol. 7, p. 276, 1940.

Hill, H. N., Compression Tests of Some 17S-T Aluminum Alloy Specimens of I-Cross Section, *NACA Tech. Note* 798, 1941.

Cassens, J., Tables for Computing Various Cases of Beam Columns, *NACA Tech. Mem.* 985, 1941.

Cassens, J., Buckling Tests on Eccentrically Loaded Beam Columns, *NACA Tech. Mem.* 989, 1941.

Van den Broeck, J. A., Columns Subject to Uniformly Distributed Transverse Loads—Illustrating a New Method of Column Analysis, *Eng. Jour.*, Vol. 24, p. 115, 1941.

Merriam, K. G., Eccentricity in Columns, *Jour. Aeronaut. Sci.*, Vol. 9, p. 135, 1942.

Ramberg, W., and W. R. Osgood, Description of Stress-Strain Curves by Three Parameters, *NACA Tech. Note* 902, 1943.

Osgood, W. R., Beam-Columns, *Jour. Aeronaut. Sci.*, Vol. 14, p. 167, 1947.

Holt, M., A Study of the Beam Column Problem, Doctor's Thesis, University of Pittsburgh, Pittsburgh, Pa., 1947.

Brunner, J., Knickstabilität, *Schweizer Bauzeitung*, Vol. 126, p. 379, 1947.

References to Arts. 16 *to* 19

Griffith, J. G., and J. G. Bragg, Tests of Large Bridge Columns, *Natl. Bur. Standards (U.S.), Technol. Papers*, Vol. 10, p. 3, 1918.

Final Report of the Special Committee on Steel Columns and Struts, *Trans. ASCE*, Vol. 83, p. 1583, 1919–1920. Comprehensive analysis of the results obtained from several hundred laboratory tests on steel columns. Report and discussion constitute important information on the various problems connected with the variation of material properties and the behavior of columns in steel structures.

Tuckermann, L. B., and A. H. Stang, Tests of Large Columns with H-shaped Sections, *Natl. Bur. Standards (U.S.), Technol. Paper* 328, 1926.

Southwell, R. V., The Strength of Struts, A Review of Progress Made in Theory and Experiment during the War, *Aeronaut. Research Committee (Gt. Brit.) Repts. and Memoranda*, No. 918, 1924.

Mayer, R., Uber die Sicherheit gegen Knicken, *Die Bautechnik*, Vol. 3, p. 729, 1925.

Progress Report of the Special Committee on Steel Column Research, *Trans. ASCE*, Vol. 89, p. 1485, 1926.

Hunley, J. B., A Simplified Column Formula of the Secant Type, *Bull. AREA*, Vol. 29, No. 300, p. 197, 1927.

Johnston, R. S., Tests of Large-size Columns of Three Grades of Structural Steel, *Eng. News-Record*, Vol. 103, p. 999, 1929.

Pigeaud, G., Note sur la flambement de certaines pièces droites ou courbes, *Génie civil*, Vol. 94, p. 448, 1929.

Progress Report of the Special Committee on Steel Column Research, *Trans. ASCE*, Vol. 95, p. 1152, 1931.

Aarflot, M. G., A New Column Formula, *Bull. Am. Soc. Swedish Engrs.*, Vol. 26, p. 7, 1931.

Edwards, J. H., H. L. Whittemore, and A. H. Stang, Compressive Tests of Jointed H-Section Columns, *Natl. Bur. Standards (U.S.), Jour. Research*, Vol. 6, p. 305, 1931.

Osgood, W. R., Column Curves and Stress-Strain Diagrams, *Natl. Bur. Standards (U.S.), Jour. Research*, Vol. 9, p. 571, 1932.

Timoshenko, S., Working Stresses for Columns and Thin-walled Structures, *Trans. ASME*, Vol. 55, Paper APM-55-20, 1932.

Final Report of the Special Committee on Steel Column Research, *Trans. ASCE*, Vol. 98, p. 1376, 1933. The committee recommended the secant formula as a working formula but, because of the difficulty of using the secant formula, suggested to approximate it by a parabolic column formula, subsequently adopted by AREA and AASHO. The formula allows for the uncertainties encountered in column design and for the effect of end restraint in columns as part of a structure.

Slater, W. A., and M. O. Fuller, Tests of Riveted and Welded Steel Columns, *Trans. ASCE*, Vol. 99, p. 112, 1934.

Stang, A. H., and H. L. Whittemore, Tests of Steel Tower Columns for the George Washington Bridge, *Natl. Bur. Standards (U.S.), Jour. Research*, Vol. 15, p. 317, 1935.

Wilson, M. W., and R. L. Brown, Effect of Residual Longitudinal Stresses upon Load-carrying Capacity of Steel Columns, *Univ. Illinois Bull.*, Vol. 33, No. 13, 1935.

Hoff, N. J., Elastically Encastered Struts, *Jour. Roy. Aeronaut. Soc.*, Vol. 40, p. 663, 1936.

Millet, A., Essais de flambage executés sur des cornières en acier 54 au chrome-cuivre et en acier 42 ordinaire, *Annales des ponts et chaussées*, Vol. 106, p. 232, 1936.

Roark, R. J., C. B. Voldrich, and E. Sollid, Column Tests of Reinforced Channels, *Welding Jour.*, Vol. 17, p. 31, 1938.

Osgood, W. R., Column Strength of Tubes Elastically Restrained against Rotation at the Ends, *NACA Tech. Rept.* 615, 1938.

Merriam, K. G., Dimensionless Coefficients Applied to the Solution of Column Problems, *Jour. Aeronaut. Sci.*, Vol. 7, p. 478, 1940.

Stang, A. H., and M. Greenspan, Perforated Cover Plates for Steel Columns, *Natl. Bur. Standards (U.S.), Jour. Research*, Vol. 28, p. 669, 1942.

Stang, A. H., and M. Greenspan, Perforated Cover Plates for Steel Columns, Compressive Properties of Plates Having Ovaloid Perforations and a Width-to-Thickness Ratio of 40, *Natl. Bur. Standards (U.S.), Jour. Research*, Vol. 28, p. 687, 1942.

Stang, A. H., and M. Greenspan, Perforated Cover Plates for Steel Columns, Compressive Properties of Plates Having Ovaloid Perforations and a Width-to-Thickness Ratio of 68, *Natl. Bur. Standards (U.S.), Jour. Research*, Vol. 29, p. 279, 1942.

Greenspan, M., Axial Rigidity of Perforated Structural Members, *Natl. Bur. Standards (U.S.), Jour. Research*, Vol. 31, p. 305, 1943.

Stang, A. H., and M. Greenspan, Perforated Cover Plates for Steel Columns, Compressive Properties of Plates Having Ovaloid Perforations and a Width-to-Thickness Ratio of 53, *Natl. Bur. Standards, Jour. Research*, Vol. 30, p. 15, 1943.

Stang, A. H., and M. Greenspan, Perforated Cover Plates for Steel Columns, Compressive Properties of Plates Having Circular Perforations and a Width-to-Thickness Ratio of 53, *Natl. Bur. Standards (U.S.), Jour. Research*, Vol. 30, p. 177, 1943.

Stang, A. H., and M. Greenspan, Perforated Cover Plates for Steel Columns, Compressive Properties of Plates Having Net-to-Gross Cross-sectional-area Ratio of 0.33, *Natl. Bur. Standards (U.S.), Jour. Research*, Vol. 30, p. 411, 1943.

Sergev, S. I., The Theoretical Behavior and Design of Initially Curved Struts under an Intermediate Concentric Axial Load, *Univ. Washington Eng. Expt. Sta. Bull.* 113, 1945.

Osgood, W. R., Column Formulas, *Trans. ASCE*, 1946, p. 165. The author defines the prime requisite of any column formula and discusses the Rankine formula, the secant formula, the formulas of Aarflot and Ylinen, his own formulas, Krüger's formula, and the formulas of parabolic or hyperbolic type. Discussion by readers of the paper constitutes a remarkable digest of current opinions of the various features of the column problem in practical design.

Ruffner, B. F., Stress Analysis of Columns and Beam Columns by the Photoelastic Method, *NACA Tech. Note* 1002, 1946.

—

CHAPTER II

THE MATHEMATICAL TREATMENT OF STABILITY PROBLEMS AND THE STABILITY CRITERIA

20. Introduction

The mathematical discussion of the fundamental column problem in Chap. I started from the linear differential equation of the theory of bending of prismatic bars which determines the deflection y of the bar under a given external loading, and it was found that the buckling load P_E could be derived from the solution of a linear homogeneous differential equation. Such differential equations actually form the basis for solving the various stability problems, and it will be seen that the peculiarities of the solutions of these equations are closely related to peculiarities of the buckling problem itself. In solving buckling problems in the structural field it is of considerable help to have insight into the well-established theory of linear homogeneous differential equations which play a dominant role in physics, especially in the theory of small vibrations. A complete analogy exists between the theory of small vibrations and the theory of elastic stability, which has its origin in the common mathematical foundation of the vibration and stability problems. The deep insight into the nature of various dynamic problems provided by the theory of homogeneous linear differential equations, which was developed by many generations of scientists, should also be utilized for the study and the better understanding of the various methods of solving buckling problems. The following Arts. 21 and 22 are not intended to give an extensive account of the mathematical theory, but those characteristic features will be discussed which are of special significance for the type of differential equation considered here. These features are of primary importance for the understanding of the nature of the stability problem as a mathematical problem and especially for the effective application of the Ritz method for the approximate solution of buckling problems.

Energy methods, with particular emphasis on the Ritz method, are discussed in Arts. 23 to 26 of this chapter. The solution of stability problems by successive approximation and by finite difference methods are considered in Arts. 27 and 28, respectively.

To make full use of the energy methods presented in this chapter it is necessary to understand the calculus of variation; no reference or text-book suitable for engineers being available, it was deemed necessary to devote Arts. 29 to 33 to an introduction into this branch of mathematics.

21. The Buckling Problem as a Characteristic Value Problem

The subsequent brief outline of the mathematical theory will be limited to the discussion of the differential equation of the column problem. This is considered sufficient to demonstrate those aspects of the theory of linear differential equations which are of importance in dealing with buckling problems.

The homogeneous differential equation which has been used in Chap. I to present the principal features of the fundamental problem of elastic stability is not of a sufficiently general nature to provide the proper basis for the discussion of the mathematical features of the buckling problem of straight columns. The general form of this differential equation, on which the solution of the stability problem of centrally loaded straight columns can be based for any type of end condition, is[1]

$$\frac{d^2}{dx^2}\left(EI_x\frac{d^2y}{dx^2}\right) + P\frac{d^2y}{dx^2} = 0 \tag{65}$$

It is assumed that the moment of inertia I_x varies along the column, so that $I_x = I\psi(x)$, where I is a constant moment of inertia and $\psi(x)$ a dimensionless function of the abscissa x.

Equation (65) is a homogeneous linear differential equation of the fourth order whose general solution involves four arbitrary constants corresponding to the number of boundary conditions of any particular column problem. It is expedient to write Eq. (65), after introducing $I_x = I\psi(x)$, in the condensed form

$$[\psi(x)y'']'' + \lambda^2y'' = 0 \tag{66}$$

in which the parameter λ is defined by

$$\lambda = \sqrt{\frac{P}{EI}} \tag{67}$$

The general solution of the differential equation (66) is

$$y = C_1\varphi_1(\lambda,x) + C_2\varphi_2(\lambda,x) + C_3\frac{x}{l} + C_4 \tag{68}$$

[1] The differential equation (6) in Chap. I is applicable to pin-ended columns, but not to columns with clamped or elastically restrained ends. For such columns an additional term due to the end moments has to be added; differentiating the resulting equation twice leads to Eq. (65), in which the additional term no longer appears because its second derivative vanishes.

in which $\varphi_1(\lambda,x)$ and $\varphi_2(\lambda,x)$ are dimensionless, transcendental functions of x and of the parameter λ. The constants C represent lengths and are determined by the condition of restraint at both the ends of the column. These boundary conditions are linear and homogeneous equations and will be referred to as homogeneous boundary conditions. To be more specific, the end conditions considered here and most frequently encountered are

For a freely supported end: $\quad y = 0 \quad$ and $\quad y'' = 0$

For a fixed end: $\qquad\qquad\quad\; y = 0 \quad$ and $\quad y' = 0$

For a free end: $\qquad\qquad\quad y'' = 0 \quad$ and $\quad [\psi(x)y'']' + \lambda^2 y' = 0*$

$$\left.\begin{array}{c} \\ \\ \\ \end{array}\right\} \quad (69)$$

Introducing the solution (68) into the four boundary conditions in any given case leads to a set of four linear homogeneous equations of the general form

$$\left.\begin{aligned} \alpha_{11}C_1 + \alpha_{21}C_2 + \alpha_{31}C_3 + \alpha_{41}C_4 &= 0 \\ \alpha_{12}C_1 + \alpha_{22}C_2 + \alpha_{32}C_3 + \alpha_{42}C_4 &= 0 \\ \alpha_{13}C_1 + \alpha_{23}C_2 + \alpha_{33}C_3 + \alpha_{43}C_4 &= 0 \\ \alpha_{14}C_1 + \alpha_{24}C_2 + \alpha_{34}C_3 + \alpha_{44}C_4 &= 0 \end{aligned}\right\} \quad (70)$$

in which some of the coefficients α are transcendental functions of the parameter λ while others are constants. For arbitrary values of the parameter λ these homogeneous equations are satisfied only when C_1 to C_4 are zero, indicating that the deflection y is zero and the column remains straight. However, Eqs. (70) have solutions different from zero if the determinant Δ of the coefficients of this system of equations vanishes, i.e., if

$$\Delta = \begin{vmatrix} \alpha_{11} & \alpha_{21} & \alpha_{31} & \alpha_{41} \\ \alpha_{12} & \alpha_{22} & \alpha_{32} & \alpha_{42} \\ \alpha_{13} & \alpha_{23} & \alpha_{33} & \alpha_{43} \\ \alpha_{14} & \alpha_{24} & \alpha_{34} & \alpha_{44} \end{vmatrix} = 0 \qquad (71)$$

On expanding the determinant Δ the condition (71) furnishes an equation for the parameter λ, the only unknown in this equation. Equation (71) is in general a transcendental equation, having an infinite number of roots $\lambda_i (i = 1, 2, \ldots)$, referred to as the *characteristic values* of the parameter λ, and defining an infinite number of critical loads P_i. Introducing one of the characteristic values λ_i into the system (70) yields four equations for the four constants C_{1i}, C_{2i}, C_{3i}, and C_{4i} associated with λ_i. However, because the determinant Δ of the coefficients of these equations is zero, one of these equations is identical with and can be obtained as a combination of the other three, leaving only three independent equations for four unknowns. From these three equations only

---

* This equation expresses the condition that the shearing force vanishes.

the three ratios $\bar{C}_{2i} = C_{2i}/C_{1i}$, $\bar{C}_{3i} = C_{3i}/C_{1i}$, and $\bar{C}_{4i} = C_{4i}/C_{1i}$ can be determined, and the solution (68) assumes the form

$$y_i = C_{1i}\left[\varphi_1(\lambda_i, x) + \bar{C}_{2i}\varphi_2(\lambda_i, x) + \bar{C}_{3i}\frac{x}{l} + \bar{C}_{4i}\right] \tag{72}$$

where C_{1i} remains an arbitrary constant. y_i are the so-called *characteristic functions* of the homogeneous differential equation (66) associated with the particular boundary condition of the case considered.

The foregoing discussion of the solution of the differential equation (66) indicates that, for certain values of the parameter λ, deflected configurations of the axially loaded column exist, indeterminate as to their magnitude but defined as to their shape by Eq. (72). The characteristic values λ_i and the characteristic functions y_i therefore determine buckling loads P_i and corresponding buckling modes y_i. Equation (71), which furnishes the λ-values, represents the stability criterion; Eq. (67) is a relation connecting the smallest root λ_1 and the corresponding critical load P_c at which the column passes from its straight and stable position to a deflected and unstable configuration.

At this point it may be worth while to refer briefly to the significant analogy, mentioned at the outset of this article, which exists between the mathematical interpretation of small oscillations and of the phenomenon of buckling. The characteristic functions y_i of any vibration problem represent an infinite set of principal modes of vibration, while the characteristic values λ_i of the vibration problem are connected with the frequencies of this mode determined from Eq. (71), $\Delta = 0$, which is called the frequency equation. The relationship between the two groups of problems is shown in the following table:

	Equation $\Delta = 0$	Characteristic values	Characteristic functions
Buckling..	Stability criterion	Buckling loads	Buckling modes
Vibrations.	Frequency equation	Frequencies	Principal modes of vibration

Recognition of the common mathematical basis may promote a deeper understanding of each of these phenomena and of the physical relations which exist between the critical loads and the frequencies of free vibrations, relations which may be of interest for experimental work in the field of buckling.[1]

[1] For example, the fundamental frequency of lateral vibrations of an axially loaded bar decreases when the load increases and becomes zero when the critical load is reached.

22. The Orthogonality Relations

The primary objective—the determination of the buckling load of a column with given end conditions—is reached when the stability condition (71) has been obtained and the smallest root λ_1 determined. However, it will be seen in the course of the discussion in this chapter that the characteristic functions of the differential equation (66) play an important part in the energy method, which will be demonstrated in the following articles. It is well, therefore, to explain here certain significant and useful relations between the characteristic functions y_i ensuing from the inherent properties of the differential equation (66) itself.

Since any characteristic function y_i satisfies the differential equation (66) if $\lambda = \lambda_i$, we may write

$$[\psi(x)y_i'']'' + \lambda_i{}^2 y_i'' = 0$$

Multiplying this equation by one of the other characteristic functions y_k and integrating over the length l of the column we obtain

$$\int_0^l [\psi(x)y_i'']''y_k\, dx + \lambda_i{}^2 \int_0^l y_i''y_k\, dx = 0 \tag{73}$$

Twofold integration by parts of the first term gives

$$\int_0^l [\psi(x)y_i'']''y_k\, dx = \Big[[\psi(x)y_i'']'y_k\Big]_0^l - \Big[\psi(x)y_i''y_k'\Big]_0^l$$
$$+ \int_0^l \psi(x)y_i''y_k''\, dx$$

and simple integration by parts of the second term,

$$\lambda_i{}^2 \int_0^l y_i''y_k\, dx = \lambda_i{}^2 \Big[y_i'y_k\Big]_0^l - \lambda_i{}^2 \int_0^l y_i'y_k'\, dx$$

Substitution of these expressions into Eq. (73) leads to

$$\Big[\{[\psi(x)y_i'']' + \lambda_i{}^2 y_i'\}y_k\Big]_0^l - \Big[\psi(x)y_i''y_k'\Big]_0^l + \int_0^l \psi(x)y_i''y_k''\, dx$$
$$- \lambda_i{}^2 \int_0^l y_i'y_k'\, dx = 0$$

The terms within the brackets vanish for any combination of the homogeneous boundary conditions (69), and there remains

$$\int_0^l \psi(x)y_i''y_k''\, dx - \lambda_i{}^2 \int_0^l y_i'y_k'\, dx = 0 \tag{74}$$

This equation holds for each combination of two different characteristic functions, and we can therefore interchange y_i and y_k and obtain

$$\int_0^l \psi(x)y_k''y_i''\, dx - \lambda_k{}^2 \int_0^l y_k'y_i'\, dx = 0$$

Subtracting the two equations leads to

$$(\lambda_i{}^2 - \lambda_k{}^2) \int_0^l y_i' y_k' \, dx = 0$$

If i is different from k, $\lambda_i{}^2 - \lambda_k{}^2$ will be different from zero, and therefore

$$\int_0^l y_i' y_k' \, dx = 0 \tag{75a}$$

Introducing (75a) into Eq. (74) yields

$$\int_0^l \psi(x) y_i'' y_k'' \, dx = 0 \tag{75b}$$

If $i = k$, the integral $\int_0^l y'^2 \, dx$ cannot be zero because the integrand is a square and necessarily positive, and since $\lambda_i{}^2$ is also different from zero, Eq. (74) requires

$$\int_0^l \psi(x) y_i''^2 \, dx \neq 0 \qquad \text{and} \qquad \int_0^l y_i'^2 \, dx \neq 0 \tag{76}$$

Equations (75) express fundamental properties of the characteristic solutions of the differential equation (66) of outstanding importance and are known as the *orthogonality relations* of the characteristic functions y_i. A family of functions consisting of all the characteristic functions y_i of Eq. (66) for particular boundary conditions will be referred to as a *complete system* of orthogonal functions.

If I_x is constant, we have $\psi(x) = 1$, and Eqs. (75) simplify to

$$\int_0^l y_i' y_k' \, dx = \int_0^l y_i'' y_k'' \, dx = 0 \tag{77}$$

The best known example of a complete system of orthogonal functions which satisfies conditions (77) is the sequence of functions

$$y_i = \sin i \frac{\pi x}{l} \ (i = 1, 2, \ldots, \infty)$$

which form the terms of a Fourier expansion. The applicability of Fourier series to the solution of countless problems in mechanics and physics rests chiefly on the orthogonality relations (77) which exist between the terms of the above set of functions. Since

$$y_i' = \frac{\pi i}{l} \cos i \frac{\pi x}{l} \qquad \text{and} \qquad y_i'' = -\frac{\pi^2 i^2}{l^2} \sin i \frac{\pi x}{l}$$

we obtain from (77) the well-known formulas:

If $i \neq k$: $\displaystyle \int_0^l \cos i \frac{\pi x}{l} \cos k \frac{\pi x}{l} \, dx = \int_0^l \sin i \frac{\pi x}{l} \sin k \frac{\pi x}{l} \, dx = 0$

whereas

$$\int_0^l \sin^2 i\frac{\pi x}{l}\, dx = \int_0^l \cos^2 i\frac{\pi x}{l}\, dx = \frac{l}{2}$$

is different from zero. It may be noted that the functions $y_i = \sin(i\pi x/l)$ are the characteristic solutions of the differential equation (66) for the end conditions $y = 0$, $y'' = 0$ at $x = 0$ and l, and have already been discussed in Chap. I in connection with the derivation of the Euler formula.

It is not generally recognized that each complete system of characteristic functions, which consists of the solutions of a homogeneous differential equation under specified boundary conditions, can be utilized for setting up an expansion like a Fourier series. Such series possess the same peculiar properties which make the Fourier series so extremely useful in mathematics, properties which are closely connected with the fact that the characteristic functions form an orthogonal system. The significance of such especially devised series for the solution of certain stability problems will be discussed in Arts. 24 to 26.

So far we have limited the discussion to the problem of individual columns, but similar orthogonality relations exist also between the buckling modes of compression members which form a system of rigidly jointed columns. A simple example is shown in Fig. 29. The column is supported at the ends and at two intermediate points like a continuous beam over three spans. The moment of inertia is assumed constant over the length L. The buckling modes must satisfy the differential equation (66), and by reasoning in the same manner as before but extending the integrals over the total length L of the compression member, one arrives at the orthogonality relations

$$\int_L y_i' y_k'\, dx = 0 \qquad \text{and} \qquad \int_L y_i'' y_k''\, dx = 0 \tag{78}$$

if y_i and y_k are different characteristic functions. These two integrals, however, are different from zero when $i = k$.[1] Figure 29 shows, for illustration, the symmetric functions y_1 and y_3 and the antisymmetric function y_2.

Orthogonality relations similar to those encountered in cases of one-dimensional problems also exist when the characteristic functions are solutions of a partial differential equation. This applies to all two-dimensional problems where the characteristic solutions are functions $u(x,y)$ of two independent variables x,y. The double Fourier series

---

[1] It may be specifically noted that Eqs. (78) are valid only when the integration is extended over the total length L.

$$\sum_m \sum_n c_{mn} \sin m\,\frac{\pi x}{a} \sin n\,\frac{\pi y}{b} \qquad (m = 1, 2, \ldots \quad \text{and} \quad n = 1, 2, \ldots)$$

is a familiar example, which we shall encounter in the theory of stability
of plates.   The orthogonality relation reads

$$\int_0^a \int_0^b \sin m\,\frac{\pi x}{a} \sin n\,\frac{\pi y}{b} \sin p\,\frac{\pi x}{a} \sin q\,\frac{\pi y}{b}\, dx\, dy = 0 \qquad (79)$$

valid if $m \neq p$ or $n \neq q$.

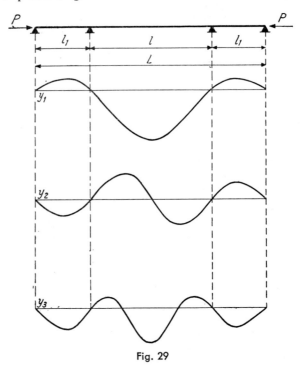

Fig. 29

After this excursion in the field of mathematics we turn again to the
real subject of this chapter.   Reviewing the previous discussion, it may
be well to stress the basic idea which underlies the method of determining
the critical load P_c of the column.   This critical load was determined by
the criterion that the stability limit is reached when a deflected configuration infinitesimally near to the straight equilibrium form of the column
is possible, indicating bifurcation of the equilibrium position.   The study
of the solution of the homogeneous differential equation (66) revealed
that for a certain characteristic value $\lambda = \sqrt{P/EI}$ such a bifurcation of
the equilibrium configuration actually occurs and that this value of λ is
the smallest root of the stability condition $\Delta = 0$.

The same concept applies, of course, to various other groups of stability problems, and this method of deriving the condition of stability from the differential equation of any particular buckling problem will be utilized in other chapters of this book.

23. The Energy Method and the Theorem of Stationary Potential Energy

The energy method for the solution of problems of elastic stability is founded on an extremum principle of mechanics utilizing an energy criterion which characterizes the condition of equilibrium in an elastic system. This principle was introduced into the theory of elasticity by Kirchhoff,[1] who derived from it the differential equation of a laterally loaded flat plate. The first to apply the principle to the solution of buckling problems was Bryan,[2] who used it as a starting point to obtain the differential equation on which the theory of the buckling strength of flat plates is based.

Credit belongs properly to Timoshenko[3] for establishing the energy method for the approximate solution of problems of elastic stability. He developed this method into a powerful tool for the treatment of various buckling problems of considerable complexity. At about the same time Ritz[4] published his classic paper in which he developed on a broad mathematical basis a general method for the direct solution of so-called minimum problems of mathematical physics. He applied the method to the investigation of the equilibrium and vibrations of rectangular plates, clamped on all four sides. The Ritz method is quite general and applies to all those problems in mechanics and physics which, mathematically speaking, may be considered as problems of the calculus of variations. Timoshenko's method was especially devised for the approximate solution of problems of elastic stability. As far as this type of problem is concerned, both the Ritz method and Timoshenko's concept lead essentially to the same procedure and to the same mathematical form of the result.

No further progress was made in this field until 1935, when Trefftz[5]

[1] Kirchhoff, G., Über das Gleichgewicht und die Bewegung einer elastischen Scheibe, *Zeitschrift für Reine und Angewandte Mathematik*, Vol. 40, p. 51, 1850.

[2] Bryan, G. H., On the Stability of a Plane Plate under Thrusts in Its Own Plane with Application on the "Buckling" of the Sides of a Ship, *Proc. London Math. Soc.*, 1891, p. 59.

[3] Published 1910 in Russian, *Bull. Polytech. Inst. Kiew*, and later in French, Sur la stabilité des systèmes élastiques, *Annales des ponts et chaussées*, 1913.

[4] Ritz, W., Über eine neue Methode zur Lösung gewisser Variationsprobleme der mathematischen Physik, *Zeitschrift für Reine und Angewandte Mathematik*, 1909, p. 1.

[5] Trefftz, E., Die Bestimmung der Knicklast gedrückter, rechteckiger Platten, *Zeitschrift für angewandte Mathematik und Mechanik*, Vol. 15, p. 339, 1935.

supplemented Ritz's method by developing a procedure for the determination of a lower limit for the critical load.   The Ritz method in its original form leads to approximate values of the critical load which are larger than the exact value, thus giving an upper limit for the critical load.   Trefftz's method, therefore, permits enclosing the solution of the problem between an upper and a lower limit, a fact of importance for judging the accuracy of the solution.   A modification of the Trefftz method was recently proposed as the Lagrangian multiplier method by Budiansky and Hu,[1] who applied it with advantage to problems of plate stability.

The principle of the energy method can readily be derived from the principle of virtual work in the following way:

Consider an elastic structure at rest under the action of a system of loads P_i.   Applying the principle of virtual work, the condition of equilibrium between internal and external forces can be expressed by the equation

$$\delta V - \Sigma P_i \delta \xi_i = 0 \tag{80}$$

where $\delta \xi_i$ represents the virtual displacement of the point of application of the force P_i projected upon the line of action of P_i and V is the internal work, i.e., the strain energy accumulated in the structure in the state of equilibrium considered.   Therefore, δV represents the change of the strain energy if the structure passes from its configuration in the state of equilibrium to an adjoining configuration defined by the infinitesimally small virtual displacements $\delta \xi_i$.

Introducing the concept of "potential energy" as employed in theoretical mechanics, the term $-\Sigma P_i \delta \xi_i$ in Eq. (80) is an expression for the change δU_w of the potential energy U_w of the external loads, and Eq. (80) can be written

$$\delta V + \delta U_w = \delta(V + U_w) = 0 \tag{81}$$

Expressed in words: The amount of total potential energy $U = V + U_w$ does not change when the structure passes from its configuration of equilibrium to an infinitesimally near adjacent configuration. $\delta(V + U_w)$ is the variation of the potential energy, and Eq. (81) can be interpreted as the mathematical condition that $U = V + U_w$ assumes a stationary value.[2]   We may write, therefore,

$$U = V + U_w = \text{stationary} \tag{82}$$

[1] Budiansky, B., and Pai C. Hu, The Lagrangian Multiplier Method of Finding Upper and Lower Limits to the Critical Stresses, NACA *Tech. Note* 1103, 1946.

[2] The structure is in stable equilibrium only if this stationary value of the potential energy U is a minimum; according to the mathematical rule, U will be a minimum if the second variation $\delta^2 U$ is positive for any virtual displacement.   In engineering applications it is rarely necessary to use this mathematical criterion, because stable equilibrium is usually evident from the physical facts.

Applying this equilibrium condition to the peculiar state of equilibrium which exists at the incipience of buckling of an elastic system, Eq. (82) is an energy criterion from which the limit of elastic stability can be determined. Thus, mathematically, the buckling problem becomes a problem of the calculus of variations.[1] We shall refer to Eq. (82) as the theorem of stationary potential energy.

When deriving values of the potential energy U it is important to note that the general expression for U contains an arbitrary additive constant.[2] The value of this arbitrary constant may be selected by making the potential energy equal to zero for a suitable reference position; in stability problems it is convenient (but not necessary) to use the loaded state just prior to buckling as such reference position. In this case, the part V of the potential energy stored in the structure is the increase in strain energy between the unbuckled and the buckled state, while the potential energy U_w of the external loads is equal to the negative product of the external forces and the displacement, due to buckling, of their points of application in direction of the forces. To illustrate this, let us investigate the stability of an axially loaded straight column (Fig. 30). The moment of inertia I_x is assumed variable.

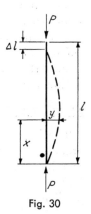

Fig. 30

Considering the column carrying a load P and using the compressed but undeflected state as reference position for which $U = 0$, the additional strain energy is due to bending only;

$$V = \frac{E}{2} \int_0^l I_x y''^2 \, dx \qquad (83)$$

in which y is the lateral deflection of the column.

The potential energy U_w of the axial load P is (Fig. 30)

$$U_w = -P \, \Delta l = -\frac{P}{2} \int_0^l y'^2 \, dx \qquad (84)$$

In the case discussed here V and U_w are integrals of quadratic functions of the unknown y and its derivatives. The condition (81),

[1] The fundamental problem of this branch of mathematics is the determination of the form of a function $y = f(x)$ which satisfies the condition that the definite integral $\int_{x_0}^{x_1} F(x,y,y',y'', \ldots) \, dx$ is to be an extremum. F may be any given function of the function y and its derivatives. A brief introduction to the calculus of variations is given in Arts. 29 to 33 of this chapter.

[2] This is due to the fact that the potential energy is basically defined by the relations $P_i = -\dfrac{\partial U}{\partial \xi_i}$, and an arbitrary constant of integration occurs in determining U.

$$\delta(V + U_w) = \delta\left(\frac{E}{2}\int_0^l I_x y''^2\, dx - \frac{P}{2}\int_0^l y'^2\, dx\right) = 0 \qquad (85)$$

permits the determination of the function y by applying the methods of the calculus of variations. The mathematical procedure leads to the Eulerian differential equation which in this case is identical with Eq. (65). This equation can be derived directly by considering the equilibrium between external and internal forces on a column element. Nevertheless, the method of solving the buckling problem on the basis of the energy criterion in the manner just outlined has special merits in some cases. It is frequently far simpler to establish the energy expressions V and U_w and derive the differential equation (or equations) of the problem by the method of the calculus of variations than to develop the differential equations in other ways. A typical example can be found in Chap. III, where the problem of bending and twisting of bars composed of thin walls is treated by means of the calculus of variations.

24. The Ritz Method

The importance of the energy criterion for the solution of stability problems becomes evident in the light of the Ritz method, which leads to a direct solution of the extremum problem arising out of the condition (82). The essentials of the method will be demonstrated on the column problem previously discussed.

Let the deflection y in the energy expressions (83) and (84) be expressed by the finite series

$$y = a_1\varphi_1 + a_2\varphi_2 + \cdots + a_n\varphi_n \qquad (86)$$

in which the φ-terms represent an arbitrarily chosen set of functions of x satisfying the same boundary conditions as the deflection y. They are called *coordinate functions*. The coefficients a are a corresponding set of parameters as yet undetermined. Introducing Eq. (86) into the energy equations (83) and (84) and performing the integrations indicated lead to an expression showing $V + U_w$ as a function of the n parameters a, having the form

$$V + U_w = F_1(a_1, \ldots, a_n) - PF_2(a_1, \ldots, a_n) \qquad (87)$$

in which F_1 and F_2 are quadratic forms of the parameters a. If y is to be regarded as a solution of the extremum problem, it must satisfy the extremum condition (82), and the parameters a must be selected to make $V + U_w = F_1 - PF_2$ stationary. The problem therefore has become an ordinary maximum-minimum problem in which the parameters a_1, $a_2, \ldots, a_n$ are the variables to be obtained from the n conditions

$$\frac{\partial(V + U_w)}{\partial a_i} = 0 \qquad (i = 1, 2, \ldots, n) \qquad (88)$$

The first derivatives of quadratic forms being linear functions, Eq. (88) represents a system of n homogeneous linear equations from which the parameters a are to be determined. This system of equations does not have solutions different from zero unless the determinant Δ of its coefficients is equal to zero. Thus,

$$\Delta = 0 \tag{89}$$

is an equation of degree n in the unknown P and is the stability condition from which P can be determined. The smallest of the roots of Eq. (89) is the critical load P_c.

On introducing $P = P_c$ into Eqs. (88) a set of n linear homogeneous equations is obtained from which, however, only $n - 1$ ratios $\alpha_i = a_i/a_1$ ($i = 2, 3, \ldots, n$) can be computed because the determinant Δ of its coefficients vanishes. $a_1 = C$ remains arbitrary. Thus, Eq. (86) defines the first buckling mode

$$y_1 = C(\varphi_1 + \alpha_2\varphi_2 + \cdots + \alpha_n\varphi_n) \tag{90}$$

When based upon an appropriate set of functions φ, the Ritz method furnishes a sequence of parameters a which decrease in many cases so rapidly that a few terms of the convergent series (86) suffice to determine the critical load $P = P_c$ with the required degree of accuracy.

The importance of the Ritz method lies in the fact that it offers the means for the approximate solution of buckling problems in those cases in which the exact solution of the underlying characteristic-value problem discussed in the previous article becomes too difficult or is not practicable. But the Ritz method can also be used with much advantage for the solution of mathematically less difficult problems, since the labor involved in calculating the critical load P_c from the Ritz determinant [Eq. (89)] is often far less than the labor necessary to compute P_c by solving a complex transcendental equation.

Success or failure in applying the Ritz method to any problem depends largely on the proper choice of the coordinate functions φ. If these functions are selected without due regard to the individuality of the problem, the analysis may become unnecessarily lengthy and laborious. There are no theoretical restrictions as to the form of these functions. They can be polynomials or transcendental functions, the chief requirement being that they satisfy the boundary conditions of the given problem. However, it must be emphasized that in the majority of cases satisfactory results can be obtained only when the coordinate functions φ form a system of orthogonal functions, from which a set of consecutive functions may be chosen for the formation of the expansion (86). The orthogonality relations which exist between the terms of such a sequence will considerably simplify the energy expression $V + U_w$ and the further analysis. This is the reason why Fourier series play such a paramount role in the numerous applications of the Ritz method in the theory of elasticity. However, the use of these series obviously is limited to problems whose boundary conditions are in accord with the boundary values of the coordinate functions φ of a Fourier expansion.

In many cases where the conditions of support preclude the use of Fourier series, the consecutive buckling modes (characteristic functions) of a related but less complex buckling problem may provide a suitable set of orthogonal coordinate functions. Such a set of functions, satisfying the boundary conditions of the given problem, assures quick convergence, because the functions reflect already some of the geometric and elastic properties of the system whose stability is considered.

As illustration, the following buckling problem may be briefly discussed. A column on unyielding supports at A, B, C, and D (Fig. 31) is in addition

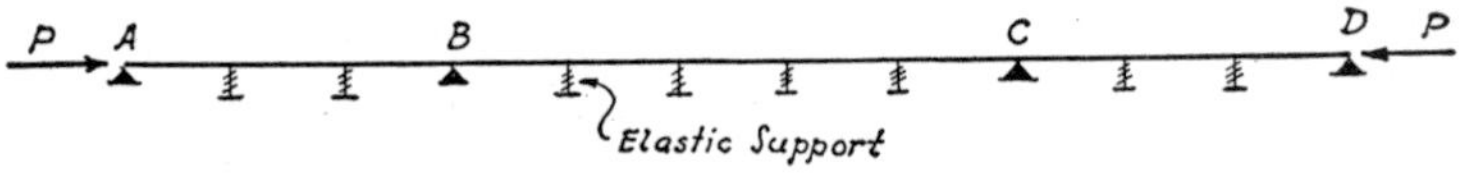

Fig. 31

elastically supported at equally spaced points between the fixed supports. The axial load is P, and assuming constant moment of inertia I, the expression for the potential energy U of the system is

$$U = V + U_w = \frac{EI}{2} \int_L y''^2 \, dx - \frac{P}{2} \int_L y'^2 \, dx + \frac{c}{2} \sum y_s^2 \qquad (91)$$

The last term represents the potential energy of the elastic supports in which c is the spring constant, indicating the degree of resistance against deflection of the points of support. The integrals extend over the entire length L of the column, and the sum over all elastic supports.

In choosing the coordinate functions φ for the expansion (86) it must be taken into account that these functions must satisfy not only the conditions at the ends A and D but also the particular conditions of constraint at the supports B and C. The buckling modes of the column $ABCD$ without the intermediate elastic supports, which can be found with comparative ease, are a suitable set of orthogonal functions φ for the solution of the buckling problem under consideration. These modes, of course, satisfy the end conditions and also the additional conditions of restraint of the buckling problem at points B and C. These functions φ approximate the shape of the buckling curve of the system investigated sufficiently well to expect that a linear combination of only a few consecutive functions[1] will furnish an approximate solution of reasonable accuracy.

[1] The functions φ to be used need not necessarily be those corresponding to the lowest critical values P of the column $ABCD$ without intermediate elastic support.

The first three modes are shown in Fig. 29, and the orthogonality relations [Eq. (78)] were briefly discussed in Art. 22. Introducing $y = a_1\varphi_1 + a_2\varphi_2 + \cdots$ into the energy expression (91) it is readily seen that the definite integrals reduce to a sum of squares, $\Sigma \alpha_i a_i{}^2$, the cross products dropping out because of the orthogonality relations (78). This simplifies the analysis considerably; when minimizing the expression (91) it is found that the two integrals only contribute terms along the diagonal of the determinant Δ, rendering these terms preponderant in magnitude, with the effect that but a few consecutive coordinate functions φ need enter the computation in order to arrive at a practically accurate result.[1]

Similar considerations concerning the selection of the coordinate functions φ apply also to two-dimensional buckling problems involving the stability of plates.

The Ritz method has one disadvantage—it is rather difficult to gauge the accuracy of the results obtained. While the accuracy obviously increases with increased number of terms used, the only way to judge the convergence of the series (86) is to compare successive results obtained with an increasing number of terms, which is cumbersome and not even foolproof. Attempts to overcome this difficulty are discussed in Art. 26.

25. Timoshenko's Concept of Solving Buckling Problems

Timoshenko[2] starts the explanation of his method with the following reasoning: A straight column under a concentric load P smaller than the critical load P_c is in stable equilibrium, for if slightly bent, the column returns to its previous position when the disturbance is removed. A certain amount of work is required to produce the displacement. This can be expressed mathematically by the inequality

$$V - W > 0 \tag{92}$$

in which V is the strain energy of bending and $W = P \, \Delta l$ the work done by the external force P. When P increases, $V - W$ decreases, approaching zero when P approaches P_c. Therefore

$$V - W = 0 \tag{93}$$

characterizes the incipient state of buckling at which the straight form of equilibrium changes to the unstable deflected configuration. Proceeding in the same manner as Ritz and introducing into the integrals which represent V and W a series of the type (86), Timoshenko arrives at the

---

[1] This problem is discussed in detail in Art. 83, Chap. VIII.

[2] Timoshenko, S., "Theory of Elastic Stability," p. 78, McGraw-Hill Book Company, Inc., 1936.

equation[1]

$$F_1(a_1 \cdots a_n) - PF_2(a_1 \cdots a_n) = 0 \qquad (94)$$

from which

$$P = \frac{F_1(a_1 \ldots a_n)}{F_2(a_1 \ldots a_n)} \qquad (95)$$

is derived. Timoshenko concludes now that the parameters a must be adjusted in such a way that P becomes a minimum. This condition leads to n equations

$$\frac{\partial P}{\partial a_i} = \frac{1}{F_2{}^2}\left(\frac{\partial F_1}{\partial a_i} F_2 - \frac{\partial F_2}{\partial a_i} F_1\right) = 0 \qquad (i = 1, 2, \ldots, n)$$

which may be transformed to

$$\frac{1}{F_2}\left(\frac{\partial F_1}{\partial a_i} - \frac{\partial F_2}{\partial a_i}\frac{F_1}{F_2}\right) = 0 \qquad (i = 1, 2, \ldots, n) \qquad (96)$$

Since $P = F_1/F_2$ [Eq. (95)], we obtain finally

$$\frac{\partial F_1}{\partial a_i} - P\frac{\partial F_2}{\partial a_i} = 0 \qquad (i = 1, 2, \ldots, n) \qquad (97)$$

These n equations are identical with Eqs. (88), which determine the parameters a and the critical load P_c, since $V + U_w = F_1 - PF_2$.

From the theorem that P as defined by Eq. (95) shall be a minimum, it can be concluded that lower values of P will be obtained the more closely the computed shape of the deflection curve y approaches the true form of the equilibrium configuration. From this it follows that the approximate value of P_c, whether derived by Timoshenko's or by the Ritz method, must always be greater than the exact value.

For certain buckling problems a good approximation can be obtained by using only one coordinate function, $y = a_1\varphi_1$. In such cases Eq. (93), which expresses the fact that the strain energy V must be equal to the work W done by the external forces, furnishes the value of the critical load without reference to any minimum principle. Expressing V and W in Eq. (93) by $a_1\varphi_1$ it is found that both contain the factor $a_1{}^2$ and after division by $a_1{}^2$ a linear equation for P results.[2] In Chap. V this simple method will be applied to determine the critical load of built-up columns.

---

[1] In order to compare Timoshenko's method with the Ritz method, it should be noted that the potential energy of the external loads U_w, as used in the previous articles, and the work W are related: $U_w = -W$. Equation (93) could therefore be written $V + U_w = 0$, and the functions F_1 and F_2 appearing in Eq. (87) occur again in Eq. (94).

[2] This procedure corresponds to Rayleigh's method of finding the natural frequencies of vibrating systems.

26. Extension of the Ritz Method

The method as originally devised by Ritz was based on the idea of expressing the deflection y of the elastic system under consideration by a sum of coordinate functions φ, where each term of the expansion should satisfy the particular boundary conditions of the problem. It is natural that this requirement restricts to a certain extent the choice of the coordinate functions, and if it could be abandoned, more freedom in the selection of these functions would be achieved with the benefit that in many cases the simplest type of coordinate functions, Fourier terms, could be applied. However, if the functions φ violate some of the boundary conditions of the problem, care must be taken that the expression y as a whole nevertheless satisfies all boundary conditions. This is achieved by requiring that the solution y not only satisfies the condition (82) but also certain additional conditions which ensue from the particular condition of restraint of the given problem.

The procedure in finding the critical load is essentially the same as described above in discussing the Ritz method. Assuming y in the form $y = a_1\varphi_1 + \cdots + a_i\varphi_i + \cdots + a_n\varphi_n$ where the φ_i are suitably chosen coordinate functions which do not, however, satisfy all the boundary conditions of the problem, the coefficients a_i must be determined so that they satisfy the energy criterion

$$V + U_w = \text{stationary} \tag{98}$$

where V and U_w are quadratic functions of the parameters a_i. But the coefficients a_i must also satisfy certain equations of the form

$$f_1(a_1 \cdots a_n) = 0, \quad f_2(a_1 \cdots a_n) = 0, \quad \cdots f_r(a_1 \cdots a_n) = 0 \tag{99}$$

expressing those conditions of constraint which are not already satisfied by the chosen functions φ_i, the number of these equations being r and $r < n$.

The problem of making the expression (98) stationary and simultaneously satisfying Eqs. (99) can be solved conveniently by Lagrange's multiplier method, which obtains the values of the parameters a from the condition that the expression

$$\bar{U} = V + U_w - \lambda_1 f_1 - \lambda_2 f_2 - \cdots - \lambda_r f_r \tag{100}$$

shall be stationary, where $\lambda_1, \ldots \lambda_r$ are multipliers to be determined in such manner that Eqs. (99) are satisfied. This leads to n equations

$$\frac{\partial \bar{U}}{\partial a_i} = 0 \quad (i = 1, 2, \ldots, n) \tag{101}$$

which together with the r equations (99) determine the n values a and the r multipliers λ.

At the first glance the procedure just outlined seems to be more complicated than the original Ritz method, for it apparently leads to a determinant of the order $n + r$ as compared with the nth-order determinant of Ritz's method. However, in certain problems it is possible to choose a set of coordinate functions φ_i which are the solutions of the buckling problem for the same structure but under different boundary conditions.[1] In this case the orthogonality relations, the importance of which has been stressed previously, result in a reduction of the final stability condition to a determinant of a system of r equations which determine the r Lagrangian multipliers $\lambda_1 \ldots \lambda_r$.

The essential features of this method can be illustrated on an elementary example, for which the exact solution is known.

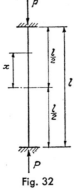

Fig. 32

Let us consider a column of length l, built in at both ends and having constant moment of inertia I (Fig. 32). The expression for the potential energy is

$$U = V + U_w = \frac{EI}{2} \int_{-\frac{l}{2}}^{\frac{l}{2}} y''^2 \, dx \; - \frac{P}{2} \int_{-\frac{l}{2}}^{\frac{l}{2}} y'^2 \, dx \quad (102)$$

The deflection curve y shall be determined from the condition that U will be stationary, the function y satisfying the boundary conditions for built-in ends:

$$y = 0 \quad \text{and} \quad y' = 0 \quad (103)$$

for $x = l/2$ and $x = -l/2$. We assume the function y to be of the form

$$y = \sum_{i=1}^{n} a_i \varphi_i = \sum_{i=1}^{n} a_i \cos \frac{(2i-1)\pi x}{l} \quad (104)$$

where $n > 2$. The terms of this sum are the subsequent symmetrical characteristic functions of the buckling problem of the same column, but with pinned ends. Each of the coordinate functions $\varphi_i = \cos \dfrac{(2i-1)\pi x}{l}$ satisfies the first but not the second boundary condition (103). To satisfy this boundary condition we must impose the additional condition

$$\sum_{i=1}^{n} (-1)^i (2i-1) a_i = 0 \quad (105)$$

According to Lagrange's multiplier method the expression

$$\bar{U} = V + U_w - \lambda \sum_{i=1}^{n} (-1)^i (2i-1) a_i \quad (106)$$

[1] When a clamped plate is being investigated, the simpler solutions of a freely supported plate may be used.

must be made stationary, where the multiplier λ is to be found from Eq. (105). Using Eqs. (102) and (104), $V + U_w$ in Eq. (106) can be expressed by the coefficients a_i:

$$\bar{U} = \sum_{i=1}^{n} \left[\frac{EI\pi^4}{4l^3} (2i - 1)^4 a_i^2 - \frac{P\pi^2}{4l} (2i - 1)^2 a_i^2 \right.$$
$$\left. - \lambda(-1)^i \frac{\pi}{l} (2i - 1)a_i \right] \quad (107)$$

The expression $\bar{U}$ will be stationary if

$$\frac{\partial \bar{U}}{\partial a_i} = \left[\frac{EI\pi^4}{2l^3} (2i - 1)^4 - \frac{P\pi^2}{2l} (2i - 1)^2 \right] a_i$$
$$- \lambda(-1)^i \frac{\pi}{l} (2i - 1) = 0 \quad (108)$$

where $i = 1, 2, \ldots, n$. Because of the orthogonality relations, no mixed terms $a_i a_k$ occur in Eq. (107), and as a result each of Eqs. (108) contains only one of the coefficients a_i, which can be determined as function of λ:

$$a_i = (-1)^i \frac{2}{(2i - 1)\pi} \frac{\lambda}{(2i - 1)^2 P_E - P} \quad (109)$$

where P_E is the Euler load $\pi^2 EI/l^2$. Substituting these values a_i into Eq. (105) furnishes the equation for the determination of the multiplier λ:

$$\frac{2\lambda}{\pi} \sum_{i=1}^{n} \frac{1}{(2i - 1)^2 P_E - P} = 0 \quad (110)$$

Values of λ other than zero can exist only if the sum in Eq. (110) vanishes, and

$$\sum_{i=1}^{n} \frac{1}{(2i - 1)^2 P_E - P} = 0 \quad (111)$$

is therefore the stability condition. Solving Eq. (111) for $n = 2, 3, 4$, and 5 gives the approximate values $P_c = 5P_E$, $4.63P_E$, $4.45P_E$, $4.35P_E$, which converge toward the exact value $P_c = 4P_E$.

The significant fact in the example is that, in spite of using n coordinate functions φ_i, we found the stability condition from the single Eq. (110) and not as determinant of a system of $n + 1$ equations. It is also noticeable that a relatively large number n of terms is required for accuracy, but this is no serious objection, because the order of the determinant does not change when the number n of the terms used increases.

In the above example we obtained approximate values of the critical load which were larger than the exact value, just as in the original Ritz method.

In order to judge the degree of approximation obtained with a given number of terms it would be highly desirable to know also an approximate value of the critical load lower than the exact value. For certain plate-buckling problems it is possible to obtain such a lower limit for the critical load by a variation of the method just discussed of using coordinate functions which do not satisfy the boundary conditions. A suitable example is the buckling of a clamped rectangular plate in shear (Fig. 33).[1]

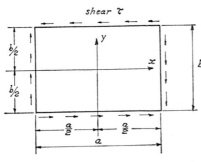

Fig. 33

Denoting the deflection of the plate by w, we approximate this deflection by the following double Fourier expansion:

$$w = \sum_{i=1}^{n} \sum_{k=1}^{n} a_{ik} \sin \frac{2i\pi x}{a} \sin \frac{2k\pi y}{b} + \sum_{i=0}^{n} \sum_{k=0}^{n} d_{ik} \cos \frac{2i\pi x}{a} \cos \frac{2k\pi y}{b} \quad (112)$$

This expression is suitable to express symmetrical deformations of the plate. The boundary conditions for the clamped plate are

For the edges $x = \pm \dfrac{a}{2}$ and $y = \pm \dfrac{b}{2}$: $w = 0$ (113a)

For the edges $x = \pm \dfrac{a}{2}$: $\dfrac{\partial w}{\partial x} = 0$ (113b)

For the edges $y = \pm \dfrac{b}{2}$: $\dfrac{\partial w}{\partial y} = 0$ (113c)

Inspection of the coordinate functions in Eq. (112) reveals that the sine terms satisfy the boundary conditions Eq. (113a) but not Eqs. (113b) and (113c), while the cosine terms satisfy Eqs. (113b) and (113c) but not Eq. (113a). In order that the deflection w satisfies the boundary conditions which the individual coordinate functions violate, additional conditions between the coefficients must be satisfied. Substituting Eq. (112) into Eqs. (113), the following additional restraining conditions can be derived:

[1] This particular problem is discussed in detail in B. Budiansky, Pai C. Hu, and R. W. Connor, Notes on the Lagrangian Multiplier Method, *NACA Tech. Note* 1558, 1948.

$$\sum_{i=0}^{n} (-1)^i d_{ik} = 0 \qquad (k = 0, 1, 2, \ldots, n) \qquad (114a)$$

$$\sum_{k=0}^{n} (-1)^k d_{ik} = 0 \qquad (i = 0, 1, 2, \ldots, n) \qquad (114b)$$

$$\sum_{i=1}^{n} i(-1)^i a_{ik} = 0 \qquad (k = 1, 2, \ldots, n) \qquad (114c)$$

$$\sum_{k=0}^{n} k(-1)^k a_{ik} = 0 \qquad (i = 1, 2, \ldots, n) \qquad (114d)$$

If we now proceed as before and use Lagrange's multiplier method to make the potential energy $V + U_w$ stationary while satisfying all the conditions (114), we should again obtain a value of the critical load necessarily higher than the actual critical load. Instead, we decide to make the potential energy stationary while disregarding some of the boundary conditions (114); we consider Eqs. (114a) and (114c) only for $k = 0$, 1, . . . , r, and Eqs. (114b) and (114d) for $i = 1, 2, \ldots, r$, where $r < n$. In doing so, we are no longer computing the critical load of a fully clamped plate, but the load of a partially restrained plate. The exact value of the critical load of a partially restrained plate is necessarily lower than the load for the fully fixed plate, and the approximate value which the computation furnishes will also be lower than the critical load of the fully fixed plate, provided the value n was selected high enough to secure a good approximation. It is important to stress that, because of the orthogonality relations between the coordinate functions used, the order of the determinant to be solved does not depend on the number of these functions, but only on the number of conditions (114) retained.

We shall not discuss this particular problem further, as this discussion is intended only to show the principle of the method which may also be applied to other suitable cases of plate buckling. The method was suggested by Courant, and its practicability demonstrated by Trefftz[1] in the case of a square plate clamped on all four sides and subjected to compressive stresses on two opposite edges. The method was further developed and extended by Budiansky and Hu.[2]

27. Solution of Column Problems by Successive Approximation

Another method of arriving at an approximate solution of a stability problem, a procedure of particular applicability in the field of column stability, is the method of successive approximation known as the Stodola-

---

[1] Trefftz, *loc. cit.* on p. 69.
[2] Budiansky and Hu, *loc. cit.* on p. 70.

Vianello method.   In its essential feature this method represents nothing else than a numerical or graphical procedure of integrating the differential equation of column stability by a sequence of successive approximations. The method was introduced into the field of engineering by Vianello,[1] who demonstrated its application to the graphical solution of column problems.   Its usefulness in solving vibration problems was first pointed out by Stodola.[2]   The mathematical proof for the convergence of the method was given by Koch.[3]

Starting from the second-order differential equation of the pin-ended column

$$EI_x y'' + Py = 0 \qquad\qquad (115)$$

we assume the moment of inertia $I_x = I\psi(x)$ to be a continuous or discontinuous function of x.   Introducing $I\psi(x)$, in which I is an arbitrary reference moment of inertia and $\psi(x)$ a given function of x, Eq. (115) can be written

$$\psi(x)y'' + \lambda^2 y = 0 \qquad\qquad (116)$$

where $\lambda = \sqrt{P/EI}$.   In order to solve the differential equation (116) by the method of successive approximations, we proceed as follows: We consider a sequence of functions

$$z_0,\ z_1,\ z_2,\ \ldots \qquad\qquad (117)$$

which satisfy the boundary conditions of the problem and are interrelated by the differential equations

$$z_n'' = -\frac{z_{n-1}}{\psi(x)} \qquad (n = 1,\ 2,\ 3,\ \ldots) \qquad\qquad (118)$$

If z_0 is chosen arbitrarily, the functions $z_1,\ z_2,\ \ldots$ can be determined step by step by direct integration of Eq. (118).   As will be shown subsequently, the functions z_n thus obtained converge into the first characteristic solution y_1 (first buckling mode) of the differential equation (116), and the associated characteristic value λ which defines the critical value of P is given by the equation

$$\lambda_1^2 = \lim_{n \to \infty} \frac{z_{n-1}}{z_n} \qquad\qquad (119)$$

When the function z_0 from which the computation starts is suitably chosen, the fraction z_{n-1}/z_n $(n = 1,\ 2,\ \ldots)$ very rapidly approaches the

[1] Vianello, L., Graphische Untersuchung der Knickfestigkeit gerader Stäbe, *Zeitschrift des Vereines deutscher Ingenieure*, Vol. 42, p. 36, 1898.

[2] Stodola, A., and L. C. Loewenstein, "Steam Turbines," 2d rev. ed., p. 185, D. Van Nostrand Company, Inc., New York, 1905.

[3] Koch, J. J., Bestimmung höherer kritischer Drehzahlen schnellaufender Wellen, *Proc. 2d Intern. Congr. Applied Mechanics*, Zürich, 1926, p. 213.

true value of the parameter $\lambda_1{}^2$. In many cases, two or three steps suffice to arrive at a practically accurate value of λ_1. However, after a limited number of steps, the two curves z_{n-1} and z_n are not yet completely similar, and the value of $\lambda_1{}^2 = z_{n-1}/z_n$ will depend on the particular abscissa x at which the ordinates z_{n-1} and z_n are read. This difficulty can be overcome by using the average of the values z:

$$\lambda_1{}^2 = \lim_{n \to \infty} \frac{\int_0^l z_{n-1}\, dx}{\int_0^l z_n\, dx} \tag{120}$$

The rapid convergence of the process on the one hand and the ease of carrying out the integration of Eq. (118) on the other hand make the

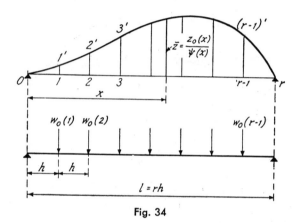

Fig. 34

above-discussed method a valuable tool for the approximate solution of column problems. According to Eq. (118) z_n can be interpreted as the moment produced by the loading $z_{n-1}/\psi(x)$, and consequently, the performance of the integrations of Eq. (118) necessary to obtain the functions $z_1, z_2, \ldots$ is reduced to the numerical determination of the ordinates of moment diagrams.

In performing the computation in an actual case, the distributed load $z_{n-1}/\psi(x)$ may be replaced by equivalent concentrated loads acting at equally spaced points of the column. If z_0 is the assumed deflection (Fig. 34), the ordinates of the curve $\bar{z}_0(x) = z_0(x)/\psi(x)$ at the points $1, 2, \ldots, r-1$ are computed first. This permits the determination of the equivalent concentrated loads $w_0\,(i)$, acting at the points $i = 1, 2, \ldots, r-1$, from the following approximate formula:[1]

---

[1] The formula is derived by replacing the curve $z_0/\psi(x)$ by the polygon **0′, 1′, 2′, 3′, . . .**

$$w_0(i) = \frac{h}{6} [\bar{z}_0(i-1) + 4\bar{z}_0(i) + \bar{z}_0(i+1)]$$

$$(i = 1, 2, \ldots, r-1) \quad (121)$$

If the curve $\bar{z}_0$ has a discontinuity at any point i, as shown in Fig. 35, the load $w_0(i)$ should be computed from

$$w_0(i) = \frac{h}{6} [\bar{z}_0(i-1) + 2(\bar{z}_0{}'(i) + \bar{z}_0{}''(i)) + \bar{z}_0(i+1)] \quad (122)$$

It is now easy to determine numerically the moment $m_1(i)$ due to the loads $w_0(i)$ by the method, familiar to the structural engineer, of computing the end reactions, finding the shear in each interval by adding the successive loads to the shear in the preceding panel, and finally obtaining

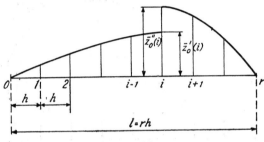

Fig. 35

the moments by adding the successive shears multiplied by the length h of the intervals.[1]   The resulting moment $m_1(i)$ is the first approximation of the deflection curve, $z_1(i) = m_1(i)$.

Repeating this procedure but starting with the curves $m_1(i)/\psi$, $m_2(i)/\psi$, . . . , improved deflection curves

$$z_n(i) = m_n(i)$$

are obtained.   Applying Eq. (120), the parameter λ_1 can be expressed

$$\lambda_1{}^2 = \frac{\int z_{n-1}\, dx}{\int z_n\, dx} = \frac{\displaystyle\sum_{i=0}^{r} m_{n-1}(i)}{\displaystyle\sum_{i=0}^{r} m_n(i)} \quad (123)$$

[1] An extensive presentation of numerical procedures in determining moments and their application to the computation of deflections and buckling loads is given by N. M. Newmark, Numerical Procedure for Computing Deflections, Moments, and Buckling Loads, Trans. ASCE, Vol. 108, p. 1161, 1943.

and the critical load is finally

$$P_c = EI \frac{\sum\limits_{i=0}^{r} m_{n-1}(i)}{\sum\limits_{i=0}^{r} m_n(i)} \tag{124}$$

So far we have assumed P constant. If P varies along the column, the method is also applicable. To adapt it for such cases it is necessary to use a more general form of Eq. (115):

$$EI_x y'' + M(x) = 0 \tag{125}$$

where $M(x)$ is the moment at the reference point x of the deflected column axis. Consider, for example, a column of length l loaded by an axial

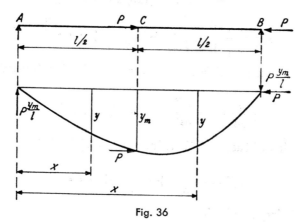

Fig. 36

force P applied at the mid-point C (Fig. 36). The moment $M(x)$ between points A and C is

$$M(x) = P y_m \frac{x}{l}$$

and between points C and B

$$M(x) = P\left[y_m \frac{x}{l} - (y_m - y) \right]$$

If we write $M(x) = P\mu(x)$, Eq. (125) takes the form

$$\psi(x) y'' + \lambda^2 \mu(x) = 0 \tag{126}$$

where $\lambda = \sqrt{P/EI}$, and instead of Eq. (118) we have the relation

$$z_n'' = - \frac{\mu_{n-1}(x)}{\psi(x)} \qquad (n = 1, 2, 3, \ldots) \tag{127}$$

By successive integrations of Eq. (127), starting for $n = 1$ with an arbitrary curve $\mu_0(x)$ and using the numerical procedure previously described, the problem can be solved in the same manner as in the case of constant P.

The method discussed in this article is entirely dependent on the theorem expressed by Eq. (119), and a proof of it is of interest.[1] The process of the successive approximation starts with a function z_0 which satisfies the boundary conditions but is otherwise arbitrary. Any such function z_0 can be expanded in the form

$$z_0 = a_1\varphi_1 + a_2\varphi_2 + a_3\varphi_3 + \cdots \tag{128}$$

where the φ_1, φ_2, . . . are the characteristic functions of the differential equation (116) associated with the characteristic values λ_1, λ_2, ... Introducing this expansion into Eq. (118) for $n = 1$ gives

$$z_1'' = -\left[a_1 \frac{\varphi_1}{\psi(x)} + a_2 \frac{\varphi_2}{\psi(x)} + \cdots \right] \tag{129}$$

Since any function φ_i satisfies the differential equation (116) if $\lambda^2 = \lambda_i^2$, we have

$$\frac{\varphi_i}{\psi(x)} = -\frac{\varphi_i''}{\lambda_i^2} \qquad (i = 1, 2, \ldots)$$

and introduction of these relations into Eq. (129) leads to

$$z_1'' = a_1 \frac{\varphi_1''}{\lambda_1^2} + a_2 \frac{\varphi_2''}{\lambda_2^2} + \cdots$$

Integrating twice, we obtain

$$z_1 = a_1 \frac{\varphi_1}{\lambda_1^2} + a_2 \frac{\varphi_2}{\lambda_2^2} + \cdots \tag{130}$$

Applying the same reasoning to z_1 gives

$$z_2 = \frac{a_1}{\lambda_1^4} \varphi_1 + \frac{a_2}{\lambda_2^4} \varphi_2 + \cdots$$

and after $n - 1$ and n steps, respectively, we have

$$z_{n-1} = \frac{1}{\lambda_1^{2n-2}} \left(a_1\varphi_1 + \frac{\lambda_1^{2n-2}}{\lambda_2^{2n-2}} a_2\varphi_2 + \cdots \right)$$

and

$$z_n = \frac{1}{\lambda_1^{2n}} \left(a_1\varphi_1 + \frac{\lambda_1^{2n}}{\lambda_2^{2n}} a_2\varphi_2 + \cdots \right)$$

[1] Koch, *loc. cit.* on p. 82.

Since λ_2, λ_3, . . . are far greater than λ_1, the functions z_{n-1} and z_n converge with increasing n toward

$$z_{n-1} = \frac{1}{\lambda_1^{2n-2}} a_1 \varphi_1 \quad \text{and} \quad z_n = \frac{1}{\lambda_1^{2n}} a_1 \varphi_1 \quad (131)$$

so that the ratio z_{n-1}/z_n approaches the lowest characteristic value λ_1^2 when $n \to \infty$.

28. Solution of Buckling Problems by Finite Differences

The finite-difference method is an approximate numerical method for the evaluation of buckling loads, based upon the use of approximate expressions for the derivatives appearing in the differential equation and the boundary conditions of the problem. The method was first introduced by Richardson[1] in 1911, extensively studied by Collatz,[2] and treated as a method of successive approximations by Salvadori.[3]

The method will be illustrated by the solution of the lateral buckling problem of a simply supported I-beam, which is governed by the differential equation[4]

$$E\Gamma\beta^{IV} - GK\beta'' - \frac{M^2}{EI_y} \beta = 0 \quad (132)$$

and the boundary conditions

$$\beta = 0 \quad \text{and} \quad \beta'' = 0 \quad (133)$$

at both ends of the beam.

Divide the span L of the beam into n equal parts of width $h = L/n$, and indicate the values of β at the subdivision points by

$$\beta_0, \beta_1, \beta_2, \ldots, \beta_{i-1}, \beta_i, \beta_{i+1}, \ldots, \beta_{n-1}, \beta_n$$

When the spacing h between the points i is sufficiently small, the slope of the curve β at the ith point may be approximated by the slope of either of the two chords AB or BC (see Fig. 37) and we may write

$$[\beta_i']_{\text{left}} \doteq \frac{\beta_i - \beta_{i-1}}{h} \quad \text{and} \quad [\beta_i']_{\text{right}} \doteq \frac{\beta_{i+1} - \beta_i}{h} \quad (134)$$

[1] Richardson, L. F., The Approximate Arithmetical Solution by Finite Differences of Physical Problems Involving Differential Equations with an Application to the Stresses in a Masonry Dam, *Phil. Trans. Royal Soc. (London)*, Vol. 210, 1911.

[2] Collatz, L., "Eigenwert Probleme und ihre numerische Behandlung," Chelsea Publishing Company, New York, 1948.

[3] Salvadori, M. G., Numerical Computation of Buckling Loads by Finite Differences, *Trans. ASCE*, Vol. 116, 1951.

[4] This equation is derived in Chap. IV as Eq. (315). We assume here that the loading is such that $\bar{a} = 0$.

The sign $\doteq$ indicates approximately equal. Similarly, the second derivative of β at i may be approximated by the difference between the slopes $[\beta_i{'}]_{\text{right}}$ and $[\beta_i{'}]_{\text{left}}$ divided by h:

$$\beta_i{''} \doteq \frac{1}{h}\left(\frac{\beta_{i+1} - \beta_i}{h} - \frac{\beta_i - \beta_{i-1}}{h}\right) = \frac{\beta_{i+1} - 2\beta_i + \beta_{i-1}}{h^2} \qquad (135)$$

and the fourth derivative may be approximately obtained by means of Eq. (135) as the second derivative of the second derivative

$$\beta_i{}^{\text{IV}} \doteq \frac{\beta_{i+1}{''} - 2\beta_i{''} + \beta_{i-1}{''}}{h^2} = \frac{\beta_{i+2} - 4\beta_{i+1} + 6\beta_i - 4\beta_{i-1} + \beta_{i-2}}{h^4} \qquad (136)$$

Dividing Eq. (132) by $E\Gamma$ and substituting the approximate values of

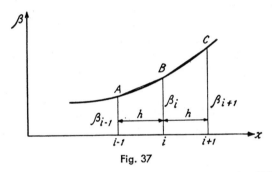

Fig. 37

β'' and β^{IV} given by Eqs. (135) and (136), we obtain the difference equation valid at each point i

$$\frac{\beta_{i+2} - 4\beta_{i+1} + 6\beta_i - 4\beta_{i-1} + \beta_{i-2}}{h^4} - \frac{GK}{E\Gamma}\frac{\beta_{i+1} - 2\beta_i + \beta_{i-1}}{h^2}$$
$$- \frac{M^2}{E^2\Gamma I_y}\beta_i = 0$$

which, when multiplied by $h^4 = L^4/n^4$, becomes

$$\beta_{i+2} - \left(4 + \frac{GKL^2}{E\Gamma n^2}\right)\beta_{i+1} + \left(6 + 2\frac{GKL^2}{E\Gamma n^2} - \frac{M^2L^4}{E^2\Gamma I_y n^4}\right)\beta_i$$
$$- \left(4 + \frac{GKL^2}{E\Gamma n^2}\right)\beta_{i-1} + \beta_{i-2} = 0 \qquad (137)$$

By means of Eq. (135), the boundary conditions (133) become

$$\beta_0 = 0 \qquad \text{and} \qquad \frac{\beta_1 - 2\beta_0 + \beta_{-1}}{h^2} = 0$$

$$\beta_n = 0 \qquad \text{and} \qquad \frac{\beta_{n+1} - 2\beta_n + \beta_{n-1}}{h^2} = 0$$

or

$$\beta_0 = 0, \qquad \beta_{-1} = -\beta_1, \qquad \beta_n = 0, \qquad \beta_{n+1} = -\beta_{n-1} \qquad (138)$$

While Eqs. (138) define the fictitious values β_{-1} and β_{n+1} beyond the beam supports in terms of the unknown values β_1 and β_{n-1} inside the supports, Eqs. (137) hold at the $n - 1$ points $i = 1, 2, \ldots, n - 1$ and constitute a system of simultaneous linear equations in the $n - 1$ unknown rotations β_i. These equations are homogeneous; hence they have a trivial solution $\beta_i = 0$, which corresponds to the unbuckled state of the beam, but they may also have a solution different from zero if the determinant of their coefficients is equal to zero. The condition on the buckling load obtained by setting this determinant equal to zero defines the critical values of the load, with an approximation which improves with an increase in the number n of subdivisions.

To illustrate the procedure, consider a 24 W, 76-lb beam simply supported over a span of 25 ft and loaded by a vertical load P applied at the centroid of the middle section. In this case

$$M = \begin{cases} \dfrac{P}{2} z & \text{if } 0 \leq z \leq \dfrac{L}{2} \\ \dfrac{P}{2} (L - z) & \text{if } \dfrac{L}{2} \leq z \leq L \end{cases}$$

and Eq. (137) becomes, for $0 \leq z \leq L/2$,

$$\beta_{i+2} - \left(4 + \frac{GKL^2}{E\Gamma n^2}\right)\beta_{i+1} + \left(6 + 2\frac{GKL^2}{E\Gamma n^2} - \frac{P^2 z_i^2 L^4}{4E^2{}_y\Gamma I n^4}\right)\beta_i$$
$$- \left(4 + \frac{GKL^2}{E\Gamma n^2}\right)\beta_{i-1} + \beta_{i-2} = 0 \qquad \text{if } 0 \leq z_i \leq \frac{L}{2}$$

or, letting

$$A = \frac{GKL}{E\Gamma}, \qquad B = \frac{P^2 L^6}{4E^2\Gamma I_y}, \qquad x_i = \frac{z_i}{L} \qquad (139)$$

and multiplying through by n^4,

$$n^4\beta_{i+2} - (4n^4 + An^2)\beta_{i+1} + (6n^4 + 2An^2 - Bx_i^2)\beta_i - (4n^4 + An^2)\beta_{i-1}$$
$$+ n^4\beta_{i-2} = 0 \qquad \text{if } 0 \leq x_i \leq \tfrac{1}{2} \quad (140)$$

The corresponding equation valid for the right half of the beam ($\tfrac{1}{2} \leq x_i \leq 1$) need not be written, since the rotation β is symmetrical with respect to the middle of the span and hence, $\beta_i = \beta_{n-i}$.

The constants for the beam under study have the following values:

$$E = 29.5 \times 10^6 \text{ lb/in.}^2, \qquad G = \tfrac{5}{13}E, \qquad K = 2.9 \text{ in.}^4$$
$$I_y = 76.5 \text{ in.}^4, \qquad d = 23.9 \text{ in.}, \qquad L = 300 \text{ in.}$$
$$A = \frac{GKL^2}{E\Gamma} = \frac{4GK}{EI_y d^2} = 9.19$$

Equation (140) can now be applied, subdividing the beam into an increasing number n of sections. The lowest value n which might be used is $n = 2$, but for purposes of demonstration we select $n = 4$.

Approximation n = 4. Applying Eq. (140) at $i = 1$ and $i = 2$ (Fig. 38), we obtain the two simultaneous equations

$$-4^4\beta_1 - 0 + \left(6 \times 4^4 + 2A \times 4^2 - \frac{B_4}{4^2}\right)\beta_1$$
$$- \left(4 \times 4^4 + A \times 4^2\right)\beta_2 + 4^4\beta_1 = 0$$

$$0 - \left(4 \times 4^4 + A \times 4^2\right)\beta_1 + \left(6 \times 4^4 + 2A \times 4^2 - \frac{B_4}{2^2}\right)\beta_2$$
$$- \left(4 \times 4^4 + A \times 4^2\right)\beta_1 + 0 = 0$$

or

$$\left(6 \times 4^4 + 2A \times 4^2 - \frac{B_4}{16}\right)\beta_1 - \left(4 \times 4^4 + A \times 4^2\right)\beta_2 = 0$$

$$-\left(8 \times 4^4 + 2A \times 4^2\right)\beta_1 + \left(6 \times 4^4 + 2A \times 4^2 - \frac{B_4}{4}\right)\beta_2 = 0$$

where B_4 is the approximation (for $n = 4$) of the value B defined in Eq. (139).

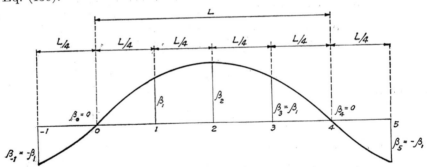

Fig. 38

The determinant of the coefficients of this system equated to zero gives the quadratic equation for B_4:

$$\begin{vmatrix} \left(1,830 - \dfrac{B_4}{16}\right) & -1,171 \\ -2,342 & \left(1,830 - \dfrac{B_4}{4}\right) \end{vmatrix} = B_4{}^2 - 36,600\,B_4 + 38,810,752 = 0$$

The smallest root of this equation, corresponding to the smallest value of the critical load, equals $B_4 = 1,093$, and hence

$$P_4 = \frac{EI_y d}{L^3}\sqrt{B_4} = 1,998\sqrt{B_4} = 66,054\text{ lb}$$

with an error of $+11.5\%$ in comparison with the value of 74,670 lb computed by means of Table 5 in Chap. IV.

The following Table 4 gives the successive values of P_n with the corresponding percentage errors.

TABLE 4

n	P_n	Error, %
2	46,860	+37.2
3	76,690	− 2.7
4	66,054	+11.5
5	74,700	0
6	70,980	+ 5.2
7	74,680	0

The results obtained by the finite-difference method may be substantially improved by assuming that the error in the value of P_n is inversely proportional to n^2.

This assumption is valid only for equations with constant coefficients[1] but gives good results whenever it is applied to a sequence of values P_n, which either increases or decreases steadily (monotonic sequence).

For example, calling P the true value of the load and using the sequence of even approximations in Table 4, we obtain

$$P - P_2 \doteq \frac{C}{2^2} \quad \text{and} \quad P - P_4 \doteq \frac{C}{4^2}$$

where C is a constant. Solving for P,

$$P_{2,4} = \tfrac{4}{3}P_4 - \tfrac{1}{3}P_2 = 72,452$$

with an error of $+3\%$, as compared with errors of $+37.2$ and 11.5% in P_2 and P_4. The value $P_{2,4}$ is obtained with a negligible amount of labor and is a better approximation than the value P_6, which requires setting up and solving a third-degree determinantal equation.

The method of finite differences may be used with advantage to determine the critical loads of columns or beams with variable moment of inertia and is also applicable to the two-dimensional problems of the stability of plates or shells.

29. Introduction to the Calculus of Variations

The calculus of variations was conceived by Bernoulli, Euler, and Lagrange for the solution of a certain group of problems in geometry and physics. Today, it is a highly advanced branch of modern mathematics,

[1] Salvadori, *loc. cit.* on p. 87.

closely related to the theory of linear differential equations, and together with this theory forms the backbone of the mathematical treatment of various problems in statics and dynamics. Knowledge of the fundamental features of the calculus of variations is indispensable for a thorough understanding of the nature of the energy method, the mathematical procedures involved in its applications, and the relationship of this method to other methods of solving mechanical problems.

The calculus of variations may be considered a generalization of the elementary theory of maxima and minima. This branch of calculus deals with the finding of a point x_0, y_0, . . . in which a function $f(x, y, . . .)$ of n variables assumes an extreme value, *i.e.*, a largest or a least value of f compared with the values of f in the close neighborhood of the point x_0, y_0, ... The criterion which determines this point is that the first derivatives $\dfrac{df}{dx}, \dfrac{df}{dy}$, . . . vanish for $x = x_0, y = y_0$, ... Such points at which these derivatives are zero are referred to as stationary points of the function f.

In the case where the variables x, y, . . . are not independent of each other but are related through r equations

$$g_1(x, y, . . .) = 0, \qquad g_2(x, y, . . .) = 0, . . .$$

(constraining conditions), the extremum criterion can be conveniently formulated by using the method of *Lagrangian multipliers*. After forming a new function $\bar{f}$ containing the parameters $\lambda_1, \lambda_2, . . . , \lambda_n$ (the Lagrangian multipliers),

$$\bar{f} = f(x, y, . . .) - \lambda_1 g_1(x, y, . . .) - \lambda_2 g_2(x, y, . . .) + \cdots \quad (141)$$

the coordinates x_0, y_0, . . . of stationary values of $\bar{f}$ are determined. The values x_0, y_0, . . . are functions of the r parameters λ, and the values of λ may be chosen so that the r equations $g_1 = 0, g_2 = 0, . . .$ are satisfied. This leads to $n + r$ equations

$$\frac{\partial \bar{f}}{\partial x} = 0, \qquad \frac{\partial \bar{f}}{\partial y} = 0 \cdots \qquad g_1 = 0, \qquad g_2 = 0 \cdots \quad (142)$$

from which the $n + r$ unknowns x_0, y_0, . . . , $\lambda_1, \lambda_2 . . . , \lambda_r$ can be computed.

The calculus of variations also deals with the problem of finding an extremum. However, the fundamental difference is that an extreme value of a given function f of a number of variables is no longer being sought but the problem now is the determination of the extremum of a function F of functions. To illustrate the problem let us consider the definite integral

$$I = \int_{x_0}^{x_1} F(x, y, y', y'', . . .) \, dx \quad (143)$$

where y itself and its derivatives y', y'', . . . with respect to x are functions of x. Therefore, I is a function of the function y which now represents the independent variable and may assume any arbitrary form between the limits x_0 and x_1. The fundamental problem of the calculus of variations is to determine the analytical form of the function $y = y(x)$ such that the integral I shall be an extremum, or, as it is often expressed, that I is stationary.

The integrand in Eq. (143) was assumed dependent on one function y only. However, the method of solving the extremum problem offered by the calculus of variations can also be extended to such problems where the integrand depends on a number of functions y, z, . . . and their derivatives of any order with respect to x.

Furthermore, if F is a function of the function $u(x,y)$ of the two independent variables x, y, the corresponding problem to be solved by the calculus of variation is to find the function $u(x,y)$ such that the double integral extended over the area A,

$$I = \iint_A F(x, y, u, u_x, u_y, u_{xx}, u_{xy}, \ldots) \, dx \, dy \qquad (144)$$

assumes an extreme value. u_x, u_y, . . . indicate the partial derivatives

$$u_x = \frac{\partial u}{\partial x}, \qquad u_y = \frac{\partial u}{\partial y}, \qquad u_{xx} = \frac{\partial^2 u}{\partial x^2}, \qquad u_{xy} = \frac{\partial^2 u}{\partial x \, \partial y}, \cdots \qquad (145)$$

It will be shown in the following articles that the unknown functions which make integral expressions of the type (143) or (144) stationary can be found from linear differential equations, the form of which depends on the function F. This is the classic way of solving the problem of the calculus of variation, and the resulting differential equations are called Eulerian equations. The Ritz method discussed in Art. 24 is an alternative method devised to solve the same problem by approximation.

30. Integrals Containing Only One Function of One Independent Variable

We consider the integral

$$I = \int_{x_0}^{x_1} F(x, y, y', y'') \, dx \qquad (146)$$

and seek the function $y = y(x)$ which makes the expression I stationary. $y(x_0)$ and $y(x_1)$ are given boundary values of the function y which may be geometrically represented by the curve AB in the system of rectangular coordinates x, y (Fig. 39). We assume that $y = y(x)$ is the function which satisfies the extremum condition. Let us consider an arbitrary but continuous function $\eta(x)$ defined in the interval $x_0 < x < x_1$, such that the function itself and its first derivative with respect to x vanish at the boundaries A and B. Denoting by ϵ a small number, we now form a new function

$$\bar{y} = y + \epsilon\eta(x) \tag{147}$$

and call the magnitude $\delta y = \epsilon\eta(x)$ the variation of $y = y(x)$. If ϵ is taken sufficiently small such that $\epsilon\eta(x)$ for all values of x remains below a previously chosen small quantity Δ, the functions $\bar{y}$ will lie in the close neighborhood of the solution y. The definite integral

$$I(\bar{y}) = I[y + \epsilon\eta(x)]$$

will be a function $\Phi(\epsilon)$ of the parameter ϵ, and this function $\Phi(\epsilon)$ must

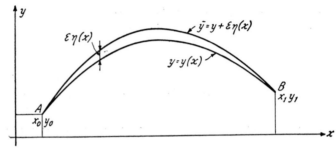

Fig. 39

have a stationary value for $\epsilon = 0$. With reference to Eq. (146) we can write

$$I(\bar{y}) = \Phi(\epsilon) = \int_{x_0}^{x_1} F(x, y + \epsilon\eta, y' + \epsilon\eta', y'' + \epsilon\eta'') \, dx \tag{148}$$

The necessary condition that $\Phi(\epsilon)$ be stationary is

$$[\Phi'(\epsilon)]_{\epsilon=0} = 0 \tag{149}$$

where the prime indicates differentiation with respect to ϵ. We now perform the differentiation indicated by Eq. (149) on the integral in Eq. (148) according to the familiar rules of the differential calculus. Since the derivative of a definite integral is identical with the integral of the derivative of the integrand, we obtain, by differentiation and then setting $\epsilon = 0$. the condition

$$\int_{x_0}^{x_1} (F_y\eta + F_{y'}\eta' + F_{y''}\eta'') \, dx = 0 \tag{150}$$

in which

$$F_y = \frac{\partial F}{\partial y}, \qquad F_{y'} = \frac{\partial F}{\partial y'}, \qquad F_{y''} = \frac{\partial F}{\partial y''}$$

$\delta y = \epsilon\eta(x)$ is the variation of the function $y(x)$ in passing from y to the neighboring curve $\bar{y} = y + \epsilon\eta(x)$. Denoting the corresponding variation of y', i.e., $\epsilon\eta'(x)$, by $\delta y'$, and the variation of y'', i.e.. $\epsilon\eta''(x)$ by $\delta y''$, Eq. (150) can be multiplied by ϵ and becomes

$$\int_{x_0}^{x_1} (F_y\, \delta y + F_{y'}\, \delta y' + F_{y''}\, \delta y'')\, dx = 0 \qquad (151)$$

This equation indicates clearly that the integrand can be obtained by a formal operation identical with the operation of differentiating the integrand in Eq. (146) and replacing the differentials dy, dy', $\ldots$ by the variations δy, $\delta y'$, $\ldots$ [1]

The left side of Eq. (151) is called the first variation δI of the integral I defined by Eq. (146), and

$$\delta I = 0 \qquad (152)$$

is the necessary condition for I being stationary.

Equation (150) or (151) will apply for any arbitrary function $\eta(x)$ having values $\eta = \eta' = 0$ at the boundaries x_0 and x_1, as stated at the beginning of this article.

In order to eliminate the variations $\delta y'$ and $\delta y''$ from Eq. (151) we transform the second and third terms at the left side by integration by parts as follows:

$$\int_{x_0}^{x_1} F_{y'}\, \delta y'\, dx = \left[F_{y'}\, \delta y \right]_{x_0}^{x_1} - \int_{x_0}^{x_1} \frac{d}{dx} F_{y'}\, \delta y\, dx = - \int_{x_0}^{x_1} \frac{d}{dx} F_{y'}\, \delta y\, dx$$

On account of the assumed boundary conditions for $\eta(x)$, the first term at the right side of the above equation containing $\delta y = \epsilon\eta(x)$ vanishes. Integrating twice by parts we obtain

$$\int_{x_0}^{x_1} F_{y''}\, \delta y''\, dx = \left[F_{y''}\, \delta y' \right]_{x_0}^{x_1} - \left[\frac{d}{dx} F_{y''}\, \delta y \right]_{x_0}^{x_1} + \int_{x_0}^{x_1} \frac{d^2}{dx^2} F_{y''}\, \delta y\, dx$$

$$= \int_{x_0}^{x_1} \frac{d^2}{dx^2} F_{y''} \delta y\, dx$$

The first and second term on the right are again zero because of the assumed boundary condition for the function $\eta(x)$. Substitution into Eq. (151) leads to

$$\delta I = \int_{x_0}^{x_1} \left(F_y - \frac{d}{dx} F_{y'} + \frac{d^2}{dx^2} F_{y''} \right) \delta y\, dx = 0 \qquad (153)$$

[1] According to differential calculus we have

$$dF = \frac{\partial F}{\partial y}\, dy + \frac{\partial F}{\partial y'}\, dy' + \cdots$$

dy, dy', $\ldots$ are the increments caused by increasing x by dx, while δy, $\delta y'$ $\ldots$ are the increments caused by increasing the parameter ϵ, thus varying the form of the functions y, y', $\ldots$

The variation δy is a function of x and may assume any arbitrary value different from zero. The integral (153) is zero for any value of δy only when the expression within the parentheses vanishes for all values of x, and this condition furnishes an equation from which the function y can be determined:

$$F_y - \frac{d}{dx} F_{y'} + \frac{d^2}{dx^2} F_{y''} = 0 \tag{154}$$

Equation (154) is known as *Eulerian differential equation.*[1] The solution of the extremum problem is reduced to the solution of the differential equation (154), which must be solved with regard to the particular boundary conditions of the case under consideration.

To illustrate the procedure of obtaining the differential equation associated with a given extremum problem, we consider the integral

$$U = \int_0^l \left(\frac{EI}{2} y''^2 - \frac{P}{2} y'^2 - wy \right) dx \tag{155}$$

which expresses the potential energy U of a beam of length l of constant moment of inertia I, acted on by a lateral load w uniformly distributed along the span l and by an axial load P. The equilibrium condition from which the deflection y is to be determined is that U must be a minimum:

$$\delta U = 0 \tag{156}$$

This condition will be satified if y is a solution of the Eulerian equation (154). Applying it to the energy expression (155) we have

$$F = \frac{EI}{2} y''^2 - \frac{P}{2} y'^2 - wy$$

and

$$F_y = \frac{\partial F}{\partial y} = -w$$

$$F_{y'} = \frac{\partial F}{\partial y'} = -Py' \quad \text{and} \quad \frac{d}{dx} \frac{\partial F}{\partial y'} = -Py''$$

$$F_{y''} = \frac{\partial F}{\partial y''} = EIy'' \quad \text{and} \quad \frac{d^2}{dx^2} \frac{\partial F}{\partial y''} = EIy^{IV}$$

Thus we obtain the equation

$$EIy^{IV} + Py'' = w \tag{157}$$

which is the familiar differential equation of fourth order of a beam loaded axially by the force P and laterally by the uniformly distributed load w.

[1] Equation (154) was first derived by Euler.

31. Integrals Containing Several Functions of One Independent Variable

If r functions $y(x)$, $z(x)$, . . . of x are to be found such that the integral

$$I = \int_{x_0}^{x_1} F(x, y, z, \ldots, y', z', \ldots, y'', z'') \, dx \qquad (158)$$

will be stationary, the procedure in deriving the r Eulerian equations which determine the functions y, z, . . . is essentially the same as in the preceding article. Again introducing arbitrary functions $\eta(x)$, $\zeta(x)$, . . . , which vanish including their first derivatives at the boundaries $x = x_0$ and $x = x_1$, we conclude that the function

$$\Phi(\epsilon_1, \epsilon_2, \ldots)$$
$$= \int_{x_0}^{x_1} F(x, y + \epsilon_1\eta, z + \epsilon_2\zeta, \ldots, y' + \epsilon_1\eta', z' + \epsilon_2\zeta', \ldots) \, dx$$

of the variables ϵ_1, ϵ_2, . . . must be stationary for $\epsilon_1 = \epsilon_2 = \cdots = 0$. This furnishes r conditions

$$\left[\frac{\partial\Phi}{\partial\epsilon_1}\right]_{\epsilon_1=\epsilon_2=0} = 0, \qquad \left[\frac{\partial\Phi}{\partial\epsilon_2}\right]_{\epsilon_1=\epsilon_2=0} = 0, \ldots$$

which transform to

$$\left.\begin{array}{l} \int_{x_0}^{x_1} (F_y \, \delta y + F_{y'} \, \delta y' + \cdots) \, dx = 0 \\ \int_{x_0}^{x_1} (F_z \, \delta z + F_{z'} \, \delta z' + \cdots) \, dx = 0 \end{array}\right\} \qquad (159)$$

Integration by parts leads finally to the r Eulerian differential equations.

$$\left.\begin{array}{l} F_y - \dfrac{d}{dx} F_{y'} + \dfrac{d^2}{dx^2} F_{y''} - \cdots = 0 \\[2mm] F_z - \dfrac{d}{dx} F_{z'} + \dfrac{d^2}{dx^2} F_{z'} - \cdots = 0 \\[2mm] \cdots\cdots\cdots\cdots\cdots\cdots\cdots \end{array}\right\} \qquad (160)$$

which determine the r functions y, z, ...[1]

32. Integrals Containing a Function of Two Independent Variables

The problem of determining stationary values of a double integral leads to a partial differential equation which defines the unknown function $w(x,y)$. Let us consider the simplest case, a double integral I extended

[1] Equations (160) will be applied in Chap. III to derive the three differential equations (244) of the problem of torsional buckling.

over the rectangular area A bounded by $x = x_0$, x_1 and $y = y_0$, y_1, respectively:

$$I = \int_{x_0}^{x_1} \int_{y_0}^{y_1} F(x, y, w, w_x, w_y) \, dx \, dy \qquad (161)$$

$w = w(x,y)$ is a function of the variables x, y, and w_x and w_y are the partial derivatives $\dfrac{\partial w}{\partial x}$ and $\dfrac{\partial w}{\partial y}$, respectively.

If $\eta(x,y)$ is an arbitrary function of the two variables x and y upon which we impose the condition $\eta = 0$ along the boundary of the area A, we obtain as a necessary condition for I being stationary

$$[\Phi'(\epsilon)]_{\epsilon=0} = 0$$

This leads to the equation

$$\int_{x_0}^{x_1} \int_{y_0}^{y_1} \left(\frac{\partial F}{\partial w} \delta w + \frac{\partial F}{\partial w_x} \delta w_x + \frac{\partial F}{\partial w_y} \delta w_y \right) dx \, dy = 0 \qquad (162)$$

which is the equivalent of Eq. (151) in Art. 30. Integrating by parts in the variable x only we have

$$\int_{x_0}^{x_1} \int_{y_0}^{y_1} \frac{\partial F}{\partial w_x} \delta w_x \, dx \, dy$$
$$= \left[\int_{y_0}^{y_1} \frac{\partial F}{\partial w_x} \delta w \, dy \right]_{x_0}^{x_1} - \int_{x_0}^{x_1} \int_{y_0}^{y_1} \frac{\partial}{\partial x} \frac{\partial F}{\partial w_x} \delta w \, dx \, dy \qquad (163)$$

Integrating by parts in the variable y only we find

$$\int_{x_0}^{x_1} \int_{y_0}^{y_1} \frac{\partial F}{\partial w_y} \delta w_y \, dx \, dy$$
$$= \left[\int_{x_0}^{x_1} \frac{\partial F}{\partial w_y} \delta w \, dx \right]_{y_0}^{y_1} - \int_{x_0}^{x_1} \int_{y_0}^{y_1} \frac{\partial}{\partial y} \frac{\partial F}{\partial w_y} \delta w \, dx \, dy \qquad (164)$$

Because of the condition $\eta = 0$ on all four boundaries, $\delta w = \epsilon \eta$ also vanishes on the boundaries, and the simple integrals in Eqs. (163) and (164) are zero. Equation (162) can therefore be written

$$\int_{x_0}^{x_1} \int_{y_0}^{y_1} \left(\frac{\partial F}{\partial w} - \frac{\partial}{\partial x} \frac{\partial F}{\partial w_x} - \frac{\partial}{\partial y} \frac{\partial F}{\partial w_y} \right) \delta w \, dx \, dy = 0$$

and we conclude that w must satisfy the Eulerian equation

$$\frac{\partial F}{\partial w} - \frac{\partial}{\partial x} \frac{\partial F}{\partial w_x} - \frac{\partial}{\partial y} \frac{\partial F}{\partial w_y} = 0 \qquad (165)$$

If the integral contains terms depending on the second derivatives of the function w, the Eulerian equation reads

$$\frac{\partial F}{\partial w} - \frac{\partial}{\partial x} \frac{\partial F}{\partial w_x} - \frac{\partial}{\partial y} \frac{\partial F}{\partial w_y} + \frac{\partial^2}{\partial x^2} \frac{\partial F}{\partial w_{xx}} + 2 \frac{\partial^2}{\partial x \, \partial y} \frac{\partial F}{\partial w_{xy}} + \frac{\partial^2}{\partial y^2} \frac{\partial F}{\partial w_{yy}} = 0 \qquad (166)$$

As an example consider the problem of the buckling of a simply supported flat rectangular plate in shear. The total potential energy U to be made stationary is[1]

$$U = \int_0^a \int_0^b \left[\frac{D}{2} (w_{xx} + w_{yy})^2 - D(1 - \nu)(w_{xx}w_{yy} - w_{xy}^2) - t\tau_{xy}w_xw_y \right] dx\, dy \quad (167)$$

When applying Eq. (167) it is useful to know that the term $w_{xx}w_{yy} - w_{xy}^2$, which appears in all plate problems, does not give any contribution to the Eulerian equation. This surprising result is due to the fact that the value of the double integral

$$\int_0^a \int_0^b (w_{xx}w_{yy} - w_{xy}^2)\, dx\, dy \quad (168)$$

may be expressed by a line integral over the boundaries of the plate; the value of the integral is therefore a constant which does not depend on the function w at all, but only on the boundary conditions.

Instead of considering the expression (167), we have therefore the simpler integral

$$I = \int_0^a \int_0^b \left[\frac{D}{2} (w_{xx} + w_{yy})^2 - t\tau_{xy}w_xw_y \right] dx\, dy \quad (169)$$

for which the Eulerian equation (166) is to be determined. The individual terms of Eq. (166) are

$$\frac{\partial F}{\partial w} = 0, \qquad \frac{\partial}{\partial x}\frac{\partial F}{\partial w_x} = -t\tau_{xy}\frac{\partial^2 w}{\partial x\, \partial y}, \qquad \frac{\partial}{\partial y}\frac{\partial F}{\partial w_y} = -t\tau_{xy}\frac{\partial^2 w}{\partial x\, \partial y}$$

$$\frac{\partial^2}{\partial x^2}\frac{\partial F}{\partial w_{xx}} = D\left(\frac{\partial^4 w}{\partial x^4} + \frac{\partial^4 w}{\partial x^2\, \partial y^2}\right)$$

$$\frac{\partial^2}{\partial y^2}\frac{\partial F}{\partial w_{yy}} = D\left(\frac{\partial^4 w}{\partial x^2\, \partial y^2} + \frac{\partial^4 w}{\partial y^4}\right) \qquad \text{and} \qquad \frac{\partial^2}{\partial x\, \partial y}\frac{\partial F}{\partial w_{xy}} = 0$$

and the Eulerian equation is finally

$$D\left(\frac{\partial^4 w}{\partial x^4} + 2\frac{\partial^4 w}{\partial x^2\, \partial y^2} + \frac{\partial^4 w}{\partial y^4}\right) + 2t\tau_{xy}\frac{\partial^2 w}{\partial x\, \partial y} = 0 \quad (170)$$

This is the well-known differential equation for a plate under the action of shear forces.

33. The Boundary Conditions

In closing the brief introduction to the calculus of variation an additional feature of the variational method remains to be discussed. In

---

[1] Equations (723) and (725) in Chap. XI.

the previous presentation it was tacitly assumed that the unknown function y or its derivatives assume predetermined values along the boundary of the system. However, in many cases there are no particular restrictions concerning the free displacement at the boundary (free boundary). Again, in various other cases the function y is restricted along the boundary by linear relations expressing restraints imposed at the boundary, caused by the interaction between the system and the supporting structure.

In the course of deriving the expression (153) for the first variation δI it was noted that a number of terms referring to the boundary occurred but were equal to zero because of the assumption that the boundary values of y and its derivatives are predetermined and are not subjected to variation; this resulted in δy, $\delta y'$, . . . being zero along the boundary. But in cases where this assumption does not apply, the condition $\delta I = 0$

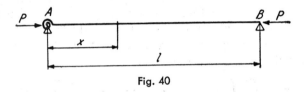

Fig. 40

furnishes not only Euler's differential equation but also additional conditions at the boundary which will be referred to as the natural boundary conditions of the problem under consideration. These boundary relations are essentially mechanical relations involving shearing forces, moments, or torques, even in the case of a free boundary. They are of a quite different nature from the geometrical conditions of fixed boundary values assumed previously.

The significant fact is that the mechanical boundary conditions, which beside the geometric conditions at the boundary affect the solution of the differential equation, can be obtained as natural boundary conditions of the corresponding variational problem. The fixed boundary values, representing the particular geometric conditions, however, must be separately imposed, for they do not ensue from the process of variation.

For illustration consider the following stability problem. The column AB under axial load P is supported at both ends and elastically restrained against rotation at the left support A while free to rotate at the right support B (Fig. 40). The expression for the potential energy U reads:

$$U = \int^{l} \left(\frac{EI}{2} y''^{2} - \frac{P}{2} y'^{2} \right) dx + \frac{C}{2} y_{0}'^{2} \qquad (171)$$

where C is the torsional spring constant defining the degree of restraint at the left support and y_{0}' the angle of rotation of the cross section at

$x = 0$. The expression U will be stationary if the variation $\delta U = 0$, and using the same approach as in Art. 30 we find

$$\delta U = \int_0^l (EIy'' \,\delta y'' - Py' \,\delta y') \, dx + Cy_0' \,\delta y_0' = 0 \qquad (172)$$

Integrating by parts we have

$$\int_0^l EIy'' \,\delta y'' \, dx = \left[EIy'' \,\delta y' \right]_0^l - \left[EIy''' \,\delta y \right]_0^l + \int_0^l EIy^{IV} \,\delta y \, dx \quad (173a)$$

and

$$- \int_0^l Py' \,\delta y' \, dx = - \left[Py' \,\delta y \right]_0^l + \int_0^l Py'' \,\delta y \, dx \qquad (173b)$$

Owing to the unyielding supports at the ends $x = 0$ and $x = l$, the deflection at these points must be $y = 0$, and the variation will also be $\delta y = 0$. The terms referring to the boundary and containing δy in Eqs. (173) are therefore zero. The first term of Eq. (173a) can be written

$$\left[EIy'' \,\delta y' \right]_0^l = EIy_l'' \,\delta y_l' - EIy_0'' \,\delta y_0'$$

where the subscript 0 and l indicates the value at $x = 0$ and l, respectively.

Equation (172) may now be rearranged

$$\delta U = EIy_l'' \,\delta y_l' + (Cy_0' - EIy_0'') \,\delta y_0'$$
$$+ \int_0^l (EIy^{IV} + Py'') \,\delta y \, dx = 0 \quad (174)$$

$\delta y_0'$ and $\delta y_l'$ not being zero, we conclude that Eq. (174) requires that the function y satisfies the Eulerian differential equation

$$EIy^{IV} + Py'' = 0 \qquad (175)$$

and the two additional conditions

$$Cy_0' - EIy_0'' = 0 \qquad (176)$$

and

$$EIy_l'' = 0 \qquad (177)$$

Equations (176) and (177) are the natural boundary conditions of the problem. Together with the two geometric conditions $y_0 = y_l = 0$ we have four boundary conditions, as required for a differential equation of fourth order.

The physical meaning of Eqs. (176) and (177) is readily recognized. Equation (176) expresses the equilibrium between the bending moment at $x = 0$ and the resisting moment of the elastic support. Equation (177) indicates that the moment at $x = l$ vanishes, agreeing with the assumption that the column is free to rotate at the support B.

The concept of natural boundary conditions outlined above leads to a conclusion of importance for the application of the Ritz method to variational problems when mechanical boundary conditions are involved. The process of variation of the energy expression U yields the Eulerian differential equation as well as the natural boundary conditions. Accordingly, a function y which satisfies the condition $\delta U = 0$ will satisfy Euler's equation and also the natural boundary conditions. The implication is that, in choosing an expansion $\Sigma a_i \varphi_i$ for the direct solution of a variational problem, the coordinate functions φ_i need satisfy only the geometric boundary conditions of the problem, the natural boundary conditions being automatically approximated by the process of the Ritz method. If the coordinate functions φ_i are part of a complete set of orthogonal functions,[1] an expansion

$$y = a_1 \varphi_1 + a_2 \varphi_2 + \cdots + a_n \varphi_n \tag{178}$$

of n terms will converge with increasing n toward a solution which also satisfies the natural boundary conditions of the problem.[2]

In applying the method just outlined it will be found that in certain cases the convergence of the series (178) is slow and a great number of coordinate functions is required to determine the buckling mode y with reasonable accuracy but that in spite of this the critical load can be obtained with a small number of coordinate functions. This difficulty occurs if the functions φ_i are badly suited to the natural boundary conditions, as may be seen in the following example.

Consider again the column AB, shown in Fig. 40. Its potential energy U is given in Eq. (171), and the natural boundary conditions are Eqs. (175) and (176). If we express y by the Fourier expansion

$$y = \sum_{i=1}^{n} a_i \sin \frac{i\pi x}{l} \tag{179}$$

and compute the values of y'' for $x = 0$ and l, we find $y_0'' = y_l'' = 0$ for any value of the coefficients a_i. While this result agrees with the second boundary condition (177), it disagrees with the correct value of y_0''. There being an elastic restraint at $x = 0$, the value of y_0'' must be different from zero, a result which cannot be obtained from Eq. (179). The series (179) will approximate the exact value of y in spite of this fact, but the second derivative of the series (179) cannot approximate y'', and if determined it would be found to be a divergent series.

These difficulties do not affect the values of the critical load determined

[1] In the sense defined on p. 66.

[2] An application of this method can be found in F. Bleich and H. Bleich, Beitrag zur Stabilitäts Üntersuchung des punktweise elastisch gestützten Stabes, *Der Stahlbau*, Vol. 18, p. 17, 1937.

by the method.   To indicate the degree of approximation, P_c was computed for a value of the spring constant $C = 3EI/l$.   The approximate values found for $n = 1, 2, 3$ were $P_c = 1.61P_E$, $P_c = 1.48P_E$, $P_c = 1.41P_E$ where P_E is the Euler load of the column, while the exact solution found by another method is $P_c = 1.40P_E$.

Additional References

References to Arts. 20 to 27

Marguerre, K., Uber die Behandlung von Stabilitätsproblemen mit Hilfe der energetischen Methode, *Zeitschrift für angewandte Mathematik und Mechanik*, Vol. 18, p. 57, 1938.

Grammel, R., Ein neues Verfahren zur Lösung technischer Eigenwertprobleme, *Ingenieur-Archiv*, Vol. 10, p. 35, 1939.

Hoff, N. J., Stable and Unstable Equilibrium of Plane Frameworks, *Jour. Aeronaut. Sci.*, Vol. 8, p. 115, 1941.

Westergaard, H. M., On the Method of Complementary Energy, *Trans. ASCE*, Vol. 107, p. 765, 1942.

Courant, R., Problems of Equilibrium and Vibrations, *Bull. Am. Math. Soc.*, Vol. 49, p. 1, 1943.

Prager, W., The General Variational Principle of the Theory of Structural Stability, *Quart. Applied Math.*, Vol. 4, p. 378, 1947.

Higgins, T. J., A Survey of the Approximate Solution of Two-dimensional Physical Problems by Variational Methods and Finite Difference Procedures, Chap. 10 of "Numerical Methods of Analysis in Engineering, in Honor of Hardy Cross," The Macmillan Company, New York, 1949.

References to Arts. 29 to 33

Courant, R., and D. Hilbert, "Methoden der mathematischen Physik I," Chaps. 4 and 6, Julius Springer, Berlin, 1924.

Margenau, H., and G. M. Murphy, "The Mathematics of Physics and Chemistry," Chap. 6, Calculus of Variations, D. Van Nostrand Company, Inc., New York, 1943.

CHAPTER III

BUCKLING OF CENTRALLY LOADED COLUMNS BY TORSION AND FLEXURE

34. Introduction

In Chap. I the fundamental case of buckling of centrally loaded columns was discussed under the tacit assumption that columns will buckle in the plane of a principal axis without rotation of the cross sections. This assumption appears reasonable for cross sections having two axes of symmetry but becomes questionable if only one of the principal axes is an axis of symmetry or if there is no symmetry. The possibility of the occurrence of torsional column failure was first recognized when open thin-walled sections were used in aircraft design, and experience revealed that columns having open cross sections showed a tendency to bend and twist simultaneously under axial load. The importance of this type of failure lies in the fact that the actual critical load of such columns, due to their small torsional rigidity, may be less than the critical load predicted by the generalized Euler formula.

Wagner[1] was the first to investigate torsional buckling of open thin-walled sections, and he introduced the concept of "unit warping" in the analysis. But Wagner based his theory upon the arbitrary assumption that the center of rotation during buckling coincides with the center of shear, which, in general, is not the case as was shown by subsequent investigators. The results of Wagner's analysis are therefore not exact. Ostenfeld[2] considered buckling by torsion and flexure of some rolled sections and was the first to present exact solutions for channel-, angle-, and T-sections. His analysis appears rather complicated and received but slight attention.

The problem of bending, twisting, and buckling of bars having thin-walled polygonal cross section was treated in a general manner by F.

---

[1] Wagner, H., Verdrehung und Knickung von offenen Profilen, 25th Anniversary Publication, Technische Hochschule Danzig, 1904–1929. Translated in *NACA Tech. Mem.* 807, 1936.

[2] Ostenfeld, A., Politecknisk Laereanstalts Laboratorium for Bygningsstatik, *Meddelelse* No. 5, Kopenhagen 1931.

Bleich and H. Bleich.[1] These authors derived the fundamental differential equations of the problem from the theorem of stationary potential energy and established the fact that the usual differential equations of bending retain their validity for sections which do not have two axes of symmetry, provided the displacements of the center of shear are used as coordinates instead of the displacements of the centroid. The method of approach in solving the problem was fundamentally different from Wagner's method, the basic differential equations being developed without using the idea of unit warping. Application of the method to the problems of torsional buckling of centrally loaded columns and lateral buckling of transversely loaded beams was discussed briefly. In dealing with the column problem the authors disregarded in the expression for the potential energy a term which attains importance for sections of very low torsional rigidity, thus impairing the exactness of the solution. This was subsequently pointed out by Kappus,[2] who presented in 1937 a refined theory applicable to any thin-walled section. He also called attention to Wagner's erroneous assumption of the location of the center of rotation. Kappus obtained his solution, as F. Bleich and H. Bleich did, from the theorem of stationary potential energy. Independent of Kappus, Lundquist and Fligg[3] published in the same year an exact theory adding to Wagner's hypothesis the theorem that the center of rotation will be in such a position that the critical load becomes a minimum. Kappus's theory as well as the theory of Lundquist and Fligg are based upon Wagner's concept of unit warping. In a more recent paper Goodier[4] discusses in a very lucid manner the effect of the assumptions made by Wagner and the subsequent writers. Goodier succeeds in reducing the equations of buckling by torsion and flexure to the simplest possible form by using the center of shear as the origin of the system of coordinates. Another comprehensive review on bending and torsion of open sections including buckling is contained in a paper by Timoshenko.[5]

All the papers mentioned make the fundamental assumption that the plane cross sections of the column warp but that their geometric shape

[1] Bleich, F. and H. Bleich, Bending Torsion and Buckling of Bars Composed of Thin Walls, *Prelim. Pub. 2d Cong. Intern. Assoc. Bridge and Structural Eng.*, English edition, p. 871, Berlin, 1936.

[2] Kappus, R., Drillknicken zentrisch gedrückter Stäbe mit offenem Profil im elastischen Bereich, *Luftfahrt-Forschung*, 1937. Translated in *NACA Tech. Mem.* 851, 1938.

[3] Lundquist, E. E., and C. M. Fligg, A Theory for Primary Failure of Straight Centrally Loaded Columns, *NACA Tech. Rept.* 582, 1937. Lundquist, E. E., On the Strength of Columns That Fail by Twisting, *Jour. Aeronaut. Sci.*, Vol. 4, p. 249, 1937.

[4] Goodier, J. N., The Buckling of Compressed Bars by Torsion and Flexure, *Cornell Univ. Eng. Expt. Sta. Bull.* 27, December, 1941.

[5] Timoshenko, S., Theory of Bending, Torsion and Buckling of Thin-walled Members of Open Cross Section, *Jour. Franklin Inst.*, 1945.

does not change during buckling; *i.e.*, the theories consider primary failure of columns as opposed to local failure characterized by distortion of the cross sections. The analysis of local failure of compression members usually requires consideration of the thin walls as plates or shells. The dividing line between primary and local failure, however, is not always sharp. Torsional buckling of equal angles, for example, was first analyzed by Timoshenko as local failure, while later authors have treated it as a primary failure.

Separate investigation of primary and local buckling can necessarily give only approximate results because, in general, there will be coupling of primary and local buckling. No attempt was ever made to estimate the accuracy of the theory of primary buckling by torsion and flexure by simultaneous analysis of primary and local buckling, as such an analysis would be extremely complicated. However, in certain cases it is possible to make some allowance for local instability in the theory of buckling by torsion and flexure, by abandoning the assumption that cross sections of the column will not deform. Nylander[1] investigated the effect of web deformations on the lateral buckling of I-beams; Goodier and Barton[2] determined the same effect on the torsional stiffness of I-beams without applying their results to the buckling problem.

The following presentation of the theory of torsional buckling is based upon the differential equations of bending and twisting of bars with open thin-walled polygonal cross section subjected to any external loading. This theory, demonstrated in Arts. 35 to 38, will serve as the common basis for the study of the buckling of centrally loaded columns in this chapter and for the investigation of the stability of axially and transversely loaded beams (lateral buckling) in the following chapter. The method of approach in setting up the expression for the strain energy of a bar with open cross section is the same as presented in the paper of F. Bleich and H. Bleich. The method regards the behavior of a member in flexure and torsion from a different angle than do the papers based on Wagner's hypothesis and sheds new light on the interaction of the plates of which the column is composed. The method applies only to members composed of flat plates, but this is no disadvantage because columns used in structural design are usually of this type.[3] The method, however, has the advantage that it can be applied to closed sections and can be readily adapted to allow for the effect of distortion of the cross section. This

[1] Nylander, H., Drehungsvorgänge und gebundene Kippung bei geraden, doppeltsymetrischen I-Trägern, *Ingeniors Vetenskaps Akademien Handlingar* 174, Stockholm, 1943.

[2] Goodier, J. N., and M. V. Barton, The Effect of Web Deformation on the Torsion of I-Beams, *Jour. Applied Mechanics*, Vol. 2, p. A-35, 1944.

[3] Wagner, Kappus, Lundquist, and Goodier developed methods applicable to curved or polygonal cross sections.

latter question will be discussed in Art. 44 in connection with the buckling of T-stiffeners.   The results of the method presented agree with those obtained by Lundquist, Kappus, and Goodier.   The relationship between the basic assumptions of the theory presented and the assumptions underlying the theories of Lundquist, Kappus, and Goodier will be clarified.

35. Potential Energy of Bent and Twisted Bars of Open Thin-walled Section

Consider a bar of constant, but otherwise arbitrary, open section composed of n thin flat plates (Fig. 41).   The plates may be of nonuniform

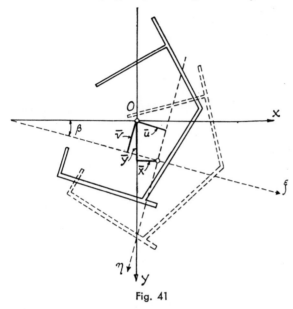

Fig. 41

thickness but shall be sufficiently thin for their lateral stiffness to be negligible in comparison with the stiffness in their own plane, and the length of the bar shall be large compared with the dimensions of the cross section.   We select a system of coordinates x, y, z, with the centroid as origin O; x and y are principal axes of the section, and z is the longitudinal center line.   In addition to the system of coordinates x, y, and z we attach to each cross section axes ξ and η through the centroid initially parallel to the principal axes.   As the sections are displaced, the axes ξ and η will move with them, and the components of the displacement of the centroid parallel to these axes are u and v, respectively.

Under the action of external loads the bar will deform; we assume that the deformation will be such that the cross sections of the bar do not distort.   The components of the displacement of any point in the plane of its cross section will, therefore, be defined by the coordinates $\bar{x}$ and $\bar{y}$ of the centroid and the angle of twist β. Alternatively, these displacements are defined by the components $\bar{u}$ and $\bar{v}$ of the displacements of the centroid and by the angle β. $\bar{x}$, $\bar{y}$, $\bar{u}$, $\bar{v}$, and β are functions of the coordinate z.

In the conventional theory of bending of bars, longitudinal deformations, i.e., parallel to the z-axis, are obtained from Navier's hypothesis, which states that, during bending, plane cross sections will remain plane. This hypothesis must be abandoned, as the cross sections will warp if a bar is twisted. But we assume that Navier's hypothesis remains valid for each of the flat plates of which the bar is composed. This assumption appears to be justified because St. Venant's theory of torsion indicates that the longitudinal center line of the cross section of a thin flat plate remains in a plane during torsion. Warping can vary only very little across the plate because of its small thickness, and the entire cross section must remain approximately plane. This subject is discussed further on page 117. As a result of this assumption the cross section of each plate between two adjacent corners will remain plane, although the planes may be different for two adjoining plates and the cross section of the entire bar will be warped.

Starting from this assumption we shall now derive the basic differential equation of bending and twisting from the theorem of stationary potential energy discussed in Chap. II. The potential energy U consists of two parts: the potential energy of the external loads and the strain energy V of the deformed bar.[1] In the case considered, V can be divided in two parts: V_1 due to the longitudinal direct stresses and V_2 due to the shear stresses. V_1 will be determined first.

We assign a number to each of the flat plates forming the bar; if there are n such plates, the numbers will be $1, 2, \ldots, n$. Figure 42a shows the ith plate and the adjacent plate elements; the center of gravity of the plate is marked O_i, and the distances from O_i to the intersections of the center lines of successive plates are a_i and a_i'. The perpendicular from the origin O to the center line of the plate will be r_i, and the angle between this perpendicular and the axis of x is φ_i. The cross-sectional area of the plate and its moment of inertia with respect to an axis through O_i at right angles to the plate will be denoted by A_i and I_i, respectively.

Figure 42 shows the ith plate in the original and in the displaced positions. The component η_i of the deflection of this plate in its own plane can be obtained by projecting point O_i in its original position on the center line of the deflected plate. β being a small angle, we may assume

---

[1] Any expression for the potential energy contains an arbitrary additive constant, which in the present case is defined by making $U = 0$ for the unloaded and undeformed state of the bar.

$\cos \beta = 1$, $\sin \beta = \beta$, and have

$$\eta_i = -\bar{u} \sin \varphi_i + \bar{v} \cos \varphi_i + \beta r_i \qquad (180)$$

According to the assumption that Navier's hypothesis applies for each of the plates individually, the portion of the strain energy V_1 stored in

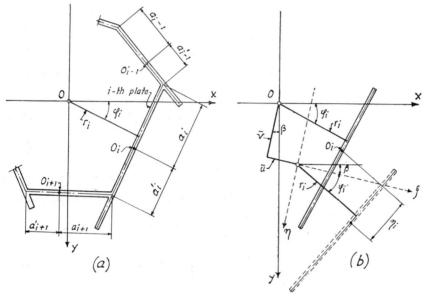

Fig. 42

the ith plate can be expressed by the curvature $\dfrac{d^2\eta_i}{dz^2} = \eta_i''$ of the plate and by the longitudinal strain $\bar{\epsilon}_i$ measured at the centroid O_i of the plate:

$$\tfrac{1}{2}\int (EI_i\eta_i''^2 + EA_i\bar{\epsilon}_i^2)\, dz \qquad (181)$$

The total strain energy for all n plates will be

$$V_1 = \tfrac{1}{2} \int \sum_{i=1}^{n} (EI_i\eta_i''^2 + EA_i\bar{\epsilon}_i^2)\, dz \qquad (182)$$

where the integral is to be taken over the entire length of the bar.

The curvatures η_i'' and strains $\bar{\epsilon}_i$ are not independent of each other, because where two plates join, the strains in both plates must be equal. If positive $\bar{\epsilon}_i$ indicates elongations, then with reference to Fig. 42a, we obtain for the junction of the $(i-1)$th and ith plate

$$\bar{\epsilon}_{i-1} + a_{i-1}'\eta_{i-1}'' = \bar{\epsilon}_i - a_i\eta_i'' \qquad (183)$$

For n plates there will be $n-1$ such equations, one equation for each corner of the cross section. We define the average strain of the entire cross section by the relation

$$A\epsilon = \sum_{i=1}^{n} A_i \bar{\epsilon}_i \qquad (184)$$

where A is the entire cross-sectional area of the bar, $A = \sum_{i=1}^{n} A_i$. Denoting by ϵ_i the difference between the strain $\bar{\epsilon}_i$ and the average strain ϵ, we have

$$\epsilon_i = \bar{\epsilon}_i - \epsilon \qquad (185)$$

Substituting $\bar{\epsilon}_i$ from Eq. (185) in Eqs. (183) and (184) we find that the terms containing the average strains ϵ cancel, leaving

$$\epsilon_{i-1} + a_{i-1}'\eta_{i-1}'' = \epsilon_i - a_i\eta_i'' \qquad (186)$$

$$\sum_{i=1}^{n} A_i \epsilon_i = 0 \qquad (187)$$

There are $n - 1$ Eqs. (186) and one Eq. (187); these n independent, linear equations can be used to determine the n values ϵ_i and to express them in terms of the curvatures η_i''.

Upon substituting $\bar{\epsilon}_i$ from Eq. (185) in Eq. (182) we obtain

$$V_1 = \frac{E}{2} \int \left[\sum_{i=1}^{n} (I_i \eta_i''^2 + A_i \epsilon_i^2) + A\epsilon^2 \right] dz \qquad (188)$$

the terms containing products of ϵ_i and ϵ disappearing because of Eq. (187).

Equations (186) and (187) define the ϵ_i as functions of η_i''. Equations (180) give after differentiation

$$\eta_i'' = -\bar{u}'' \sin \varphi + \bar{v}'' \cos \varphi + r_i\beta'' \qquad (189)$$

and all the curvatures η_i'' and strains ϵ_i can therefore be expressed as linear functions of $\bar{u}''$, $\bar{v}''$, and β''. If the values of η_i'' and ϵ_i are substituted in Eq. (188), the expression under the integral must be quadratic in the three variables $\bar{u}''$, $\bar{v}''$, and β''. The most general form of such a quadratic expression would be

$$V_1 = \frac{E}{2} \int (\alpha_1 \bar{u}''^2 + \alpha_2 \bar{v}''^2 + \alpha_3 \beta''^2 + \alpha_4 \bar{u}''\bar{v}'' + \alpha_5 \bar{u}''\beta''$$
$$+ \alpha_6 \bar{v}''\beta'' + A\epsilon^2) \, dz \qquad (190)$$

where $\alpha_1, \alpha_2, \ldots, \alpha_6$ depend only on the geometrical properties of the cross sections. It can be shown that α_1, α_2, and α_4 are equal to the moments and product of inertia of the entire cross section:

$$\alpha_y = I_y, \qquad \alpha_2 = I_x, \qquad \alpha_4 = I_{xy} = 0 \qquad (191)$$

I_x and I_y are referred to the axes x and y, respectively; I_{xy} is zero because x and y are principal axes. The coefficients α_3, α_5, and α_6 do not occur in the conventional theory of bending. Using the notations

$$\alpha_5 = 2R_y, \qquad \alpha_6 = 2R_x, \qquad \alpha_3 = R_\beta \qquad (192)$$

Eq. (190) takes the form

$$V_1 = \tfrac{1}{2}\int (EI_y\bar{u}''^2 + EI_x\bar{v}''^2 + 2ER_y\bar{u}''\beta''$$
$$+ 2ER_x\bar{v}''\beta'' + ER_\beta\beta''^2 + EA\epsilon^2)\,dz \quad (193)$$

The coefficients R_x, R_y, and R_β can be determined from Eqs. (186) to (189). If the section is symmetrical with respect to the x- or y-axis, R_y or R_x, respectively, will be zero. For double symmetry R_x and R_y, but not R_β, will be zero.

We now have to determine the strain energy V_2 of the shearing stresses. Such stresses may be due to two causes: External shearing forces must be balanced by shearing stresses in each cross section, and furthermore, a twisting of the bar $\dfrac{d\beta}{dz}$ will also produce shearing stresses. For bars which are long compared with the dimensions of the cross section, the strain energy of shearing stresses due to external shear is but small, and in the theory of nontorsional buckling it was found to have no effect of practical importance.[1] We therefore feel justified in neglecting this part of the strain energy.

The shearing stresses due to twisting are assumed to be the same as in St. Venant's theory of torsion.[2] The resultant of these shear forces will be a torque T, and the relation

$$T = GK\frac{d\beta}{dz} = GK\beta' \qquad (194)$$

defines the torsion constant K. G is the modulus of rigidity. The strain energy of these shearing stresses for an element of the bar of length dz must be equal to the work done by the torque T. The strain energy V_2 for the entire bar is, therefore,

$$V_2 = \frac{1}{2}\int T\frac{d\beta}{dz}\,dz = \frac{1}{2}\int GK\beta'^2\,dz \qquad (195)$$

The value of the torsion constant K for a narrow rectangle of depth d and thickness t is $K = \tfrac{1}{3}dt^3$. For open sections composed of narrow rectangles K is approximately equal to the sum of the values K of its parts. More accurate values allowing for the slope of flanges and for

[1] Chapter I, Art. 8.

[2] Timoshenko, S., "Theory of Elasticity," p. 229, McGraw-Hill Book Company, Inc., New York, 1934.

fillets of rolled sections can be determined according to a paper by Lyse and Johnston.[1] Numerical values of K for rolled beams are available in some handbooks.[2]

Adding Eqs. (193) and (195) we find the entire strain energy of the deformed bar

$$V = V_1 + V_2 = \tfrac{1}{2}\int (EI_y\bar{u}''^2 + EI_x\bar{v}''^2 + 2ER_y\bar{u}''\beta'' + 2ER_x\bar{v}''\beta''$$
$$+ ER_\beta\beta''^2 + GK\beta'^2 + AE\epsilon^2)\,dz \quad (196)$$

We now turn to the determination of the potential energy of the external loads. In order to discuss the action of the bar in bending and torsion we consider the bar under distributed transverse loads w which in general do not act at the center of gravity of the section (Fig. 43). The load acting on an element of length dz is $w\,dz$; we can replace this load by its components $w_x\,dz$, $w_y\,dz$ acting at the centroid and by a torsion moment $\bar{m}_t\,dz = \bar{e}w\,dz$. The displacement of the cross section is given by the components $\bar{x}$ and $\bar{y}$ of the deflection of the centroidal axis and by the angle of rotation β. For an element of length dz of the bar the potential energy of the forces w, assumed zero in the undeflected position, will be

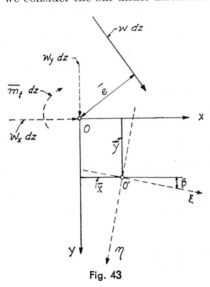

Fig. 43

$$dU_w = -(\bar{x}w_x + \bar{y}w_y + \beta\bar{m}_t)\,dz \quad (197)$$

If the bar is supported in such a manner that the external reaction forces will not do any work, these forces will not contribute to the potential energy, and we obtain the total potential energy of the loads by integrating Eq. (197) over the entire length of the bar:

$$U_w = -\int (\bar{x}w_x + \bar{y}w_y + \beta\bar{m}_t)\,dz \quad (198)$$

Equation (196) gives the potential energy of the distorted bar as a function of $\bar{u}$ and $\bar{v}$, while Eq. (198) contains $\bar{x}$ and $\bar{y}$. We can easily express $\bar{x}$ and $\bar{y}$ as functions of $\bar{u}$ and $\bar{v}$. Referring to Fig. 41 we have

[1] Lyse, I., and B. G. Johnston, Structural Beams in Torsion, *Trans. ASCE*, 1936, pp. 857–944.

[2] "Torsional Stresses in Structural Beams," Booklet S-57, Bethlehem Steel Co., 1950.

$$\left.\begin{array}{l} \bar{x} = \bar{u} \cos \beta - \bar{v} \sin \beta \\ \bar{y} = \bar{u} \sin \beta + \bar{v} \cos \beta \end{array}\right\} \qquad (199)$$

Due to the fact that only small displacements $\bar{u}$, $\bar{v}$, and β are considered, we may use $\cos \beta = 1$ and $\sin \beta = \beta$; we may also neglect the products $\bar{u}\beta$ and $\bar{v}\beta$ as being small of the second order[1] and obtain

$$\bar{x} = \bar{u} \qquad \text{and} \qquad \bar{y} = \bar{v} \qquad (200)$$

and

$$U_w = - \int (\bar{u}w_x + \bar{v}w_y + \beta\bar{m}_t)\, dz \qquad (201)$$

The expression for the total potential energy U is

$$U = V + U_w = \tfrac{1}{2}\int (EI_y\bar{u}''^2 + EI_x\bar{v}''^2 + 2ER_y\bar{u}''\beta'' + 2ER_x\bar{v}''\beta''$$
$$+ ER_\beta\beta''^2 + GK\beta'^2 + EA\epsilon^2 - 2\bar{u}w_x - 2\bar{v}w_y - 2\beta\bar{m}_t)\, dz \qquad (202)$$

36. The Differential Equations of Bending and Torsion

According to the theorem of stationary potential energy the deformations $\bar{u}$, $\bar{v}$, β, and ϵ shall be such that the integral in Eq. (202) is a minimum. This problem can be solved by the calculus of variation; U will be stationary if the Eulerian equations are satisfied.[2] There are four unknowns $\bar{u}$, $\bar{v}$, β and ϵ and the four Eulerian equations are

$$EI_y\bar{u}^{\mathrm{IV}} + ER_y\beta^{\mathrm{IV}} = w_x \qquad (203a)$$
$$EI_x\bar{v}^{\mathrm{IV}} + ER_x\beta^{\mathrm{IV}} = w_y \qquad (203b)$$
$$ER_y\bar{u}^{\mathrm{IV}} + ER_x\bar{v}^{\mathrm{IV}} + ER_\beta\beta^{\mathrm{IV}} - GK\beta'' = \bar{m}_t \qquad (203c)$$
$$EA\epsilon = 0 \qquad (203d)$$

According to the convential theory of bending we should expect the equations

$$EI_y\bar{u}'' = -M_y \qquad \text{and} \qquad EI_x\bar{v}'' = -M_x$$

or differentiating twice,

$$EI_y\bar{u}^{\mathrm{IV}} = w_x \qquad \text{and} \qquad EI_x\bar{v}^{\mathrm{IV}} = w_y \qquad (204a)$$

These equations differ from Eqs. (203a) and (203b), which contain additional terms depending on R_x and R_y.

Timoshenko[3] derived an equation for the torsion of I-beams:

$$C\beta' - \frac{Dh^2}{2}\beta''' = M_z$$

[1] It would not be permissible to neglect such terms in stability problems, because in such problems the potential energy of the external forces does not contain terms of the first order in at least some of the variables.

[2] Chapter II, Art. 31.

[3] Timoshenko, S., "Theory of Elastic Stability," p. 257, McGraw-Hill Book Company, Inc., New York, 1936.

where M_z is the acting torque and C is identical with GK in Eq. (203c). By differentiation of this equation and considering that $\dfrac{dM_z}{dz} = -\bar{m}_t$, we obtain

$$\frac{Dh^2}{2}\beta^{\mathrm{IV}} - GK\beta'' = \bar{m}_t \qquad (204b)$$

If we identify ER_β with the term $Dh^2/2$, Eq. (203c) agrees with (204b), except again for the terms containing R_x and R_y.

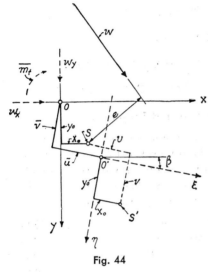

Fig. 44

Equation (203d) requires no discussion; it simply states that the average longitudinal strain is zero, which is rather obvious as there are no longitudinal forces.

Equations (203a), (203b), and (203c) can be simplified by a suitable choice of coordinates. We consider a point S in each cross section having coordinates x_0, y_0; as the bar deflects, this point will move to S' (Fig. 44). We define the coordinates u and v as the components of the displacement of S parallel to the displaced system of axes ξ and η. For small values of β, cos $\beta = 1$ and sin $\beta = \beta$, and we obtain from Fig. 44 the relations

$$\bar{u} = u + y_0\beta \qquad \text{and} \qquad \bar{v} = v - x_0\beta \qquad (205)$$

Any values of x_0 and y_0 may be used. If we choose

$$y_0 = -\frac{R_y}{I_y} \qquad \text{and} \qquad x_0 = \frac{R_x}{I_x} \qquad (206)$$

Eqs. (205) become

$$\bar{u} = u - \frac{R_y}{I_y}\beta \qquad \text{and} \qquad \bar{v} = v - \frac{R_x}{I_x}\beta \qquad (207)$$

Upon introducing these equations into Eqs. (203a), (203b), and (203c), we obtain

$$EI_y u^{\mathrm{IV}} = w_x \qquad (208a)$$

$$EI_x v^{\mathrm{IV}} = w_y \qquad (208b)$$

$$ER_y u^{\mathrm{IV}} + ER_x v^{\mathrm{IV}} + E\left(R_\beta - \frac{R_y{}^2}{I_y} - \frac{R_x{}^2}{I_x}\right)\beta^{\mathrm{IV}} - GK\beta'' = \bar{m}_t \qquad (208c)$$

The first two equations may be used to eliminate u^{IV} and v^{IV} from the third one; using also Eq. (206) we obtain

$$E\left(R_\beta - \frac{R_y{}^2}{I_y} - \frac{R_x{}^2}{I_x}\right)\beta^{IV} - GK\beta'' = \bar{m}_t + y_0 w_x - x_0 w_y \qquad (209)$$

Figure 44 indicates the components of the external loads w_x, w_y, and $\bar{m}_t$. If these loads are replaced by loads acting at point S, w_x and w_y will be unchanged but the torsional moment will be $m_t = ew$. From Fig. 44 it can be verified that

$$m_t = \bar{m}_t + y_0 w_x - x_0 w_y \qquad (210)$$

which is identical with the expression on the right-hand side of Eq. (209). If we further define the constant Γ by

$$\Gamma = R_\beta - \frac{R_y{}^2}{I_y} - \frac{R_x{}^2}{I_x} \qquad (211)$$

we obtain Eqs. (208a), (208b), and (209) in the simple form

$$EI_y u^{IV} = w_x \qquad (212a)$$
$$EI_x v^{IV} = w_y \qquad (212b)$$
$$E\Gamma\beta^{IV} - GK\beta'' = m_t \qquad (212c)$$

These three equations are identical in their form with Eqs. (204a) and (204b) of the conventional theory of bending or torsion, but the coordinates u, v, β must be referred to the origin S and the torque m_t must be determined with respect to the same point. From Eq. (212c) we may conclude that, if the bar is not to twist, $\beta = 0$, m_t must be zero, which means that the resultant w of the loads must pass through point S. This is the property by which the center of shear of a section is defined, and S must be the center of shear. If the bar twists but does not deflect, $u = v = 0$, Eqs. (212a) and (212b) give $w_x = w_y = 0$, which indicates that the center of shear S is the center of rotation of the section in pure torsion.

The use of the displacements u and v of the center of shear simplifies the differential equations of bending considerably. The expression (196) for the potential energy of the deformed bar also becomes simpler if the displacements u and v are used as coordinates. Substituting u and v from Eqs. (207) and using Eq. (211), we obtain the expression for V in its final form:

$$V = \tfrac{1}{2}\int (EI_y u''^2 + EI_x v''^2 + E\Gamma\beta''^2 + GK\beta'^2 + EA\epsilon^2)\,dz \qquad (213)$$

In the preceding discussion it was tacitly assumed that the center of shear S is uniquely defined by the condition that the bar will not twist if the resultant of the external loads passes through point S. Osgood[1] has

[1] Osgood, W. R., The Center of Shear Again, *Trans. ASME*, 1943, p. A-62.

shown that the location of the center of shear is influenced by the boundary conditions at the end surfaces of the bar. The assumption that cross sections of the bar do not change their geometric form applies also to the end cross sections, and this boundary condition defines the center of shear uniquely. This assumption implies that Poisson's ratio is equal to zero. It is understandable that difficulties concerning the definition of the center of shear arise if the assumption that cross sections of the bar will not deform is not made. If the cross sections are permitted to distort, each part of the section will have its separate center of rotation, and the center of shear can no longer be defined as the common center of rotation of the entire section but must be defined in some other way as proposed by Osgood.

37. Comparison with Goodier's Theory

Kappus and Goodier derived expressions for the strain energy based on Wagner's hypothesis. Their results are necessarily equivalent, and it will suffice to compare Eq. (213) and the expression found in one of these papers. Goodier's paper is selected for convenience.

Expression (213) is in agreement with Goodier's[1] expression for the strain energy if the symbol Γ is synonymous, which we shall demonstrate. Equation (29) of his paper contains an additional term with $u''v''$ which is due to the fact that his coordinates are not parallel to the principal axes. The last term in Eq. (213) above, the work done by the compressive stresses which act on the bar, does not appear in Goodier's paper because he reckons the potential energy from the compressed state of the bar. This is, however, no disagreement; it requires only that the potential energy of the external loads be reckoned in the same manner.

Instead of proving numerically that the value of Γ in Eq. (213) and the one used by Goodier are equal, we shall show that the theory which leads to Eq. (213) is equivalent to Goodier's theory, except for a minor difference which will become apparent. As only the term containing Γ is in doubt, we can simplify the discussion by considering a bar which is twisted about an axis going through the center of shear of the section. u and v will be zero, and the term

$$\tfrac{1}{2}E\Gamma\beta''^2\,dz \tag{214}$$

represents the strain energy of the longitudinal stresses in an element of the bar. To obtain this expression we made two assumptions. The first, that the shape of the cross section is maintained, is made by Goodier too. The second assumption, that Navier's hypothesis remains valid for each of the flat plates of which the bar is composed, is not used by Goodier,

[1] Goodier, *loc. cit.* on p. 105.

who bases his theory upon a hypothesis first introduced by Wagner.[1] It is necessary to show that these two assumptions are equivalent.

Consider a bar twisted at a uniform rate $\dfrac{d\beta}{dz} = \theta$ with the center of shear as the center of rotation. If the cross sections are not restrained against warping, the torsion moment must be constant and the twisted bar represents a case of pure torsion also called St. Venant torsion. Only shearing stresses will occur in the cross sections, the longitudinal stresses will be zero, but the cross sections will warp. We denote the warping displacement which is parallel to the z-axis by w.

Figure 45a shows a cross section of the bar and its center line. At point A on the center line we have a system of coordinates s and n in the direction of the tangent and normal to the center line, respectively. The figure also indicates the displaced center line of a section at the distance dz from the first section. The displaced center line can be found by rotating the section around point S by an angle $\theta\,dz$.

Now consider longitudinal fibers of the bar through two adjacent points A and B a distance ds apart. Owing to the deformation these fibers will move into the positions AA' and BB'. If these fibers are projected on a longitudinal plane containing the s-axis, we obtain Fig. 45b. The relative movement of A' in the s direction is $\theta r_s\,dz$, where r_s is the distance of point S from the s-axis.

From St. Venant's theory of torsion of thin sections it is known that the component of the shearing stress tangential to the center line must vanish. The points $AA'B'B$, forming a rectangle before the bar was twisted, must, therefore, still form a rectangle as indicated in Fig. 45b. The relative movement of point B with respect to A in the z-direction, indicating the change in warping, is $dw = \theta r_s\,ds$. By integration along the center line we obtain w for any point on the center line:

$$w = w_0 + \theta \int_0^s r_s\,ds$$

A similar consideration can be made for two fibers through adjacent points C and A lying on the normal n (Fig. 45c). The component of the shearing stress in the n-direction is not exactly zero, but it must be very small because it must be zero at both faces of the bar. $CC'A'A$ will remain a rectangle, at least approximately, and we obtain $dw = \theta r_n\,dn$. The value of w at any point of the section is, finally,

$$w = w_0 + \theta \left(\int_0^s r_s\,ds + \int_0^n r_n\,dn \right) = w_0 + \theta \left(\int_0^s r_s\,ds + n r_n \right) \quad (215)$$

[1] Wagner, *loc. cit.* on p. 104.

The expression within the parentheses is a geometrical property of the section which we designate by w_1:[1]

$$w_1 = \int_0^s r_s \, ds + n r_n \tag{216}$$

$$w = w_0 + \theta w_1 \tag{217}$$

So far we have considered θ to be constant, which implies that adjacent sections will have the same warping w. Goodier now makes the assump-

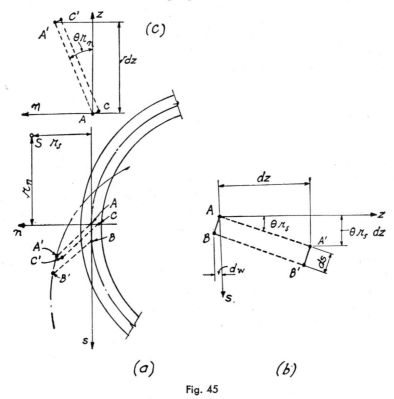

Fig. 45

tion, originated by Wagner, that Eqs. (217) will remain in force even if θ varies; this means that in two adjacent sections a distance dz apart the warping will change by

$$dw = dw_0 + d(\theta w_1)$$

The change of warping indicates that a piece of a longitudinal fiber of length dz will be elongated by dw; this requires a longitudinal fiber stress

$$\sigma_z = E \frac{dw}{dz} = E \left[\frac{dw_0}{dz} + \frac{d(\theta w_1)}{dz} \right]$$

[1] Attention is drawn to the fact that w_1 is not of the same dimensions as w and w_0.

As w_1 does not depend on z and $\dfrac{d\theta}{dz} = \beta''$, we may write

$$\sigma_z = E\left(\frac{dw_0}{dz} + w_1\beta''\right) \tag{218}$$

Goodier now makes use of equilibrium conditions. As a case of pure torsion is being considered, the resultant of the stresses σ_z must be zero, and the moments of these stresses about the x- and y-axes must vanish. The first of these conditions is used to determine w_0, which is a function of z, $w_0 = -\bar{w}_1\beta'$, where $\bar{w}_1$ is the average value of the warping function w_1. This results in

$$\sigma_z = E\beta''(w_1 - \bar{w}_1) \tag{219}$$

It is further proved that the moments of the stresses σ_z for the x- and y-axes vanish if the center of rotation S coincides with the center of shear. The strain energy of the longitudinal stresses σ_z is finally found by integration over the cross section:

$$dV = \frac{dz}{2E}\int \sigma_z\, dA = \frac{E\, dz}{2}\beta''^2 \int (w_1 - \bar{w}_1)^2\, dA = \frac{1}{2}E\Gamma\beta''^2\, dz \tag{220}$$

where

$$\Gamma = \int(w_1 - \bar{w}_1)^2\, dA \tag{221}$$

To determine Γ the warping function w_1 must be substituted from Eq. (216). w_1 is the sum of two terms, the second of which is usually negligible in relation to the first, because the maximum value of n is half the thickness of the section. Kappus[1] neglects this term completely and gives w_1 in the simplified form

$$w_1 = \int_0^s r_s\, ds \tag{222}$$

It may be noted that Eq. (222), in general, is sufficiently accurate and may replace Eq. (216), except for angle- or T-sections. For such sections the shear center lies at the intersection of the center lines of the plate elements making $r_s = 0$ everywhere, which would result in $\Gamma = 0$, while Eq. (216) leads to a small but finite value of Γ. The effect of the second term in Eq. (216) is, however, insignificant except for extremely short members.

Applying Eqs. (222) and (217) to a bar consisting of flat plates (Fig. 46), we find, for a point A lying on the flat plate BC,

$$w = w_0 + \theta w_1 = w_0 + \theta \int_0^s r_s\, ds$$

[1] Kappus, *loc. cit.* on p. 105.

The rate of change of w is

$$\frac{dw}{ds} = \frac{d}{ds}\left(w_0 + \theta \int_0^s r_s\, ds\right) = \theta r_s \qquad (223)$$

r_s being constant between the points B and C, w must be a linear function; this means geometrically that the cross section of the flat plate BC remains plane during twisting. It may be seen from this that Wagner's hypothesis as used by Kappus and Goodier is equivalent to the assumption that Navier's hypothesis remains valid for the thin flat plates of which the section is composed as long as the warping is defined by Eq. (222). If the more accurate Eq. (216) is used, one finds that

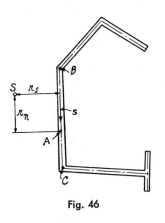

$$\frac{dw}{ds} = \theta(r_s + n) \qquad (224)$$

$\dfrac{dw}{ds}$ is no longer constant but depends on n.

As n is necessarily very small for thin sections, this term is unimportant unless r_s is also small for all parts of the section, as in the case of angles or T-sections. The value of Γ in Eq. (213) must be the same as found by Goodier, except for angles and T-sections, where Goodier obtains more accurate values for Γ.

Fig. 46

tions, where Goodier obtains more accurate values for Γ.

38. Properties of Sections

The value of Γ and of the coordinates x_0 and y_0 of the center of shear were determined for a number of sections and are listed here. The results were simplified considerably by expressing Γ, x_0, and y_0 in terms of the area and moments of inertia of the entire section wherever possible.

The values for the angle- and T-sections were derived by the Goodier theory, using Eq. (216) for the warping. The location of the shear centers for these sections was assumed to be at the intersection of the center lines of the legs. This is only approximately true, but the distance of the center of shear from this point is always a very small fraction of the thickness of the leg and can be neglected. The value Γ for these sections is small, and for many applications $\Gamma = 0$ may be used.

Angle, Equal Legs (Fig. 47):

$$x_0 = 0, \qquad y_0 = e, \qquad \Gamma = \frac{A^3}{144} \qquad (225)$$

where A is the cross-sectional area of the angle.

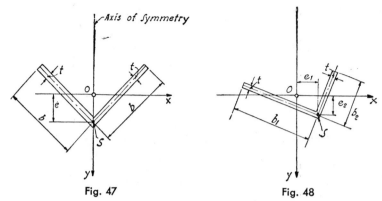

Fig. 47   Fig. 48

Angle, Unequal Legs (Fig. 48):

$$x_0 = e_1 \quad \text{and} \quad y_0 = e_2 \left. \vphantom{\frac{t^3}{36}} \right\} $$
$$\Gamma = \frac{t^3}{36}(b_1{}^3 + b_2{}^3) \tag{226}$$

T-section (Fig. 49):

$$x_0 = 0 \quad \text{and} \quad y_0 = e \left. \vphantom{\frac{t_1{}^3}{144}} \right\}$$
$$\Gamma = \frac{t_1{}^3 b^3}{144} + \frac{t_2{}^3 d^3}{36} \tag{227}$$

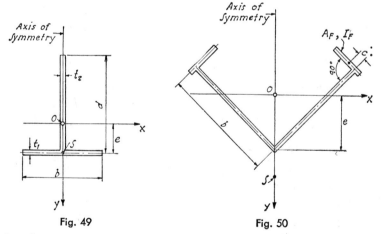

Fig. 49   Fig. 50

Section According to Fig. 50:

$$x_0 = 0 \quad \text{and} \quad y_0 = \sqrt{2}\left(e + cb^2\frac{A_F}{I_y} - b\frac{I_F}{I_y}\right) \left. \vphantom{\frac{A_F}{I_y}} \right\}$$
$$\Gamma = (2e^2 - y_0{}^2)I_y + 2b(b - 2e)I_F + 4eb^2 cA_F \tag{228}$$

A_F is the area of each of the flanges, I_F its moment of inertia with reference to the center line of the adjacent leg of the angle, and c the distance of the center of gravity of the flange from this line.

Channel-section (Figs. 51a and b):

$$x_0 = 0 \quad \text{and} \quad y_0 = -e\left(1 + \frac{d^2A}{4I_y}\right)$$

$$\Gamma = \frac{d^2}{4}\left[I_x + e^2A\left(1 - \frac{d^2A}{4I_y}\right)\right] \tag{229}$$

where A is the cross-sectional area and I_x, I_y the moments of inertia of

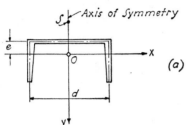

(a)

the channel. Equations (229) were derived for channels with tapered flanges; these equations are also valid for the more general section shown in Fig. 51b. As a limiting case, if the x-axis is an axis of symmetry, Eqs. (229) agree with Eqs. (230) for the symmetrical I-beam.

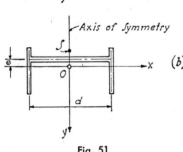

(b)

Fig. 51

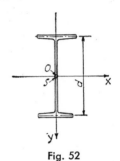

Fig. 52

Symmetrical I-beam (Fig. 52):

$$x_0 = y_0 = 0 \quad \text{and} \quad \Gamma = \frac{d^2I_y}{4} \tag{230}$$

where I_y is the moment of inertia of the beam with reference to the y-axis.

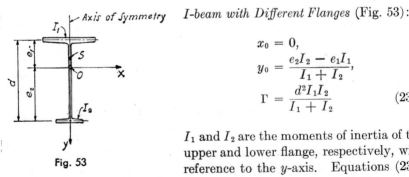

Fig. 53

I-beam with Different Flanges (Fig. 53):

$$x_0 = 0,$$

$$y_0 = \frac{e_2I_2 - e_1I_1}{I_1 + I_2},$$

$$\Gamma = \frac{d^2I_1I_2}{I_1 + I_2} \tag{231}$$

I_1 and I_2 are the moments of inertia of the upper and lower flange, respectively, with reference to the y-axis. Equations (231) are valid for tapered or otherwise variable flange and web thickness.

Section According to Fig. 54

The thickness of the webs and flanges for this section may be constant or variable without affecting the validity of Eqs. (232).

$$x_0 = 0 \quad \text{and} \quad y_0 = -e\left(1 + \frac{b^2 A}{4I_y}\right) + 2d\frac{I_F}{I_y}$$

$$\Gamma = \frac{b^2}{4}\left[I_x + e^2 A\left(1 - \frac{b^2 A}{4I_y}\right)\right] + 2d^2 I_F - 2bcd^2 A_F + b^2 deA\frac{I_F}{I_y} - 4d^2\frac{I_F{}^2}{I_y}$$

$$(232)$$

A, I_x, I_y are the area and moments of inertia, respectively, of the entire section; A_F and I_F are the area and the moment of inertia of one lower flange with respect to the axis of the web to which it is connected; and c is the distance of the center of gravity of the flange from this axis. The first terms of Eqs. (232) agree with Eqs. (229) for channel-sections.

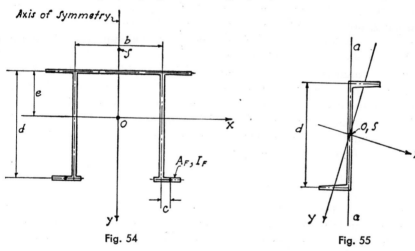

Fig. 54   Fig. 55

Z-section (Fig. 55):

$$x_0 = 0, \qquad y_0 = 0, \qquad \Gamma = \frac{d^2}{4}I_{a-a} \qquad (233)$$

where I_{a-a} is the moment of inertia of the cross section with reference to the center line $a\text{-}a$ of the web.

39. The Potential Energy of Centrally Loaded Columns

The differential equation of buckling can be obtained from the theorem of stationary potential energy. The total potential energy U of the system under consideration consists of the internal strain energy V and the potential energy U_w of the external loads.

In the previous section it was found that the strain energy V assumes its simplest form if expressed in terms of the displacements u and v of the center of shear. We shall therefore use u and v as coordinates. The expression (213) for the strain energy V was derived under the assumption of completely elastic behavior of the material, and in order to cover elastic and inelastic buckling we have to modify this expression in an adequate manner. Equation (213) reads:

$$V = \tfrac{1}{2} \int_0^l (EI_y u''^2 + EI_x v''^2 + E\Gamma\beta''^2 + GK\beta'^2 + EA\epsilon^2)\, dz \quad (213)$$

We reason as follows: A column remains practically straight until the buckling load is reached, and the first four terms of Eq. (213), which represent the strain energy of bending and twisting, will therefore remain zero until the critical load is reached. According to the tangent-modulus theory instantaneous values E_t and G_t will then be effective while the bending and torsional deformations occur, and we need only replace E and G in the first four terms of Eq. (213) by E_t and G_t.* This simple reasoning, however, does not apply to the last term $EA\epsilon^2$, which represents the strain energy of compression. We can, however, avoid the evaluation of this term. We are permitted to reckon the potential energy from the value zero for the compressed but undeflected state of the column. This will not change the final results provided the potential energy of the external loads is determined on the same basis. As the potential energy is zero for the straight column carrying its critical compressive load, the potential energy in the deformed state will be expressed by the first four terms of Eq. (213):

$$V = \tfrac{1}{2} \int_0^l (E_t I_y u''^2 + E_t I_x v''^2 + E_t \Gamma\beta''^2 + G_t K\beta'^2)\, dz \quad (234)$$

In Chap. I the tangent-modulus E_t was expressed by the elastic modulus E and the ratio τ [Chap. I, Eq. (18)] in the form $E_t = E\tau$, where τ is dependent on the stress. No definite information is available concerning the tangent-modulus of rigidity G_t, but it can be shown that the assumptions made in the theory of Local Buckling of Plate Elements of Columns, Chap. IX, are equivalent to the assumption $G_t = G\sqrt{\tau}$.† Application of this relation leads, however, to complicated methods of design, and as for most cases of torsional buckling the shearing stresses play only a minor role, we introduce the relation $G_t = G\tau$ instead. We are thus using a smaller value than the actual value for G_t, which leads to lower critical stresses, and the results will be on the safe side. The assumption $G_t = G\tau$ makes it possible to treat inelastic buckling in a

---

* E_t and G_t are defined by $E_t = \dfrac{d\sigma}{d\epsilon}$ and $G_t = \dfrac{d\tau}{d\gamma}$ as tangents to the stress-strain diagrams for compression and shear.

† See the discussion of torsional buckling of angles in Art. 42.

relatively simple manner. The expression (234) for the strain energy V becomes finally

$$V = \frac{1}{2} \int_0^l \left(E_T I_y u''^2 + E_T I_x v''^2 + E_T \Gamma \beta''^2 + G_T K \beta'^2 \right) dz \quad (235)$$

Inelastic torsional buckling was considered by Lundquist[1] and later by Ramberg and Levy.[2] Both papers are based on the double-modulus theory using effective moduli $\bar{E}$ and $\bar{G}$. Ramberg and Levy use $\bar{G} = (\bar{E}/E)G$; Lundquist assumes $\bar{G} = (\tau + \sqrt{\tau}G/2)$, which leads to rather complicated and inconvenient design methods.

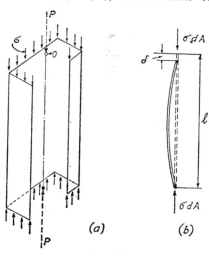

In addition to Eq. (235) giving the strain energy of the distorted column, we must determine the potential energy U_w of the external loads. As explained in Chap. II, this potential energy U_w is equal to the sum of the negative products of the external forces and the displacements of their points of application in direction of the forces. In accordance with the derivation of Eqs. (234) and (235) U_w must be reckoned from zero for the fully loaded but undeflected column, and U_w therefore represents the change

Fig. 56

of potential energy due to lateral bending and twisting of the column only. Figure 56 shows a column under the action of equally distributed compressive stresses $\sigma = P/A$ on the end surfaces. The resultant of these stresses σ goes through the centroid of the cross section, and we have the case of a centrally loaded column. As the member buckles, the stresses on the end surfaces may change to $\sigma + d\sigma$. We consider small deformations only and assume, furthermore, that the end conditions are such that the work done by $d\sigma$ may be neglected in comparison with the work done by the stresses σ.

Figure 56 shows a fiber of the column carrying a load σdA at each end. The change of potential energy is $dU_w = -\sigma dA \delta$. The relative displacement δ of the top and bottom of the column is due to two causes: the curvature of the fibers and the change in the longitudinal stresses. During buckling, the longitudinal stresses will change by an amount $\Delta\sigma_z$,

[1] Lundquist and Fligg, *loc. cit.* on p. 105.

[2] Ramberg, W., and S. Levy, Instability of Extrusions under Compressive Loads, *Jour. Aeronaut. Sci.*, 1945, p. 485.

causing a change of strain $\Delta\epsilon_z/E_t$ in the elements of the fiber. With the change in the length of the fiber due to the curvature designated by δ_c we have

$$dU_w = -\sigma \, dA \left(\delta_c + \frac{1}{E_t} \int_0^l \Delta\sigma_z \, dz \right) \tag{236}$$

For the entire column we obtain by integration

$$U_w = -\sigma \int_A \delta_c \, dA - \frac{\sigma}{E_t} \int_A \int_0^l \Delta\sigma_z \, dz \, dA = -\sigma \int_A \delta_c \, dA$$
$$- \frac{\sigma}{E_t} \int_0^l \left(\int_A \Delta\sigma_z \, dA \right) dz \tag{237}$$

The letter A at the bottom of the integrals indicates integration over the entire cross-sectional area of the column. The integral in the parentheses

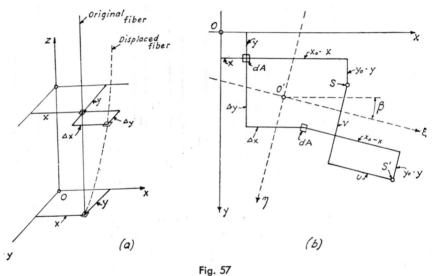

Fig. 57

in Eq. (237) is the component in the z-direction of the resultant of the additional stresses $\Delta\sigma_z$ during buckling. The stresses $\Delta\sigma_z$ will have moments about the x- and y-axes, but their resultant in the z-direction must vanish because the external load does not change. We have therefore

$$U_w = -\sigma \int_A \delta_c \, dA \tag{238}$$

In order to determine the relative displacement δ_c due to the curvature of the fibers, we consider Fig. 57a. The system of coordinates x,y,z shown is the system defined at the beginning of Art. 35. We consider a fiber having the coordinates x and y before deformation. Owing to the deformation, the coordinates will change to $x + \Delta x$ and $y + \Delta y$, where Δx and Δy are functions of z. We now consider a cross section at the distance z from the origin. Figure 57b shows the element dA, the centroid O of the section, the center of shear S having the coordinates x_0 and y_0, and the displaced positions of these points. The displacement of the section is defined by the movements u, v, and β of the center of shear, and Δx and Δy can be determined from Fig. 57b:

$$\left. \begin{aligned} \Delta x &= x_0 - x + (u - x_0 + x)\cos\beta - (v - y_0 + y)\sin\beta \\ &= u + (y_0 - y)\beta \\ \Delta y &= y_0 - y + (u - x_0 + x)\sin\beta + (v - y_0 + y)\cos\beta \\ &= v - (x_0 - x)\beta \end{aligned} \right\} \quad (239)$$

The simplification on the right-hand side of these equations is permissible because we consider small deformations only.

The shortening δ_c of the fiber due to its curvature is the difference between the length of the curve and the length of the chord of the deflection curve. This difference can be expressed by the derivatives of Δx and Δy:

$$\delta_c = \int_0^l \left[\sqrt{1 + \left(\frac{d\,\Delta x}{dz}\right)^2 + \left(\frac{d\,\Delta y}{dz}\right)^2} - 1 \right] dz$$

Considering that $\dfrac{d\,\Delta x}{dz}$ and $\dfrac{d\,\Delta y}{dz}$ are small, we obtain

$$\delta_c = \frac{1}{2}\int_0^l \left[\left(\frac{d\,\Delta x}{dz}\right)^2 + \left(\frac{d\,\Delta y}{dz}\right)^2 \right] dz \quad (240)$$

Introduction of Eqs. (239) and (240) into Eq. (238) leads to a double integral, the elements of the variables being dz and dA. The variables in this integral can be separated, and by using the geometrical relations

$$\int_A dA = A, \qquad \int_A x\,dA = 0, \qquad \int_A y\,dA = 0,$$

$$\int_A [(x - x_0)^2 + (y - y_0)^2]\,dA = I_p \quad (241)$$

the expression

$$U_w = \tfrac{1}{2}\int_0^l [-\sigma A (u'^2 + v'^2) - 2\sigma A y_0 u'\beta' + 2\sigma A x_0 v'\beta'$$
$$- \sigma I_p \beta'^2]\,dz \quad (242)$$

is obtained. I_p is the polar moment of inertia of the cross section with reference to the center of shear S.

The complete expression for the potential energy U is the sum of Eqs. (235) and (242):

$$U = V + U_w = \tfrac{1}{2}\int_0^l [E_T I_y u''^2 + E_T I_x v''^2 + E_T \Gamma \beta''^2 + G_T K \beta'^2$$
$$- \sigma A (u'^2 + v'^2) - 2\sigma A y_0 u'\beta' + 2\sigma A x_0 v'\beta' - \sigma I_p \beta'^2]\,dz \quad (243)$$

40. The Differential Equations of Buckling

The theorem of stationary potential energy, discussed in Chap. II, requires U to be a minimum if considered as a function of the three variables u, v, and β. According to the rules of the calculus of variations, U will be stationary if the three Eulerian equations are satisfied:[1]

$$E\tau I_y u^{IV} + \sigma A u'' + \sigma A y_0 \beta'' = 0 \qquad (244a)$$
$$E\tau I_x v^{IV} + \sigma A v'' - \sigma A x_0 \beta'' = 0 \qquad (244b)$$
$$\sigma A y_0 u'' - \sigma A x_0 v'' + E\tau \Gamma \beta^{IV} + (\sigma I_p - G\tau K)\beta'' = 0 \qquad (244c)$$

These three equations are the simultaneous differential equations of buckling by torsion and flexure in their most general form. Each of these differential equations is of the fourth order, and their general solution will contain $3 \times 4 = 12$ arbitrary constants which may be used to satisfy an equal number of boundary conditions.

Taking into account that x_0, y_0 are defined differently and therefore have opposite signs, Eqs. (244) agree in principle with Eqs. (15), (16), and (18) in Goodier's paper.[2] However, Goodier's differential equations are of the second and third order only, since they were developed for pin-ended columns. Equations (244) are more general and apply to any type of boundary condition; Goodier's equations may be derived by integrating Eqs. (244) and observing that the constants of integration will be zero for the particular case of pin-ended columns.

Equations (244) may be applied to columns with pinned, fixed, or free ends as in the usual theory of buckling. Although no other cases can be found in the literature, it is possible to consider additional cases where the conditions of support for individual flanges or webs at the same end of the column differ. An illustration of such a case would be an I-beam the top flange and web of which are fully restrained while the bottom flange is free to rotate in its own plane. It is, however, not permissible to prescribe entirely arbitrary boundary conditions because the assumption that the cross sections of the column do not distort imposes restrictions. In general, boundary conditions which can be expressed without contradiction in terms of the variables u, v, β, and their derivatives are permissible.

41. Columns for Which the Center of Shear Coincides with the Centroid

For sections having two axes of symmetry or for sections with point symmetry, the center of shear is at the centroid and we can substitute $x_0 = 0$ and $y_0 = 0$ into Eqs. (244):

---

[1] See Chap. II, Art. 31.

[2] Goodier, *loc. cit.* on p. 105.

$$E_T I_y u^{\mathrm{IV}} + \sigma A u'' = 0 \qquad (245a)$$
$$E_T I_x v^{\mathrm{IV}} + \sigma A v'' = 0 \qquad (245b)$$
$$E_T \Gamma \beta^{\mathrm{IV}} + (\sigma I_p - G_T K)\beta'' = 0 \qquad (245c)$$

In this case each of the three differential equations contains only one of the variables u, v, and β. The first two equations are identical in form with the differential equation of the tangent-modulus theory [Chap. I, Eq. (19)]. For pin-ended columns the stresses at which buckling parallel to the x- and y-axes, respectively, takes place are [Chap. I, Eq. (20)]

$$\sigma_x = \frac{\pi^2 E_T}{(l/r_y)^2} \qquad \text{and} \qquad \sigma_y = \frac{\pi^2 E_T}{(l/r_x)^2} \qquad (246)$$

The third Eq. (245) is an addition to the usual theory of buckling and describes the buckling of the column by twisting. We shall solve Eq. (245c) for a pin-ended column and determine whether or not such buckling is possible. To obtain the boundary conditions we must describe the conditions of support in detail. We consider an I-beam column and assume that the end cross sections are prevented from twisting and that the two flanges at the ends of the column are free to rotate in their own planes. If the column is twisted about its center line, the components η_1 and η_2 of the displacement of the flanges in their own planes are (Fig. 58)

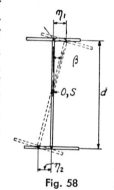

$$\eta_1 = \frac{d}{2}\beta \qquad \text{and} \qquad \eta_2 = \frac{d}{2}\beta \qquad (247a)$$

Fig. 58

The curvature of each flange is the second derivative of the displacement,

$$\eta_1'' = \frac{d}{2}\beta'' \qquad \text{and} \qquad \eta_2'' = \frac{d}{2}\beta'' \qquad (247b)$$

At the ends of the column twisting is prevented, and $\beta = 0$. Furthermore, if each flange is free to rotate, the bending moment in the flanges must be zero; this requires that the curvatures at the end are $\eta_1'' = \eta_2'' = 0$, too, and we arrive at the four boundary conditions:

For $z = 0$ and $z = l$: $\beta = 0$ and $\beta'' = 0$ (248)

The differential equation (245c) and the boundary conditions (248) are homogeneous equations, and it can be shown that nonvanishing solutions exist only for certain values of the stress. The displacement is found to be of the form

$$\beta = C \sin \frac{n\pi z}{l}$$

where C is an arbitrary constant and n an integer. The value of σ is

$$\sigma = \frac{\pi^2 E \tau}{l^2} \left(n^2 \frac{\Gamma}{I_p} + \frac{l^2}{\pi^2} \frac{GK}{EI_p} \right) \tag{249}$$

where K and Γ are cross-sectional properties defined in Arts. 35 and 36 and I_p is the polar moment of inertia referred to the center of shear.

The lowest stress, σ_β, for which torsional buckling occurs is obviously obtained for $n = 1$. σ_β can be expressed as a function of an equivalent radius of gyration r_β:

$$\sigma_\beta = \frac{\pi^2 E \tau}{(l/r_\beta)^2} \tag{250}$$

The value of the equivalent radius of gyration r_β is, with $\nu = 0.30$ and $G/E = 1/2(1 + \nu) = 1/2.60$,

$$r_\beta = \sqrt{\frac{\Gamma}{I_p} + \frac{G}{\pi^2 E} \frac{l^2 K}{I_p}} = \sqrt{\frac{\Gamma}{I_p} + 0.0390 \frac{l^2 K}{I_p}} \tag{251}$$

Equation (250) is of the same form as Eqs. (246) for the lateral buckling according to the tangent-modulus theory, and we can therefore state that the column will be torsionally unstable at a critical stress σ_β which is equal to the critical stress for lateral buckling of an equivalent column having the slenderness ratio l/r_β. This statement applies to both elastic and inelastic buckling. r_β has the dimension of a length and is a function of the shape of the cross section and of the length of the column. The critical stress of the column will be the lowest of the three stresses σ_x, σ_y, and σ_β, and it will correspond to the smallest of the radii r_x, r_y, and r_β.

So far we have considered pin-ended columns only; for other end conditions the critical loads for lateral buckling can be written

$$\sigma_{cr} = \frac{\pi^2 E \tau}{(kl/r)^2} \tag{252}$$

where kl is the effective length of the column [Chap. 1, Eq. (21)]. When the boundary conditions for β are the same as for the lateral displacements u and v (this is the case for fixed-ended columns and for columns with one end free), torsional buckling will occur at the stress given by Eq. (252) for an equivalent column of slenderness ratio kl/r_β. The equivalent radius of gyration r_β is in these cases

$$r_\beta = \sqrt{\frac{\Gamma}{I_p} + 0.0390 \frac{k^2 l^2 K}{I_p}} \tag{253}$$

Applying Eq. (253) to rolled beam sections, we use Eq. (230), $\Gamma = (d^2/4) I_y$. As the center of shear lies at the centroid, we have

$I_p = I_x + I_y$ and find the equivalent radius of gyration

$$r_\beta = \sqrt{\frac{d^2}{4}\frac{I_y}{I_x + I_y} + 0.0390\frac{k^2 l^2 K}{I_x + I_y}} \tag{254}$$

An investigation of standard steel beam sections indicates that r_β is in most cases larger than r_y and the column will buckle laterally; only

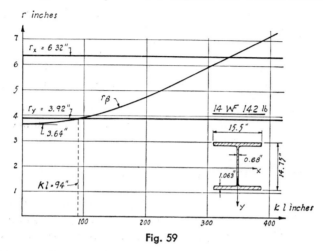

Fig. 59

columns of short length l with very wide flanges have values r_β slightly smaller than r_y, and such columns will buckle torsionally. Figure 59 indicates the variation of r_β as a function of kl for a 14-in. W̄ 142-lb beam. Torsional buckling in this particular case will be critical if the effective length is less than 94 in. The increase in the slenderness ratio remains below 8%, and because kl/r is under 25, the effect on the critical stress is quite insignificant. Similar conditions prevail for commonly used built-up columns of H-section as long as the cross sections are symmetrical for the x- and y-axes. Torsional buckling must, however, not be considered unimportant for all sections where center of shear and centroid coincide; torsional buckling may be critical for cruciform sections similar to that shown in Fig. 60.

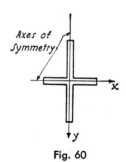

Fig. 60

Summing up, we have found that, when the center of shear coincides with the centroid, flexural buckling of columns occurs, without simultaneous twisting and at the critical stress given by the tangent-modulus theory. There is, however, the possibility of purely torsional buckling about an axis which goes through the center of shear. The critical stress can be obtained from Eq. (252) as function of an equivalent slenderness ratio kl/r_β. For conventional columns of I-sections torsional buckling will not reduce the critical stress appreciably. This statement does not necessarily apply to other types of cross sections with two axes of symmetry.

42. Columns with One Axis of Symmetry

If the cross section of the column has an axis of symmetry, say the y-axis, we have $x_0 = 0$ and Eqs. (244) become

$$E\tau I_y u^{IV} + \sigma A u'' + \sigma A y_0 \beta'' = 0 \tag{255a}$$
$$E\tau I_x v^{IV} + \sigma A v'' = 0 \tag{255b}$$
$$\sigma A y_0 u'' + E\tau \Gamma \beta^{IV} + (\sigma I_p - G\tau K)\beta'' = 0 \tag{255c}$$

The second of these equations contains the displacement v only and is the usual differential equation of flexural buckling in the y-direction, giving for pin-ended columns the critical stress.

$$\sigma_y = \frac{\pi^2 E\tau}{(l/r_x)^2} \tag{256}$$

The first and third equations contain u and β, but not v. This indicates that buckling in the x-direction and twisting will occur simultaneously and that the buckling stress found by the conventional theory is no longer correct. Assuming that the ends of the pin-ended column are prevented from twisting, the boundary conditions are

For $x = 0$ and $x = l$: $u = 0$, $\beta = 0$, $u'' = 0$, $\beta'' = 0$ (257)

The general solution of the two simultaneous differential equations (255a) and (255c) will contain eight arbitrary constants. Owing to the boundary conditions it can be shown that all but two of these constants vanish and the solutions are of the form

$$u = C_1 \sin \frac{n\pi z}{l} \quad \text{and} \quad \beta = C_2 \sin \frac{n\pi z}{l}$$

Substituting these expressions in the differential equations, two homogeneous equations for the constants C_1 and C_2 are obtained. Nonvanishing solutions for C_1 and C_2 can exist only if the determinant of the coefficients of these equations is zero. This condition can be used to determine the critical values of the stress σ. The lowest critical stress occurs for buckling in one half wave, $n = 1$, and this stress can be expressed in the form

$$\sigma_{x\beta} = \frac{\pi^2 E\tau}{(l/r_e)^2} \tag{258}$$

where r_e is an equivalent radius of gyration to be found from the following quadratic equation in r_e^2:

$$\begin{vmatrix} 1 - \dfrac{r_y^2}{r_e^2} & y_0 \\ y_0 & \dfrac{I_p}{A}\left(1 - \dfrac{r_\beta^2}{r_e^2}\right) \end{vmatrix} = \left(1 - \dfrac{r_y^2}{r_e^2}\right)\left(1 - \dfrac{r_\beta^2}{r_e^2}\right) - \dfrac{A y_0^2}{I_p} = 0 \quad (259)$$

r_y is the radius of gyration of the cross section referred to the y-axis, and r_β is defined by

$$r_\beta = \sqrt{\dfrac{\Gamma}{I_p} + \dfrac{l^2}{\pi^2}\dfrac{GK}{EI_p}} = \sqrt{\dfrac{\Gamma}{I_p} + 0.0390\dfrac{Kl^2}{I_p}} \quad (260)$$

Γ and K are properties of the cross section defined in Arts. 35 and 36; I_p is the polar moment of inertia referred to the center of shear.

Equation (258) has the same form as Eq. (256) for ordinary buckling. The critical stress $\sigma_{x\beta}$ for buckling by torsion and flexure will therefore be the same as the critical stress in the ordinary column theory for an equivalent column having the slenderness ratio l/r_e. This applies equally in the elastic and in the inelastic range.

The deformations corresponding to the roots r_e of Eq. (259) can be determined, and it is found that each cross section rotates around a point C having the coordinates

$$x_c = 0 \qquad \text{and} \qquad y_c = \dfrac{y_0}{1 - (r_e^2/r_y^2)} \quad (261)$$

Figure 61 shows the location of the center of rotation for an angle section.

Equation (259) always has two positive roots r_e, one of which is smaller than both r_y and r_β. If the torsional resistance of the section is very small, r_β is also small compared with r_y, and one root r_e will be close to r_β. From Eq. (261) we may conclude that in such a case y_c will differ only a little from y_0 which means that the center of rotation will be close to the center of shear.

Speaking generally, the column will buckle at a stress σ according to Eqs. (256) and (258) corresponding to the smaller one of the values r_x and r_e. If r_x is smaller, the column will buckle in the y-direction without twisting; if the root r_e of Eq. (259) is smaller than r_x, the column will deflect in the x-direction and twist simultaneously. As r_e is always smaller than r_y, the critical stress is also smaller than that given by the conventional column theory for buckling in the x-direction.

Equations (258) to (260) can be used for other end conditions too, if l is replaced by the equivalent length kl, provided the boundary conditions for β and u are the same.

The results found indicate that the conventional theory of buckling by flexure is no longer applicable for buckling perpendicular to the axis of symmetry of the cross section. The consequences of this result for a few typical cases will be discussed in the following.

For angles with equal legs (Fig. 61), r_x is considerably smaller than r_y, and from the usual theory of buckling we expect the angle to buckle in the y-direction. However, one of the roots r_e of Eq. (259) may become smaller than r_x, and in such a case the angle will buckle torsionally. Figure 62 illustrates the relationship between r_e and r_x for an angle

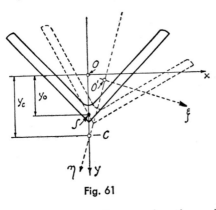

Fig. 61

6 by 6 by ⅜ in.; r_x is constant, but r_e is a function of the length l. It will be seen that r_e is smaller than r_x for length under 97 in. Figure 62 also contains the distance $y_c - y_0$ of the center of rotation from the center of shear. For short lengths y_c is only a little larger than y_0, which means that the angle twists approximately around the center of shear. The values r_β, indicated by a dotted line, differ only a little from r_e, and for angles one can use

$r_e = r_\beta$ as a good approximation. Figure 62 contains also the critical design values max l/r; this line differs considerably from the values l/r_x as given by the conventional theory. The ratio of leg thickness to width, t/b, for this angle is 16, which is the largest ratio used in steel structures. For thicker angles the differences reduce markedly

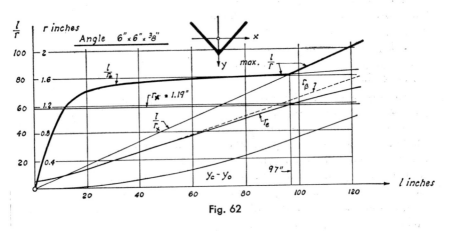

Fig. 62

as can be seen from Fig. 63, which shows the corresponding curves for angles 6 by 6 by ¾ in. Torsional buckling will occur only for less than 47 in. length, but the differences in the effective slenderness ratios are still substantial. It must, however, be remembered that for small values of l/r_e the critical stress is not sensitive to changes in the slenderness ratio, and the large differences between l/r_x and l/r_e are not quite so serious as might appear on first sight.

At the beginning of this chapter it was pointed out that for equal angles there is no rational division between primary and local buckling, and the phenomenon of torsional buckling of an angle can alternatively be considered as local failure of the outstanding legs of the angle. Considering each leg of the angle as a plate simply supported along the long side while the opposite side is entirely free, we can find σ_c from Eq. (647) of Chap. IX. For the boundary conditions stated, the coefficient of

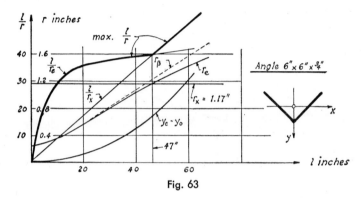

Fig. 63

restraint is $\zeta = \infty$, and from Fig. 163 we have $p = 0.425$, $q = 0$. The angle will buckle in one wave $n = 1$, the ratio $\alpha = l/b$, and the theory of the buckling of plates gives the critical stress

$$\sigma_c = \frac{\pi^2 E \sqrt{\tau}}{12 (1 - \nu^2)} \left(\frac{t}{b}\right)^2 \left[\frac{b^2 \sqrt{\tau}}{l^2} + 0.425\right] \tag{262}$$

If we use the approximation $r_e = r_\beta$, which is permissible for angles as indicated by Figs. 62 and 63, we can find the critical stress from Eqs. (258) and (260):

$$\sigma_{x\beta} = \frac{\pi^2 E \tau}{(l/r_e)^2} = \frac{\pi^2 E \tau}{l^2} \left(\frac{\Gamma}{I_p} + 0.0390 \frac{K l^2}{I_p}\right) \tag{263}$$

Expressing Γ, K, and I_p by the width b and thickness t of the angle, $\Gamma = b^3 t^3/18$, $K = 2bt^3/3$, and using $\nu = 0.30$, $I_p = 2b^3 t/3$,

$$\sigma_{x\beta} = \frac{\pi^2 E \sqrt{\tau}}{12(1 - \nu^2)} \left(\frac{t}{b}\right)^2 \left[(1 - \nu^2) \frac{b^2}{l^2} \sqrt{\tau} + 0.425 \sqrt{\tau}\right] \tag{264}$$

Equations (262) and (264) are very similar but not identical. The first term in the bracket in Eq. (264) contains an additional factor $1 - \nu^2$. This difference must be due to neglecting the effect of Poisson's ratio in the derivation of the value of Γ. The last term contains an additional

$\sqrt{\tau}$, which is due to the fact that we used $G_t = G\tau$ instead of $G_t = G\sqrt{\tau}$ when obtaining Eq. (235).

Due to its derivation from the theory of plates Eq. (262) must be considered more accurate. The numerical effect of the factor $1 - \nu^2$ in Eq. (264) is quite unimportant because this term is very small compared with the last term in the bracket; the effect of the term $\sqrt{\tau}$ may be noticeable for short angles. Equation (264) gives too low a critical stress, and its use is therefore on the safe side. The advantage of the designer's being able to express the critical stress as function of an equivalent radius of gyration r_e outweighs the loss of accuracy due to the use of the approximation $G_t = G\tau$.

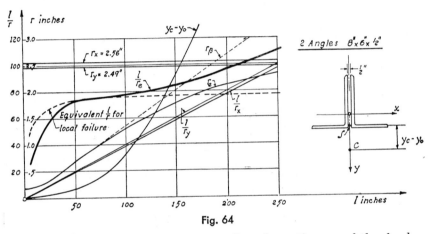

Fig. 64

Figure 64 indicates the equivalent radius of gyration r_e and the slenderness ratio l/r_e for a T-section consisting of two angles. Such sections are in frequent use and therefore important. For a short length l the differences between l/r_e and l/r_y are very large and remain more than 10% of l/r_y even for slender members. The critical load of such members may be reduced by as much as 20%. The distance of the center of rotation C from the center of shear $y_c - y_0$ is also shown in Fig. 64. Except for short columns the center of rotation is not close to the center of shear.

For T-sections, whether rolled or built up by two angles, it is no longer possible to explain torsional buckling alternatively as local failure of the outstanding legs. For the case shown in Fig. 64 the equivalent slenderness ratios l/r due to local failure were determined from the theory of plates. For very short columns local buckling will occur at a lower stress than torsional buckling, making consideration of torsional buckling unnecessary; for longer columns, from $l = 80$ in. up, torsional buckling is critical and requires consideration for this type of section.

Figures 65 to 67 indicate the slenderness ratios l/r_e, l/r_x, and l/r_y for other typical sections. The differences between the equivalent slenderness ratio l/r_e and the ratios l/r_x and l/r_y used in the conventional design are noticeable but not very large in the cases of the channel- and unsymmetrical beam-sections (Figs. 65 and 66). The differences indicated in

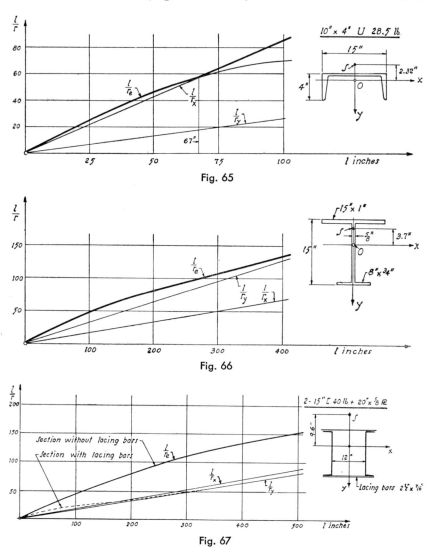

Fig. 65

Fig. 66

Fig. 67

Fig. 67 for an open built-up section, however, are considerable and rather alarming. However, such sections are usually provided with lacing bars connecting the lower flanges of the channels, and the section then becomes a closed section with considerably increased torsional stiffness.

An approximate analysis of the section with lacing bars as a closed section[1] resulted in the values l/r_e indicated by the dotted line which differs only very little from the line l/r_x.   Figure 67 is a striking proof of the necessity of providing lacing bars or batten plates connecting the lower flanges.

Primary buckling and local failure of webs and flanges for the channel-, I-, and built-up columns indicated in Figs. 65 to 67 are obviously two quite different types of failure, each of which requires separate analysis.

Reviewing the examples shown in Figs. 62 to 67 we can state that an increase in the slenderness ratio l/r_e due to the possibility of torsional buckling is noticeable for all open sections with one axis of symmetry. Among the sections employed in steel construction and shipbuilding thin angles and T-sections show the largest reductions in carrying capacity. For single angles torsional buckling and local buckling of the outstanding legs are the same phenomenon, and a single-angle column designed to be safe against local buckling will automatically be safe against torsional buckling and vice versa.

43. Torsional Buckling with Enforced Axis of Rotation

Longitudinal stiffeners attached to a plate in compression are special cases of the problem of buckling of columns by torsion and flexure where an axis of rotation is enforced by external conditions.   The plate prevents

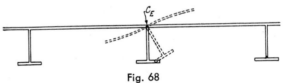

Fig. 68

the stiffener from moving laterally in any other way except by rotation around point C_E (Fig. 68).   Even this rotation is resisted by the stiffness of the plate in bending.

To obtain a basis for the design of stiffeners we shall consider in this section the buckling of symmetrical columns with an enforced axis of rotation in the plane of symmetry.   For I-beams this problem was first considered by Bleich;[2] for general sections solutions were first given by Kappus[3] and by Lundquist and Fligg.[4]

Figure 69a shows a section which is symmetrical to the y-axis.   The enforced center of rotation is marked C_E.   The distance a from C_E to the center of shear S is reckoned positive if S is between O and C_E.

[1] Closed sections were considered in the papers of Bleich and Bleich, *loc. cit.* on p. 105, and of Lundquist and Fligg, *loc. cit.* on p. 105.

[2] Bleich, F., "Stahlhochbauten," Vol. 2, p. 927, Julius Springer, Berlin, 1933.

[3] Kappus, *loc. cit.* on p. 105.

[4] Lundquist and Fligg, *loc. cit.* on p. 105.

The potential energy U is given by Eq. (243) as function of the displacements u, v, and β. The cross sections of the column being forced to rotate around point C_E, the displacements u and v can be expressed by the angle of twist β (see Fig. 69b):

$$u = a \sin \beta \quad \text{and} \quad v = (\cos \beta - 1)a$$

If we restrict the investigation to small deflections $\sin \beta = \beta$, $\cos \beta = 1$, we obtain

$$u = a\beta \quad \text{and} \quad v = 0 \tag{265}$$

Substitution of these values of u and v in Eq. (243) leads to

$$U = \tfrac{1}{2} \int_0^l [E_T(a^2 I_y + \Gamma)\beta''^2 + G_T K \beta'^2 - \sigma(Aa^2 + 2Aay_0 + I_p)\beta'^2]\, dz$$

The last term containing I_p can be simplified by considering that the polar moment of inertia I_p of the cross section with reference to the center

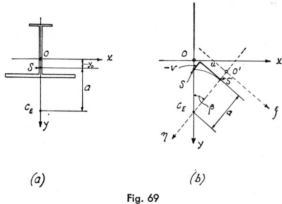

(a) (b)

Fig. 69

of shear can be expressed in the form $I_p = I_x + I_y + Ay_0^2$, I_x, I_y being the principal moments of inertia of the cross section. We have

$$Aa^2 + 2Aay_0 + I_p = I_x + I_y + A(a + y_0)^2 = I_{pc}$$

where I_{pc} is the polar moment of inertia of the cross section with reference to the enforced center of rotation C_E.

The potential energy U assumes the simple form

$$U = \tfrac{1}{2} \int_0^l [E_T(a^2 I_y + \Gamma)\beta''^2 + (G_T K - \sigma I_{pc})\beta'^2]\, dz \tag{266}$$

The theorem of stationary potential energy requires that U shall be a minimum considered as a function of β. According to the rules of the calculus of variation, U will be stationary if the following Eulerian equation is satisfied:

$$E_T(a^2 I_y + \Gamma)\beta^{IV} + (\sigma I_{pc} - G_T K)\beta'' = 0 \tag{267}$$

The boundary conditions for simply supported ends are $\beta = 0$ and $\beta'' = 0$ at both ends $z = 0$, $z = l$. Equation (267) and the boundary conditions being homogeneous, nonvanishing solutions will exist only for certain values of the stress σ. The displacement β is found to be

$$\beta = C \sin \frac{n\pi z}{l}$$

where C is an arbitrary constant, and the value of σ is

$$\sigma = \frac{\pi^2 E\tau}{l^2} \left(n^2 \frac{a^2 I_y + \Gamma}{I_{pc}} + \frac{G}{\pi^2 E} \frac{l^2 K}{I_{pc}} \right)$$

The lowest value of σ will occur for buckling in one wave, $n = 1$:

$$\sigma_c = \frac{\pi^2 E\tau}{l^2} \left(\frac{a^2 I_y + \Gamma}{I_{pc}} + \frac{G}{\pi^2 E} \frac{l^2 K}{I_{pc}} \right) = \frac{\pi^2 E\tau}{(l/r_e)^2} \tag{268}$$

The equivalent radius of gyration r_e in Eq. (268) is defined by

$$r_e = \sqrt{\frac{a^2 I_y + \Gamma}{I_{pc}} + \frac{G}{\pi^2 E} \frac{l^2 K}{I_{pc}}} = \sqrt{\frac{a^2 I_y + \Gamma}{I_{pc}} + 0.0390 \frac{l^2 K}{I_{pc}}} \tag{269}$$

where I_{pc} is the polar moment of inertia of the cross section with reference to the enforced center of rotation C_E.

Equation (268) is of the same form as Eqs. (246) for the lateral buckling of columns according to the tangent-modulus theory and the column will buckle torsionally at the critical stress belonging to the equivalent slenderness ratio l/r_e.

Equations (268) and (269) were derived for columns which can rotate without restraint around the enforced axis of rotation. It is possible to investigate the case of columns where this rotation is elastically restrained.[1] If the restraining moment m_t is proportional to the angle of twist β, a relationship

$$m_t = C\beta \tag{270}$$

exists, where C is a "spring constant." The critical stress again can be expressed by an equivalent radius of gyration r_e in the form

$$\sigma_{cr} = \frac{\pi^2 E\tau}{(l/r_e)^2} \tag{271}$$

where

$$r_e = \sqrt{\frac{n^2(\Gamma + a^2 I_y) + 0.0390 K l^2 + \dfrac{1}{n^2} \dfrac{l^4}{\pi^4} \dfrac{C}{E}}{I_{pc}}} \qquad (n = 1, 2, \ldots) \tag{272}$$

[1] The more general case of a column which is elastically restrained against displacement and rotation was treated by V. Z. Vlasov and is discussed in Timoshenko, Theory of Bending, Torsion and Buckling of Thin-walled Members of Open Cross Section, *Jour. Franklin Inst.*, 1945, p. 348.

The equivalent radius of gyration r_e is a function of the number of waves n in which the column buckles.

To obtain the critical stress, n must be selected in such a way that r_e becomes a minimum. From $\dfrac{\partial r_e}{\partial n} = 0$ we obtain

$$n = \frac{l}{\pi} \sqrt[4]{\frac{C}{E(\Gamma + a^2 I_y)}}$$

Introducing this value into Eq. (272) r_e^2 becomes

$$\min r_e{}^2 = \frac{l^2}{\pi^2 I_{pc}} \left[0.0390 K\pi^2 + 2 \sqrt{\frac{(\Gamma + a^2 I_y)C}{E}} \right] \tag{273}$$

It will be noticed that min r_e^2 according to Eq. (273) does not depend on the number of half waves n and that, because min r_e^2 is proportional to

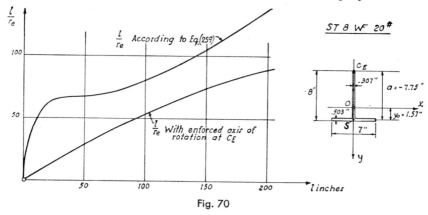

Fig. 70

l^2, the slenderness ratio and the critical stress do not depend on the length l. Similar independence of n and l is found repeatedly for the critical stresses of compressed rectangular plates (see Chap. IX, page 321).

Figure 70 shows the values of l/r_e according to Eq. (269) for a T-section which rotates without restraint around the toe of the web. For comparison Fig. 70 contains also the values of l/r_e according to Eq. (259) for a column which is not forced to rotate around point C_E but can buckle freely. The difference in carrying capacity between the two columns is very substantial; the column with enforced axis of rotation is capable of carrying much higher load. Figure 71 shows the typical displacement of a cross section of each of the two columns. In Fig. 71a the cross section is forced to rotate around point C_E; in Fig. 71b the cross section will rotate around a point C the coordinates of which are given by Eq. (261). For the free column the toe of the web has a tendency to move ahead of the flange; this is prevented in Fig. 71a by external reactions H acting at C_E. These external reactions are opposed to the displacement of the column as a whole and are the cause for the increase in the critical load.

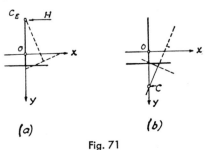

The occurrence of the reactions H which are distributed along the enforced center line of rotation introduces an additional problem. Owing to the forces H the web will bend, and the deformation of the web may affect the critical load of the column. We shall investigate this problem in the next article.

Fig. 71

The more general case of unsymmetrical stiffeners attached to a flexible sheet is discussed in a paper by Goodier;[1] the results permit the determination of the critical stress of stiffeners of channel- or Z-section.

44. Effect of Web Deformations on Torsional Buckling of T-stiffeners

Figure 72a shows the T-section in its original and in its displaced state. The axes x and y are the principal axes of the cross section in its original position. In addition to the axes x and y we use a system of coordinates

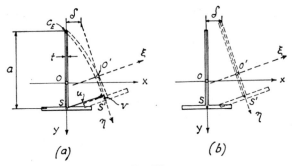

Fig. 72

ξ and η which are attached to the cross section and coincide with x and y in the undisplaced position. As the cross section is displaced, η shall remain parallel to the flange and η shall go through the displaced center of shear S'. The center line of the web in the displaced position is curved, and the maximum deflection of the web is δ.

The deformations are defined by the displacements u and v of the center of shear, by the angle of twist β, and by the deflection of the web δ. u and v are measured parallel to the axes ζ and η, and β is positive if the rotation is clockwise. Because small deformations only are considered,

[1] Goodier, *loc. cit.* on p. 105.

we have the relations

$$v = 0 \quad \text{and} \quad \delta = u + a\beta \tag{274}$$

If the web did not distort, the displaced position of the cross section would be as shown in Fig. 72b. The strain energy V corresponding to this displaced position can be found from Eq. (235) by introducing $v = 0$:

$$V = \tfrac{1}{2} \int_0^l (E_T I_y u''^2 + E_T \Gamma \beta''^2 + G_T K \beta'^2)\, dz \tag{275}$$

The strain energy of the column with deformed web will be the expression (275) plus a term representing the additional strain energy of the deformation of the web.

The strain energy stored in an element of the web of thickness t considered as a cantilever of span a is

$$dV = \frac{1}{2} \frac{E t^3 \delta^2}{4a^3}\, dz$$

If we consider the column at stresses above the elastic limit, E can be replaced approximately by E_T; from Eq. (274) we substitute $\delta = u + a\beta$, and the total strain energy of the column becomes

$$V = \frac{1}{2} \int_0^l \left[E_T I_y u''^2 + E_T \Gamma \beta''^2 + G_T K \beta'^2 + E_T \frac{t^3}{4a^3} (u + a\beta)^2 \right] dz \tag{276}$$

The entire potential energy of the column consists of the strain energy V and of the potential of the external loads. The derivation of the value of the latter in Art. 39 remains valid except for Eqs. (239), (242), and (243). Equations (239) define the displacements Δx and Δy of the elements of the cross section. Because of the deformation of the web, different equations apply for the flange and for the web. For the flange, Eqs. (239) remain valid, and considering $v = 0$, $x_0 = 0$, $y = y_0$, we have

$$\Delta x = u \quad \text{and} \quad \Delta y = -(x_0 - x)\beta \tag{277}$$

The displacements Δx and Δy of the web are

$$\Delta x = u + (y_0 - y)\beta - \delta \left(\frac{y_0 - y}{a} \right)^2 \left(\frac{3}{2} - \frac{y_0 - y}{2a} \right) \quad \text{and} \quad \Delta y = 0 \tag{278}$$

where the last term in the expression for Δx represents the deflection of the web considered as a cantilever under the action of a concentrated load. Substitution of these expressions into Eqs. (238) and (240) leads to the following expression for the potential energy of the external loads:

$$U_w = -\tfrac{1}{2} \int_0^l [\sigma(A - \tfrac{18}{35}\, ta)u'^2 + 2\sigma(Ay_0 - \tfrac{29}{70}\, ta^2)u'\beta'$$
$$+ \sigma(I_p - \tfrac{11}{35}\, ta^3)\beta'^2]\, dz \tag{279}$$

where I_p is the polar moment of inertia of the cross section with reference to the center of shear.

The entire potential energy is the sum of the expressions (276) and (279):

$$
\begin{aligned}
U = V + U_w = \frac{1}{2} \int_0^l \bigg[& E_\tau I_y u''^2 + E_\tau \Gamma \beta''^2 + G_\tau K \beta'^2 \\
& + E_\tau \frac{t^3}{4a^3}(u + a\beta)^2 - \sigma\left(A - \frac{18}{35}ta\right)u'^2 - 2\sigma\left(Ay_0 - \frac{29}{70}ta^2\right)u'\beta' \\
& - \sigma\left(I_p - \frac{11}{35}ta^3\right)\beta'^2 \bigg]dz \quad (280)
\end{aligned}
$$

The theorem of stationary potential energy requires the integral in Eq. (280) to be a minimum and leads to the following two Eulerian equations:

$$
\left.
\begin{aligned}
E_\tau I_y u^{IV} + \sigma\left(A - \frac{18}{35}ta\right)u'' + \frac{E_\tau t^3}{4a^3}u + \sigma\left(Ay_0 - \frac{29}{70}ta^2\right)\beta'' & \\
+ \frac{E_\tau t^3}{4a}\beta = 0 & \\[2mm]
\sigma\left(Ay_0 - \frac{29}{70}ta^2\right)u'' + \frac{E_\tau t^3}{4a^2}u + E_\tau \Gamma \beta^{IV} + \left[\sigma\left(I_p - \frac{11}{35}ta^3\right)\right. & \\
\left. - G_\tau K\right]\beta'' + \frac{E_\tau t^3}{4a}\beta = 0 &
\end{aligned}
\right\} \quad (281)
$$

For columns with hinged ends the solutions of Eqs. (281) are of the form

$$
u = C_1 \sin\frac{n\pi z}{l} \quad \text{and} \quad \beta = C_2 \sin\frac{n\pi z}{l} \quad (282)
$$

Substituting these expressions in the differential equations, two homogeneous equations for the constants C_1 and C_2 are obtained. Nonvanishing solutions C_1 and C_2 can exist only if the determinant of the coefficients of these equations is zero. This condition can be used to determine the values of σ for which the solutions (282) occur. Expressing σ by an equivalent radius of gyration r_e, the result is

$$
\sigma = \frac{\pi^2 E_\tau}{(l/r_e)^2} \quad (283)
$$

where r_e^2 can be found from the following quadratic equation:

$$
\begin{aligned}
\left[Ar_y^2 - \left(A - \frac{18}{35}ta\right)\frac{r_e^2}{n^2} + \frac{t^3}{4\pi^4 a^3}\left(\frac{l}{n}\right)^4\right]&\left[\Gamma + 0.0390K\left(\frac{l}{n}\right)^2\right. \\
\left. - \left(I_p - \frac{11}{35}ta^3\right)\frac{r_e^2}{n^2} + \frac{t^3}{4\pi^4 a}\left(\frac{l}{n}\right)^4\right] - \left[\left(Ay_0 - \frac{29}{70}ta^2\right)\frac{r_e^2}{n^2}\right. & \\
\left. - \frac{t^3}{4\pi^4 a^2}\left(\frac{l}{n}\right)^4\right]^2 = 0 \quad (284)
\end{aligned}
$$

The lowest critical stress will be obtained from Eq. (284) if the number of half waves n in which the column buckles is selected in such manner that the equivalent radius of gyration r_e becomes a minimum.

The terms containing t in Eq. (284) represent the effect of the flexibility of the web.   It can be shown that for the limit $t^3(l/n)^4 \to \infty$ Eqs. (284) and (269) give the same root r_e.

Figure 73 shows the equivalent slenderness ratio l/r_e for a T-section ST 8 W 20 for $n = 1, 2, 3$.   The subsequent curves for $n = 1, 2, 3, \ldots$ are similar to each other but are distorted in the l-direction.   For lengths up to 22 in. the column will buckle in one half wave; as the column becomes longer, the equivalent slenderness ratio l/r_e for buckling in two

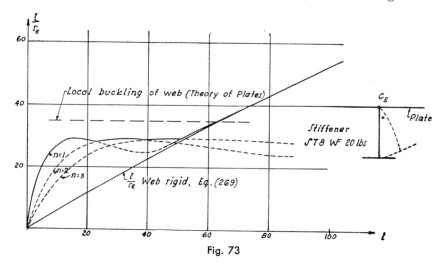

Fig. 73

half waves is larger than for one half wave, and the column must buckle in two half waves.   As the length increases further, the column buckles in three half waves until a length of approximately 51 in. is reached.   At this point l/r_e for one half wave becomes critical again and buckling for all larger values of l occurs in one half wave.   Figure 73 also indicates l/r_e for buckling with rigid web according to Eq. (269).   For $l > 51$ in. there is practically no difference between the results according to Eq. (269) and according to Eq. (284) for $n = 1$.   For short lengths the values l/r_e differ sharply, and the critical stress is noticeably smaller if the deformation of the web is considered.

If $l < 51$ in., buckling occurs in very short half waves of but 15 in. length.   The displacements u and β were determined from the differential equations (281), and it was found that for buckling in short waves u is very small and the deformations are of the type shown in Fig. 74a.   The deformations consist mainly of buckling of the web and twisting of the flange around its center line and represent clearly a case of local buckling. It is possible to find the critical load for local buckling of the web restrained by the flange from the theory of buckling of plates.[1] The equivalent value of l/r_e is shown in Fig. 73. The theory of plates yields larger values l/r_e than Eq. (284), indicating that local buckling occurs at lower stresses than expected from Eq. (284). The reason for this difference becomes apparent if we compare the distorted form of the cross section as shown in Fig. 74a with the deformations of the cross section for local buckling according to the theory of plates (Fig. 75). It will be seen that the web is restrained by the flange and that there must be a point of contraflexure in the web; this is not in agreement with the assumption, made earlier in this article, that the web deformation will be the deflection of a cantilever due to a concentrated load. Equation (284) cannot therefore give accurate results for buckling in short waves. On the other hand Eq. (284) remains reliable for buckling in longer waves, $n = 1$, where the deformation is according to Fig. 74b.

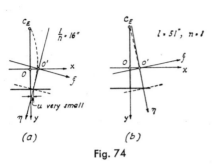

(a)   (b)

Fig. 74

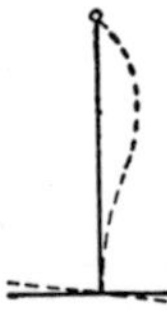

Fig. 75

Reviewing the results found in this article it can be stated that Eq. (269) is reliable for the primary buckling of T-stiffeners but that the possibility of local buckling of the web must be investigated by the theory of plates.

45. Corroboration of the Theory by Tests

The earliest tests were made by Wagner and Pretschner[2] to confirm Wagner's theoretical results. The tests were made on plain and on flanged angles of aluminum alloy. The results of the tests showed good agreement with the theory.

A series of tests of aluminum-alloy panels stiffened by Z-sections were made by Ramberg, McPherson, and Levy.[3] Observations of torsional buckling of the stiffeners were made, and the test results were subsequently compared by Goodier[4] with the results of his theory.

[1] Chap. X, Art. 102.

[2] Wagner, H., and W. Pretschner, Verdrehung und Knickung von offenen Profilen, *Luftfahrt-Forschung* 1934. Translated in *NACA Tech. Note* 784, 1936.

[3] Ramberg, W., A. E. McPherson, and S. Levy, *NACA Tech. Note* 684, 1939.

[4] Goodier, *loc. cit.* on p. 105.

A further series of tests made by Niles[1] on aluminum-alloy channels showed good agreement with the theory.

Aluminum-alloy sheet panels stiffened by bulb angles were tested by Dunn.[2]

Tests on thin angle struts, including steel specimens, were made by Thomas.[3]

An extensive series of tests on many extruded sections of aluminum and magnesium alloys were made more recently by Ramberg and Levy.[4] The tests include cases of elastic and inelastic buckling, and good agreement is claimed between these tests and theoretical results based on the double-modulus theory.

All these tests, except those by Thomas, were made on aluminum and magnesium alloys, and the cross sections were of the types employed in aircraft construction. One series of tests using steel specimens which can be used to check theoretical results on torsional buckling were made by Kollbrunner[5] on equal angles. These tests are discussed in detail in Art. 95 of Chap. IX, where good agreement with results obtained from the theory of plates is shown. As pointed out on pages 106 and 135, the critical load of angle columns determined from the theory of buckling by torsion and flexure agrees closely with the critical loads according to the theory of buckling of plates. Kollbrunner's tests therefore support the results found in this chapter.

No other tests on sections of the type used in steel construction are available. From an inspection of Figs. 59, 64 to 67, and 70 indicating the effects of torsional buckling on various sections it becomes clear that such tests would be of value only for T-sections according to Figs. 64 and 70, because in all other cases the effect of torsional buckling is so small that tests would be inconclusive.

Additional References

Pugsley, A. G., Torsional Instability in Struts, *Aircraft Eng.*, Vol. 4, No. 43, p. 229, 1932.

[1] Niles, A. S., Experimental Study of Torsional Column Failure, *NACA Tech. Note* 733, 1939. These experiments are also discussed in A. S. Niles and J. S. Newell, "Airplane Structures," 3d ed., p. 351, John Wiley & Sons, Inc., New York.

[2] Dunn, L. G., An Investigation of Sheet-stiffener Panels Subjected to Compression Loads with Particular Reference to Torsionally Weak Stiffeners, *NACA Tech. Note* 752, 1940.

[3] Thomas, E. W., Torsion Instability of Thin Angle Section Struts, *Structural Engr.*, Vol. 19, No. 5, p. 77, 1941.

[4] Ramberg and Levy, *loc. cit.* on p. 125.

[5] Kollbrunner, C. F., Das Ausbeulen des auf Druck beanspruchten freistehenden Winkels, *Mitteilungen*, 4, *Institut für Baustatik, Eidgenössische Technische Hochschule, Zurich*, 1935; and Das Ausbeulen der auf einseitigen, gleichmässig verteilten Druck beanspruchten Platten im elastischen und plastischen Bereich, *Mitteilungen*, 17, *Institut für Baustatik, Eidgenössische Technische Hochschule, Zurich*, 1946.

Bridget, F. J., C. C. Jerome, and A. B. Voseller, Some New Experiments on Buckling of Thin-wall Construction, *Trans. ASME*, Vol. 56, 1934.

M. Kuranisi, Torsional Buckling of Centrally Loaded Thin-walled Columns, *Trans. Soc. Mech. Engrs. (Japan)*, Vol. 1, No. 5, p. 415, 1935 (in Japanese).

de Marneffe, A., Flambage par torsion, *Rev. universelle mines*, Vol. 15, No. 10, p. 501, 1939.

Arutinyan, N. C., Approximate Solution of Problems of Torsion of Bars Having Polygonal Cross Section, *Prikladnaya Matematika Mechanika*, Vol. 6, No. 1, p. 19, 1943 (in Russian).

Goodier, J. N., Torsional and Flexural Buckling of Bars of Thin-walled Open Section under Compressive and Bending Loads, *Jour. Applied Mechanics*, Vol. 10, p. A-110, June, 1943.

Hoff, N. J., Strain Energy Derivation of Torsional-Flexural Buckling Loads of Straight Columns of Thin-walled Open Sections, Brown University, *Quart. Applied Math.*, Vol. 1, No. 4, p. 341, June, 1944.

Goodier, J. N., Flexural Buckling of a Twisted Bar, *Quart. Applied Math.*, Vol. 2, p. 93, 1944.

Levy, S., and W. D. Kroll, Primary Instability of Open Section Stringers Attached to Sheet, *Jour. Aeronaut. Sci.*, Vol. 15, p. 580, 1948.

CHAPTER IV

LATERAL BUCKLING OF BEAMS

46. Introduction

In the previous chapters we were concerned with the investigation of the stability of centrally and eccentrically loaded columns. We now consider a more complex buckling problem, which is a generalization of the problem of the stability of columns with open thin-walled sections which was discussed in Chap. III. The close relationship between the two problems is seen from the fact that the basic theory developed in the foregoing chapter can be used again for the solution of the various problems of lateral buckling of beams.

An I-beam supported at the ends and loaded longitudinally and transversely in the plane of the web may buckle sideways if laterally unsupported except at the supports A and B (Fig. 76). If the flexural rigidity of the beam in the plane of the web is many times greater than its lateral rigidity, the beam may buckle and collapse long before the bending stresses due to the transverse load reach the yield point. As long as the loads which act in the plane of the web remain below a certain intensity, the equilibrium of the structure is stable; i.e., if slightly twisted or bent laterally, the structure returns to its plane configuration when the force which caused the slight distortion ceases to act. With increasing load intensity, however, the restoring forces become smaller and smaller, until a loading is reached at which, besides the plane equilibrium form of the beam, a deflected and twisted equilibrium position becomes equally possible. The plane form is no longer stable, and the lowest load at which such an alternative equilibrium form becomes possible is the critical load of the structure.

The problem of lateral buckling of beams of deep but narrow rectangular cross section was first considered by Prandtl[1] and Michell.[2] Independent of each other, both published in the same year a theory of lateral buckling of beams under transverse loading, arriving at substantially

[1] Prandtl, L., Kipperscheinungen, Thesis, Munich, 1899.
[2] Michell, A. G. M., Elastic Stability of Long Beams under Transverse Forces, *Phil. Mag.*, Vol. 48, p. 298, 1899.

the same solution, a differential equation of the second order with variable coefficients which controls the problem.

Further progress was due to Timoshenko,[1] who derived the fundamental differential equation of torsion of symmetric I-beams and investigated on this basis the lateral buckling of transversely loaded, deep I-beams. In 1913 Timoshenko[2] solved this particular stability problem, as an example of the application of the energy method developed by him especially for the treatment of buckling problems.

I-shaped beams with unequal flanges under simultaneous axial compression and equal end moments in the plane of the web were considered first by Bleich,[3] who established the stability condition in a general form, valid in the elastic and plastic range of stresses at failure. The theory was also applied to the problem of I-beams having the tension flange restrained against lateral displacement, a case of buckling with enforced axis of rotation.

Stüssi[4] suggested in 1935 a solution of the stability problem of rectangular beams and symmetrical I-beams under transverse loading by a method of successive approximation. He applied the method to some typical loading conditions and obtained simple formulas, suitable for routine design.

An extensive presentation of the problem with a comprehensive discussion of the fundamentals was published in 1939 by Chwalla.[5] The study is restricted to symmetrical I-sections and contains a detailed and critical investigation of some special problems in the field of lateral buckling, most of them already studied by previous investigators. In particular, the stability condition of beams, elastically restrained at the ends, under combined axial thrust and constant flexure is discussed in detail. However, the author did not recognize certain limitations concerning the validity of the differential equations of equilibrium for slender bars which form the basis of his analysis, and as a consequence, the theory of beams under combined bending and axial loading is incomplete; the solutions in the paper are not entirely accurate and do not agree with those of other investigators.

[1] Timoshenko, S., Einige Stabilitätsprobleme der Elasticitätstheorie, *Zeitschrift für Mathematik und Physik*, Vol. 58, p. 337, 1910. Published first in Russian, 1906–1907. See also Timoshenko, Beams without Lateral Support, *Trans. ASCE*, Vol. 87, p. 1247, 1924, and "Theory of Elastic Stability," Chap. V, p. 273, McGraw-Hill Book Company, Inc., New York, 1936.

[2] Timoshenko, S., Sur la stabilité des systèmes élastiques, *Annales des ponts et chaussées*, 1913, Parts III, IV, V.

[3] Bleich, F., "Stahlhochbauten," Vol. II, p. 925, Julius Springer, Berlin, 1933.

[4] Stüssi, F., Die Stabilität des auf Biegung beanspruchten Trägers, *Pubs. Intern. Assoc. Bridge and Structural Eng.*, Vol. 3, p. 401, 1935.

[5] Chwalla, E., Die Kipp-Stabilität gerader Träger mit doppelt symmetrischem I-Querschnitt, *Forschungshefte auf dem Gebiete des Stahlbaues*, No. 2, Berlin, 1939.

Winter[1] presented in 1941 approximate formulas for lateral buckling of nonsymmetrical I-beams, derived by Rayleigh's energy method. The author also discussed the buckling of rectangular and unsymmetrical I-shaped beams having the tension edge restrained against lateral displacement. The problem of lateral buckling of unsymmetrical I-beams subjected to a constant bending moment was treated in a more exact manner by H. N. Hill.[2]

An extensive treatment of the problem under discussion was offered by Goodier,[3] who presented the solution of the general problem of stability of bars of thin-walled open sections under thrust, bending, and twisting as a logical extension of the theory of buckling of columns by torsion and flexure. The study is not restricted to any special condition of symmetry of the cross section but considers only the effect of longitudinal forces and of moments acting at the ends of the bar. Beams under transverse loads are not discussed.

De Vries[4] derived simple rules for rolled I-beams. The critical stress in the elastic range of buckling is expressed by a simple function of one parameter, ld/bt, in which l and d are span length and depth of beam and b and t the flange dimensions, respectively. Such a simple approach can naturally lead only to approximate results, but the formula has a rational basis and is suitable for design purposes.

Many suggestions have been made to overcome the difficulty of determining the stability limit when at the instant of buckling the proportional limit in the highest stressed fibers of the beam is exceeded. Except in the case of constant bending and axial thrust, in which the effect of varying modulus of elasticity can be handled in a rational way, this problem does not readily yield to a reasonably exact theoretical solution. Far-reaching simplifying assumptions are necessary to adapt the results obtained for buckling in the elastic region to plastic buckling. Timoshenko,[5] Stüssi,[6] and Chwalla[7] discussed the problem, which has not yet been solved in a really satisfactory manner.

[1] Winter, G., Lateral Stability of Unsymmetrical I-beams and Trusses in Bending, *Trans. ASCE*, 1943, p. 247.

[2] Hill, H. N., The Lateral Instability of Unsymmetrical I-beams, *Jour. Aeronaut. Sci.*, Vol. 9, p. 175, 1942.

[3] Goodier, J. N., Flexural-Torsional Buckling of Bars of Open Sections, under Bending, Eccentric Thrust or Torsional Loads, *Cornell Univ. Eng. Exp. Sta. Bull.* 28, Ithaca, N.Y., 1942.

[4] De Vries, K., Strength of Beams as Determined by Lateral Buckling, *Trans. ASCE*, Vol. 112, p. 1245, 1947.

[5] Timoshenko, S., Beams without Lateral Support, *Trans. ASCE*, Vol. 87, p. 1247, 1924. Also "Theory of Elastic Stability," Chap. V, p. 273, McGraw-Hill Book Company, Inc., New York, 1936.

[6] Stüssi, *loc cit.* on p. 150.

[7] Chwalla, *loc. cit.* on p. 150.

Michell, who presented the theory of rectangular beams in 1899, gave in the same paper the results of tests with steel bars which agreed fairly well with the theoretical predictions.

Tests on the failure of beams by "lateral buckling" were made by Moore[1] in 1913 as part of a series of tests on the strength of standard I-beams in flexure; similar tests for light beams were made by Ketchum and Draffin[2] in 1932. The results of these tests are not at all in agreement with the theoretical results, the tests indicating very much higher critical stresses. The loading arrangement as shown in Figs. 2 and 10 of the paper by Ketchum and Draffin leads to the suspicion that the testing arrangement forced the beams to rotate around the spherical block through which the load was applied instead of buckling freely. A clue that the loading arrangement introduced some restraint is given in a statement by the investigators that an earlier arrangement using spherical blocks instead of rollers to transmit the load to the top flanges of the beams was abandoned because of instability of the loading apparatus. It would appear important to repeat these tests under conditions eliminating the doubts concerning the method of support.

No further report on experimental investigations in this field can be found until 1937, when Dumont and Hill[3] reported on a series of experiments with rectangular beams of aluminum alloy. The results obtained in the elastic range indicated rather good agreement with the theory. These investigators also made experiments on the lateral buckling of I-beams of 27 ST aluminum alloy under constant bending and found the theory in agreement with the results of the experiments.[4]

Careful tests conducted by Johnston and Cheney,[5] already discussed in Chap. I, must be mentioned, since a group of the tests were made on columns of I-sections loaded eccentrically in the plane of the web. This loading constitutes the basic case of lateral buckling under combined constant bending and axial compression. Unfortunately, the results of these experiments were never precisely interpreted in the light of the exact theory and with proper regard to the actual conditions of restraint at the ends of the columns.

In the subsequent presentation of the subject the problem of lateral

[1] Moore, H. F., The Strength of I-beams in Flexure, *Univ. Illinois Bull.* 68, pp. 20, 21, 1913.

[2] Ketchum, M. S., and J. O. Draffin, Strength of Light I-Beams, *Univ. Illinois Bull.* 241, pp. 25, 26, 1932.

[3] Dumont, C., and H. N. Hill, The Lateral Stability of Deep Rectangular Beams, *NACA Tech. Note* 601, 1937.

[4] Dumont, C., and H. N. Hill, The Lateral Stability of Equal Flanged Aluminum Alloy I-beams Subjected to Pure Bending, *NACA Tech. Note* 770, 1940.

[5] Johnston, B. G., and L. Cheney, Steel Columns of Rolled Wide Flange Section, *Committee on Tech. Research, Am. Inst. Steel Construction, Progress Rept.* 2, 1942.

buckling will be discussed in general form by utilizing the results obtained in the previous chapter. Thus, a common basis will be provided from which the critical discussion of each particular problem may start conveniently. Following the procedure set forth in Chap. III, the general expression for the potential energy of the beam in its compressed, bent, and twisted state will be developed and will serve as the fundamental equation for the application of the theorem of stationary potential energy. Once in possession of the expression for the potential energy, we are free either to derive from it the differential equations of any specific problem or to use the energy expression in conjunction with the Ritz method for the approximate solution of the particular buckling problem. Since both methods have been applied in the past by various investigators, we have the benefit of having a unified basis which yields quickly in each case the appropriate equations for the analysis.

47. Lateral Buckling of I-beams under Axial and Transverse Loads

We consider a beam AB of span l (Fig. 76) loaded in the plane of the web by an eccentric axial force P and by transverse forces w_y. Concentrated transverse loads can be considered as a special case of this general type of loading.

As defined in Chap. III, x and y are the principal axes of the I-section which may have unequal flanges; the coordinates of the center of

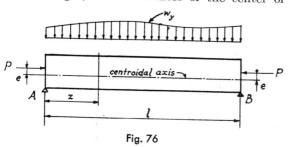

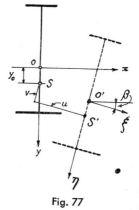

Fig. 76

Fig. 77

shear generally are x_0 and y_0, but because of the symmetry about the y-axis we have $x_0 = 0$; u and v are the components of the displacement of the center of shear parallel to the axes ξ and η (Fig. 77).

The analysis is based upon the following assumptions:

1. The cross section of the beam is constant.
2. The fiber stresses due to the external load do not exceed the proportional limit at the instant of buckling.
3. The deformation of the beam when bent and twisted is such that its cross section does not change its shape.

4. The external loads remain parallel to their original direction when the points of application of these loads are displaced.

We shall consider the beam in its deflected and compressed state just prior to buckling and shall then determine an expression for the change of potential energy associated with the lateral displacement and twisting which occur when the beam buckles.

The potential energy U consists of the internal strain energy V of the deformed beam and of the potential energy of the external loads P and w_y. Equation (213), Chap. III, for the strain energy V remains applicable, but the terms $EI_z v''^2$ and $EA\epsilon^2$ representing the strain energy of bending and compression prior to buckling are omitted:

$$V = \tfrac{1}{2} \int_0^l (EI_y u''^2 + E\Gamma\beta''^2 + GK\beta'^2)\, dz \qquad (285)$$

The potential energy U_w of the external loads will be computed separately for the vertical loads w_y and for the axial forces P. To determine the potential energy $\bar{U}_w$ of the force P we use the same reasoning that led to Eq. (242), Chap. III. As indicated in Fig. 76 the end loading has an eccentricity e which is counted positive if P acts above the centroid; the stress distribution from this loading over the end surface is

$$\sigma = \frac{P}{A} - \frac{eP}{I_z} y \qquad (286)$$

where positive values of σ indicate compression. The work done by the stress σ on an element of area dA is given by Eq. (236), except that E_t is to be changed to E because we consider buckling in the elastic range only:

$$d\bar{U}_w = -\sigma\, dA \left(\delta_c + \frac{1}{E} \int_0^l \Delta\sigma_z\, dz \right) \qquad (287)$$

$\Delta\sigma_z$ is the change in stress due to buckling as in Chap. III, while δ_c now must be interpreted as the additional shortening of the fibers due to the deformation associated with lateral buckling. Integrating over the entire end surface A of the beam, we obtain

$$\bar{U}_w = -\int_A \sigma\delta_c\, dA - \frac{1}{E} \int_0^l \left(\int_A \sigma\, \Delta\sigma_z\, dA \right) dz \qquad (288)$$

The changes $\Delta\sigma_z$ in the stresses in the beam must be such that their resultant parallel to the z-axis and their resultant moment about the x-axis vanish,

$$\int_A \Delta\sigma_z\, dA = 0 \quad \text{and} \quad \int_A y\, \Delta\sigma_z\, dA = 0 \qquad (289)$$

Substituting Eq. (286) into Eq. (288), it will be found that, because of Eqs. (289), the second term in (288) vanishes:

$$\bar{U}_w = -\frac{P}{A}\int_A \delta_c \, dA + \frac{eP}{I_x}\int_A y\delta_c \, dA \tag{290}$$

Equation (240), Chap. III, is an expression for the entire shortening δ_c of the fibers from the unloaded to the loaded and buckled state of the beam; introducing Eq. (240) into (290) will therefore give an expression for the entire change of potential energy starting from the unloaded state. Using also Eqs. (239) and (241), the expression

$$\bar{U}_w = -\frac{1}{2}\int_0^l \left[P(u'^2 + v'^2) + 2P(y_0 + e)u'\beta' \right.$$
$$\left. + P\left(\frac{I_p}{A} + e\frac{Z}{I_x}\right)\beta'^2 \right] dz \tag{291}$$

is obtained, where Z is defined by

$$Z = 2y_0 I_x - \int_A y(x^2 + y^2) \, dA \tag{292}$$

Z is a property of the cross section of the beam; if the section is symmetrical with respect to the x-axis, Z vanishes.

The change of potential energy between the unloaded state and the deflected state just prior to buckling can be obtained from Eq. (291) by introducing $u' = \beta' = 0$, which furnishes the well-known expression

$$\bar{U}_w = -\frac{1}{2}\int_0^l Pv'^2 \, dz \tag{293}$$

The change of potential energy at the instant of buckling which we require is the difference between expressions (291) and (293).

$$\bar{\bar{U}}_w = -\frac{1}{2}\int_0^l \left[Pu'^2 + 2P(y_0 + e)u'\beta' + P\left(\frac{I_p}{A} + e\frac{Z}{I_x}\right)\beta'^2 \right] dz \tag{294}$$

To determine the potential energy $\bar{U}_w$ of the loads w_y, consider Fig. 78. The cross section is shown in its original and in its displaced location. In order to define the behavior of the loads w_y we have stated at the beginning of this article that the line of action of the loads will remain parallel to the original line of action; Fig. 78 indicates further that the loads will act on the cross section at a point a distance $\bar{a}$ above the center of shear. If the vertical component of the movement of the center of shear is designated by y_s, the change in potential energy will be equal to the negative work done by the forces w_y. The loads are lowered a distance $y_s + \bar{a}(1 - \cos\beta)$; because β is small, $1 - \cos\beta = \beta^2/2$, and we obtain

$$\bar{U}_w = -\int_0^l w_y y_s \, dz - \frac{\bar{a}}{2}\int_0^l w_y\beta^2 \, dz \tag{295}$$

The first integral in Eq. (295) can be transformed by partial integration; denoting by Q_w and M_w the shear and moment in a simple beam of span l under the loads w_y, we have the relations

$$\frac{dQ_w}{dz} = -w_y \quad \text{and} \quad \frac{dM_w}{dz} = Q_w \tag{296}$$

and obtain by successive integration by parts

$$-\int_0^l w_y y_s\, dz = \left[Q_w y_s\right]_0^l - \int_0^l Q_w \frac{dy_s}{dz}\, dz = \left[Q_w y_s\right]_0^l$$
$$- \left[M_w \frac{dy_s}{dz}\right]_0^l + \int_0^l M_w \frac{d^2y_s}{dz^2}\, dz \tag{297}$$

The term $\left[Q_w y_s\right]_0^l$ vanishes because the deflection y_s is zero at the ends of

the beam; the term $\left[M_w \dfrac{dy_s}{dz}\right]_0^l$ vanishes also because the moment M_w was

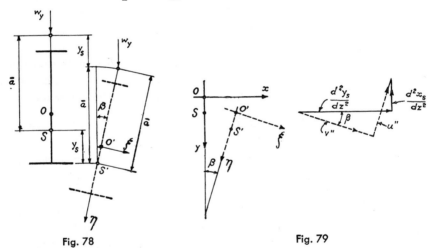

Fig. 78   Fig. 79

defined as simple beam moment and is zero at the ends of the beam. Equations (295) and (297) therefore furnish

$$\bar{U}_w = \int_0^l M_w \frac{d^2y_s}{dz^2}\, dz - \frac{\bar{a}}{2} \int_0^l w_y \beta^2\, dz \tag{298}$$

Equation (298) for $\bar{U}_w$ can be modified by replacing the deflection y_s of the center of shear parallel to the y-axis by the deflections u and v parallel to the ξ- and η-axes. The term $\dfrac{d^2y_s}{dz^2}$ represents the curvature of the beam in the yz-plane; all deformations being small, we may consider this curvature as a vector to be drawn at right angles to the plane of the curvature (Fig. 79). Similarly, the curvature in the xz-, ξz-, and ηz-planes may be expressed by the vectors $\dfrac{d^2 x_s}{dz^2}$, u'', and v'', respectively. β being a small angle, $\dfrac{d^2 y_s}{dz^2}$ can be expressed by u'' and v''

$$\frac{d^2 y_s}{dz^2} = v'' + \beta u'' \; .$$ (299)

and by substitution into Eq. (298)

$$\bar{U}_w = \int_0^l M_w v'' \, dz + \int_0^l M_w \beta u'' \, dz - \frac{\bar{a}}{2} \int_0^l w_y \beta^2 \, dz$$ (300)

Equation (300) is the change of potential energy from the unloaded to the buckled state. Just prior to buckling $\beta = u'' = 0$, and the potential energy will be

$$\bar{U}_w = \int_0^l M_w v'' \, dz$$ (301)

The change of potential energy at the instant of buckling is the difference between these two values, and we have the result

$$\bar{\bar{U}}_w = \int_0^l M_w \beta u'' \, dz - \frac{\bar{a}}{2} \int_0^l w_y \beta^2 \, dz$$ (302)

In order to avoid misunderstanding, it is repeated that M_w in Eq. (302) is not the actual bending moment in the beam, but the simple beam moment due to the loads w_y.

Adding Eqs. (285), (294), and (302) furnishes an expression for the entire change of the potential energy U in the state of buckling:

$$U = V + \bar{U}_w + \bar{\bar{U}}_w = \frac{1}{2} \int_0^l \left[EI_y u''^2 + E\gamma \beta''^2 + GK\beta'^2 - Pu'^2 \right.$$
$$\left. - 2P(y_0 + e)u'\beta' + 2M_w u''\beta - P\left(\frac{I_p}{A} + e\frac{Z}{I_x}\right)\beta'^2 - \bar{a}w_y\beta^2 \right] dz \quad (303)$$

A slight simplification of this expression is obtained if integration by parts is applied to one of the terms of Eq. (303):

$$\int_0^l [-2P(y_0 + e)u'\beta'] \, dz = -2P(y_0 + e) \left[u'\beta \right]_0^l$$
$$+ \int_0^l 2P(y_0 + e)u''\beta \, dz \quad (304)$$

The first term vanishes because $\beta = 0$ for $z = 0$ or l; the remaining expression under the integral can be united with the term $2M_w u''\beta$ in Eq. (303):

$$2P(y_0 + e)u''\beta + 2M_w u''\beta = 2(Py_0 + Pe + M_w)u''\beta = 2Mu''\beta \quad (305)$$

where
$$M = M_w + Py_0 + Pe \tag{306}$$

M as defined by Eq. (306) is the moment of the external forces w_y and P with reference to an axis parallel to the x-axis through the center of shear. This moment M differs from the conventional bending moment in a beam which is referred to the x-axis through the centroid; if the section is symmetrical and $y_0 = 0$, or if $P = 0$, this difference disappears and M becomes the conventional bending moment.

The final expression for the potential energy is

$$U = \frac{1}{2} \int_0^l \left[EI_y u''^2 + E\Gamma\beta''^2 + GK\beta'^2 - Pu'^2 + 2Mu''\beta \right.$$
$$\left. - P\left(\frac{I_p}{A} + \frac{eZ}{I_x}\right)\beta'^2 - \bar{a}w_y\beta^2 \right] dz \tag{307}$$

The theorem of stationary potential energy applied to Eq. (307) furnishes the stability conditions for the buckling of the beam. We shall apply the rules of the calculus of variation and derive the differential equations of the problem, but Eq. (307) could also be used to find the critical load by the Ritz method or by any similar approach.

According to Chap. II, Euler's equations are

$$EI_y u^{IV} + Pu'' + \frac{d}{dz^2}(M\beta) = 0 \tag{308a}$$

$$E\Gamma\beta^{IV} + \left(P\frac{I_p}{A} - GK + eP\frac{Z}{I_x}\right)\beta'' - \bar{a}w_y\beta + Mu'' = 0 \tag{308b}$$

Equation (308a) can be integrated twice:

$$EI_y u'' + Pu + M\beta = C_1 + C_2 z \tag{309}$$

where C_1 and C_2 are arbitrary constants. For the usual boundary conditions $u = u'' = \beta = 0$ at both ends of the beam, $C_1 = C_2 = 0$, and the differential equations become

$$EI_y u'' + Pu + M\beta = 0 \tag{310a}$$

$$E\Gamma\beta^{IV} + \left(P\frac{I_p}{A} - GK + eP\frac{Z}{I_x}\right)\beta'' - \bar{a}w_y\beta + Mu'' = 0 \tag{310b}$$

48. Beams without Transverse Loads

If the beam carries no transverse load, but only an axial load P having an eccentricity e in the plane of the web, we obtain from Eqs. (310), with $w_y = 0$ and $M = P(y_0 + e)$,

$$EI_y u'' + Pu + P(y_0 + e)\beta = 0 \tag{311a}$$

$$E\gamma\beta^{IV} + \left(P\frac{I_p}{A} - GK + eP\frac{Z}{I_x}\right)\beta'' + P(y_0 + e)u'' = 0 \tag{311b}$$

For a centrical load, $e = 0$, these equations agree with Eqs. (255), Chap. III, for torsional buckling of sections with one axis of symmetry.

We can further compare Eqs. (311) with Goodier's results;[1] his differential equations are more general, as no symmetry is assumed and the load may be eccentric in the x- and y-directions. eP and $P(y_0 + e)$ in Eqs. (311) correspond to M_2 and $M_2 - Py_0$, while Z proves to be identical with the expression κ_2 of Goodier's paper. The term Z occurs only for unsymmetrical sections and was not obtained by any other investigator. It is of value to note that this term is obtained here by the energy method, while Goodier establishes it independently from equilibrium considerations.

Equations (311) can also be compared with the results of Chwalla,[2] who obtained a differential equation of the sixth order in β. If u is eliminated from Eqs. (311) and $Z = 0$ because of the symmetry considered, the result still differs from Chwalla's because the terms resulting from the expression PI_p/A in Eq. (311b) do not occur. There can be no doubt about the term PI_p/A, because it appears not only in Goodier's derivation but also in the theory of torsional buckling of columns. The fact that this investigator does not obtain this term is not due to an error but to the fact that he approximates the beam as a line having bending and torsional stiffness, while the beam is actually a three-dimensional body.

Simple solutions of Eqs. (311) can be found if the beam is hinged and held against twisting at the ends, resulting in the boundary condition $u = u'' = \beta = 0$; it is easily verified that

$$u = C_1 \sin \frac{\pi z}{l} \qquad \text{and} \qquad \beta = C_2 \sin \frac{\pi z}{l} \tag{312}$$

satisfy Eqs. (311). Substitution of (312) into (311) leads to two linear and homogeneous equations for the arbitrary constants C_1 and C_2; nonvanishing values C_1 and C_2 exist only if the determinant of these equations is zero. This condition leads to the following quadratic equation for the critical load P_{cr}:

$$(P_E - P_{cr}) \left[E\Gamma \frac{\pi^2}{l^2} + GK - P_{cr} \frac{I_p}{A} \left(1 + e \frac{AZ}{I_p I_x} \right) \right] - P_{cr}^2 (y_0 + e)^2 = 0 \tag{313}$$

where $P_E = \pi^2 EI_y/l^2$ is the Euler load for buckling in the direction of the axis x.

A study of Eq. (313) indicates that it has always a root $P_{cr} \leq P_E$; the largest possible value $P_{cr} = P_E$ will be reached only if the second term in

[1] Goodier, op. cit. p. 8.
[2] Chwalla, op. cit. p. 17, Eq. (C3).

Eq. (313) is zero, for $e = -y_0$. This means (see Figs. 76 and 77) that the beam will carry the full Euler load if this load acts at the shear center; this is an interesting and little-known fact.

49. Beams without Axial Forces

If no axial force P is present, Eqs. (310) simplify to

$$EI_y u'' + M\beta = 0 \tag{314a}$$
$$E\Gamma\beta^{\mathrm{IV}} - GK\beta'' - \bar{a}w_y\beta + Mu'' = 0 \tag{314b}$$

where M is now the external bending moment in the plane of the web.

These equations can be compared with the equations derived by Timoshenko[1] for symmetrical I-beams carrying a concentrated load at the center. Noting that M is equivalent to $-\dfrac{P}{2}\left(\dfrac{l}{2} - z\right)$, Eq. (314a) is identical, while (314b) is obtained by differentiation from the second equation (a) in the source quoted.

It is possible to eliminate u from the system of simultaneous differential equations (314), and obtaining the single differential equation for the angle of twist β,

$$E\Gamma\beta^{\mathrm{IV}} - GK\beta'' - \left(\bar{a}w_y + \frac{M^2}{EI_y}\right)\beta = 0 \tag{315}$$

Equations of this form were derived and used by many investigators. Attention is called to the term $\bar{a}w_y\beta$ which defines the location of the load; this term has considerable influence on the critical load and must not be neglected.

If the moment M is constant, the load w_y is zero, and Eq. (315) becomes

$$E\Gamma\beta^{\mathrm{IV}} - GK\beta'' - \frac{M^2}{EI_y}\beta = 0 \tag{316}$$

This differential equation has constant coefficients and can be solved readily. The critical moment for a beam of span l with simply supported ends, $\beta = \beta'' = 0$, is

$$M_{cr} = \frac{\pi}{l}\sqrt{EI_y GK}\sqrt{1 + \pi^2\frac{E\Gamma}{l^2 GK}} \tag{317}$$

If the moment M is not constant, simple exact solutions of Eq. (315) do not exist, and approximate solutions by the Ritz or similar methods may be used. The values of the critical load where determined by Timoshenko[2] for beams with equal flanges for a concentrated load W at the

[1] Timoshenko, S., "Theory of Elastic Stability," p. 265, McGraw-Hill Book Company, Inc., New York, 1936.
[2] *Ibid.*, pp. 267, 268.

center (Fig. 80), and for a uniformly distributed load w (Fig. 81). The following Tables 5 and 6 can be used to determine the critical values of the load for the three cases: load acting at centroid, at top, and at bottom flange. As pointed out previously, the differences between the three cases are quite substantial.

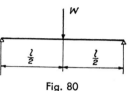

For a concentrated load at the center (Fig. 80), the critical load is

$$W_{cr} = k\,\frac{\sqrt{EI_yGK}}{l^2} \qquad (318)$$

Fig. 80

where k is a coefficient to be taken from Table 5. k is a function of the parameter $GKl^2/E\Gamma$; for symmetrical sections $\Gamma = I_yd^2/4$, where d is the depth of the section.

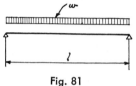

For an equally distributed load (Fig. 81), the critical load is

$$w_{cr} = k\,\frac{\sqrt{EI_yGK}}{l^3} \qquad (319)$$

Fig. 81

where k is to be taken from Table 6.

Equations (318) and (319) were derived for beams with equal top and bottom flanges; however, the fact that the basic differential equation

TABLE 5. Coefficients k in Eq. (318)

$\dfrac{GK}{E\Gamma}\,l^2$	The load acts at —		
	The centroid	The top flange	The bottom flange
0.4	86.4	51.3	145.6
4	31.9	20.2	50.0
8	25.6	17.0	38.2
16	21.8	15.4	30.4
24	20.3	15.0	27.2
32	19.6	14.8	26.3
48	19.0	14.8	23.5
64	18.3	14.9	22.4
80	18.1	14.9	21.7
96	17.9	15.1	21.1
160	17.5	15.3	20.0
240	17.4	15.6	19.3
320	17.2	15.7	18.9
400	17.2	15.8	18.7

TABLE 6.   Coefficients k in Eq. (319)

$\dfrac{GK}{E\Gamma} l^2$	The load acts at —		
	The centroid	The top flange	The bottom flange
0.4	143.0	92.9	222.0
4	53.0	36.3	77.3
8	42.6	30.4	59.4
16	36.3	27.4	48.0
24	33.8	26.6	43.4
32	32.6	26.1	40.4
48	31.5	25.8	37.6
64	30.5	25.7	36.2
80	30.1	25.7	35.1
128	29.0	26.0	33.3
200	29.0	26.4	32.1
280	28.8	26.5	31.4
360	28.7	26.6	31.0
400	28.6	26.6	30.7

(315) does not change if the flanges are unequal indicates that Eqs. (318) and (319) and Tables 5 and 6 may also be used if the section is not sym-

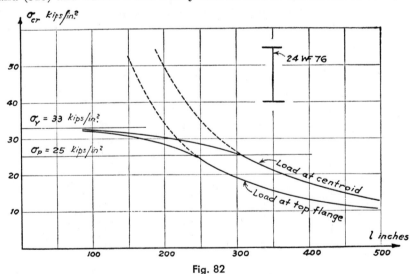

Fig. 82

metrical with respect to the x-axis, but with the following modification: The values k given for loads acting at the top flange, at the centroid, and at the bottom flange apply instead to loads acting at a distance

$\bar{a} = \sqrt{\Gamma/I_y}$ above the center of shear, at the center of shear, and at a distance $\bar{a} = -\sqrt{\Gamma/I_y}$ below the center of shear, respectively. Values k for loads acting at other points can be determined approximately by interpolation.

To illustrate the theoretical discussion, Figs. 82 and 83 show the maximum stresses σ_{cr} at which a 24 W 76-lb beam and the same beam with a 9- by ½-in. cover plate on the top flange will buckle laterally. In both cases the difference between the load acting at the top flange and at the centroid (or center of shear) is very pronounced.

The stresses were determined from Eq. (319) and Table 6; obviously the critical stresses can be valid only if they are below the proportional

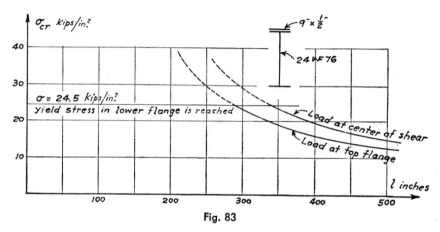

Fig. 83

limit σ_p. The critical stresses above the proportional limit in the case of the beam without cover plate (Fig. 82) will be discussed further in Art. 51. In the case of the beam with a cover plate the question of inelastic buckling does not arise because the lower flange of the beam will yield before the proportional limit in the upper flange is reached. This fact eliminates in some practical cases the necessity of considering the troublesome question of inelastic lateral buckling.

50. Lateral Buckling with Enforced Center of Rotation and Other Refinements of the Theory

If the beam is restrained in such manner that each section rotates around a point C_E a distance a below the shear center (Fig. 84), the relation

$$u = a\beta \tag{320}$$

is enforced. Substituting (320) in Eq. (307) furnishes an expression for the potential energy U

$$U = \frac{1}{2} \int_0^l \left[E(\Gamma + a^2 I_y)\beta''^2 + \left(GK - Pa^2 - P\frac{I_p}{A} - P\frac{eZ}{I_x} \right) \beta'^2 \right.$$
$$\left. + 2aM\beta\beta'' - \bar{a}w_y\beta^2 \right] dz \quad (321)$$

U is a function of the angle of twist β only.

The critical values of P and M may be obtained from Eq. (321) by applying any of the methods discussed in Chap. II. It is possible to consider additional elastic restraints by adding appropriate terms to the expression (321); such cases were studied by Nylander,[1] who considered cases of lateral buckling with enforced center of rotation and elastic torsional restraints.

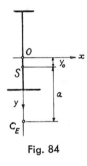

The same author investigated the effects of the deformations of the web on the critical load for lateral buckling. These effects are very small for beams of conventional construction but may be of interest with regard to unusual types of thin-walled welded structures.

In the same paper Nylander also studies the effects of various novel types of bracing which resist the warping of the cross section; the bracing proposed increases the torsional rigidity and, therefore, the critical load for lateral buckling.

Fig. 84

A refinement of a different nature was considered by Chwalla,[2] who investigated the effect of the deflection of the beam prior to buckling on the critical load of a narrow rectangle. No similar analysis for I-sections is available, but Chwalla concludes that this effect for I-sections can be taken care of approximately by replacing the moment of inertia I_y in Eq. (310a) by $I_y \dfrac{1}{1 - (I_y/I_x)}$; this modification results in slightly higher critical loads. The term I_y/I_x is usually small, but there are a few commonly used rolled wide-flanged sections where the effect is noticeable. Equivalent corrective terms for I-beams were obtained by Hall[3] and Julian.[4] The special value of Chwalla's investigation is that it indicates that the correction is essentially due to the deflection of the beam prior to buckling; caution is therefore required, and the beneficial effect of this term should not be allowed for in cases where initial cambering is used to compensate for all or part of the expected deflection.

[1] Nylander, H., Drehungsvorgänge und gebundene Kippung bei geraden, doppeltsymetrischen I-Trägern, *Ingeniors Vetenskaps Akademien Handlingar* 174, Stockholm, 1943.

[2] Chwalla, *loc. cit.* on p. 150.

[3] *Trans. ASCE*, Vol. 112, p. 1276, 1947.

[4] *Ibid.*, p. 1303, and Errata, Vol. 113, p. XIII, 1948.

51. Lateral Buckling in the Inelastic Range

If the stresses in the beam exceed the proportional limit at the instant of buckling, the modulus of elasticity E and modulus of rigidity G in any element of the beam will change into E_t and G_t, where E_t and G_t are the effective values according to the tangent-modulus theory. Compared with the problem of inelastic buckling of columns, we have the added difficulty that, owing to the different stresses in different elements of a beam, E_t and G_t are also variable, making the problem too complicated for a rational solution.

It is possible to obtain a lower limit for the critical load by assuming that the values E and G everywhere in the beam will be reduced to $E_t = E\tau$ and $G_t = G\tau$ where τ is the value applicable to the maximum compressive stress occurring anywhere in the beam. If this is done, the general expression for the potential energy (307) becomes

$$U = \frac{1}{2}\int_0^l \left[E\tau I_y u''^2 + E\tau \Gamma \beta''^2 + G\tau K \beta'^2 + Pu'^2 + 2Mu''\beta \right.$$
$$\left. - P\left(\frac{I_p}{A} + e\frac{Z}{I_x}\right)\beta'^2 - \bar{a}w_y\beta^2 \right] dz \quad (322)$$

The critical loads can be determined from Eq. (322), and the new values of the critical load or stress will be the values for elastic buckling multiplied by τ. It will therefore be possible to find the value of the critical stress σ_{cr}/τ, and σ_{cr} can be determined in the same manner as in the case of inelastic buckling of columns.

Consider as an example the case of a simple beam carrying uniformly distributed load (Fig. 81). The critical load for elastic buckling is given by Eq. (319); replacing E and G by $E\tau$ and $G\tau$, we obtain

$$w_{cr} = k\tau \frac{\sqrt{EI_yGK}}{l^3} \quad (323)$$

The stress in the beam will be

$$\sigma_{cr} = k\tau \frac{\sqrt{EI_yGK}}{8Sl} \quad (324)$$

where S is the section modulus of the beam and k is to be taken from Table 6. It should be noted that the value $(GK/E\Gamma)l^2$ which occurs in this table does not change, because we assume that the ratio $G\tau/E\tau = G/E$ remains unchanged.

The left portion of Fig. 82 indicates the critical stress determined in this way for a 24 W beam. As stated before, this stress is only a lower limit for the actual critical stress, but the difference cannot be very large because the actual critical stress must necessarily be below the yield point.   A similar procedure can be used in other cases and will always result in conservative values for the critical stress.

Additional References

Prescott, J., "Applied Elasticity," p. 499, Chapman & Hall, Ltd., London, 1924.

Richmond, H. S., Elastic Equilibrium in the Theory of Structures, *Trans. ASCE*, Vol. 94, p. 845, 1930.

Trayer, G. W., and H. W. March, Elastic Instability of Members Having Sections Common in Aircraft Construction, *NACA Tech. Rept.* 382, 1931.

Stüssi, F., Excentrisches Kippen, *Schweizerische Bauzeitung*, Vol. 105, p. 123, 1935.

Hartmann, F., "Knickung, Kippung und Beulung," F. Deuticke, Leipzig and Vienna, 1937.

Dohrenwend, C. O., Action of Deep Beams under Combined Vertical, Lateral and Torsional Loads, *Jour. Applied Mechanics,* 1941, p. A-130.

Madsen, I., Report of Crane Girder Tests, *Iron Steel Engr.*, November, 1941.

Johnston, B. G., Lateral Buckling of I-section Columns with Eccentric Loads in Plane of Web, *Jour. Applied Mechanics*, 1941, p. 180.

Winter, G., Strength of Slender Beams, *Trans. ASCE*, Vol. 109, p. 1321, 1944.

Hill, H. N. and J. W. Clark, Lateral Buckling of Eccentrically Loaded I-section Columns, *Proc. ASCE* 34, 1950.

CHAPTER V

BUILT-UP COLUMNS AND COLUMNS OF VARIABLE STIFFNESS

52. Introduction

The effect of the shearing forces which occur when a column deflects at the instant of buckling has been discussed in Chap. I. Their influence on the critical axial load was found practically negligible in columns of solid cross section of the types conventional in structural design. This is entirely due to the fact that the shearing stresses and the distortion caused by these stresses are very small, even in the worst case of an I-section buckling in the plane of the web. The conditions are different in built-up columns. The contribution of the shearing forces to the total deflection of the column is much greater when the components of the column are connected by a system of lacing bars or batten plates. The decrease in buckling strength due to the shear deflection is therefore much greater than in the case of columns with solid cross section and depends upon the dimensions and the structural make-up of the lacing elements. Long ago, failures of built-up compression members called attention to certain deficiencies of this type of column and gave rise to various theoretical and experimental investigations into the behavior of built-up columns.

The earliest treatment of the problem was by Engesser[1] in a publication in 1889 in which he presented approximate formulas for the buckling load of latticed columns as well as that of columns with batten plates. In 1909 Engesser[2] published a refined analysis of the same problem, taking into account secondary effects of the shearing forces.

A built-up column represents a framework, the stability of which can be investigated more accurately by the methods of framework analysis developed in Chap. VI. Many attempts have been made to approach the problem in this manner and to arrive at exact solutions of the column

[1] Engesser, F., Die Knickfestigkeit gerader Stäbe, *Zentralblatt der Bauverwaltung*, Vol. 11, p. 483, 1891, and *Zeitschrift des Architekten und Ingenieur Vereins zu Hannover*, Vol. 35, p. 455. 1889

[2] Engesser, F., Uber die Knickfestigkeit von Rahmenstäben, *Zentralblatt der Bauverwaltung*, Vol. 29, p. 136, 1909.

problem. A paper by Mann,[1] who gave the exact analysis for columns with batten plates, is the first to be mentioned. Ljungberg[2] in 1922 and Mises and Ratzersdorfer[3] in 1925 presented the theory of the laced column, considering it as a triangular articulated framework. A further refinement of this theory was given by Wentzel,[4] who investigated the triangular framework under the more realistic condition that the chords are continuous but that the web members (lacing bars) are hinged to the chords. The problem of battened columns was taken up by Mises and Ratzersdorfer,[5] who arrived at a formula for the critical load which is essentially identical with Mann's result. Chwalla[6] investigated the effect of slip in the rivets which connect the battens to the components of the column. He also confirmed Mann's results.

All these studies, which considered the column as a framework, did not add much new knowledge concerning the performance of built-up columns beyond that already furnished by Engesser's work. They confirmed the results first derived by Engesser, and this is their importance. The exact solutions differ from the approximate formulas, in that the number n of panels in which the column is subdivided appears only in the exact expressions for the critical load developed on the basis of the framework theory, but n affects the result only in cases where it is a small number. In practice n is usually greater than 4, and the exact and the approximate methods furnish nearly the same results. Engesser's formulas, derived in a quite simple way, may be considered sufficiently accurate to be used for practical design.

In Arts. 53 and 54, laced columns and columns with batten plates will be discussed. Expressions for the critical load will be derived by means of the energy method. However, there is another aspect of the problem of built-up columns which is of great importance in investigating this type of column. It is the question of designing the lacing elements of built-up columns in such a manner that the lacing does not fail before the load-carrying capacity of the entire column is reached. This problem and the question of secondary stresses in laced columns prior to buckling will be considered in Arts. 55 and 56, respectively.

[1] Mann, L., Die Berechnung steifer Vierecknetze, *Zeitschrift für Bauwesen*, Vol. 59, p. 539, 1909.

[2] Ljungberg, K., Auf Knickung beanspruchte Gitterstäbe, *Der Eisenbau*, Vol. 13, p. 100, 1922.

[3] von Mises, R., and J. Ratzersdorfer, Die Knicksicherheit von Fachwerken, *Zeitschrift für angewandte Mathematik und Mechanik*, Vol. 5, p. 218, 1925.

[4] Wentzel, W., Uber die Stabilität des Gleichgewichtes ebener elastischer Stabwerke und die Knickfestigkeit des Gitterträgers, Thesis, Berlin, 1929.

[5] von Mises, R., and J. Ratzersdorfer, Die Knicksicherheit von Rahmentragwerken, *Zeitschrift für angewandte Mathematik und Mechanik*, Vol. 6, p. 181, 1926.

[6] Chwalla, E., Die Stabilität des Rahmenstabes, *Sitzungsberichte der Akademie der Wissenschaften in Wien*, Vol. 136, p. 487, 1927.

Columns using perforated cover plates, instead of lacing bars or batten plates, have been used in recent years. The design of such columns hinges on the effective area of the perforated plates, as tests made on such columns have not indicated any weakness due to shear deformations.[1] The methods in this chapter essentially evaluate the effect of shear deformations on the buckling strength, and application of these methods to columns with perforated cover plates accordingly seems unnecessary.

The last article of this chapter is devoted to the study of columns with varying moment of inertia. Built-up compression members frequently vary in width or depth, resulting in varying moments of inertia, and it seems proper to deal in this chapter with the buckling strength of such columns.

53. Buckling Strength of Laced Columns

The subsequent analysis is based on the assumption that the shape of the deflected axis of the column for buckling in the plane of the lacing elements is the same as in the case of a column of solid cross section. Considering a pin-ended column as the fundamental case to be treated, the deflected axis of the column assumes the form of a half sine wave.

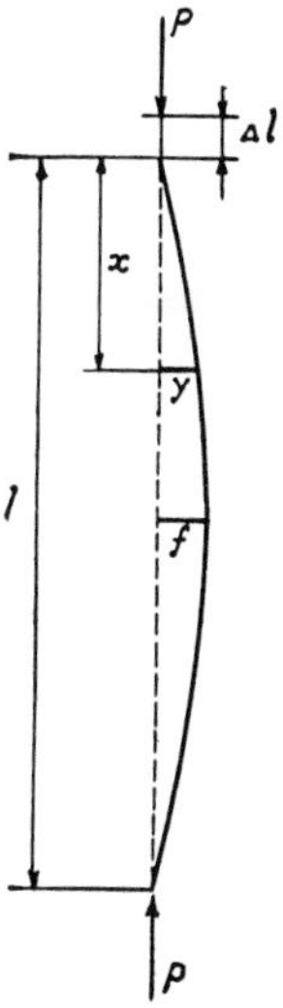

The transition from stable to unstable equilibrium of any elastic system is characterized by the energy condition[2]

$$V - W = 0 \qquad (325)$$

in which V is the strain energy due to the deflection and W is the work done by the external forces due to the displacements of their points of application caused by the deflection. V and W are functions of the deflection y and of the load P (Fig. 85). Upon assuming

Fig. 85

$$y = f \sin \frac{\pi x}{l} \qquad (326)$$

Eq. (325) permits the determination of the load P_c, the critical load, at which deflections y different from zero can exist, indicating the transition from the straight and stable configuration to the unstable form of equilibrium.[3]

---

[1] Stang, A. H., and M. Greenspan, Perforated Cover Plates for Steel Columns, *Natl. Bur. Standards (U.S.), Jour. Research*, Vol. 28, 1942, Research Papers RP 1473 and RP 1474, and Vol. 40, 1948, Research Papers RP 1861 and RP 1880.

[2] See Eq. (93), Chap. II.

[3] Refer to the last paragraph of Art. 25, p. 76.

In Fig. 86a the column is shown in its deflected state. It is assumed that in accordance with Shanley's theory, explained in Chap. I, the tangent-modulus E_t controls the strain-stress relationship in both of the chords when the buckling stress P_c/A exceeds the proportional limit. Assumption of an infinitely small amplitude f of the deflection implies that the distortion of the lacing bars is elastic, and Young's modulus E will be used in setting up the expressions for the strain energy of these members.

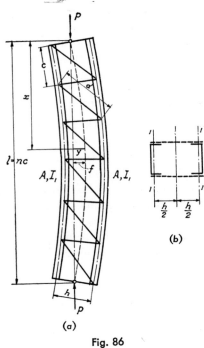

(a)

(b)

Fig. 86

With reference to Fig. 86 the following notation is introduced:

F = the change of the axial force in one chord caused by flexure of the column in the state of buckling

A = the cross-sectional area of one chord

I = the moment of inertia of one chord about the centroidal axis 1-1, (see Fig. 86b)

D and A_d = the force and cross-sectional area of the diagonals

B and A_b = the force and cross-sectional area of the transverse bars

h = the distance between the center lines of the chords

d = the length of diagonals

$c = l/n$ = panel length

If the column has two planes of lacing, D, B, and A_d, A_b denote the forces and areas of two diagonals and two transverse bars.

Strain Energy V. In setting up the equation for the strain energy we neglect at first the bending energy of the chords, taking into account only the work done by the axial forces in the chords and lacing bars, thus disregarding the continuity of the two column shafts. The effect of chord continuity will be introduced later into the resulting formula by a simple consideration. The expression for the strain energy reads:

$$V = \frac{1}{2}\left(2\sum \frac{F^2 c}{E_t A} + \sum \frac{D^2 d}{EA_d} + \sum \frac{B^2 h}{EA_b}\right) \tag{327}$$

in which the first term within the parentheses is the elastic energy accumulated in the chord members, and the last two terms indicate the strain energy of the lacing bars.

The bending moment at any point on the column axis is

$$M_x = P_c y = P_c f \sin \frac{\pi x}{l}$$

and the shearing force

$$Q_x = \frac{dM_x}{dx} = P_c f \frac{\pi}{l} \cos \frac{\pi x}{l}$$

whence

$$F = \frac{M_x}{h} = \pm P_c \frac{f}{h} \sin \frac{\pi x}{l} \tag{328a}$$

$$D = Q_x \frac{d}{h} = \pm P_c f \frac{d}{h} \frac{\pi}{l} \cos \frac{\pi x}{l} \tag{328b}$$

$$B = Q_x = \pm P_c f \frac{\pi}{l} \cos \frac{\pi x}{l} \tag{328c}$$

The $\pm$ signs in Eqs. (328) indicate that some members get tension, others compression, depending on their location.

We assume that the reference point x for determining F, D, and B in each panel is at mid-point of the panel. The error involved in this assumption is negligible when the number of panels n is greater than four. Accordingly, by introducing $\frac{\pi x}{l} = \frac{2r - 1}{2n}\pi$, where $r = 1, 2, \ldots,$ $n - 1$, n are the numbers of the panel points, Eq. (327) becomes

$$V = \frac{P_c^2 f^2}{2} \frac{c}{h^2} \frac{2}{E_t A} \sum_{r=1}^{n} \sin^2 \frac{2r-1}{2n}\pi + \frac{P_c^2 f^2}{2} \frac{d^3}{h^2} \frac{\pi^2}{l^2} \frac{l}{EA_d} \sum_{r=1}^{n} \cos^2 \frac{2r-1}{2n}\pi$$

$$+ \frac{P_c^2 f^2}{2} \frac{\pi^2}{l^2} \frac{h}{EA_b} \sum_{r=1}^{n} \cos^2 \frac{2r-1}{2n}\pi$$

Introducing the moment of inertia $I_0 = Ah^2/2$, it is readily seen that

$$\frac{P_c^2 f^2}{2} \frac{c}{h^2} \frac{2}{E_t A} = \frac{P_c^2 f^2}{2} \frac{c}{E_t I_0}$$

and since

$$\sum_{r=1}^{n} \sin^2 \frac{2r-1}{2n} \pi = \sum_{r=1}^{n} \cos^2 \frac{2r-1}{2n} \pi = \frac{n}{2} = \frac{l}{2c} \tag{329}$$

the strain energy V assumes the form

$$V = P_c^2 \frac{f^2 l}{4} \left(\frac{1}{E_t I_0} + \frac{d^3}{ch^2} \frac{\pi^2}{l^2} \frac{1}{EA_d} + \frac{h}{c} \frac{\pi^2}{l^2} \frac{1}{EA_b} \right) \tag{330}$$

Work W of the External Forces.   The work done by the external forces P_c is, with reference to Fig. 85,

$$W = P_c \, \Delta l = \frac{P_c}{2} \int_0^l y'^2 \, dx$$

and since $y' = (\pi/l) f \cos (\pi x/l)$, we obtain after performing the integration

$$W = P_c \frac{\pi^2 f^2}{4l} \tag{331}$$

Substituting V and W from Eqs. (330) and (331) into Eq. (325) leads to the condition of stability, which reads after division by $P_c^2 f^2/4$

$$\frac{\pi^2}{l} - P_c l \left(\frac{1}{E_t I_0} + \frac{\pi^2}{l^2} \frac{d^3}{ch^2} \frac{1}{EA_d} + \frac{\pi^2}{l^2} \frac{h}{c} \frac{1}{EA_b} \right) = 0$$

The expression for the critical load is finally

$$P_c = \frac{\pi^2 E_t I_0}{l^2} \frac{1}{1 + \dfrac{\pi^2 E_t I_0}{l^2} \dfrac{1}{Ech^2} \left(\dfrac{d^3}{A_d} + \dfrac{h^3}{A_b} \right)} \tag{332}$$

If the lacing were absolutely rigid, $A_d = A_b = \infty$, Eq. (332) would furnish a critical load $\pi^2 E_t I_0/l^2$, which is the critical load of a column having the moment of inertia $I_0 = Ah^2/2$. The actual moment of inertia of the column section is, however,

$$I = I_0 + 2I_1 \tag{333}$$

where I_1 is the moment of inertia of each chord about axis 1-1, as indicated in Fig. 86b. We have so far neglected the stiffness of the chord represented by I_1, and it seems a logical step to allow for this neglected influence now by substituting I for I_0 in the first term of Eq.(332).[1] The critical load P_c of the built-up column can then be represented finally by

$$P_c = \frac{\pi^2 E_t I}{(kl)^2} \tag{334}$$

in which

$$k = \sqrt{1 + \frac{\pi^2 E_t I_0}{l^2} \frac{1}{Ech^2} \left(\frac{d^3}{A_d} + \frac{h^3}{A_b} \right)} \tag{335}$$

The failure load of a laced column for buckling in the plane of the lacing can be computed from the column formula for the given material by using the effective length kl, where k is defined by formula (335). k is always greater than unity. $\pi^2 E_t I_0/l^2$ in Eq. (335) is the buckling load P_0 of a column of solid cross section, having the moment of inertia $I_0 = Ah^2/2$. The formula developed above has been derived in another way by Engesser in 1891.

Equation (335) is valid for the system of lacing shown in Fig. 86. For lacing of the type indicated by Fig. 87a the factor k is given by

$$k = \sqrt{1 + \frac{\pi^2 E_t I_0}{l^2} \frac{d^3}{Ech^2 A_d}} \tag{336}$$

and for double lacing (Figs. 86b and 86c)

$$k = \sqrt{1 + \frac{\pi^2 E_t I_0}{l^2} \frac{d}{2Ech^2 A_d}} \tag{337}$$

Columns with lacing according to Fig. 87a have been investigated on the basis of the framework theory by Wentzel.[2] Equation (336) is in good agreement with the expression derived from the framework theory, specialized for a large number n of panels,

$$k = \sqrt{1 + \frac{\pi^2 E_t I_0}{l^2} \frac{d^3}{Ech^2 A_d} \frac{1}{1 + 4I_1/Ah^2}} \tag{338}$$

Equation (338) differs from Eq. (336) by the factor $\dfrac{1}{1 + 4I_1/Ah^2}$ in the radicand, which factor is close to unity. Its effect on k in case of a conventionally designed column is negligible.

In order to show the effect of the shear forces upon the buckling

---

[1] It may appear arbitrary that I_0 in the denominator of Eq. (332) is not replaced by I. This is not done because the accurate framework analysis shows that I_0, not I, occurs in this term [see Eq. (338)]. In any case, the effect on the critical load P_c of changing I_0 in the second term would be very small, as the value of the denominator is close to unity.

[2] Wentzel, loc. cit. on p. 168.

strength of laced struts, the case shown in Fig. 87a may be discussed. If $2A$ is the cross-sectional area of the column, we can replace $\pi^2 E_t I_0/l^2$ in Eq. (336) by $2A\sigma_c{}^\circ$, where $\sigma_c{}^\circ$ is the critical stress of the column of solid cross section having the moment of inertia I_0. Furthermore we express the ratio d^3/ch^2 in terms of the angle α between the diagonals and

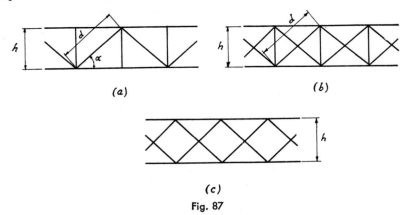

(a)   (b)

(c)

Fig. 87

the column axis, thus reducing the number of variables in the expression for k. We obtain in this manner

$$k = \sqrt{1 + \frac{\sigma_c{}^\circ}{E} \frac{2A}{A_d} \frac{1}{\sin^2 \alpha \cos \alpha}} \tag{339}$$

Table 7 shows the effect of α and of the ratio $2A/A_d$ upon k for two selected values of $\sigma_c{}^\circ$. The values are $\sigma_c{}^\circ = 32$ kips/in.², which is slightly

TABLE 7. k Computed from Eq. (339)

Stress, $\sigma_c{}^\circ$, kips/in.²	α, degrees	Ratio $2A/A_d$				
		30	25	20	15	10
32	30	1.072	1.061	1.049	1.037	1.025
	45	1.045	1.038	1.030	1.023	1.015
	60	1.042	1.035	1.028	1.021	1.014
25	30	1.057	1.048	1.039	1.029	1.019
	45	1.035	1.030	1.024	1.018	1.012
	60	1.033	1.028	1.023	1.017	1.011

less than the yield strength of 33 kips/in.², and $\sigma_c{}^\circ = 25$ kips/in.², which is the proportional limit for structural steel.

Since the length factor k has a minor effect on the buckling strength of short columns, the P_c-values of short laced columns will deviate only slightly from the buckling strength of columns with solid cross section having the same moment of inertia I. The lacing, however, has greater influence in case of slender columns where the reduction in strength in extreme cases may amount to about 10%.

54. Columns with Batten Plates

The procedure in deriving the buckling load is essentially the same as in the preceding article. The battened column, subdivided by the battens into panels, is a highly redundant structure whose exact analysis

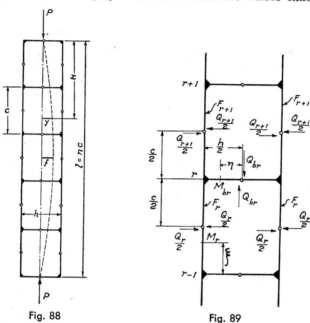

Fig. 88   Fig. 89

would be rather laborious. However, in studying the stability problem of this system, simplifying assumptions concerning the local deformations of the framework can be made, permitting approximate relations to be established which determine the internal forces of the system. From the theory of rectangular frameworks it is known that the distorted form of such a framework is characterized by points of inflection at the center of the transverse members, and approximately at the mid-point of each chord member. We can therefore replace the redundant system by a statically determinate framework having articulated links at the mid-point of each member as shown in Fig. 88.

Shear forces and moments acting in the members of the framework in the deflected state of buckling are indicated in Fig. 89, showing two adjacent panels of the column.

We list the following quantities which will appear in the analysis and the notation used:

F_r = change of the axial force in the chord between panel points $r - 1$ and r caused by flexure of the column in the state of buckling

Q_r = the shearing force between the panel points $r - 1$, r

Q_{br} = the longitudinal shearing force acting on the transverse member at joint r

M_r = the bending moment at any point ξ of the chord member $r - 1$, r

M_{br} = the bending moment at any point η of the transverse member r

A = the cross-sectional area of one chord

I_1, I_b = the moments of inertia of chord and of transverse member, respectively, each with respect to the centroidal axis of its cross section perpendicular to the plane of buckling

$I_0 = Ah^2/2$

The elastic energy of the distorted column consists of the work done by the axial forces F_r in the two chords and the energy of local bending accumulated in the chords and in the battens. The bending energy of the chords associated with the sinusoidal deformation of the column axis will at first be neglected but will be taken into account later in the final formula for the buckling load. The effect of the distortion of the chord members and battens due to the shear stresses which occur with bending will be disregarded. The equation for V therefore reads:

$$V = \frac{1}{2}\left(2\sum_{r=1}^{n}\frac{F_r{}^2 c}{E_t A} + 2\sum_{r=1}^{n}\int_0^c \frac{M_r{}^2}{E_t I_1}\,d\xi + \sum_{r=1}^{n}\int_{-\frac{h}{2}}^{\frac{h}{2}}\frac{M_{br}{}^2}{E I_b}\,d\eta\right) \quad (340)$$

The first two terms refer to the chords whose distortion due to axial force and flexure in the state of buckling is controlled by the tangent-modulus E_t. The third term represents the strain energy of the battens which are assumed unstressed when buckling starts, and Young's modulus appears in the denominator of this term.

Under the assumption that the column deflects in a sine curve, $y = f \sin (\pi x/l)$, as indicated in Fig. 88, the bending moment M_r at the point $x = (2r - 1/2n)l$, corresponding to the mid-point of panel $r - 1$, r is

$$M_r = P_c y = P_c f \sin \frac{2r - 1}{2n}\pi \quad (341)$$

and the shearing force Q_r for the same reference point is

$$Q_r = \frac{dM_r}{dx} = P_c f \frac{\pi}{l}\cos \frac{2r - 1}{2n}\pi \quad (342)$$

Considering the equilibrium of the moments acting on joint r we derive from Fig. 89

$$Q_{br} \frac{h}{2} - \left(\frac{Q_r}{2} + \frac{Q_{r+1}}{2}\right) \frac{c}{2} = 0$$

from which

$$Q_{br} = \frac{Q_r + Q_{r+1}}{2} \frac{c}{h}$$

follows. To simplify the analysis this expression will be replaced by the approximation

$$Q_{br} = \frac{c}{h} \bar{Q}_r \tag{343}$$

in which

$$\bar{Q}_r = P_c f \frac{\pi}{l} \cos \frac{r}{n} \pi \tag{344}$$

Since $F_r = M_r/h$, we obtain with reference to Eqs. (341) and (329)

$$\sum_{r=1}^{n} \frac{F_r{}^2 c}{E_t A} = \frac{P_c{}^2 f^2}{E_t A} \frac{c}{h^2} \sum_{r=1}^{n} \sin^2 \frac{2r-1}{2n} \pi = \frac{P_c{}^2 f^2}{E_t A} \frac{l}{2h^2} = \frac{P_c{}^2 f^2 l}{4E_t I_0} \tag{345}$$

where $I_0 = Ah^2/2$.

With reference to Fig. 89 we have

$$\int_0^c \frac{M_r{}^2}{E_t I_1} d\xi = \int_0^c \frac{Q_r{}^2 \left(\xi - \frac{c}{2}\right)^2}{4E_t I_1} d\xi = \frac{Q_r{}^2 c^3}{48 E_t I_1}$$

and

$$\int_{-\frac{h}{2}}^{\frac{h}{2}} \frac{M_{br}{}^2}{E I_b} d\eta = \int_{-\frac{h}{2}}^{\frac{h}{2}} \frac{\bar{Q}_r{}^2 c^2}{E I_b h^2} \eta^2 d\eta = \frac{\bar{Q}_r{}^2 c^2 h}{12 E I_b}$$

hence, by using Eqs. (342) and (329), we obtain

$$\sum_{r=1}^{n} \int_0^c \frac{M_r{}^2}{E_t I_1} d\xi = \sum_{r=1}^{n} \frac{Q_r{}^2 c^3}{48 E_t I_1} = \frac{\pi^2 P_c{}^2 f^2 c^3}{48 E_t I_1 l^2} \sum_{r=1}^{n} \cos^2 \frac{2r-1}{2n} \pi = \frac{\pi^2}{96} \frac{P_c{}^2 f^2 c^2}{E_t I_1 l}$$

$$\tag{346}$$

Applying Eqs. (344) and observing that $\sum\limits_{r=1}^{n} \cos^2 \pi \frac{r}{n} = \frac{n}{2} = \frac{l}{2c}$,

$$\frac{1}{2} \sum_{r=1}^{n} \int_{-\frac{h}{2}}^{\frac{h}{2}} \frac{M_{br}{}^2}{E I_b} d\eta = \frac{1}{2} \sum_{r=1}^{n} \frac{\bar{Q}_r{}^2 c^2 h}{12 E I_b} = \frac{\pi^2 P_c{}^2 f^2 c^2 h}{24 E I_b l^2} \sum_{r=1}^{n} \cos^2 \pi \frac{r}{n} = \frac{\pi^2}{48} \frac{P_c{}^2 f^2 c h}{E I_b l}$$

$$\tag{347}$$

The expression for the work W of the external forces is again given by Eq. (331). Using Eqs. (340), (345), (346), and (347), and canceling the factor $P_c f^2/4$, the energy condition (325) reads:

$$\frac{\pi^2}{l} - P_c \left(\frac{l}{E_t I_0} + \frac{\pi^2}{24} \frac{c^2}{E_t I_1 l} + \frac{\pi^2}{12} \frac{ch}{EI_b l} \right) = 0$$

Solving for P_c leads to

$$P_c = \frac{\pi^2 E_t I_0}{l^2} \frac{1}{1 + \dfrac{\pi^2}{24} \dfrac{I_0}{I_1} \left(\dfrac{c}{l}\right)^2 + \dfrac{\pi^2 E_t I_0}{l^2} \dfrac{ch}{12 E I_b}} \tag{348}$$

Reasoning in the same manner as in the preceding section, we may replace I_0 in the numerator by the moment of inertia $I = I_0 + 2I_1$ of the column. In this way we account for the flexural rigidity of the chords disregarded in the foregoing investigation. P_c can be expressed

$$P_c = \frac{\pi^2 E_t I}{(kl)^2} \tag{349}$$

where k is given by

$$k = \sqrt{1 + \frac{\pi^2 I_0}{24 I_1}\left(\frac{c}{l}\right)^2 + \frac{\pi^2}{12} \frac{I_0}{I_b} \frac{ch}{l^2}} \tag{350}$$

In the last term of Eq. (350) E_t/E was replaced by unity, a simplification which leads to a slightly larger value for k.

The second term of the radicand in Eq. (350) depends on the flexibility of the chords; the last term on the flexural rigidity of the batten plates. For a properly designed column this last term is small compared with $1 + \dfrac{\pi^2 I_0}{24 I_1}\left(\dfrac{c}{l}\right)^2$ and, as a rule, can be disregarded.

Formula (348) has been derived by Engesser, and its validity was proved by comparison with the results of the exact investigation of Mann and others. It is also well confirmed by tests.

Multiplying Eq. (350) on both sides by the slenderness ratio l/r of the column, $r = \sqrt{I/2A}$, and omitting the last term, we obtain

$$\frac{kl}{r} = \sqrt{\left(\frac{l}{r}\right)^2 + \frac{\pi^2 I_0}{24 I_1}\left(\frac{c}{r}\right)^2}$$

Replacing l/r^2 in the second term by $2A/I$, approximating I_0/I by unity, and introducing the radius of gyration of the chord, $r_1 = \sqrt{I_1/A}$, this equation becomes

$$\frac{kl}{r} = \sqrt{\left(\frac{l}{r}\right)^2 + \frac{\pi^2}{12}\left(\frac{c}{r_1}\right)^2} \tag{351}$$

where c/r_1 is the slenderness ratio of the chord. Equation (351) gives the equivalent slenderness ratio kl/r of the battened column in a very convenient form.

Table 8 shows the value of k computed from Eq. (351) for various slenderness ratios l/r under the assumption that $c/r_1 = 40$. It will be seen from the discussion in the next article that battened columns should be designed so that c/r_1 does not exceed the values of l/r appreciably. In order to judge the effect of k on the buckling strength, the σ_c-value which pertains to the slenderness ratio l/r is compared with the $\sigma_c{}'$-value computed for the slenderness ratio kl/r. Table 8 shows the ratio $\sigma_c{}'/\sigma_c$.

TABLE 8*

l/r.............	40	50	60	80	100	108†	120	140	160
k...............	1.350	1.235	1.168	1.099	1.064	1.056	1.045	1.032	1.025
Ratio $\sigma_c{}'/\sigma_c$.......	0.97	0.97	0.97	0.97	0.96	0.90	0.92	0.94	0.95

* Computed for structural steel. $\sigma_p = 25$ kips/in.^{2}, $\sigma_y = 33$ kips/in.^{2}
† Corresponds to $\sigma_c = \sigma_p$.

The reduction of buckling strength amounts to about 3% for columns with $l/r \leqq 80$ and reaches a maximum of 10% for slender columns. However, it must be recalled that the above figures were derived under the assumption of $c/r_1 = 40$. Increase of the spacing c would lead to a further reduction of the load-carrying capacity of a battened column.

55. Local Failure of Built-up Columns

The purpose of the investigations in Arts. 53 and 54 was the determination of the buckling load of a built-up column with due regard to the effect that lacing or batten plates may have upon the load-carrying capacity of the column. But these studies do not afford any clue for the proper design of the lateral system itself in order to prevent failure of these members prior to primary failure of the column. A built-up column represents a framework which will collapse if any member of the structure begins to yield locally before the critical load P_c is reached for which the column was designed. It is therefore necessary to establish rules for the design of the details of build-up columns to prevent premature failure of the column.

It is an obvious conclusion that each of the two chords must be able to carry a load of $P_c/2$ safely over the length c between two adjacent joints of the lacing (Fig. 90a) or over the spacing c' of rivets in the batten plates (Fig. 90b). If kl/r is the critical slenderness ratio of the column and c/r_1 the slenderness ratio of one chord of a laced column, where r_1 refers to the centroidal axis 1-1 as shown in Fig. 86b, the condition

$$\frac{c}{r_1} \leq \frac{kl}{r}$$

must be satisfied. This condition is valid regardless of whether buckling occurs below or above the elastic limit. Since k in practical cases is

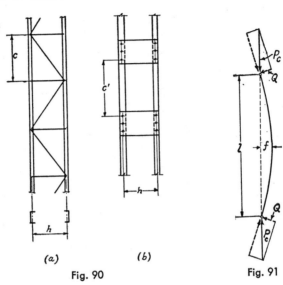

(a)   (b)

Fig. 90   Fig. 91

close to unity, it is conventional practice to calculate the upper limit of c from the equation

$$c = \frac{r_1 l}{r} \qquad (352)$$

A similar reasoning can be applied to columns with batten plates. The critical slenderness ratio of the chord should be smaller than the slenderness ratio of the column:

$$\frac{k_1 c'}{r_1} \leq \frac{kl}{r}$$

where k_1 indicates the effect of the restraint of the battens. k_1 lies between unity and 0.7. For design purposes it is on the safe side to use $k_1 = 1$, and if we also use $k = 1$, we obtain finally

$$c' = \frac{r_1 l}{r} \qquad (353)$$

To avoid any misunderstanding, Eqs. (352) and (353) give the upper limit of c or c' to prevent local failure of the chord. But the actual value of c or c' must be selected below this limit in order that the reduction of buckling strength of the built-up column may remain small in comparison with that of a solid column of the same ratio l/r.

The function of the connecting members of a laced or battened column is to carry the shearing forces which occur when the column deflects under the critical load. The shear forces Q at the ends of the column (Fig. 91) are the components of the critical load P_c at right angles to the deflected center line of the column and are a function of the deflection f. Since in the unstable state of equilibrium f remains indeterminate, there is no uniquely defined value of Q indicating the magnitude of the shear forces. Nevertheless the following reasoning leads to a rational criterion for the magnitude of Q upon which the safe design of the lacing members can be based to avert premature failure of any member of the lacing system. It appears logical to design the lacing system so that its members are just strong enough to carry the shearing forces which arise when the deflection reaches the magnitude at which the chord on the concave side of the bent column begins to yield. Then the highest stressed parts of the column will yield or collapse simultaneously.[1]

The maximum chord stress σ_1 associated with the deflection f is

$$\sigma_1 = \frac{P_c}{2A} + \frac{P_c f}{Ah} = \sigma_c + \frac{P_c f}{Ah}$$

when the influence of the chord stiffness is disregarded. From this equation follows the value of f for which σ_1 will be equal to the yield point σ_y:

$$f = \frac{\sigma_y - \sigma_c}{P_c} Ah \tag{354}$$

Assuming sinusoidal deformation, the shearing force Q reaches its maximum value at the ends of the column:

$$Q_{max} = P_c \frac{\pi}{l} f$$

Substituting f from Eq. (354), and approximating h by $2r$, where r is the radius of gyration of the column in the plane of the lacing, give the design formula

$$Q_{max} = (\sigma_y - \sigma_c) \frac{\pi}{l} Ah = 2\pi(\sigma_y - \sigma_c)A \frac{r}{l} \tag{355}$$

Q_{max} varies considerably with the slenderness ratio l/r as can be seen from an inspection of the graph in Fig. 92, in which the values Q_{max}/A are plotted against the slenderness ratio l/r. The curve was computed

[1] Engesser, F., Zum Einsturz der Brücke über den St. Lorenzstrom bei Quebeck, *Zentralblatt der Bauverwaltung*, Vol. 27, p. 609, 1907.

from Eq. (355) for structural steel, $\sigma_p = 25$ kips/in.^{2} and $\sigma_y = 33$ kips/in.^{2}, for values of l/r between 40 and 200.   Below $l/r = 40$, σ_1 may become greater than σ_y and Eq. (355) is not applicable.   The part of the Q_{max}/A curve between $l/r = 0$ and 40 which approaches zero with decreasing l/r has been replaced, somewhat arbitrarily, by a horizontal line.

Attempts have been made to base the determination of the shearing forces Q on the concept that imperfections of the column, such as initial crookedness or initial eccentricity of the axial load, may produce shearing forces which must be carried by the members of the lacing system.[1]   The initial deflection or eccentricity of the load was assumed a small fraction of the length l.   But in this manner an arbitrary factor which has no

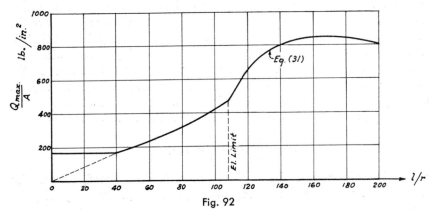

Fig. 92

real relationship to the buckling problem is introduced into the analysis, in contrast to the above-discussed method, which considers the actual performance of the structure in the state of instability.

Using Eq. (355), the design of the details of built-up columns should be based on the yield strength for parts in tension or flexure and on buckling strength for compression members.

Diagonals in Laced Columns.   With Q_{max} computed from Eq. (355) the maximum force in the diagonals for lacing systems of the type indicated in Figs. 86 and 87a is given by

$$D_{max} = Q_{max} \frac{d}{h} \tag{356}$$

and for columns having double lacing (Fig. 87b),

$$D_{max} = Q_{max} \frac{d}{2h} \tag{357}$$

[1] Young, D. H., Rational Design of Steel Columns, *Trans. ASCE*, Vol. 101, p. 422, 1936.

In columns with double lacing, as shown in Fig. 87b, allowance should be made for additional forces in the lacing bars due to secondary stresses discussed in the next article.

Attention may be drawn here to the fact that any eccentricity in connecting lacing bars to the chords of columns should be held to the minimum possible, as such eccentricities increase the shear deformations and reduce the critical load of the column.[1]

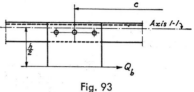

Fig. 93

Batten Plates. The maximum value of longitudinal shear Q_b causing bending of the battens (see Figs. 89 and 93) is

$$Q_{b_{max}} = Q_{max} \frac{c}{h} \tag{358}$$

56. Secondary Stresses in Laced Columns

Since a laced column is essentially a triangular framework with stiff joints, secondary stresses arise which are caused by the distortion of the chords due to the axial load P prior to buckling. The stresses in diagonals or horizontal bars may assume considerable magnitude, especially in the case of double lacing, as will be shown hereafter.

Let us consider the panel $abcd$ of a column with a double lacing system as shown in Fig. 94a in its original shape and in its distorted form after the axial load P is applied. Owing to the shortening of the chord members ac and bd, the rectangular panel deforms as indicated by the dotted lines, causing compressive stresses in the diagonals and tensile stresses in the vertical and horizontal members of the panel. If X is the unknown diagonal stress, than $-X \sin \alpha$ is the additional stress in each chord and $-2X \cos \alpha$ the stress in the horizontal bars, it being noted that the latter must balance the diagonal forces of two adjacent panels (Fig. 94b). The diagonal force X can be assumed to be the same in all panels, and in determining this force it is sufficiently accurate to consider only one panel independent of the others.

By applying the principle of least work, the redundant force X in the framework system shown in Fig. 94c can be expressed in the form

$$X = \frac{\Sigma F_0 F_1 l / EA'}{\Sigma F_1^2 l / EA'} \tag{359}$$

where F_0 indicates the forces in the residual system due to the loading P and F_1 the forces in this system due to the loading condition $X = 1$.

[1] Amstütz, E., Die Knicklast gegliederter Stäbe, *Schweizerische Bauzeitung*, Vol. 118, p. 97, 1941.

l are the lengths of the members, l_c, l_h, or l_d, and A' their areas, A, A_h, or A_d, respectively. The sums extend over the five elements of the residual system. The forces in the statically indeterminate system are finally given by

$$F = F_0 - F_1 X \tag{360}$$

The simple analysis leads to the following expression for the diagonal stress X:

$$X = \frac{P/2A_c}{\dfrac{\sin \alpha}{A} + 2\dfrac{\cot^2 \alpha \cos \alpha}{A_h} + \dfrac{1}{A_d \sin^2 \alpha}} \tag{361}$$

where A, A_h, and A_d are the cross-sectional areas of one chord, of one horizontal bar, and one diagonal, respectively. The factor 2 in the mid-

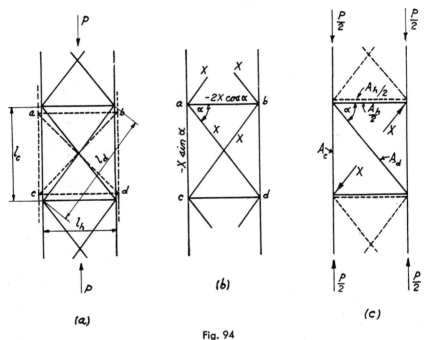

Fig. 94

dle term of the denominator is due to the fact that in setting up this term the horizontal member was considered as split into two components as indicated in Fig. 94c, each having the cross sectional area $A_h/2$ and belonging to one of the two adjacent panels.

The force in the chord therefore reduces to

$$F_c = \frac{P}{2} - X \sin \alpha \tag{362}$$

and the horizontal members are stressed by

$$F_h = -2X \cos \alpha \tag{363}$$

On introducing $\sigma_0 = P/2A$ and $\sigma_d = X/A_d$ Eq. (361) becomes

$$\frac{\sigma_d}{\sigma_0} = \frac{1}{\dfrac{A_d}{A} \sin \alpha + 2 \dfrac{A_d}{A_h} \cot^2 \alpha \cos \alpha + \dfrac{1}{\sin^2 \alpha}} \tag{364}$$

The ratio σ_d/σ_0 depends on the angle α and the ratios A_d/A and A_d/A_h. As A_d/A is small compared with unity, the first term can be disregarded and Eq. (364) simplifies to

$$\frac{\sigma_d}{\sigma_0} = \frac{\sin^2 \alpha}{1 + 2 \dfrac{A_d}{A_h} \cos^3 \alpha} \tag{365}$$

Table 9 gives the values of σ_d/σ_0 for $\alpha = 30°, 45°, 60°$ and for

$$\frac{A_d}{A_h} = 1 \text{ and } 2.$$

These considerable stresses are already present in the lacing members prior to buckling and, if not taken care of, will reduce the resistance of the lacing system. To keep these stresses within reasonable limits it is recommended that angles α greater than 45° be avoided and the cross sections of the horizontal members be reduced as far as possible. In proportioning the diagonals of columns with double lacing on the basis

TABLE 9. Ratios σ_d/σ_0

α, deg	30	45	60
$A_d/A_h = 1$	0.268	0.354	0.464
$A_d/A_h = 2$	0.183	0.234	0.317

of Eq. (355), it is advisable to provide some margin in the cross-sectional area of these members to allow for the initial stresses indicated by Eq. (365). Since the cross-sectional area of the chords is many times greater than that of the diagonals, the influence of the second term in Eq. (362) amounts to only a few per cent of $P/2$. Thus, the part of the axial load P carried by the diagonal members is relatively small and has no noticeable effect upon the buckling load of the column.

Tests made by Hartmann, Moore, and Holt[1] with laced structural frames indicate that about 6% of the total axial load is carried by the

[1] Hartmann, E. C., R. L. Moore, and M. Holt, Model Tests of Latticed Structural Frames, *Aluminum Research Lab.*, *Tech. Paper 2*, Aluminum Company of America, 1938.

diagonal lacing bars. For the specimen tested the above analysis gives a 5.8% reduction of the chord stresses.

57. Built-up Columns of Varying Moment of Inertia

For practical reasons built-up compression members sometimes are designed with varying width or depth. Several examples are presented in Fig. 95. With a constant cross section $2A$ of the column, the effective moment of inertia I for bending in the plane of the lacing varies with the square of the distance h:

$$I = \frac{2Ah^2}{4} \tag{366}$$

The exact solution of the special column problem under consideration involves the determination of the characteristic values of a homogeneous

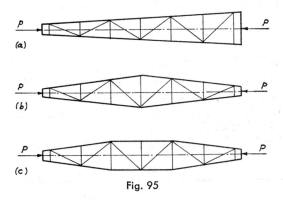

Fig. 95

differential equation of the second order with variable coefficients. This equation can be solved in some cases of practical importance by means of elementary transcendental functions as will be shown hereafter.

The stability problem of build-up columns of varying stiffness was treated in 1914 by Dinnik[1] and by Bairstow and Stedman.[2] Dinnik presented numerical tables for a generalized type of column, illustrated in Fig. 95c, assuming various parabolic laws for the stiffness in the end portions of the column. Approximate solutions based on the energy method for some shapes of columns were given in 1924 by the author.[3]

---

[1] Published in Russian. Also A. N. Dinnik, Design of Columns of Varying Cross Sections, *Trans. ASME*, Vol. 51, Part 1, APM-51-11, 1929, and Vol. 54, APM-54-16, 1932.

[2] Critical Loads for Long Struts of Varying Sections, *Engineering*, Vol. 98, p. 403, 1914.

[3] Bleich, F., "Theorie und Berechnung der eisernen Brücken," p. 136, Julius Springer, Berlin, 1924.

Powerful numerical methods applicable to this problem were developed by Newmark[1] and by Salvadori.[2]

Symmetrical Column with Straight Chords (Fig. 96):

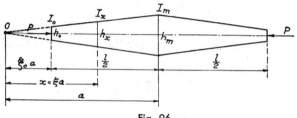

Fig. 96

Denoting by I_m the moment of inertia at the mid-point and by I_x its value at the reference point x, we may write

$$I_x = I_m \frac{h_x^2}{h_m^2} = I_m \frac{x^2}{a^2} = I_m \xi^2 \tag{367}$$

where $\xi = x/a$ is a dimensionless quantity. The differential equation of the column problem is

$$E_t I_x \frac{d^2y}{dx^2} + Py = 0$$

Substituting I_x from Eq. (367) and introducing

$$\alpha^2 = \frac{Pa^2}{E_t I_m} \tag{368}$$

leads to a differential equation with variable coefficients:

$$\xi^2 \frac{d^2y}{d\xi^2} + \alpha^2 y = 0 \tag{369}$$

The general solution of this equation, containing two arbitrary constants A and B, reads:

$$y = \sqrt{\xi}\,[A \sin (k \log_e \xi) + B \cos (k \log_e \xi)] \tag{370}$$

in which the parameter k is defined by

$$k = \sqrt{\alpha^2 - \tfrac{1}{4}} \tag{371}$$

[1] Newmark, N. M., Numerical Procedure for Computing Deflections, Moments and Buckling Loads, *Trans. ASCE*, Vol. 108, p. 1172, 1943.

[2] Salvadori, M. G., Numerical Computation of Buckling Loads by Finite Differences, *Trans. ASCE*, Vol. 116, 1951.

Substituting Eq. (370) into the boundary conditions (see Fig. 96)

$$\xi = \xi_0 = \frac{h_0}{h_m} : y = 0$$

$$\xi = 1: \quad \frac{dy}{d\xi} = 0$$

results in two homogeneous equations for the constants A and B:

$$A \sin \left(k \log_e \frac{h_0}{h_m} \right) + B \cos \left(k \log_e \frac{h_0}{h_m} \right) = 0$$

$$Ak + B/2 = 0$$

Solutions for A and B different from zero exist only if the determinant condition

$$\tan \left(k \log_e \frac{h_0}{h_m} \right) - 2k = 0 \tag{372}$$

which has an infinite number of roots k, the smallest root k_1 defining the critical load P_c. From Eqs. (368) and (371) the buckling load follows

$$P_c = \frac{E_t I_m}{4a^2} (1 + 4k_1^2)$$

which can be written

$$P_c = \mu \frac{\pi^2 E_t I_m}{l^2} \tag{373}$$

where the factor μ is defined by

$$\mu = \frac{1 + 4k_1^2}{4\pi^2} \left(\frac{l}{a} \right)^2 = \frac{1 + 4k_1^2}{\pi^2} \left(1 - \frac{h_0}{h_m} \right)^2 \tag{374}$$

Thus, the critical load P_c is found as the buckling load of a column of constant cross section having an equivalent moment of inertia $I = \mu I_m$, where μ is given by Eq. (374). Table 10 gives the values of μ for various ratios h_0/h_m.

TABLE 10.   Values for μ in Eq. (373) for Columns as Shown in Fig. 96

h_0/h_m ...	0	0.1	0.2	0.4	0.6	0.8	1.0
μ^*	0.101	0.349	0.449	0.610	0.749	0.881	1.000

* For intermediate values of h_0/h_m use linear interpolation.

Nonsymmetrical Column with Straight Chords (Fig. 97):

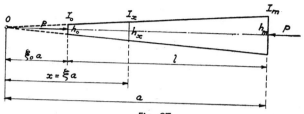

Fig. 97

The investigation of this type of column leads again to the solution given by Eq. (370). Applying it now to the boundary conditions

$$\xi = \xi_0 = \frac{h_0}{h_m}: \qquad y = 0$$

$$\xi = 1: \qquad y = 0$$

yields the two equations

$$A \sin\left(k \log_e \frac{h_0}{h_m}\right) + B \cos\left(k \log_e \frac{h_0}{h_m}\right) = 0$$

$$B = 0$$

for A and B. The stability condition therefore reads:

$$\sin\left(k \log_e \frac{h_0}{h_m}\right) = 0 \tag{375}$$

The smallest nontrivial root is

$$k_1 = \frac{\pi}{\log_e h_0 - \log_e h_m}$$

and using Eqs. (368) and (371) the following expression for the critical load P_c is found:

$$P_c = \mu \frac{\pi^2 E_t I_m}{l^2} \tag{376}$$

in which

$$\mu = \frac{1}{4}\left(1 - \frac{h_0}{h_m}\right)^2 \left[\frac{1}{\pi^2} + \frac{4}{(\log_e h_0 - \log_e h_m)^2}\right] \tag{377}$$

Table 11 shows values of μ computed from Eq. (377) for various ratios h_0/h_m.

TABLE 11. Values for μ in Eq. (376) for Columns as Shown in Eq. (97)

h_0/h_m ...	0	0.1	0.2	0.4	0.6	0.8	1.0
μ^*	0.025	0.173	0.263	0.438	0.618	0.804	1.000

* For intermediate values of h_0/h_m use linear interpolation.

Symmetrical Column with Parabolic Chords (Fig. 98):

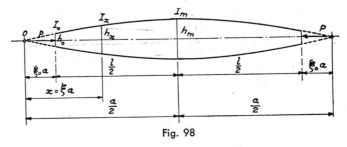

Fig. 98

In terms of the notation in Fig. 98, the moment of inertia I_x is given by

$$I_x = I_m \frac{h_x^2}{h_m^2} = \frac{16 I_m}{a^4} x^2 (a - x)^2$$

The differential equation of the stability problem assumes, with $x = \xi a$, the form

$$\xi^2 (1 - \xi)^2 \frac{d^2 y}{d\xi^2} + \alpha^2 y = 0 \qquad (378)$$

in which

$$\alpha^2 = \frac{P a^2}{16 E_t I_m} \qquad (379)$$

The general solution of Eq. (378) is

$$y = \sqrt{\xi(1 - \xi)} \left[A \cos\left(\frac{k}{2} \log_e \frac{\xi}{1 - \xi} \right) + B \sin\left(\frac{k}{2} \log_e \frac{\xi}{1 - \xi} \right) \right] \qquad (380)$$

where

$$k = \sqrt{4\alpha^2 - 1}$$

The boundary conditions

$$\xi = \xi_0: \qquad y = 0$$
$$\xi = 1 - \xi_0: \qquad y = 0$$

furnish two linear and homogeneous equations:

$$A \cos\left(\frac{k}{2} \log_e \frac{\xi_0}{1 - \xi_0} \right) + B \sin\left(\frac{k}{2} \log_e \frac{\xi_0}{1 - \xi_0} \right) = 0$$

$$A \cos\left(\frac{k}{2} \log_e \frac{1 - \xi_0}{\xi_0} \right) + B \sin\left(\frac{k}{2} \log_e \frac{1 - \xi_0}{\xi_0} \right) = 0$$

The determinant of the coefficients of the two equations equated to zero leads to the stability condition

$$\sin\left(k \log_e \frac{\xi_0}{1 - \xi_0} \right) = \qquad (381)$$

Its smallest root

$$k_1 = \frac{\pi}{\log_e (\xi_0/1 - \xi_0)} \tag{382}$$

defines the characteristic value k_1 which is associated with the buckling load P_c.

Again we can write

$$P_c = \mu \frac{\pi^2 E_t I_m}{l^2} \tag{383}$$

where μ is now defined by

$$\mu = \frac{4(k_1^2 + 1)}{\pi^2} \left(\frac{l}{a}\right)^2 \tag{384}$$

k_1 is given by Eq. (382). Table 12 shows μ as a function of the ratio h_0/h_m.

TABLE 12. Values for μ in Eq. (383) for Columns as Shown in Fig. 98

h_0/h_m...	0	0.1	0.2	0.4	0.6	0.8	1.0
μ^*......	0.405	0.636	0.709	0.807	0.882	0.945	1.000

* For intermediate values of h_0/h_m use linear interpolation.

Additional References

References to Arts. 52 to 56

v. Emperger, F., Welchen Querverband bedarf eine Eisensäule, *Beton und Eisen*, Vol. 7, pp. 71, 96, 119, 148, 193, 1908.

Talbot, A. N., and H. F. Moore, An Investigation of Built-up Columns under Load, *Univ. Illinois Eng. Expt. Sta. Bull.* 44, 1910.

Rudeloff, H., Knickversuch mit einer Strebe des eingestürzten Hamburger Gas-behälters, *Zeitschrift des Vereins deutscher Ingenieure*, Vol. 57, p. 615, 1913.

Petermann, A., Müller-Breslau's Knickversuche mit Rahmenstäben. *Der Bauin-genieur*, Vol. 7, pp. 979, 1009, 1926.

Kayser, H., Knickversuche mit doppelteiligen Rahmenstäben, *Die Bautechnik*. Vol. 12, 1930.

American Society of Civil Engineers, Steel Column Research, *2d Progress Rept. Special Committee, Trans. ASCE*, Vol. 95, p. 1152, 1931.

American Society of Civil Engineers, Steel Column Research, *Final Rept. Special Committee, Trans. ASCE*, Vol. 98, pp. 1414–1432, 1933.

Ratzersdorfer, J., "Die Knickfestigkeit von Stäben und Stabwerken," pp. 201–243, Julius Springer, Vienna, 1936.

Sergev, S. I., Shear Effect on the Strength of Struts, *Trans. ASCE*, Vol. 110, p. 391, 1945.

References to Art. 57

Morley, A., Critical Loads for Long Tapering Struts, *Engineering,* Vol. 104, p. 295, 1917.

Barling, W. H., and H. A. Webb, Design of Aeroplane Struts, *Jour. Roy. Aeronaut. Soc.,* Vol. 22, p. 313, 1918.

Webb, H. A., and E. D. Long, Struts of Conical Taper, *Jour. Roy. Aeronaut. Soc.,* Vol. 23, p. 179, 1919.

Ono, A., On the Stability of Long Struts of Variable Section, *Mem. Coll. Eng., Kyushu Imp. Univ.,* Vol. 1, No. 5, 1919.

Boyd, J. E., Tapered Struts, a Theoretical and Experimental Investigation, *Ohio State Univ. Eng. Exp. Sta. Bull.* 25, 1923.

Wilcken, J. A., The Bending of Columns of Varying Cross Section, *Phil. Mag.,* Series 7, Vol. 3, pp. 418, 1065, 1927, and Vol. 13, p. 845, 1932.

Lockschin, A., Ueber die Knickung eines doppelwandigen Druckstabes mit parabolisch veränderlicher Querschnittshöhe, *Zeitschrift für angewandte Mathematik und Mechanik,* Vol. 10, p. 160, 1930.

Kiessling, F., Eine Methode zur approximativen Berechnung einseitig eingespannter Druckstäbe mit veränderlichem Querschnitt, *Zeitschrift für angewandte Mathematik und Mechanik,* Vol. 10, p. 594, 1930.

Radomski, B., Compression Struts with Non Progressively Variable Moment of Inertia, *NACA Tech. Mem.* 861, 1938, translated from *Luftfahrt-Forschung,* Vol. 14, p. 438, 1937.

Harris, C. O., Suggestions for Columns of Varying Sections, *Jour. Aeronaut. Sci.,* Vol. 9, p. 97, 1942.

Turton, F. J., Pinned-pinned Solid Strut with Parabolic Taper, *Jour. Roy. Aeronaut. Soc.,* Vol. 46, p. 146, 1942.

Ratzersdorfer, J., Determination of the Buckling Load of Struts by Successive Approximations, *Jour. Roy. Aeronaut. Soc.,* Vol. 47, p. 103, 1943.

Templeton, H., Approximate Solution for Tapered Pin Ended Struts, *Jour. Roy. Aeronaut. Soc.,* Vol. 48, p. 6, 1944.

Young, D. H., Inelastic Buckling of Variable Section Columns, *Trans. ASME,* Vol. 67, p. A-165, 1945.

Miesse, C. C., Determination of the Buckling Load for Columns of Variable Stiffness, *Jour. Applied Mechanics,* Vol. 71, p. 406, 1949.

CHAPTER VI

THE STABILITY OF FRAMEWORKS

58. Introduction

Various types of framework, such as riveted or welded trusses, rigid frames, columns having intermediate fixed or elastic supports, and similar structures, play an important role in structural design, and the performance of a compression member as part of a truss or the stability of the entire system of a rigid frame is of primary concern to the structural engineer. Because of the rigid connections between the members of a framework, deflection of one member in the buckling state causes distortion of the other members of the structure. Each member is elastically restrained by the others, and the degree of restraint of any particular element depends upon the flexural rigidity and the axial loading of all other elements. Thus, the study of the stability of framework systems is necessary to obtain the actual buckling condition of the entire system or to clarify on a rational basis the behavior of a compressed member or a particular group of such members which are parts of a framework. This chapter is primarily devoted to the discussion of general methods of approach which have been developed for the solution of the various buckling problems involved in the investigation of framed structures. The application of these methods to the study of special types of frameworks will be the subject of the following two chapters.

The theory of stability of frameworks is well established as far as structures are concerned where the members are subject to axial forces only. The following discussion will deal primarily with such systems. Not much effort has been made to study the effect of primary or secondary bending moments already present in many frameworks at the instant when the system passes from stable to unstable equilibrium. The significance of this question and the outlook for a solution of this highly involved problem will be discussed in the last article of this chapter.

In viewing the various methods which have been used to solve problems of framework stability, three essentially different ways of approach can be visualized, which correspond to the methods in use for the analysis of statically indeterminate rigid frames. These methods are (1) the direct analytical solution by setting up a system of linear homogeneous equations, expressing the interrelations between axial forces, moments at the rigid joints, joint displacements, and joint rotations, leading to a determinant as criterion of stability; (2) the energy method based on the energy criterion of stability which also yields a system of linear equations, the vanishing determinant of which furnishes the stability condition; (3) convergence methods utilizing the principles of moment distribution modified to include the bending effect of the axial forces.

The problem of framework buckling was considered by Zimmermann,[1] who, in a series of papers, discussed straight columns with intermediate fixed or elastic supports. He clearly recognized the stability problem of a system of rigidly jointed bars which form a straight column and developed the determinant criterion for the critical axial load. Problems pertaining to the stability of systems of rigidly jointed bars in connection with the study of the buckling of the top chord of the trusses of half-through bridges were treated by Müller-Breslau.[2]

In 1919 Bleich[3] presented a systematic analysis of the stability of plane frameworks with rigid joints, suitable for the general solution of the problem for all types of framed structures considered in this chapter. By introducing into the analysis a reduced modulus, the theory was rendered applicable in the elastic and plastic range of buckling. Osgood[4] applied the four-moment equations of this theory to the special problem of the free length of compression members in aircraft frameworks. A general method for the solution of buckling problems in the related field of space frameworks, based on the same principles as the before-mentioned two-dimensional theory, was published in 1928 by F. Bleich and H. Bleich.[5]

The stability of pin-connected frameworks was treated in a generalized manner by Mises and Ratzersdorfer,[6] who applied the theory to a comprehensive study of the pin-connected truss with parallel chords, considering it as the idealized system of a latticed strut.

[1] Zimmermann, H., Die Knickfestigkeit des geraden Stabes mit mehreren Feldern, *Sitzungsberichte der preussischen Akademie der Wissenschaften,* 1909, p. 180; "Die Knickfestigkeit der Druckgurte offener Brücken," W. Ernst und Sohn, Berlin, 1910; "Die Knickfestigkeit der Stabverbindungen," W. Ernst und Sohn, Berlin, 1925.

[2] Müller-Breslau, H., "Die graphische Statik der Bau-Konstructionen," Vol. II.2, A. Kröner, Berlin, 1908.

[3] Bleich, F., Die Knickfestigkeit elastischer Stabverbindungen, *Der Eisenbau,* Vol. 10, p. 27, 1919; Einige Aufgaben über die Knickfestigkeit elastischer Stabverbindungen, *Der Eisenbau,* Vol. 13, p. 34, 1922.

[4] Osgood, W. R., Contribution to the Design of Compression Members in Aircraft, *Natl. Bur. Standards (U.S.), Jour. Research,* Research Paper RP 698, 1934.

[5] Bleich, F., and H. Bleich, Die Stabilität räumlicher Stabverbindungen, *Zeitschrift des Österreichischen Ingenieur- und Architektenvereines,* 1928, p. 345.

[6] von Mises, R., and J. Ratzersdorfer, Die Knicksicherheit von Fachwerken, *Zeitschrift für angewandte Mathematik und Mechanik,* Vol. 5, p. 218, 1925.

Mises and Ratzersdorfer[1] in another paper gave a detailed presentation of the problem of rigid-jointed frameworks, extending the investigations also to systems in which the change in length of the members due to the axial forces affects the stability condition. The mathematical treatment of the problem is essentially the same as in Bleich's paper and differs from it in the choice of the type of the basic moment relations from which the analysis starts.

The slope deflection method of stability analysis, applied by Chwalla and Jokisch[2] to the investigation of multistory frames belongs also in the category of analytical methods discussed above. Prager[3] developed in 1936 a method for the stability analysis of frameworks utilizing the analytical stability condition of a column with elastic rotational and translational restraints.

The energy method was applied by Kasarnowsky and Zetterholm[4] to the investigation of the stability of long columns elastically supported at equidistant intermediate points. A more general solution of this problem by means of the energy method was presented in 1937 by F. Bleich and H. Bleich.[5]

Utilizing a method of indeterminate analysis based on the principle of moment distribution, Lundquist[6] developed in 1937 a method for the investigation of the stability of frameworks with rigid joints by devising the fundamental "series" and "stiffness" criteria for stability.

Hoff[7] gave, by means of energy considerations, the rigorous proof

[1] von Mises, R., and J. Ratzersdorfer, Die Knicksicherheit von Rahmentragwerken, *Zeitschrift für angewandte Mathematik und Mechanik,* Vol. 6, p. 181, 1926. See also J. Ratzersdorfer, "Die Knicksicherheit von Stäben und Stabwerken," Julius Springer, Vienna, 1936.

[2] Chwalla, E., and F. Jokisch, Über das ebene Knickproblem des Stockwerkrahmens, *Der Stahlbau,* Vol. 14, p. 33, 1941.

[3] Prager, W., Elastic Stability of Plane Frameworks, *Jour. Aeronaut. Sci.,* Vol. 3, p. 388, 1936.

[4] Kasarnowsky, S., and D. Zetterholm, Zur Theorie der Seitensteifigkeit offener Fachwerkbrücken, *Der Bauingenier,* Vol. 8, p. 760, 1927.

[5] Bleich, F., and H. Bleich, Beitrag zur Stabilitätsuntersuchung des punkweise elastisch gestützten Stabes, *Der Stahlbau,* Vol. 10, p. 17, 1937.

[6] Lundquist, E. E., Stability of Structural Members under Axial Load, *NACA Tech. Note* 617, 1937; Method for Estimating the Critical Buckling Load for Structural Members, *NACA Tech. Note* 717, 1939; Principles of Moment Distribution Applied to Stability of Structural Members, *Proc. 5th Intern. Congr. Applied Mechanics,* 1938, p. 145.

[7] Hoff, N. J., Instability of Aircraft Frameworks, Paper presented at the 2d Annual Summer Meeting of the Institute of Aeronautical Sciences, California, 1940; Stable and Unstable Equilibrium of Plane Frameworks, *Jour. Aeronaut. Sci.,* Vol. 8, p. 115, 1941; The Proportioning of Aircraft Frameworks, *Jour. Aeronaut. Sci.,* Vol. 8, p. 319, 1941; Stress Analysis of Aircraft Frameworks, *Proc. Roy. Aeronaut. Soc.,* Vol. 45, No. 367, p. 241, 1941.

of the convergence of the moment distribution method and of the uniqueness of the results obtained by this method in the case of stable equilibrium under external loads. The proof leads directly to Hoff's criterion of stability.

Southwell's relaxation method was recently applied by Boley[1] to the analysis of the stability of frameworks.

Antisymmetrical buckling (sidesway) of simple rectangular rigid frames was discussed by Winter et al.[2]

Little experimental work in the field of framework stability has been done. In 1918 Engesser[3] reported tests made on small-scale models of elastically supported columns. Careful tests leading to conclusive results were made recently by Hoff[4] on truss models in order to check the computed failure load.

59. The Analytical Stability Criterion for Plane Frameworks—Bleich's Method

The theory discussed hereafter[5] is limited to the investigation of the stability of plane frameworks within their plane. It is based on the assumption that, before buckling sets in, the members are subjected to axial forces only and that no bending moments of any kind are induced in the members by the external forces which act upon the system. It is assumed that the members are straight, of constant cross section, and centrally loaded and that the direction of the external forces remains unchanged by deformation of the structure.

External and internal forces are in general in a state of stable equilibrium. However, under certain loading conditions another state of equilibrium may exist, characterized by the appearance of bending moments in the members of the framework. An example is demonstrated in Fig. 99. As will be subsequently shown, the case is one of unstable equilibrium between internal and external forces, similar to that studied in Chap. I on the pin-ended column. In this state of instability the external loads and the axial forces in the members, being in equilibrium just before the transition from the stable to the unstable configuration, no longer form a balanced group of forces, since the external loads change their position (but not direction) because of the distortion of the

[1] Boley, B. A., Numerical Methods for the Calculation of Elastic Instability; Paper presented at the Institute of Aeronautical Sciences, January, 1947.

[2] Winter, G., P. T. Hsu, B. Koo, and M. H. Loh, Buckling of Trusses and Rigid Frames, *Cornell Univ.* Eng. Expt. Sta. Bull. 36, Ithaca, N.Y.

[3] Engesser, F., Versuche und Untersuchungen über den Knickwiderstand des seitlich gestützten Stabes, *Der Eisenbau*, Vol. 9, p. 28, 1918.

[4] Hoff, N. J., B. A. Boley, S. V. Nardo, and S. Kaufman, Summary of Buckling of Rigid Jointed Plane Trusses, *Trans. ASCE*, 1951.

[5] Bleich, *loc. cit.* on p. 194.

whole system.   Additional axial and shear forces and additional moments[1] occur to restore equilibrium.   These forces and moments have the same order of magnitude as the displacements in the state of unstable equilibrium.

The relations between the displacements of the joints and the additional forces and additional moments represent the basic equations for the derivation of the stability condition of the framework.   These relations, referred to as stability equations, form a system of homogeneous linear equations.   The unknowns in these equations are the additional forces and moments and the joint displacements and rotations of the bars, whereas the coefficients of these unknowns are functions of the dimensions of the structure and of the axial forces P due to the loads which act on the structure.

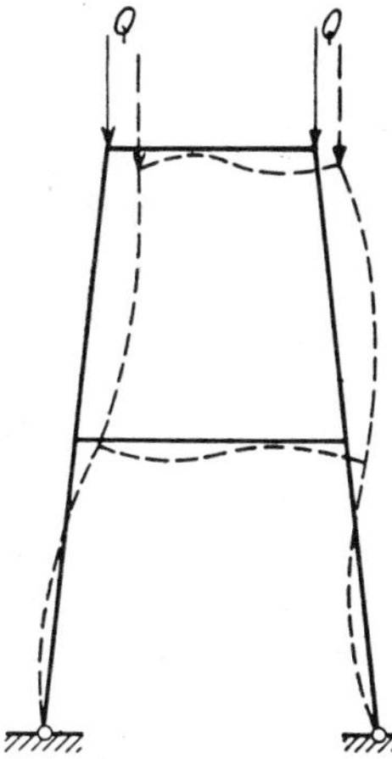

Since the stability equations are linear and homogeneous, the unknowns have, in general, zero values.   This means that no distortions or additional forces occur and the framework is in a state of stable equilibrium.   Finite values of the unknowns, indicating the appearance of additional forces and deformation, exist only when the determinant Δ of the system of stability equations vanishes.   The criterion $\Delta = 0$, therefore, determines those particular values of the external forces which correspond to the special state of equilibrium here considered.   In general, there is an infinite number of solutions of the equation $\Delta = 0$ determining an infinite number of different unstable equilibrium configurations.   The con-

Fig. 99

figuration which is associated with the smallest value of the loading determines the critical loading of the framework.

The equilibrium configurations defined by the condition $\Delta = 0$ are characterized by the fact that the distortion of the system is indeterminate as to its magnitude, for the finite solutions of a system of homogeneous linear equations always include an arbitrary factor.   Furthermore, replacing one of the zeros at the right-hand side of the equations by a loading term, expressing the effect of a small load added to the critical loading already present, would render infinite the solutions of the system of equations.   The physical meaning is that the slightest disturbing moment acting on a member will suffice to cause a large distortion of the entire framework and that it will not return to its original position when

---

[1] The forces and moments which appear in the state of buckling are referred to as additional shear forces and additional moments, although no shear forces and moments are supposed to act on the members prior to buckling.

the disturbing force ceases to act. As already pointed out, the system is in a state of unstable equilibrium.

The equation $\Delta = 0$ defines the stability limit, or, speaking more accurately, the transition from stable to unstable equilibrium, and represents the analytical stability criterion for the framework.

The determinant Δ is a function of the combination of loads which act on the framework. The magnitude of this loading can be expressed by a load parameter λ which finally represents the unknown quantity in the stability condition $\Delta = 0$. Since Δ is a transcendental function of λ, the stability condition furnishes an infinite number of roots λ, thus determining an infinite number of unstable equilibrium configurations. The configuration which is associated with the smallest root λ_1 defines the first possible state of buckling, indicating the existence of an unstable state of equilibrium infinitely close to the stable configuration (bifurcation of the equilibrium position). λ_1 therefore determines the critical loading.

It is not difficult to solve analytically the stability problem for a simple framework consisting of a few members. Starting from the differential equation of the deflected center line of the straight bar and solving the ensuing system of simultaneous differential equations with regard to the particular end conditions of each of the members, a system of linear equations is obtained, the determinant of which leads to the stability condition. In early papers some work has been done along this line. However, this procedure becomes highly involved and even hopeless when a more complex framework system is to be investigated.

The method subsequently outlined is based upon the idea of establishing a system of linear relations between the moments at the joints and the angles which measure the bar rotations. These two groups of parameters, as will be demonstrated later on, are sufficient to describe uniquely any configuration of the framework system in the state of instability. Moments and bar rotations were chosen because they represent the most natural variables apt to depict stress and strain of a distorted framework in the simplest mathematical form.

The limitations of the theory have already been discussed at the outset of this article, namely, the assumption of straight and centrally loaded bars of constant cross section and of unchanged direction of the external forces. The following points may be added:

The joints of the framework are considered as perfectly rigid, but individual members may be pin-connected to the joints.

The members are centrally loaded in compression or tension, but some members may carry no load.

The theory of stability of a two-dimensional framework composed of straight members and subject to loading in its plane is based on the fundamental differential equation of the tangent-modulus theory outlined in Chap. I:[1]

$$EI\tau \frac{d^2y}{dx^2} + M_x = 0 \tag{385}$$

where $y =$ the deflection at the distance x from the left end of the member

$M_x =$ the bending moment at x due to the forces acting on the deflected member in its displaced position

$I =$ the constant moment of inertia of the member for bending in the plane of the framework

$\tau = E_t/E$, where E_t is the tangent modulus. $\tau = 1$ if the average stress P/A lies in the elastic range, but a function of P/A if the average stress exceeds the proportional limit

Consider the member AB of length l shown in Fig. 100.   In its deflected state the following forces act on the member: the initial axial load P due to the loads to which the framework is subjected, the additional forces ΔP and Q, and the additional moments M^r and M^l. Deflections, forces, and moments are indicated in Fig. 100 in their positive directions. If a bar is part of a closed rigid frame, the above sign convention applies when each member is viewed from the interior of the frame.   Thus, the

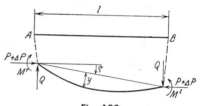

Fig. 100

deflection y is counted positive when the bar arches toward the interior, and the moment is counted positive when it induces tension in the inside flange of the member.   The bar rotation ρ is positive when the member rotates clockwise about its left end.   Displacements, additional forces, and moments are considered small as compared with the dimensions of the bar, so that their products and squares may be neglected, an assumption which leads to a linear theory of the stability of frameworks.

The bending moment at the distance x from point A, after eliminating the shear force Q, can be written in the form

$$M_x = M^r \left(1 - \frac{x}{l} \right) + M^l \frac{x}{l} + Py$$

omitting the product ΔPy which is of the second order.   Equation (385) therefore becomes

[1] Equation (19) is obtained from (385) if $M_x = Py$ is substituted.

$$EI_\tau \frac{d^2y}{dx^2} + Py + M^r \left(1 - \frac{x}{l}\right) + M^l \frac{x}{l} = 0 \qquad (386)$$

It is readily checked that the expression

$$y = \frac{M^r}{P}\left[\frac{\sin\phi\left(1 - \frac{x}{l}\right)}{\sin\phi} - 1 + \frac{x}{l}\right] + \frac{M^l}{P}\left[\frac{\sin\phi\frac{x}{l}}{\sin\phi} - \frac{x}{l}\right] \qquad (387)$$

satisfies the differential equation (386) and the condition at the ends, $y = 0$ for $x = 0$ and $x = l$. The parameter ϕ, referred to as the stability factor, is defined by

$$\phi = l\sqrt{\frac{P}{EI_\tau}} \qquad (388)$$

Equation (387) is valid when the second term Py in Eq. (386) is positive, i.e., when P is a compressive force. In the case of axial tension, Py becomes negative and ϕ imaginary, but the expression (387) remains valid provided the trigonometric functions are replaced by the corresponding hyperbolic functions.

The Four-moment Equations. The first group of stability equations expressing the condition of continuity at a point where two or more

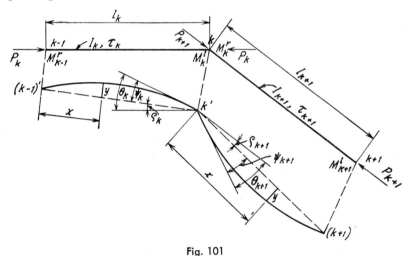

Fig. 101

members are rigidly jointed can be derived from Eq. (387). In Fig. 101 two consecutive bars l_k and l_{k+1} of a framework acted upon by the compressive forces P_k and P_{k+1} are shown in their original position and displaced and distorted in the state of buckling. The flexural rigidities of the two bars are $EI_k\tau_k$ and $EI_{k+1}\tau_{k+1}$, taking into account that τ may vary from member to member.

The two bars meet at the rigid joint k, and to be general, it is assumed that other bars, too, are rigidly framed at the same point. The additional end moments in the two elements under consideration are $M_{k-1}{}^r$, $M_k{}^l$ and $M_k{}^r$, $M_{k+1}{}^l$. Since k is assumed to be a perfectly rigid joint, the angle $\theta_k = \rho_k + \psi_k$ must be equal to $\theta_{k+1} = \rho_{k+1} + \psi_{k+1}$. Therefore the condition of continuity is expressed by

$$\rho_k + \psi_k = \rho_{k+1} + \psi_{k+1} \tag{389}$$

ρ_k and ρ_{k+1} are the bar rotations; ψ_k and ψ_{k+1} the slopes of the elastic curves at k. Since

$$\psi_k = \left[\frac{dy_k}{dx}\right]_{x=l_k} \qquad \text{and} \qquad \psi_{k+1} = \left[\frac{dy_{k+1}}{dx}\right]_{x=0}$$

the following relations can be derived from Eq. (387):

$$\left.\begin{aligned}
\psi_k &= \frac{M_{k-1}{}^r}{P_k l_k}\left(-\frac{\phi_k}{\sin \phi_k}+1\right) + \frac{M_k{}^l}{P_k l_k}(\phi_k \cot \phi_k - 1) \\
\psi_{k+1} &= \frac{M_k{}^r}{P_{k+1} l_{k+1}}(-\phi_{k+1}\cot \phi_{k+1}+1) + \frac{M_{k+1}{}^l}{P_{k+1} l_{k+1}}\left(\frac{\phi_{k+1}}{\sin \phi_{k+1}}-1\right)
\end{aligned}\right\} \tag{390}$$

By virtue of definition (388) we have

$$P_k l_k = \frac{EI_k \tau_k}{l_k}\phi_k^2 \qquad \text{and} \qquad P_{k+1}l_{k+1} = \frac{EI_{k+1}\tau_{k+1}}{l_{k+1}}\phi_{k+1}^2 \tag{391}$$

It is convenient to introduce the "reduced lengths"

$$l_k' = \frac{I}{I_k \tau_k}l_k \qquad \text{and} \qquad l_{k+1}' = \frac{I}{I_{k+1}\tau_{k+1}}l_{k+1} \tag{392}$$

in which I is an arbitrary moment of inertia. Equations (391), therefore, can be written

$$P_k l_k = \frac{EI}{l_k'}\phi_k^2 \qquad \text{and} \qquad P_{k+1}l_{k+1} = \frac{EI}{l_{k+1}'}\phi_{k+1}^2 \tag{393}$$

Upon introducing the expressions (393) and the transcendental functions

$$s = \frac{1}{\phi^2}\left(\frac{\phi}{\sin \phi}-1\right) \qquad \text{and} \qquad c = \frac{1}{\phi^2}(1-\phi\cot \phi) \tag{394}$$

into Eqs. (390), these equations assume the form

$$\left.\begin{aligned}
\psi_k &= -\frac{1}{EI}(M_{k-1}{}^r l_k' s_k + M_k{}^l l_k' c_k) \\
\psi_{k+1} &= \frac{1}{EI}(M_k{}^r l_{k+1}' c_{k+1} + M_{k+1}{}^l l_{k+1}' s_{k+1})
\end{aligned}\right\} \tag{395}$$

Substitution of ψ_k and ψ_{k+1} in the continuity condition (389) leads finally to

$$M_{k-1}{}^r l_k{}' s_k + M_k{}^l l_k{}' c_k + M_k{}^r l_{k+1}{}' c_{k+1} + M_{k+1}{}^l l_{k+1}{}' s_{k+1} - EI(\rho_k - \rho_{k+1}) = 0 \tag{396}$$

Equation (396) represents a relation between the four terminal moments of two adjacent members which are rigidly jointed and the bar rotations ρ. It is called the *four-moment equation*.[1] Equations of this type form the first group of the stability equations.

If only two members meet at k, $M_k{}^l$ becomes equal to $M_k{}^r$ and Eq. (396) simplifies to the three-moment equation

$$M_{k-1} l_k{}' s_k + M_k(l_k{}' c_k + l_{k+1}{}' c_{k+1}) + M_{k+1} l_{k+1}{}' s_{k+1} \\ - EI\ (\rho_k - \rho_{k+1}) = 0 \tag{397}$$

Equations (396) and (397) were derived under the assumption that the two members under consideration are under axial compression. If any member is in axial tension, the functions s and c in the respective terms must be replaced by

$$s = \frac{1}{\phi^2}\left(1 - \frac{\phi}{\sinh\ \phi}\right) \qquad \text{and} \qquad c = \frac{1}{\phi^2}\ (\phi \coth\ \phi - 1) \tag{398}$$

If $P = 0$, that is, when no axial force due to the external loads acts upon the member, then

$$s = \tfrac{1}{6} \qquad \text{and} \qquad c = \tfrac{1}{3} \tag{399}$$

In the case of any bar being clamped at point k (see Fig. 102), a continuity condition occurs which differs from Eq. (396). Replacing the rigid support by an imaginary member $k + 1$ which is rigidly supported and has infinite rigidity $I_{k+1} = \infty$, we have $l_{k+1}{}' = l_{k+1}/I_{k+1} = 0$ and $\rho_{k+1} = 0$, leading to the condition

$$M_{k-1}{}^r l_k{}' s_k + M_k{}^l l_k{}' c_k - EI\rho_k = 0 \tag{400}$$

The number of continuity equations which may be set up depends upon the number of rigid joints and the number of bars meeting at each

---

[1] This equation will be familiar to the structural engineer from the theory of beam columns. See A. S. Niles and J. S. Newell, "Airplane Structures," 3d ed., Vol. II, John Wiley & Sons, Inc., New York, 1943, where a special case of this equation, $\rho_k = \rho_{k+1} = 0$, is discussed. Using the above notation for the moments, the equation reads:

$$M_{k-1}{}^r \frac{l_k}{I_k} \alpha_k + 2M_k{}^l \frac{l_k}{I_k} \beta_k + 2M_k{}^r \frac{l_{k+1}}{I_{k+1}} \beta_{k+1} + M_{k+1}{}^l \frac{l_{k+1}}{I_{k+1}} \alpha_{k+1} = W$$

where W is the loading term, equal to zero in the case here considered. The parameters α and β are related to s and c by the equations

$$\alpha = 6s \qquad \text{and} \qquad \beta = 3c$$

joint.   For each joint into which n bars are rigidly framed, $n - 1$ independent four-moment equations (396) can be written.

To facilitate application of the four-moment equation, Table 13 contains the values of the coefficients s and c according to Eq. (394).

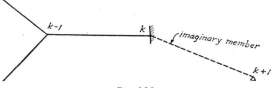

Fig. 102

Geometric Relations.   Any type of framework can be considered to be a closed circuit of bars or can be broken up into a series of closed circuits. Any open alignment of bars can be closed by a suitable imaginary member.   For example, the rigid frame A-B in Fig. 103, fixed at the left support and hinged at the right support, can be made into an equivalent closed circuit by including the phantom member A-B having $I = A = \infty$.

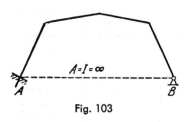

Fig. 103

Consider a closed circuit of rigidly jointed members as indicated in Fig. 104.   Proceeding from left to right as viewed from the interior of the circuit, the joints are numbered continuously around the circuit.   The angles γ defining the slope of the members in the undistorted shape of the frame are counted clockwise from the arbitrarily chosen x-axis at

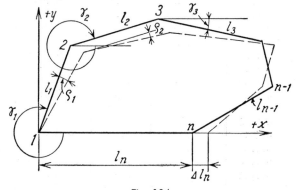

Fig. 104

the lower numbered end of the member.   The bar rotations ρ are assumed positive when they increase the angles γ.*   We denote by Δl the change

---

* The sign rule concerning the bar rotations ρ conforms with the sign convention for these angles, already assumed in setting up the four-moment equations.

TABLE 13. Values for s and c According to Eq. (394)

ϕ	$s(\phi)$	$c(\phi)$	ϕ	$s(\phi)$	$c(\phi)$
0	0.1667	0.3333	0.80	0.1800	0.3485
0.02	0.1667	0.3333	0.82	0.1807	0.3493
0.04	0.1667	0.3334	0.84	0.1815	0.3501
0.06	0.1667	0.3334	0.86	0.1823	0.3510
0.08	0.1668	0.3335	0.88	0.1831	0.3519
0.10	0.1669	0.3336	0.90	0.1839	0.3529
0.12	0.1670	0.3337	0.92	0.1847	0.3538
0.14	0.1671	0.3338	0.94	0.1856	0.3548
0.16	0.1672	0.3339	0.96	0.1865	0.3558
0.18	0.1673	0.3341	0.98	0.1874	0.3568
0.20	0.1675	0.3342	1.00	0.1884	0.3579
0.22	0.1676	0.3344	1.02	0.1894	0.3590
0.24	0.1678	0.3346	1.04	0.1904	0.3602
0.26	0.1680	0.3348	1.06	0.1914	0.3613
0.28	0.1682	0.3351	1.08	0.1925	0.3625
0.30	0.1684	0.3353	1.10	0.1936	0.3638
0.32	0.1687	0.3356	1.12	0.1948	0.3650
0.34	0.1689	0.3359	1.14	0.1959	0.3663
0.36	0.1692	0.3362	1.16	0.1971	0.3677
0.38	0.1695	0.3366	1.18	0.1984	0.3690
0.40	0.1698	0.3369	1.20	0.1997	0.3705
0.42	0.1702	0.3373	1.22	0.2010	0.3719
0.44	0.1705	0.3377	1.24	0.2023	0.3734
0.46	0.1709	0.3381	1.26	0.2037	0.3750
0.48	0.1713	0.3386	1.28	0.2051	0.3765
0.50	0.1717	0.3390	1.30	0.2066	0.3781
0.52	0.1721	0.3395	1.32	0.2081	0.3798
0.54	0.1725	0.3400	1.34	0.2097	0.3816
0.56	0.1730	0.3405	1.36	0.2113	0.3833
0.58	0.1735	0.3411	1.38	0.2129	0.3851
0.60	0.1739	0.3416	1.40	0.2146	0.3870
0.62	0.1745	0.3422	1.42	0.2164	0.3889
0.64	0.1750	0.3428	1.44	0.2182	0.3909
0.66	0.1755	0.3434	1.46	0.2200	0.3929
0.68	0.1761	0.3441	1.48	0.2219	0.3950
0.70	0.1767	0.3448	1.50	0.2239	0.3972
0.72	0.1773	0.3455	1.52	0.2259	0.3994
0.74	0.1780	0.3462	1.54	0.2280	0.4017
0.76	0.1786	0.3469	1.56	0.2302	0.4040
0.78	0.1793	0.3477	1.58	0.2324	0.4064

TABLE 13. Values for s and c According to Eq. (394). (Continued)

ϕ	$s(\phi)$	$c(\phi)$	ϕ	$s(\phi)$	$c(\phi)$
1.60	0.2346	0.4089	2.40	0.4433	0.6285
1.62	0.2370	0.4114	2.42	0.4548	0.6404
1.64	0.2394	0.4141	2.44	0.4670	0.6530
1.66	0.2419	0.4168	2.46	0.4800	0.6663
1.68	0.2445	0.4196	2.48	0.4937	0.6804
1.70	0.2472	0.4225	2.50	0.5084	0.6955
1.72	0.2499	0.4254	2.52	0.5240	0.7115
1.74	0.2527	0.4285	2.54	0.5406	0.7285
1.76	0.2557	0.4316	2.56	0.5585	0.7467
1.78	0.2587	0.4349	2.58	0.5776	0.7663
1.80	0.2618	0.4383	2.60	0.5982	0.7873
1.82	0.2651	0.4417	2.62	0.6203	0.8098
1.84	0.2684	0.4453	2.64	0.6443	0.8342
1.86	0.2719	0.4490	2.66	0.6703	0.8607
1.88	0.2755	0.4529	2.68	0.6986	0.8894
1.90	0.2792	0.4568	2.70	0.7294	0.9210
1.92	0.2830	0.4609	2.72	0.7633	0.9549
1.94	0.2870	0.4652	2.74	0.8005	0.9926
1.96	0.2911	0.4696	2.76	0.8417	1.0342
1.98	0.2954	0.4741	2.78	0.8874	1.0807
2.00	0.2999	0.4788	2.80	0.9386	1.1321
2.02	0.3045	0.4837	2.82	0.9962	1.1902
2.04	0.3093	0.4888	2.84	1.0614	1.2559
2.06	0.3143	0.4941	2.86	1.1360	1.3310
2.08	0.3195	0.4996	2.88	1.2220	1.4175
2.10	0.3249	0.5053	2.90	1.3224	1.5183
2.12	0.3305	0.5112	2.92	1.4409	1.6374
2.14	0.3364	0.5174	2.94	1.5830	1.7800
2.16	0.3425	0.5238	2.96	1.7566	1.9541
2.18	0.3489	0.5305	2.98	1.9731	2.1712
2.20	0.3556	0.5375	3.00	2.2509	2.4495
2.22	0.3626	0.5448	3.02	2.6203	2.8195
2.24	0.3699	0.5524	3.04	3.1353	3.3350
2.26	0.3776	0.5604	3.06	3.9029	4.1031
2.28	0.3856	0.5688	3.08	5.1693	5.3701
2.30	0.3940	0.5775	3.10	7.6539	7.8553
2.32	0.4029	0.5867	3.12	14.7421	14.9440
2.34	0.4122	0.5964	3.14	199.862	200.064
2.36	0.4220	0.6065	π	$\pm \infty$	$\pm \infty$
2.38	0.4323	0.6172	3.16	-17.2929	-17.0898

TABLE 13.   Values for s and c According to Eq. (394).   (Continued)

ϕ	$s(\phi)$	$c(\phi)$	ϕ	$s(\phi)$	$c(\phi)$
3.18	-8.2885	-8.0847	3.98	-0.4010	-0.1628
3.20	-5.4511	-5.2466			
3.22	-4.0614	-3.8563	4.00	-0.3928	-0.1534
3.24	-3.2367	-3.0310	4.02	-0.3851	-0.1444
3.26	-2.6908	-2.4844	4.04	-0.3777	-0.1358
			4.06	-0.3706	-0.1275
3.28	-2.3028	-2.0957	4.08	-0.3639	-0.1195
3.30	-2.0128	-1.8051	4.10	-0.3576	-0.1119
3.32	-1.7880	-1.5796			
3.34	-1.6086	-1.3995	4.12	-0.3515	-0.1044
3.36	-1.4622	-1.2524	4.14	-0.3457	-0.0973
			4.16	-0.3402	-0.0904
3.38	-1.3403	-1.1298	4.18	-0.3349	-0.0837
3.40	-1.2375	-1.0262	4.20	-0.3299	-0.0772
3.42	-1.1494	-0.9375			
3.44	-1.0733	-0.8606	4.22	-0.3251	-0.0710
3.46	-1.0068	-0.7933	4.24	-0.3205	-0.0649
			4.26	-0.3161	-0.0590
3.48	-0.9481	-0.7339	4.28	-0.3119	-0.0532
3.50	-0.8961	-0.6811	4.30	-0.3079	-0.0476
3.52	-0.8497	-0.6339			
3.54	-0.8080	-0.5913	4.32	-0.3041	-0.0422
3.56	-0.7703	-0.5528	4.34	-0.3005	-0.0369
3.58	-0.7361	-0.5178	4.36	-0.2970	-0.0317
			4.38	-0.2937	-0.0267
3.60	-0.7049	-0.4858	4.40	-0.2905	-0.0217
3.62	-0.6764	-0.4564			
3.64	-0.6502	-0.4293	4.42	-0.2875	-0.0169
3.66	-0.6261	-0.4043	4.44	-0.2846	-0.0122
3.68	-0.6038	-0.3812	4.46	-0.2818	-0.0076
			4.48	-0.2792	-0.0030
3.70	-0.5832	-0.3596	4.50	-0.2767	0.0015
3.72	-0.5640	-0.3395			
3.74	-0.5461	-0.3207	4.52	-0.2744	0.0059
3.76	-0.5295	-0.3031	4.54	-0.2721	0.0102
3.78	-0.5139	-0.2865	4.56	-0.2700	0.0144
			4.58	-0.2679	0.0186
3.80	-0.4994	-0.2709	4.60	-0.2660	0.0227
3.82	-0.4857	-0.2563			
3.84	-0.4728	-0.2424	4.62	-0.2642	0.0268
3.86	-0.4607	-0.2292	4.64	-0.2625	0.0308
3.88	-0.4493	-0.2167	4.66	-0.2609	0.0348
			4.68	-0.2594	0.0387
3.90	-0.4386	-0.2049	4.70	-0.2581	0.0426
3.92	-0.4284	-0.1936			
3.94	-0.4188	-0.1829	4.72	-0.2568	0.0465
3.96	-0.4097	-0.1726	4.74	-0.2556	0.0503

TABLE 13. Values for s and c According to Eq. (394). (Continued)

ϕ	$s(\phi)$	$c(\phi)$	ϕ	$s(\phi)$	$c(\phi)$
4.76	−0.2545	0.0542	5.52	−0.2949	0.2222
4.78	−0.2535	0.0579	5.54	−0.2994	0.2290
4.80	−0.2525	0.0617	5.56	−0.3041	0.2361
			5.58	−0.3093	0.2435
4.82	−0.2517	0.0655	5.60	−0.3148	0.2513
4.84	−0.2510	0.0692			
4.86	−0.2504	0.0729	5.62	−0.3207	0.2594
4.88	−0.2498	0.0767	5.64	−0.3271	0.2680
4.90	−0.2494	0.0804	5.66	−0.3339	0.2770
			5.68	−0.3414	0.2866
4.92	−0.2490	0.0841	5.70	−0.3494	0.2967
4.94	−0.2488	0.0879			
4.96	−0.2486	0.0916	5.72	−0.3580	0.3075
4.98	−0.2485	0.0954	5.74	−0.3674	0.3189
5.00	−0.2486	0.0992	5.76	−0.3776	0.3311
			5.78	−0.3887	0.3442
5.02	−0.2487	0.1030	5.80	−0.4008	0.3583
5.04	−0.2489	0.1068			
5.06	−0.2493	0.1107	5.82	−0.4141	0.3736
5.08	−0.2497	0.1146	5.84	−0.4286	0.3901
5.10	−0.2502	0.1185	5.86	−0.4447	0.4080
			5.88	−0.4624	0.4276
5.12	−0.2509	0.1225	5.90	−0.4821	0.4492
5.14	−0.2517	0.1265			
5.16	−0.2525	0.1306	5.92	−0.5040	0.4730
5.18	−0.2535	0.1348	5.94	−0.5287	0.4995
5.20	−0.2547	0.1390	5.96	−0.5565	0.5291
			5.98	−0.5881	0.5625
5.22	−0.2559	0.1433	6.00	−0.6243	0.6005
5.24	−0.2573	0.1476			
5.26	−0.2588	0.1521	6.02	−0.6661	0.6441
5.28	−0.2605	0.1566	6.04	−0.7150	0.6948
5.30	−0.2623	0.1613	6.06	−0.7728	0.7543
			6.08	−0.8421	0.8254
5.32	−0.2643	0.1660	6.10	−0.9268	0.9118
5.34	−0.2664	0.1709			
5.36	−0.2687	0.1759	6.12	−1.0325	1.0191
5.38	−0.2712	0.1811	6.14	−1.1679	1.1562
5.40	−0.2739	0.1864	6.16	−1.3475	1.3375
			6.18	−1.5971	1.5888
5.42	−0.2768	0.1919	6.20	−1.9672	1.9605
5.44	−0.2800	0.1975			
5.46	−0.2833	0.2034	6.22	−2.5720	2.5669
5.48	−0.2869	0.2094	6.24	−3.7377	3.7343
5.50	−0.2908	0.2157	6.26	−6.9160	6.9142
			6.28	−50.0163	50.0160
			2π	$\mp \infty$	$\pm \infty$

in length of a member due to the additional force ΔP, Δl being positive for tension members.

The sum of the rectangular projections upon the arbitrary axes x and y, respectively, of all members before buckling must be zero. Therefore

$$\Sigma l \cos \gamma = 0 \quad \text{and} \quad \Sigma l \sin \gamma = 0 \qquad (401)$$

Since the closed circuit must remain closed after distortion, whereby the lengths l have changed to $l + \Delta l$ and the angles γ to $\gamma + \rho$, we have

$$\begin{aligned} \Sigma(l + \Delta l) \cos (\gamma + \rho) = 0 \\ \Sigma(l + \Delta l) \sin (\gamma + \rho) = 0 \end{aligned} \Bigg\} \qquad (402)$$

Δl and ρ are of small magnitude as compared with l. Setting $\cos \rho = 1$ and $\sin \rho = \rho$, and disregarding the products $\Delta l \rho$, we may write

$$\Sigma l \cos \gamma + \Sigma \Delta l \cos \gamma - \Sigma \rho l \sin \gamma = 0$$
$$\Sigma l \sin \gamma + \Sigma \Delta l \sin \gamma + \Sigma \rho l \cos \gamma = 0$$

By virtue of Eqs. (401) the first term in each equation vanishes and the geometric relations assume the form

$$\begin{aligned} \Sigma \Delta l \cos \gamma - \Sigma \rho l \sin \gamma = 0 \\ \Sigma \Delta l \sin \gamma + \Sigma \rho l \cos \gamma = 0 \end{aligned} \Bigg\} \qquad (403)$$

For each closed framework two equations of the type (403) can be written.

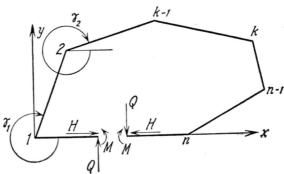

Fig. 105

In the majority of cases the first term in each of Eqs. (403) is small compared with the second term and can be disregarded. The exceptions are framework systems the dimensions of which in the direction of the acting external forces are many times larger than in the direction perpendicular to it.

Equilibrium Equations. In any closed circuit of bars, displaced and deformed in the state of buckling, in addition to the moments at the rigid joints, also there arise forces H and Q as indicated in Fig. 105. With reference to Fig. 106, showing the member $k - 1$, k removed from the circuit, the following equilibrium equation applies for each individual member:

$$M_k = M_{k-1} + P_k l_k \rho_k + Q_k l_k \qquad (404)$$

in which the term $\Delta P_k l_k \rho_k$ is omitted as small of second order. If P_k is a tensile force, the second term at the right-hand side becomes negative.

From inspection of Fig. 105 the relation

$$Q_k = Q \cos \gamma_k + H \sin \gamma_k \qquad (405)$$

is readily found, expressing Q_k ($k = 1, 2, \ldots, n$) by the forces Q and H associated with the circuit under consideration. The signs of

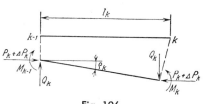

Fig. 106

the trigonometric functions in Eq. (405) are determined by the angles γ_k which must be measured clockwise from the x-axis at the lower numbered end of the member as explained by Fig. 104.

The Stability Equations. The three groups of equations developed above, the four-moment equations, the geometric relations, and the equilibrium equations, constitute the complete system of stability equations involving the following unknown quantities: moments M, additional forces Q and H, and the bar rotations ρ. It can be shown that the number of equations of the types (396), (400), (403), (404), and (405) suffice to determine the unknowns M, Q, H, and ρ.

Confining the reasoning first to a single closed circuit of n bars, there are n moments M, n bar rotations ρ, and two additional forces Q and H—

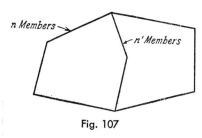

Fig. 107

altogether $2n + 2$ unknowns. They are determined by n four-moment equations, n equilibrium equations, and two geometric relations, or a total of $2n + 2$ equations. If two bars are hinged at a joint, one unknown moment and one four-moment equation drop out for each articulated joint.

If the single-circuit framework is transformed into a double-circuit framework by addition of n' bars as shown in Fig. 107, there would be $n' + 1$ additional moments, n' additional bar rotations ρ, and another two forces Q and H—altogether $2n' + 3$ additional unknowns—balanced by $n' + 1$ four-moment equation, n' equilibrium equations, and two geometric relations, a total of $2n' + 3$ additional equations.

Since any kind of framework can be formed by repeating the above-outlined procedure, it is evident that the three sets of equations, which constitute the system of stability equations, will suffice to determine the internal forces and the deformation of the buckled framework.

In closing the discussion on the stability equations it is necessary to make some general remarks concerning the application of these equations in any particular case. In setting up the four-moment equations the following sign rule must be observed. Starting from any arbitrary joint in each closed circuit the joints should be numbered continuously in a clockwise sense. In writing the four-moment equations for each circuit in the sequence as given by the number of joints, all end moments are considered positive, and Eqs. (396) apply without any consideration concerning the signs of moments or bar rotations. An exception are members which are common to two circuits, for which the end moments must be considered positive in one circuit and therefore negative in the other one. As for the geometric relations the sign convention for the initial angles γ stated above (see Fig. 104) must be observed in each closed circuit, leading automatically to a set of geometric relations which are consistent with the four-moment equations.

The Stability Condition. Inspection shows that Eqs. (396), (403), (404), and (405) are all linear, homogeneous equations, and nonzero solutions exist only if the determinant Δ of the coefficients of these equations vanishes. The condition $\Delta = 0$ is the stability condition and defines, as was already pointed out, the critical loading condition of the framework.

At first glance the number of stability equations looks formidable. However, in many cases of practical significance it is possible to reduce their number substantially by simple elimination procedures. Moreover, the use of finite difference equations sometimes permits obtaining the solution of the stability problem in simple form, regardless of the number of stability equations. The advantage of the method discussed above and of related analytical methods is that they facilitate establishment of expedient design methods and of rules for routine design, based upon a rational solution of the problem. This feature of the analytical methods constitutes their importance in the design of civil engineering structures. It is not possible to discuss the treatment of the stability condition $\Delta = 0$ in a general manner, since it depends to a great extent upon the special nature of the problem. Chapters VII and VIII will deal with the application of the analytical method to various buckling problems in the field of engineering structures, and there will be opportunities to demonstrate the various methods of handling the mathematical analysis.

60. Modification of the Analytical Method Using Joint Rotations as Unknowns

It was pointed out above that the chief concern in dealing with the stability problem of rigidly jointed frameworks is the question of reducing the number of stability equations which finally lead to the stability criterion $\Delta = 0$. For some types of framework systems it is of advantage to eliminate from the beginning the terminal moments M by considering the angular rotation θ of the joints and the bar rotations ρ as variables in the stability equations. When the number of unknown angles ρ is zero or very small compared with the number of joint rotations θ, the method indicated will prove of great advantage. The idea of introducing the joint rotation θ into the indeterminate analysis goes back to Manderla (1878) and Mohr (1892), who devised the method as a means for the study of secondary stresses in trusses.

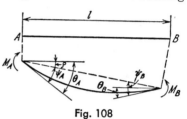

Fig. 108

Figure 108 shows a member AB of a framework in its original position and displaced and deflected after buckling, acted on by the positive end moments M_A and M_B. The rotations of the ends are $\theta = \psi + \rho$. ψ_A and ψ_B can be obtained from Eqs. (395):

$$\psi_A = \frac{l'}{EI}(cM_A + sM_B) \qquad \text{and} \qquad \psi_B = -\frac{l'}{EI}(sM_A + cM_B)$$

s and c are defined by Eqs. (394) for compression members, (398) for tension members, and (399) for members carrying no axial load.

We have therefore

$$\left. \begin{aligned} \theta_A &= \frac{l'}{EI}(cM_A + sM_B) + \rho \\ \theta_B &= -\frac{l'}{EI}(sM_A + cM_B) + \rho \end{aligned} \right\} \tag{406}$$

Solving for M_A and M_B leads to the following equations for axially loaded bars:

$$\left. \begin{aligned} M_A &= \frac{EI}{l'(c^2 - s^2)}[c\theta_A + s\theta_B - \rho(c + s)] \\ M_B &= -\frac{EI}{l'(c^2 - s^2)}[s\theta_A + c\theta_B - \rho(c + s)] \end{aligned} \right\} \tag{407}$$

By introducing the substitution factors

$$C = \frac{c}{c^2 - s^2} \qquad \text{and} \qquad S = \frac{s}{c^2 - s^2} \tag{408}$$

Eqs. (407) can be written more compactly:

$$\left. \begin{aligned} M_A &= \frac{EI}{l'}[C\theta_A + S\theta_B - \rho(C + S)] \\ M_B &= -\frac{EI}{l'}[S\theta_A + C\theta_B - \rho(C + S)] \end{aligned} \right\} \tag{409}$$

These equations are valid under the sign convention adopted previously. which implies that joint rotations and bar rotations in a clockwise sense are positive.

If a number of bars AB, AC, AD, . . . are rigidly connected to the joint A, the bars will have the same angular rotation θ_A at that point so that, on assigning an individual value θ to each of the j joints of a framework, the number of unknown angles θ will be j. The bar rotations ρ are not independent of each other but are interrelated by geometric equations of the type (403), and the angles ρ can be expressed by a restricted number r of unknown angles ρ. The total number of unknowns is therefore $j + r$.

To determine these $j + r$ unknowns two groups of equations can be set up. The first group is obtained by applying the equilibrium condition

$$\Sigma M = 0 \qquad\qquad (410)$$

to each joint, in which the values M are the moments transmitted by the members to the common joint at which they meet. j such equation can be written. The second group, determining the r unknown angles ρ, are equilibrium equations of the type (404) in which the additional forces Q always can be expressed by terms involving end moments M and axial forces P. Thus, a system of $j + r$ equations in the variables M and ρ is

TABLE 14.   Values S and C According to Eq. (408)

ϕ	$S(\phi)$	$C(\phi)$	ϕ	$S(\phi)$	$C(\phi)$
0.00	2.000	4.000	3.00	2.412	2.624
0.10	2.000	3.999	3.20	2.492	2.399
0.20	2.001	3.995	3.40	2.588	2.146
0.30	2.003	3.988	3.60	2.702	1.862
0.40	2.005	3.979	3.80	2.838	1.540
0.60	2.012	3.952	4.00	3.004	1.173
0.80	2.022	3.914	4.20	3.207	0.751
1.00	2.034	3.865	4.40	3.462	0.259
1.20	2.050	3.804	4.60	3.787	− 0.323
1.40	2.070	3.732	4.80	4.211	− 1.029
1.60	2.093	3.647	5.00	4.785	− 1.909
1.80	2.120	3.548	5.20	5.592	− 3.052
2.00	2.152	3.436	5.40	6.798	− 4.625
2.20	2.189	3.309	5.60	8.759	− 6.992
2.40	2.233	3.166	5.80	12.428	−11.111
2.60	2.283	3.005	6.00	21.454	−20.637
2.80	2.343	2.825			

arrived at. If the moments are expressed by means of Eqs. (409), the number of variables in these equations is reduced to $j + r$. These equations are linear and homogeneous in θ and ρ, and when the determinant Δ of their coefficients is set equal to zero, the stability condition is obtained. It is not difficult to decide in each individual case whether the four-moment-equation method outlined in the previous article or the joint-rotation method is more appropriate. In general, it can be said that, in investigating framework systems in which the number r of free bar rotations is very small compared with the number of the unknown moments M, the latter method will afford some advantage.[1] However, for many problems of importance in structural analysis, the four-moment-equation method leads to a straightforward solution of satisfactory simplicity.

To facilitate the application of the method outlined in this article Table 14 has been provided. This table gives the numerical values of S and C for compression members.

61. Numerical Methods Using the Principles of the Moment Distribution Method

In 1935 James[2] extended the Cross method of moment distribution to the analysis of framed members subject to axial loads. Lundquist applied James's generalized equations to the investigation of the stability of compression members in framed structures and developed an appropriate procedure for the solution of the stability problem.

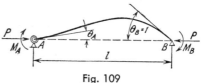

Fig. 109

Consider a member on unyielding supports at each end, elastically restrained at the end A and acted on by the axial force P, as shown in Fig. 109. The stiffness of such a member is defined as the moment at the end B necessary to produce a rotation of 1 radian of this end.[3] It is obvious that the stiffness will depend upon the degree of restraint at the far end. For the derivation of the criterion for stability three types of restraint are considered and the following symbols for stiffness used:[4]

[1] For a detailed discussion of this subject see F. Bleich, "Berechnung statisch unbestimmter Tragwerke nach der Methode des Viermomentensatzes," 2d ed., Julius Springer, Berlin, 1926.

[2] James, B. W., Principal Effects of Axial Load on Moment Distribution Analysis of Rigid Structures, *NACA Tech. Note* 534, 1935.

[3] James's and Lundquist's definition of stiffness is based on a rotation of $\frac{1}{4}$ radian, whereas other authors consider rotation of 1 radian.

[4] The symbols S and C used in this article do not have the same meaning as in the previous article.

$$S = \text{the far end fixed}$$
$$S' = \text{far end elastically restrained}$$
$$S'' = \text{far end pinned}$$

The carry-over factor for a member on unyielding supports at the ends is defined as the ratio of the moment developed at the far end A to the moment applied at the near end B. As in the case of stiffness, the

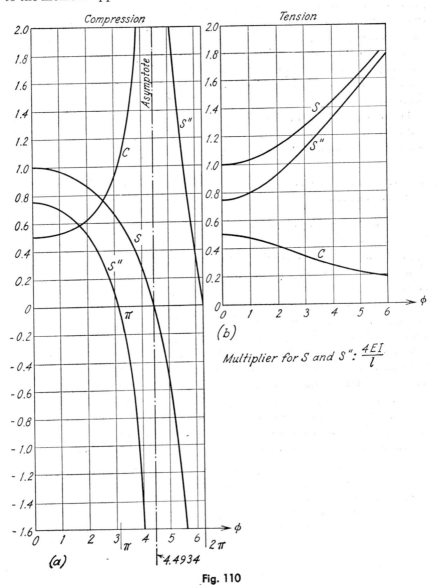

Multiplier for S and S'': $\frac{4EI}{l}$

Fig. 110

carry-over factor depends on the amount of restraint at the far end of the member. For the three types of restraint considered previously the following symbols for the carry-over factor are used.

$$C = \text{the far end fixed}$$
$$C' = \text{the far end elastically restrained}$$
$$C'' = \text{the far end pinned}$$

Values for the quantities S, S'', and C were calculated and presented by James and by Lundquist and Kroll.[1]

S, S'', and C are shown in Fig. 110, where these quantities are plotted versus $\phi = l \sqrt{P/EI\tau}$.[2] Figure 110a represents the graphs for S and S'' for axial compression for values of ϕ between 0 and 2π. It is important to take note of the fact that S and S'' may become negative for certain values of ϕ as a glance at the graphs shows. The curves S and S'', in the interval here considered, have asymptotes at $\phi = 2\pi$ and $\phi = 4.4934 \ldots$,[3] respectively. The stiffness S'' and the carry-over factor C change sign at $\phi = 4.4934$, having asymptotes at this value. Figure 110b represents the graphs for S, S'', and C for members in tension.

From the values of S and C for the far end fixed, the values of S' and C' for the elastically restrained far end can be found by the moment distribution procedure indicated in Fig. 111 leading to the relations

$$S' = S\left(1 - \frac{C^2 S}{K + S}\right) \quad (411)$$

$$C' = \frac{C}{1 + \frac{S}{K}(1 - C^2)} \quad (412)$$

Fig. 111

in which K is the spring constant at the far end A.

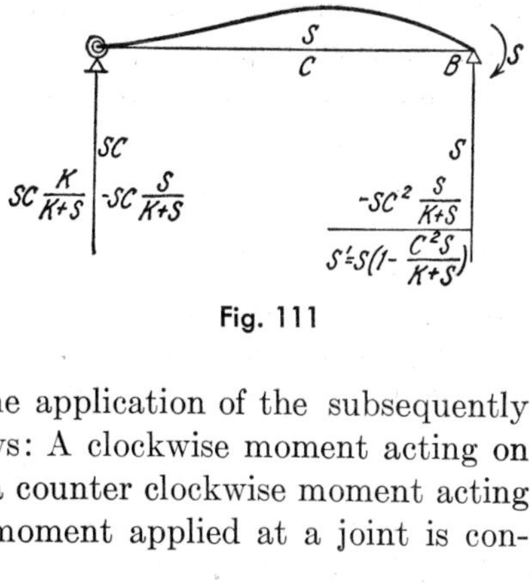

The sign convention adopted for the application of the subsequently discussed stability criteria is as follows: A clockwise moment acting on the end of a member is positive, and a counter clockwise moment acting on a joint is positive. An external moment applied at a joint is considered to act on the joint.

Stability Criteria for Frameworks with No Joint Translation Possible. If an elastic framework with joints fixed is in stable equilibrium under the action of external forces, then an arbitrary moment m applied at any joint of the framework will cause a finite distortion of the structure.

[1] Lundquist, E. E., and W. D. Kroll, Tables of Stiffness and Carry-over Factors for Structural Members under Axial Load, *NACA Tech. Note* 652, 1938.

[2] ϕ is identical with $(L/j)_{\text{eff}}$ in Lundquist's paper.

[3] This transcendental value is the second root of the equation tan $\phi = \phi$.

When the moment ceases to act, the structure will return to its original form. As the external loading is gradually increased, producing larger and larger axial loads P within the members of the framework, the resistance against bending (stiffness) of the compression members will decrease, at first slowly and then more rapidly. This results in an increasingly greater effect of the applied moment m upon the deformation of the members until a loading condition is reached at which displacements of the joints and deflections of the bars become infinite, thus indicating the critical loading conditions. These physical features of stable and unstable equilibrium of frameworks have been used for the formulation of stability criteria in those convergence methods which utilize the principle of moment distribution for the investigation of the stability of frameworks.

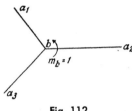

Fig. 112

Consider a part of a framework comprising one joint b as shown in Fig. 112. The elastic restraints of the joints a_1, a_2, . . . are furnished by the members beyond these points, and it may be assumed that the restraining effect of these members is expressed by certain spring constants K_1, K_2, . . . defining the degree of restraint at the joints a_1, a_2, ... A moment $m_b = +1$ applied at joint b will cause a rotation θ_b of this joint, the magnitude of which depends upon the stiffnesses S_1', S_2', . . . of the members which meet at b. According to the definition of stiffness we have

$$\theta_b = \frac{m_b}{\Sigma S_i'} \qquad (413)$$

and θ_b will be finite when $\Sigma S_i'$ is finite. For small values of the axial forces produced by the external loads, the values of the stiffnesses S_i' are all positive but tend to diminish with increasing load. Therefore, the condition for stability of a framework is expressed by

$$\Sigma S_i' > 0 \qquad (414)$$

Condition (414), when satisfied for any arbitrarily chosen joint b, ensures stability of all other joints and stability of every member of the structure.

If with increasing external loads the total stiffness $\Sigma S_i'$ of any arbitrarily chosen joint approaches zero, the limit of stability is reached. Thus

$$\Sigma S_i' = 0 \qquad (415)$$

represents the *stiffness criterion* for buckling of a framework.[1]

---

[1] The criterion (415) corresponds to the analytical condition $\Delta = 0$ for the limit of stability.

Lundquist's Series Criterion. However, the stiffness criterion has only theoretical significance and must be interpreted in an appropriate manner in order to render possible the direct application of the procedure of moment distribution.

Applying Eq. (411) to each of the members meeting at joint b in Fig. 112, we obtain

$$\sum S_i' = S_1\left(1 - \frac{C_1{}^2 S_1}{K_1 + S_1}\right) + S_2\left(1 - \frac{C_2{}^2 S_2}{K_2 + S_2}\right) + \cdots \quad (416)$$

Upon introducing the dimensionless quantities

$$r_1 = \frac{C_1{}^2 S_1}{K_1 + S_1}\frac{S_1}{\Sigma S_i}, \qquad r_2 = \frac{C_2{}^2 S_2}{K_2 + S_2}\frac{S_2}{\Sigma S_i}, \cdots \quad (417)$$

Eq. (416) can be written as follows:

$$\Sigma S_i' = (S_1 + S_2 + \cdots) - (r_1 + r_2 + \cdots)\Sigma S_i$$

Introducing $r = r_1 + r_2 + \cdots$, this equation finally takes the form

$$\Sigma S_i' = (1 - r)\Sigma S_i \quad (418)$$

Application of the stiffness criteria (415) and (416) leads directly to the two criteria[1]

$$\begin{array}{ll}
\text{For stability:} & r < 1 \\
\text{For the stability limit (buckling):} & r = 1
\end{array}\Bigg\} \quad (419)$$

With regard to the previously outlined procedure for the derivation of formula (411) for the stiffness of an elastically restrained bar, the quantity r can be interpreted in the following manner: An external unit moment is applied at joint b, with all other joints of the framework, except b, rigidly fixed against rotation. If joint b is then clamped while the other joints are successively released, balanced, and fixed for a sufficient number of cycles of moment distribution, the total unbalanced moment, carried back to b after all the other joints have been balanced, will be equal to r.

Lundquist showed that the criteria (419) can be immediately derived by using the above interpretation of r. An initial unbalanced moment $m_b = 1$ after the distribution procedure adds an unbalanced moment r at joint b. If the procedure is continued and the moment r at b is distributed in the manner described for the initial unit moment, it will be found that the unbalanced moment at joint b is r^2. In repeating the procedure we arrive at the result that the total unbalanced moment at

[1] Kavanagh, T. C., Instability of Plane Truss Frameworks, Doctor's Thesis, New York University, 1948.

joint b is

$$1 + r + r^2 + \cdots$$

This is a geometric series, the sum of which is $1/(1 - r)$. For stability the sum $1(/1 - r)$ must be finite, which condition is satisfied when $r < 1$. On the other hand, the stability limit is reached when $r = 1$. These two criteria are identical with Eqs. (419) and are called *series criteria* by Lundquist, because of the geometric series from which they are derived.

It must be borne in mind that the application of the Lundquist series criterion does not lead directly to the critical loading condition of the framework but requires the carrying out of a trial-and-error procedure which can be broken down into the following steps:

1. Assume a series of multiple nW of the given load system W and calculate for each nW the axial loads P of all members.[1]
2. For each multiple nW calculate for each member P/A, E_τ and ϕ, and determine the corresponding values of carry-over factors, stiffness factors and distribution factors.
3. For each multiple nW, starting at the lowest, apply an initial moment $+1$ at some joint, carry out a routine moment distribution, and determine the total unbalanced moment at that joint after balancing all other joints of the framework.
4. The load system nW which first yields $r = 1$ is the critical load, and n is the factor of safety.

Hoff's Convergence Method. Hoff[2] based the application of the moment distribution method for the determination of the stability of frameworks upon the following theorem:

"If a frameword (truss) is subject to external moments and the Cross method as modified for axial loads is used in the calculation of the distribution of bending moments of the bars, and a finite, unique set of values is obtained, then this result is a necessary and sufficient condition for stability."

A finite set of values means convergence of the moment distribution procedure, and uniqueness means independence of the results of the order of balancing.

If the procedure fails to yield finite results, or, in exceptional cases, if by changing the order of a few steps in the procedure different values are obtained, the structure is unstable.

The convergence of the conventional moment distribution process for

---

[1] W represents the balanced system of external loads which act upon the structure. nW means that each load of this system is multiplied by n.

[2] Hoff, N. J., Stable and Unstable Equilibrium of Plane Framework, *Jour. Aeronaut. Sci.*, Vol. 8, p. 115, 1941.

the determination of bending moments in a framework in which no axial forces are present is beyond question. The share of each member after each cycle of distribution is smaller than the unbalanced moment at the start of the cycle, and the carry-over factor is $\frac{1}{2}$ for members of constant moment of inertia. However, if the individual members are under action of compressive or tensile forces, an elaborate investigation is necessary to prove the convergence of the Cross procedure, since the stiffness factor for a compressed member assumes positive or negative values and the carry-over factor is often greater than unity. The proof is not altogether simple, but Hoff, who recognized the necessity of such an investigation, succeeded in presenting the proof, thus providing the real rational basis for the application of the moment distribution method to systems the members of which are subject to axial forces.

The procedure in applying the criterion for stability quoted above is described by Hoff as follows:

1. Determine the axial loads in all the members of the framework corresponding to an assumed value of the external loads. Compute the ϕ-value for each bar. When the ϕ-values are smaller than π in all the compression bars, the framework is necessarily stable. When in any one compression bar ϕ is greater than 2π, the entire framework is unstable.

2. Compute the stiffnesses S and the carry-over factors C with the aid of tables or graphs. Compute the sum of the stiffnesses ΣS for each joint. For stability, ΣS at every joint must be positive.

3. The conditions on ϕ and ΣS establish upper and lower limits for the critical value of the applied load.

4. The stability can be checked by applying a moment of arbitrary magnitude at any one of the joints and determining the end moments by the usual process of moment distribution. Generally, when finite values for the end moments are obtained, the framework is stable. Repeat the entire procedure with successively increased loads (each load is increased in the same proportion) until it is found that the unbalanced moments increase rather than decrease after a number of balancing operations. Then the framework is unstable under the load system considered.

5. In exceptional cases, finite values of the moments may result for an actually unstable loading condition. Change the order of a few steps of the moment distribution procedure. If, thereby, the same values of the end moments again result, the structure is stable. If different values are obtained, the structure is unstable.

Hoff based the proof of the convergence theorem upon the properties of the total potential energy of the loaded framework system, resorting to a geometric interpretation of the energy function as a potential energy surface.[1]   In essence, it was shown that in each cycle of steps of the Cross balancing procedure the total potential of the framework system decreases and thus approaches the minimum value which corresponds to stable equilibrium.   Simultaneously, the moments at the ends of the members approach the values associated with the equilibrium of the system.   However, when the framework is unstable under loading, equilibrium corresponds to either a maximum or a saddle point of the potential energy surface.   Consequently, the moment distribution procedure which diminishes the potential energy with each step can never lead to a state of equilibrium, and the end moments cannot approach values that correspond to equilibrium.   In case of instability the moment distribution procedure is divergent.

The above-outlined theory of stability has been extended to include frameworks with members having a variable flexural rigidity between the joints.[2]   In order to take into account the effect of gusset plates, each bar is considered to have its actual constant bending rigidity between the gusset plates, and this rigidity increases according to a hyperbolic law from the edge of the gusset plate to the mathematical end point of the member where the rigidity becomes infinite.   The paper contains the derivation of stiffness factors and carry-over factors for compression members and members in tension and charts from which these factors can be read for bars having equal gusset plates on both ends and various ratios of plate length to theoretical bar length.

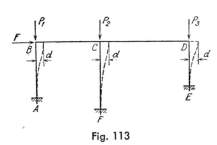

Fig. 113

Framework Systems with Joint Translation.   No general extension of the method of moment distribution has been developed to include systems where joint translations are possible.   However, the moment distribution procedure has been applied recently to the investigation of lateral buckling of a rigid frame as illustrated by Fig. 113.[3]

If the rigid frame is given an arbitrary lateral displacement d, the corresponding fixed-end moments at B, C, and D can be computed, and after these moments have been distributed and balanced in a sufficient number of cycles, the moments at the ends of the columns can be deter-

[1] The proof is presented in N. J. Hoff, Stable and Unstable Equilibrium of Plane Frameworks, *Jour. Aeronaut. Sci.*, Vol. 8, p. 115, 1941; Stress Analysis of Aircraft Frameworks, *Proc. Roy. Aeronaut. Soc.*, Vol. 45, No. 367, p. 241, 1941.   See also Niles and Newell, *op. cit.* (on p. 202), Vol. II, p. 303.

[2] Hoff, Boley, Nardo, and Kaufman, *loc. cit.* on p. 196.

[3] Winter, Hsu, Koo, and Loh, *loc. cit.* on p. 196.

mined. By applying the equilibrium equations (404) in Art. 59 to each of the columns, the shearing forces Q_1, Q_2, Q_3 which act on the columns can be expressed by the end moments of these members. With the sign convention of the paper and with $Pl\rho = Pd$ and $H = 0$, the equilibrium equation takes the form

$$M + M' - Pd - Ql = 0 \tag{420}$$

in which M and M' are the end moments and l the length of the column.

The following reasoning leads to the stability criterion. When the system is in stable equilibrium under the given loading condition, a finite force F must be applied at joint B to produce the displacement d. The shearing forces Q and the force F are connected by the equilibrium condition

$$\Sigma Q = F \tag{421}$$

The closer the external loads P_1, P_2, P_3 approach their critical values, the smaller becomes the force F necessary to sustain the displacement d, and the force approaches the value $F = 0$ when the actual stability limit is reached. Therefore, the condition

$$\Sigma Q = 0 \tag{422}$$

is the buckling condition.

Concluding Remarks. The convergence methods discussed in this section have been developed especially for application to the design of trusses in aircraft structures, in order to determine as accurately as possible the buckling load of frameworks. However, with the increasing number of bars which compose the truss the necessary computations become more and more cumbersome. When the actual end restraints acting upon a member are to be determined, which means that the effective length of a compression member as part of a truss is wanted, the computation can be simplified by considering only a group of members comprising the bars in the neighborhood of the bar to be investigated. Members of the group are assumed to be rigidly connected, whereas the far ends of those members of the group which join with the other parts of the framework are considered pin-connected. Satisfactory approximation will be obtained by considering groupings of at least six to eight members, so that the investigation still involves lengthy calculations.[1] On the other hand, if only the influence of the end restraint of the immediately adjoining members is taken into account, the result may deviate noticeably from the actual degree of restraint.[2]

As far as the design of bridges and buildings is concerned, the moment

[1] Lundquist, E. E., Stability of Members under Axial Load, *NACA Tech. Note* **717**, 1939.

[2] See Winter, Hsu, Koo, and Loh, *loc. cit.* on p. 196.

distribution method for stability determination has not received much attention, because of the inherent complexity of the computations which makes it unsuitable for routine design of bridges, roof trusses, and the like. The situation is radically different from that in aircraft structures. The structural engineer needs simple rules of design, covering as wide a range of cases as possible, which can be applied directly to the determination of the effective length of truss members. Slender compression members occur comparatively seldom in bridges and heavy roof trusses. In the majority of cases, slenderness ratios below 80 are the rule, and in this range an error in determining the degree of restraint does not materially affect the economy of the design, even though the applied approximate formula may yield somewhat conservative results. Fortunately, the analytical methods outlined in the previous articles afford the possibility of obtaining the solution of many stability problems of practical significance in such a form that the reduction of the results to readily available design rules becomes feasible.

62. Effect of Bending Moments in the Members of Frameworks upon the Buckling Strength

The problem of framework stability has been discussed previously under the implied assumption that no bending moments are present in the individual members at the instant at which buckling begins. In reality in many framework systems of practical importance this condition is not fulfilled, and the question arises to what extent do these moments affect the critical load of the structure and how can the effect be taken into account.

The most common example is the beam column continuous over several supports under combined axial and transverse loading. Neither the analytical nor the numerical methods outlined in the foregoing articles apply because the stability criteria of these methods were derived explicitly on the assumption that the members of the framework are subject to axial loads only. However, there is no doubt that transverse loads may affect the critical load to a considerable extent. Consider a beam column carrying transverse loads. This is only the case of a column under the action of end moments or side load, discussed extensively in Chap. I. The same is true when any truss member is loaded transversely between the joints. The buckling strength of the entire structure is markedly reduced by the localized load, as tests with model trusses indicate.[1] Secondary bending stresses due to the rigid connection of the members at the joints, and caused by the loads applied at the joints, certainly affect the carrying capacity of the truss. Substantial bending moments are set up in the columns of continuous multistory rigid frames with heavily

[1] See Art. 63.

loaded beams under certain loading conditions, and in studying the buckling of such columns the influence of these moments should not be neglected.

Though in the majority of cases the local moments tend to reduce the buckling strength of the structure, there are also cases where the bending moments may have a beneficial effect upon the critical load. Furthermore, from the theory of the eccentrically loaded column we know that the effect of eccentricity upon buckling strength is considerable in the plastic range of buckling but tapers off in the elastic range with increasing slenderness ratio of the column. The implication is that the moment effect may influence sturdy compression members to a larger extent than slender members. This fact makes it the more advisable to consider this effect in the design of conventional steel structures.

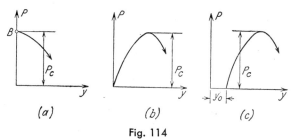

Fig. 114

However, the solution of the stability problem with proper regard to the moment effect becomes very involved, and this explains why only a few attempts have been made to attack particular problems of this type. The real nature of the extended buckling theory of frameworks, including the effect upon stability of initial moments present in the members before buckling, is not generally recognized. The following consideration may afford some insight into the characteristic features of these stability problems and into the difficulties encountered.

It may be recalled that the limit of stability of an axially loaded column was defined as that load P_c at which the straight form of equilibrium and the deflected form are equally possible—a bifurcation of the equilibrium position. Point B in Fig. 114a, where the load P is plotted against the deflection y of the center of the column, indicates the point of bifurcation.[1] Bifurcation of the equilibrium position also defines the limit of stability of a framework the members of which are subjected to axial forces only.

The buckling of an eccentrically loaded column represents another type of instability as shown by the curve in Fig. 114b. Deflection of the column begins at $P = 0$ and increases steadily until the critical load P_c is reached.[2] Thus no bifurcation of the equilibrium position takes place.

[1] Chapter I, p. 7.

[2] See the discussion on p. 30 of Chap. I.

The same holds true in the case of a framework where members are transversely loaded between the joints. Transverse loading of any member causes deflection of all members of the system, and when P increases from zero to its maximum value P_c, the initial deflection y_0, due to the transverse load, increases steadily to a maximum value at which the framework fails, as shown in Fig. 114c. The type of instability is essentially the same as indicated by Fig. 114b. This implies that a rational solution of the stability problem of a framework with proper regard to the effect of

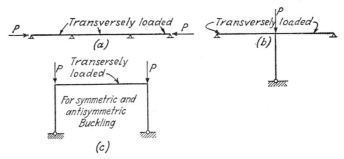

Fig. 115

initial moments upon the stability of the structure necessarily must be based upon the involved methods of investigation of eccentrically or transversely loaded columns discussed in Chap. I. This is a formidable problem, practically impossible to solve when the framework is made up of a great number of rigidly jointed bars. However, valuable information, which can be applied to more complex frameworks, could be derived by a systematic investigation of simple frameworks of the type shown in Figs. 115a to 115c. The analytical solution of these stability problems is feasible when the investigation is based upon a simplified stress-strain diagram as indicated in Fig. 116 and under the assumption that the shape of the distorted system is approximately given by a suitable chosen buckling mode of the system, computed from the theory in Art. 59. Thus, for the solution of the stability problems considered, it is suggested that Ježek's concept discussed in Chap. I be adopted.[1] That such simple frameworks can be successfully treated and an even more exact solution of the stability problem be obtained have been shown by Chwalla, who

Fig. 116

[1] In a recent paper a theory of plastic bending has been developed on the basis of a stress-strain diagram composed of two straight lines of different slopes, which includes as a limiting case the diagram in Fig. 116. See "A Study of Column Analysis" by Annabel Yuen-Wai Lee, Doctor's Thesis, Cornell University, June, 1949. The paper also contains an exact solution of the problem of eccentrically loaded columns based upon the simplified stress-strain diagram in Fig. 116.

applied his method, described in Chap. I, to a three-bay column, the center bay acted on by external moments applied at the ends of this bay. Chwalla's[1] investigation is based on the actual stress-strain graph of structural steel. It may be expected, therefore, that after the simplified stress-strain curve (Fig. 116) has been introduced, the stability conditions for the frameworks in Figs. 115 can be derived without excessive analytical work.

The extreme difficulty of calculating the buckling strength of framework members under combined axial and transverse load led to the suggestion of applying the principle which underlies the secant formula for eccentrically loaded columns to the investigation of frameworks. This means the application of the criterion that the carrying capacity of a structure is reached if in one of the members the extreme fiber stress becomes equal to the yield point. Thus, the solution of any stability problem would be reduced to an exact stress analysis of the framework, which takes into account the effect of bar deflections on the equilibrium equations. However, the same objections as made in Chap. I in discussing the secant formula can be made here. The yield-strength criterion does not take into account the substantial reserve of strength which is present in ductile material and which comes into play after the yield point is reached. The effect becomes especially prominent in statically indeterminate systems, such as rigid frames. However, in the absence of a fundamentally correct solution of a stability problem, the yield-strength concept may in some cases supply valuable information of a general and qualitative nature. This will be seen in the following discussion of the effect upon buckling load of secondary bending in trusses.

There are, however, other buckling problems where the stress criterion fails completely. This happens when the deflected but stable equilibrium form, to which the stress analysis is applied, suddenly changes to a completely different and unstable equilibrium configuration which determines the actual limit of stability. The critical load, derived by means of the yield-strength criterion for the stable-equilibrium form, has in such a case no relationship to the actual critical load associated with a completely different configuration. The case of lateral buckling of a rigid frame considered at the end of this article may serve as an illustration of the foregoing remark.

There is also some doubt whether a purely experimental approach to the solution of the above-mentioned rigid-frame problems is possible because of the great number and wide range of the variables which characterize each individual problem. These variables are the axial forces, stiffness ratios, shape of the cross section, and the various possible trans-

---

[1] Chwalla, E., Aussermittig gedrückte Baustahlstäbe mit elastisch eingespannten Enden und verschieden grossen Angriffshebeln, *Die Bautechnik*, Vol. 10, 1937.

verse loading conditions. Success can be achieved only by a close cooperation of theoretical and experimental research, resulting in a test program based on the analytical solution of the problem. The primary purpose of such tests is to supply experimental data for the determination of those coefficients in the theoretical results which cannot be derived mathematically or the computation of which becomes too cumbersome.

Only a few investigations can be considered contributions to the solution of the stability problems with which we are concerned in this article.

In 1936 Parcel and Murer[1] presented a paper in which they discussed the question of the effect of secondary stresses on the ultimate strength of truss members, in particular the effect upon the buckling strength of compression members. The study is based upon stress-analysis considerations, taking into account the particular behavior of secondary stresses after the nonlinear (plastic) region of the stress-strain relation is reached.

As far as compression members are concerned, the authors summarize the following significant features of secondary stress action:

"1. Compression members bent in single curvature may be seriously affected as regards primary failure if the transverse deflection due to secondary bending stresses becomes large. This can only occur, however, in the case of large secondary moments and flexible members, a combination that is not ordinarily realizable. For values of $l/r \leq 70$ the effect of secondary action in inducing primary failure is small. In such a case the rigid-joint action which gives rise to secondary stress acts as a brake on the long-column deflection before the point of ultimate column strength is reached.

"2. For a column bent in double curvature, the secondary action, by forcing the curvature into two waves, may actually have a beneficial effect[2] as regards primary failure.

"3. For stocky members ($l/r \leq 40$), which are ordinarily the only members that develop high secondary stresses, failure is nearly always due to local overstrain. Until the average stress approaches the yield point, the transverse deflection is negligible, and column action in the ordinary sense cannot occur. For such members the secondary stresses, whether resulting in single or double curvature, will merely result in high stresses on the compressive face, which are rapidly relieved by plastic flow of the material as the yield point is approached."

---

[1] Parcel, J. I., and E. B. Murer, Effect of Secondary Stresses upon Ultimate Strength, *Trans. ASCE*, Vol. 101, p. 289, 1936.

[2] The author is inclined to question this conclusion. A column bent in two waves may suddenly change to a one-wave configuration when the critical load associated with the lowest buckling mode is approached. The above statement, depending on the previously discussed deficiency of the yield-strength concept, should read: For a column bent in double curvature the secondary action . . . has no unfavorable effect as regards primary failure.

The first attempt—it remains the only one—to solve a framework problem by the exact method applied in the investigation of eccentrically loaded columns was made by Chwalla,[1] who studied the effect of elastic restraint on the buckling strength of a column under eccentric axial load. The elastic restraint is provided by the adjoining unstressed members indicated in Fig. 117. This is a typical problem of the kind suggested previously for investigation. Chwalla gave the numerical results for special cases, and these results are available as a check on

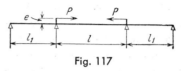

Fig. 117

any future simplified method for the investigation of the same or related problems. This is the significance of the paper.

In another article, Chwalla[2] investigates the problem of lateral stability of a rigid frame under transverse load as shown in Fig. 118a. This paper is of considerable interest, since it deals with a type of stability of a rigid frame not investigated previously. Figure 118a represents the deflection form under a loading symmetrical to the vertical axis $y - y$. When P approaches a certain critical value P_c, the symmetric form changes to an a symmetric configuration (Fig. 118b). If for the symmetric configuration the load P is

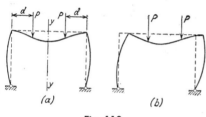

Fig. 118

plotted against the transverse deflection η of any point of the column axis, curve a in Fig. 119 is obtained, which shows a maximum at A corresponding to the critical load $\bar{P}_c$, which can be approached only when sidesway of the bent is prevented. If this is not the case, the framework becomes unstable under a lower critical load P_c (point B in Fig. 119), and the load-deflection relation is indicated by curve b. This type of instability is essentially the same as discussed in connection with Fig. 114a, characterized by a bifurcation of the equilibrium position. Consequently, the critical load P_c in the case of lateral buckling of the bent can be found from the criterion that for $P = P_c$ both the symmetric and the antisymmetric configuration become equally possible.

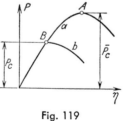

Fig. 119

Figure 120a shows the framework in its symmetric deflected form before lateral buckling. The moment of inertia of the columns is I_1;

[1] Chwalla, *loc. cit.* on p. 225.

[2] Chwalla, E., Die Stabilität lotrecht belasteter Rechteckrahmen, *Der Bauingenieur*, Vol. 19, p. 69, 1938.

that of the horizontal member I_2. η is the horizontal deflection at any point of the column, and y the deflection at any point of the member C-D. In order to check the stability of the equilibrium we superimpose on the symmetric deflection form an infinitely small antisymmetric deformation associated with a lateral displacement Δw of the joints C and D as shown in Fig. 120b. The corresponding deflections are $\Delta\eta$ and Δy. The resulting antisymmetric deformation is represented by Fig. 120c, the deflections being $\eta = \eta_0 - \Delta\eta$, $y = y_0 + \Delta y$, and $\nu = \eta_0 + \Delta\eta$.

Chwalla then investigates the conditions under which the assumed state of deformation (Fig. 120c) is compatible with the condition of

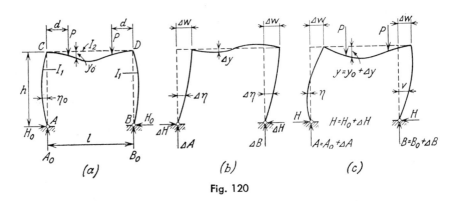

Fig. 120

equilibrium between the internal and external forces. He starts the analysis by setting up the linear differential equations which determine the deflection curves of the framework members. With reference to Fig. 121, which is self-explanatory, the following five differential equations can be readily written:

$$\left.\begin{array}{r} EI_1 \dfrac{d^2\eta}{d\xi^2} + A\eta + H\xi = 0 \\[2mm] EI_2 \dfrac{d^2y_1}{dx^2} + Hy_1 + Ax - M_1 = 0 \\[2mm] EI_2 \dfrac{d^2y_3}{dx^2} + Hy_3 + Ax - P(x-d) - M_1 = 0 \\[2mm] -EI_2 \dfrac{d^2y_2}{dx^2} + Hy_2 + B(l-x) - M_2 = 0 \\[2mm] EI_1 \dfrac{d^2\nu}{d\xi^2} + B\nu + H\xi = 0 \end{array}\right\} \qquad (423)$$

where

$$\left.\begin{array}{lll} A = A_0 - 2P\dfrac{\Delta w}{l}, & B = B_0 + 2P\dfrac{\Delta w}{l}, & H = H_0 + \Delta H \\[2mm] M_1 = Hh - A\,\Delta w & \text{and} & M_2 = Hh + B\,\Delta w. \end{array}\right\} \quad (424)$$

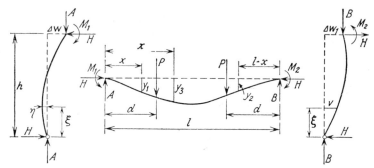

Fig. 121

The solutions of these five differential equations of second order contain 10 constants and the 2 unknowns Δw and ΔH, a total of 12 unknowns. They are determined by 12 boundary and continuity conditions, namely,

$$\left.
\begin{aligned}
[\eta]_{\xi=0} &= 0 & \text{and} && [\eta]_{\xi=h} &= -\Delta w \\[4pt]
[y_1]_{x=0} &= 0 & \text{and} && \left[\frac{dy_1}{dx}\right]_{x=0} &= -\left[\frac{d\eta}{d\xi}\right]_{\xi=h} \\[4pt]
[y_3 = y_1]_{x=d} & & \text{and} && \left[\frac{dy_3}{dx} = \frac{dy_1}{dx}\right]_{x=d} & \\[4pt]
[\nu]_{\xi=0} &= 0 & \text{and} && [\nu]_{\xi=h} &= \Delta w \\[4pt]
[y_2]_{x=l} &= 0 & \text{and} && \left[\frac{dy_2}{dx}\right]_{x=l} &= \left[\frac{d\nu}{d\xi}\right]_{\xi=h} \\[4pt]
[y_3 = y_2]_{x=l-d} & & \text{and} && \left[\frac{dy_3}{dx} = \frac{dy_2}{dx}\right]_{x=l-d} &
\end{aligned}
\right\} \quad (425)$$

When the solutions of Eqs. (423) are introduced into Eqs. (425) and the 10 constants eliminated, two equations in the unknowns Δw and ΔH remain:

$$\left.
\begin{aligned}
\frac{P}{H_0}\Gamma - \frac{\Delta w}{h}\Lambda \cos\frac{\psi l}{2}\tan^2\frac{\psi l}{2} - \frac{\Delta H}{H_0}\frac{P}{2H_0}\Theta &= 0 \\[4pt]
\frac{P}{H_0}\Gamma - \frac{\Delta w}{h}\Lambda \cos\frac{\psi l}{2} - \frac{\Delta H}{H_0}\frac{P}{2H_0}\Theta &= 0
\end{aligned}
\right\} \quad (426)$$

Γ, Λ, and Θ are transcendental functions of

$$\phi = \sqrt{\frac{P}{EI_1}} \quad \text{and} \quad \psi = \sqrt{\frac{H_0}{EI_2}} \qquad (427)$$

Assuming $\Delta H = 0$ and $\Delta w = 0$, Eqs. (426) lead to the relation

$$\frac{P}{H_0}\Gamma = 0 \qquad (428)$$

which defines the horizontal thrust H_0 due to the loads P for the symmetric configuration before buckling. We reason now as follows: If at a certain value of $P = P_c$ both the symmetric and asymmetric configurations are equally possible, then P_c must satisfy Eqs. (426) and (428) simultaneously. By using the relation (428), Eqs. (426) may be simplified to

$$\left.\begin{array}{l} \dfrac{\Delta w}{h} \Lambda \cos \dfrac{\psi l}{2} \tan^2 \dfrac{\psi l}{2} + \dfrac{\Delta H}{H_0} \dfrac{P}{2H_0} \Theta = 0 \\[3mm] \dfrac{\Delta w}{h} \Lambda \cos \dfrac{\psi l}{2} - \dfrac{\Delta H}{H_0} \dfrac{P}{2H_0} \Theta = 0 \end{array}\right\} \qquad (429)$$

These equations are compatible with a finite value of Δw if $\Lambda = 0$ and $\Delta H = 0$. The condition $\Lambda = 0$ leads to the equation

$$\phi h \cot \phi h - \frac{2Ph}{H_0 l}\left(1 - \frac{\psi l}{2}\cot\frac{\psi l}{2}\right) + \frac{H_0 h}{Pl}\left(2 - \phi h \cot \phi h \right.$$

$$\left. - \frac{\phi^2 h^2}{\sin^2 \phi h}\right) = 0 \quad (430)$$

This condition together with Eq. (428) permits the determination of P_c and H_0. From the fact that $\Delta H = 0$, we may infer that the unstable configuration is obtained by superimposing upon the stable symmetric configuration an antisymmetric deformation form, for which necessarily $\Delta H = 0$.

Chwalla's procedure is, however, unnecessarily involved. Equations (426) can be obtained in a far simpler way by using the method outlined in Art. 59. Only two three-moment equations, especially suitable for the type of stability problem considered here, and two equilibrium equations (404) are necessary to solve the problem. The latter two equations are identical with the expression for the moments M_1 and M_2 contained in the group of Eqs. (424). The elimination of M_1 and M_2 from the three-moment equations by means of these two expressions leads to two equations which should be equivalent with Eqs. (426).

Chwalla discusses in his paper two numerical examples, assuming that the loads P are applied at the third points of the horizontal member. Case 1 considers the ratio $l/h = 1$; Case 2 the ratio $l/h = 3$. In both cases the moments of inertia were assumed $I_1 = I_2 = I$.

The critical loads where found to be

$$\begin{array}{ll} \text{Case 1:} & P_c = 1.775EI/h^2 \\ \text{Case 2:} & P_c = 1.058EI/h^2 \end{array}$$

values which are many times smaller than the Euler load $P_E = \pi^2 EI/h^2$ of the column.

A comparison of these results with the critical loads obtained when the loads P act along the center line of the columns, as illustrated by Fig. 122, leads to significant conclusions. Since in this case only axial forces are present in the members of the rigid frame, the methods discussed in the previous articles are readily applicable and lateral buckling of such types of rigid frames has been frequently investigated. Chwalla gives the critical loads, when the external loads P are applied at the top of the columns, as follows:

$$\text{Case 1:} \quad P_c' = 1.816 EI/h^2$$
$$\text{Case 2:} \quad P_c' = 1.090 EI/h^2$$

We note the important fact that the initial moments, which are present at the instant of buckling, reduce the failure load of the framework only slightly. The differences between P_c and P_c' are 2.3 and 3.0%, respectively, and the conclusion can be drawn that the critical load for lateral buckling of rigid frames, made up of columns and horizontal members, can be computed without regard to the moments induced in the members by the external loads.

The study presented previously was based upon the assumption that nowhere in the structure is the proportional limit exceeded when the stability limit is reached. The theory developed is therefore more or less academic and may be considered only as the beginning of the proper research into the field of stability problems

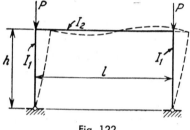

Fig. 122

which have been discussed in this article. In practical cases, in some parts of the structure the fiber stresses due to bending may already exceed the proportional limit prior to buckling, and the plasticity of these parts may reduce to a certain extent the critical load of the rigid frame.

63. Experimental Research in the Field of Framework Stability

Remarkable tests with eight specimens were made at the Polytechnic Institute of Brooklyn. The purpose of these tests was to check the validity of Hoff's convergence criterion and to investigate the effect of gusset plates of various lengths.[1] Of the specimens all but one failed by buckling. Of the seven that buckled two were designed to fail in the inelastic range; the other five buckled at stresses below the proportional limit.

Two specimens were made of solid steel rods, welded at the joints so that no gusset plate action was present. All the other model trusses were fitted with riveted gusset plates.

[1] Hoff, Boley, Nardo, and Kaufman, *loc. cit.* on p. 196.

Table 15 shows a comparison of calculated and measured buckling loads.

TABLE 15

Specimen No.	Gusset-plate size, % of bar length	Calculated buckling loads, lb		Experimental buckling loads,	%, error based on the experimental value
		Elastic range	Inelastic range		
1	..	440	.....	435	+ 1.1
2	..	440	.....	445	− 1.1
3	9	178	.....	184	− 3.2
4	9	205	.....	216	− 5.1
5	13	300	.....	300	0
5	20	320	.....	443	−22.7
6	20	...	.....	Did not fail by buckling	
7	20	...	5,875	5,600	+ 4.9
8	15	...	5,875	5,420	+ 8.4

The computed and observed buckling loads are in good agreement, except the second test series on specimen 5, the result indicating that the method for computing the gusset plate action in this particular case under-estimated the stiffening effect of the plates.

Buckling loads were also observed when one of the truss members was subjected to transverse loads of varying intensity. The transverse load-ing consisted of a concentrated load of 5, 10, 15, or 20 lb. at the mid-point of the member. The buckling load was always reduced by the applica-tion of a transverse load.

"The deflected pattern of the frameworks at buckling was always the same with specimens of the same configuration. The largest transverse load applied, 20 lbs., was not sufficient to alter this shape in any speci-men, even when the initial deflection caused by the transverse load was in direction opposite to that prevailing at the moment of failure.

"The largest decrease in the buckling load was measured under the application of 20 lbs. transverse load and amounted to 16.7, 15.0, and 23.9 percent of the buckling load without transverse load for specimens 3, 4, and 5, respectively."

CHAPTER VII

THE EFFECTIVE LENGTH OF COMPRESSION MEMBERS IN TRUSSES AND THE STABILITY OF RIGID-FRAME STRUCTURES

64. Introduction

In Chap. VI we were concerned with the study of the various methods of approach for solving the stability problems arising in the design of frameworks. The general objective of this chapter is the application of the analytical methods set forth in Arts. 59 and 60 of the preceding chapter to two groups of problems. The first part of the chapter will deal with problems concerning the approximate determination of the free length of compression members in trusses and the derivation of design rules and workable formulas for routine design. The purpose is to enable the structural engineer to estimate the effective length of a truss member without resorting to tedious computations. In the second part of this chapter the stability of rectangular rigid-frame structures, especially buckling of multistory frames, will be discussed.

Application of analytical methods to the determination of the effective length of compression members in trusses by subdividing the truss into small groups of bars was made by the author in 1919.[1] The growing interest of the aircraft designer in this problem gave rise to various attempts to approach the problem essentially along the same line, with the aim to devise tables and graphs for use in routine work in aircraft design. Borkmann[2] presented a series of valuable charts for the investigation of two- and three-bay systems. Cassens[3] tried to develop workable formulas for two- and three-bay bars by approximating the transcendental functions in the analysis by simple algebraic functions and by

---

[1] Bleich, F., Die Knickfestigkeit elastischer Stabverbindungen, *Der Eisenbau*, Vol. 10, p. 27, 1919.

[2] Borkmann, K., Charts for Checking Stability of Compression Members in Trusses, *NACA Tech. Mem.* 800, 1936; Charts for Checking the Stability of Plane Systems of Rods, *NACA Tech. Mem.* 837, 1937.

[3] Cassens, J., Der elastisch eingespannte Knickstab, *Luftfahrt-Forschung*, Vol. 14, p. 501, 1937.

assuming the parameter τ to be a linear function of the stress as was done previously by German investigators. A general stability condition for three-bay systems in a convenient form was given by Osgood.[1]

65. Stability of Compression Members in Trusses

Compression members in welded or riveted trusses behave as columns with elastically restrained ends. The restraint of any individual member is the result of the interaction between that member and the other parts of the framed structure, but its exact determination requires a rather complex procedure. Therefore, it appears rational to obtain an approximate value of the degree of restraint by disregarding the influence of

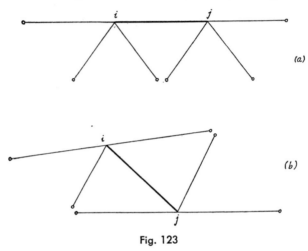

Fig. 123

members remote from the member under consideration. In this way one arrives at three-bay groups of members more amenable to simple analysis. Examples are given in Figs. 123a and 123b, in which ij indicates the compression member to be studied. It has been frequently maintained that, when the performance of a member of a truss is investigated, only an inadequate approximation is obtained when the analysis is limited to the study of the effect upon the member under consideration of those two groups of bars which join this member and when their far ends are assumed to be freely supported. From the viewpoint of the designing engineer this somewhat vague statement will be briefly examined in order to clarify the actual degree of approximation which can be expected by studying the simplified system and to decide whether the approximation is sufficient to meet the requirements of a safe and economical design.

[1] Osgood, W. R., Contribution to the Design of Compression Members in Aircraft, *Natl. Bur. Standards (U.S.), Jour. Research*, Research Paper RP 698, p. 157, 1932.

In order to obtain an insight into the magnitude of the error involved by neglecting the influence of members remote from the member ij, it is expedient to study an idealized problem. The numerical results obtained will serve as a clue for estimating the effect of remote elements on the degree of restraint of a compression member.

We consider the bar AB in Fig. 124a, freely supported at the end points A, B and at the intermediate supports h, i, j, k. The axial forces in the members l and l_1, referred to as primary members, are compressive forces, while the forces acting on the end spans may be compressive or tensile forces. It is obvious that the two members l_2 (secondary members) exert upon the three-member system $hijk$ a certain positive or negative restraining effect depending on their length l_2, flexural rigidity, and the magnitude and sign of the axial forces. The members l_2 may be

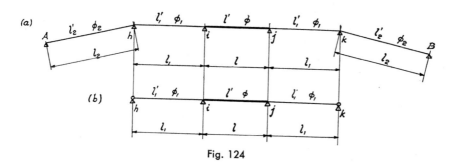

Fig. 124

considered as representing the restraint provided by truss members remote from the member ij under consideration. Since the performance of members of the system and their effect on the other members depend on the stability factor $\phi = l \sqrt{P/EI\tau}$ and the reduced length l' [defined by Eq. (392) in Chap. VI], we assign the factors ϕ, ϕ_1, ϕ_2 and the lengths l', l_1', l_2', as indicated in Fig. 124a, to the members l, l_1, l_2, respectively. Thus the problem to be considered is reduced to the investigation of the effect of varying values ϕ_2 and l_2' upon the stability factor ϕ which finally defines the effective length of the member ij. Comparison of the computed effective length kl of member ij in Fig. 124a with the free length $k_0 l$ calculated for the primary system (Fig. 124b), in which the ends h and k are hinged to the supports, will show the effect upon the critical load of any additional restraint supplied by the secondary members l_2.

The buckling problem indicated is readily solved by applying the three-moment equations (397) developed in Art. 59. Because of the symmetry of the system under consideration and since the smallest value of the critical load, obviously, is associated with a symmetric buckling configuration, the moments at the supports at the point of buckling are interrelated as follows:

$$M_A = M_B = 0, \qquad M_h = M_k, \qquad M_i = M_j \tag{431}$$

M_h and M_i are determined by the three-moment equations

$$\left. \begin{array}{l} M_h(c_2 l_2' + c_1 l_1') + M_i s_1 l_1' = 0 \\ M_h s_1 l_1' + M_i(c_1 l_1' + c l' + s l') = 0 \end{array} \right\} \tag{432}$$

in which the parameters c and s are functions of ϕ, ϕ_1 or ϕ_2, respectively. c and s are defined by Eqs. (394) or (398) depending on whether the axial force is a compressive or tensile force.

Expanding the determinant of the coefficients of Eqs. (432) leads, after dividing by l'^2, to the stability condition

$$\left(c_2 \frac{l_2'}{l'} + c_1 \frac{l_1'}{l'} \right) \left(c_1 \frac{l_1'}{l'} + c + s \right) - s_1^2 \left(\frac{l_1'}{l'} \right)^2 = 0 \tag{433}$$

It is obvious that in conducting any investigation on the basis of Eq. (433) certain limitations must be imposed on the range of variability of the design factors which control the problem. These limitations are necessary in order to obtain realistic results which reflect the actual conditions prevailing in a well-designed truss of the type used in civil engineering structures. With this in mind reasonable limits for the stiffness ratios l_1'/l', l_2'/l' and for the ratio ϕ_1/ϕ have been chosen, and the effect upon buckling strength of the primary members, exerted by the secondary members, has been investigated for a wide range of ϕ_2-values.

Within the range of possible variations considered, which cover the majority of cases encountered in the design of steel trusses in buildings and bridges, it was found that the secondary members affect the free length of the central member by an amount between zero and about 10%. It yet remains to decide whether the neglect of this effect in designing trusses would materially influence the economy of the design. In viewing this question it should be kept in mind that in the overwhelming majority of cases the compression members of trusses of the type common in civil engineering structures are built-up columns of small or medium slenderness ratios. The critical stresses are well beyond the proportional limit, at least in the heavier members which determine the weight of the structure. An error within the limits pointed out above has a rather limited effect upon the critical stress and therefore on the weight of the structure.

The following figures may illustrate the effect of a maximum error of 10% in estimating the degree of restraint on the critical stress for various slenderness ratios $l/r \leq 100$. The critical stress σ_c associated with l/r is compared with the stress σ_c' when the slenderness ratio is reduced to $0.9l/r$. Table 16 shows the increase of σ_c' over σ_c in percent of the stress σ_c and is computed for structural steel with $\sigma_p = 25$ kips/in.[2] and $\sigma_y = 33$ kips/in.[2].

TABLE 16

Slenderness ratio..........	40	60	80	100
Increase of σ_c', %........	0.5	1.5	2.8	3.8

The error involved in neglecting the influence of members remote from the member under consideration amounts to 4% or less when the member buckles beyond the proportional limit.

The implication of the foregoing reasoning is that, in an attempt to derive in a rational way simple rules of design for the determination of the effective length of truss members in compression, we may dismiss the effect of remote members and concentrate the investigation on the influence of adjacent members. Such a simplification, considered from a practical viewpoint, does not impair either the safety of the structure or its economy.

66. Stability Condition of a Three-bay Group of Truss Members

In order to simplify the discussion of problems which will be treated hereafter, it is expedient to have at hand a general solution of the stability

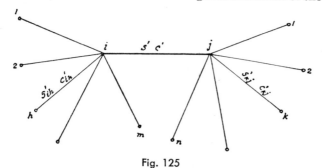

Fig. 125

problem of the group of bars illustrated by Fig. 125 for buckling in the plane of the members. Using the four-moment equation as a basis, Osgood[1] succeeded in developing the solution of the problem in a very convenient form, yielding directly the analytical stability condition for any special case. As an introduction to the subsequent investigation of specific problems in the field considered here, the derivation of this stability condition will be briefly discussed.

[1] *Ibid.*

Let the bar ij in Fig. 125 be a compression member, considered elastically restrained against rotation at its ends by the two groups of members which meet at i and j, respectively. The joints i and j are fixed against translation. The members ih ($h = 1, 2, \ldots, m$) and jk ($k = 1, 2, \ldots, n$) may be under axial tension or compression, and their far ends $1, 2, \ldots, m$ and $1, 2, \ldots, n$ are assumed freely supported.

The following notation will be used:

l = the length of the member ij

l_{hi} and l_{kj} = the lengths of the restraining members ih and jk, respectively ($h = 1, 2, \ldots, m; k = 1, 2, \ldots, n$)

M_i and M_j = the terminal moments of the member ij

M_{hi}, M_{kj} = the terminal moments at i and j of the members hi and jk, respectively ($h = 1, 2, \ldots, m; k = 1, 2, \ldots, n$)

By applying the four-moment equations successively to the pairs of members $1i$ and ij, $2i$ and ij, etc., and then to the pairs of members ij and $j1$, ij and $j2$, etc., the following two systems of equations are obtained:

$$M_{hi}c_{hi}' + M_i c' + M_j s' = 0 \qquad (h = 1, 2, \ldots, m) \qquad (434a)$$

and

$$M_{kj}c_{kj}' + M_j c' + M_i s' = 0 \qquad (k = 1, 2, \ldots, n) \qquad (434b)$$

in which

$$c_{hi}' = c_{hi}l_{hi}', \qquad c_{kj}' = c_{kj}l_{kj}', \qquad c' = cl', \qquad s' = sl' \qquad (435)$$

The values c, s, and l' are defined by Eqs. (392), (394), and (398).

The moments M are interrelated by two equations expressing the condition that the sum of all the moments acting at the joints i and j, respectively, must be equal to zero. With reference to the sign convention adopted in Art. 59 these equations are

$$\left.\begin{array}{c} -M_i + \displaystyle\sum_{h=1}^{m} M_{hi} = 0 \\[3mm] -M_j + \displaystyle\sum_{k=1}^{n} M_{kj} = 0 \end{array}\right\} \qquad (436)$$

On introducing M_i and M_j from Eqs. (436) into Eqs. (434) $m + n$ linear homogeneous equations are obtained, namely, m equations of the form

$$c'M_{1i} + c'M_{2i} + \cdots + (c' + c_{hi}')M_{hi} + \cdots + c'M_{mi}$$
$$+ s'M_{1j} + s'M_{2j} + \cdots + s'M_{kj} + \cdots + s'M_{nj} = 0 \qquad (437a)$$

and n equations of the form

$$s'M_{1i} + s'M_{2i} + \cdots + s'M_{hi} + \cdots + s'M_{mi} + c'M_{1j} + c'M_{2j}$$
$$+ \cdots + (c' + c_{kj}')M_{kj} + \cdots + c'M_{nj} = 0 \qquad (437b)$$

The determinant of the coefficients of the system of $m + n$ equations equated to zero is the condition for the limit of stability. Upon expanding the determinant the condition of stability assumes the form

$$\left(\frac{1}{c_{1i}'} + \frac{1}{c_{2i}'} + \cdots + \frac{1}{c_{mi}'}\right)\left(\frac{1}{c_{1j}'} + \frac{1}{c_{2j}'} + \cdots + \frac{1}{c_{nj}'}\right)(c'^2 - s'^2)$$
$$+ \left(\frac{1}{c_{1i}'} + \frac{1}{c_{2i}'} + \cdots + \frac{1}{c_{mi}'} + \frac{1}{c_{1j}'} + \frac{1}{c_{2j}'} + \cdots + \frac{1}{c_{nj}'}\right)$$
$$c' + 1 = 0 \quad (438)$$

When the member ij is pin-connected at j to the adjoining members, Eq. (438) simplifies because of $1/c_{1j}' = 1/c_{2j}' = \cdots = 0$:

$$\left(\frac{1}{c_{1i}'} + \frac{1}{c_{2i}'} + \cdots + \frac{1}{c_{mi}'}\right)c' + 1 = 0 \quad (439)$$

67. Buckling of Chord Members in the Plane of the Truss

In judging the behavior of compression chords of single-span trusses, the influence of any restraint effected by the attached web members will

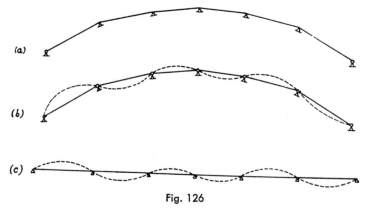

(a)

(b)

(c)

Fig. 126

be disregarded. Their stiffness, in general, is small in comparison with that of the chord members, and their restraining effect, accordingly, is of minor degree. The chord therefore may be considered as a sequence of bars on unyielding supports, free to rotate at the joints (Fig. 126a).

We now suppose that all chord members are designed so that under a certain loading condition each member just reaches its stability limit, assumed to be $\phi = l\sqrt{P/EI\tau} = \pi$, where l is the length of the member under consideration. This represents, of course, an ideal case, but in an economically designed truss this condition will be approximately fulfilled. The above assumption represents the worst condition for the stability of each individual member, since if this condition is not satisfied, any element having some reserve of buckling strength will support the others, thus increasing the stability limit of the entire system. Since each member is designed for $P_c = \pi^2 EI\tau/l^2$, i.e., the buckling load of a pin-ended column of the theoretical length l, we may assume that the members are hinged at the supports, as shown in Fig. 126b. At the instant of buckling each member will deflect in a half sine wave, whereby sign and magnitude of the deflection of each member are independent of those of the other members. Among the infinite number of possible configurations of the system there will be one configuration where the half waves, if laid off along a straight line (Fig. 126c), would join continuously, thereby satisfying the actual boundary conditions of the chord members which are rigidly connected to each other. Therefore:

> A compression chord designed so that all members within the limitation of routine design are equally safe is to be designed as if the members were hinged at the joints. The free length of each member is the theoretical length l (distance between panel points).

68. Trusses with Constant Cross Section of the Compression Chord

Trusses of moderate span are frequently designed with a constant cross section of the compression chord. Since in a single-span truss the chord forces increase from the supports to the center of the span, the members nearer the supports are considerably less stressed than those at mid-span, thus supplying additional buckling strength to these members. For the sake of economy, this beneficial effect should be taken into account in computing the critical stress of the central member which determines the cross section of the entire chord. The problem of determining the effective length to be applied in designing the chord can be readily solved and a simple rule of design established if some simplifications are introduced into the analysis.

The truss shown in Fig. 127a is assumed to be uniformly loaded, resulting in top chord forces $P_1', P_2', \ldots, P_i', \ldots, P_n'$. We assign to each joint a force P_i ($i = 1, 2, \ldots, n - 1$) representing an average value of the forces in the two members which meet at i. P_i may be given by the ordinate at i of a parabola having the maximum ordinate P_m, P_m being the chord stress at mid-span (Fig. 127b). Applying the three-moment equation (397) and considering the top chord as a bar with unyielding supports, we may write

$$M_{i-1}s_il + M_i(c_i + c_{i+1})l + M_{i+1}s_{i+1}l = 0$$

observing that $l_i' = l_{i+1}' = l$, since equal lengths and equal moments of inertia are assumed. In this equation we replace s_i and s_{i+1} as well as c_i and c_{i+1} by average values s_i and c_i of the argument $\phi_i = l\sqrt{P_i/EI\tau}$.

Upon dividing by $s_i l$ we have

$$M_{i-1} + 2\frac{c_i}{s_i} M_i + M_{i+1} = 0 \qquad (440)$$

in which

$$\frac{c_i}{s_i} = \frac{\sin \phi_i - \phi_i \cos \phi_i}{\phi_i - \sin \phi_i} \qquad (441)$$

For the sake of simplicity, the value of τ in the expressions for l' and φ_i is assumed constant and associated with the stress P_m/A at mid-span. This assumption obviously leads to conservative values of the factor k, which defines the free length of the chord members.

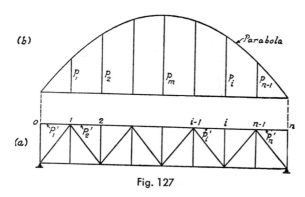

Fig. 127

Within the range of φ_i considered here, Eq. (441) can be approximated by

$$\frac{c_i}{s_i} = 2 - \left(\frac{\phi_i}{\pi}\right)^2$$

Since

$$P_i = \frac{4P_m}{n^2} i(n - i)$$

and using the notation $P_t = \pi^2 E I \tau / l^2$, we obtain

$$\left(\frac{\phi_i}{\pi}\right)^2 = \frac{P_i}{P_t} = \frac{4P_m}{n^2 P_t} i(n - i)$$

and finally the system of stability equations

$$M_{i-1} + 4\left[1 - \frac{2P_m}{n^2 P_t} i(n - i)\right] M_i + M_{i+1} = 0 \qquad (442)$$

Denoting the term within the brackets by r_i the stability condition is given by the equation

$$\begin{vmatrix} 4r_1 & 1 & 0 & \ldots & 0 & 0 & 0 \\ 1 & 4r_2 & 1 & \ldots & 0 & 0 & 0 \\ \cdots & \cdots & \cdots & \cdots & \cdots & \cdots & \cdots \\ 0 & 0 & & 1 & 4r_{n-2} & & 1 \\ 0 & 0 & & 0 & 1 & 4r_{n-1} \end{vmatrix} = 0 \qquad (443)$$

which defines the ratio P_m/P_t. The evaluation of this determinant for values up to $n = 10$ is relatively simple because of the symmetry $r_i = r_{n-i}$. We express P_m by means of the equivalent length kl in the form

$$P_m = \frac{\pi^2 EI \tau}{(kl)^2} \qquad (444)$$

where k is given by

$$k = \sqrt{\frac{P_t}{P_m}} \qquad (445)$$

The following Table 17 gives the values of k for $n = 3$ to 10.

TABLE 17.   Length Factor k in Eq. (444)

n	3	4	6	8	10
k	0.769	0.830	0.899	0.917	0.927

k can be expressed with reasonable accuracy by the formula

$$k = \sqrt{1 - \frac{5}{4n}} \qquad (446)$$

and we have the conclusion:

Top chords of trusses of constant cross section can be designed with an effective length kl, where k is given by Eq. (446).

69. Chords of Continuous Trusses

Special conditions may be present in continuous trusses. In the region where the bending moment changes its sign, one of two adjacent chord members will be in compression and the other one in tension. For the sake of economy the restraint sometimes provided by the tension member should not be disregarded. In order to arrive at a simple design formula,

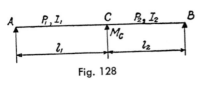

Fig. 128

we consider the system of two bars (Fig. 128), neglecting the influence of other chord and web members which join at A, B, and C. P_1 is the axial compressive force in member l_1; P_2 the tensile force in member l_2. I_1 and I_2 are the respective moments of inertia. The solution of the problem can be derived from Eq. (439). Substituting $c_{1i}' = c_1 l_1'$ and $c' = c_2 l_2'$ we obtain

$$\frac{c_2 l_2'}{c_1 l_1'} + 1 = 0 \qquad (447)$$

where

$$c_1 = \frac{1}{\phi_1^2}(1 - \phi_1 \cot \phi_1) \qquad \text{and} \qquad c_2 = \frac{1}{\phi_2^2}(\coth \phi_2 - 1) \quad (448)$$

On introducing the expressions for l_1' and l_2' [Eqs. (392)], the stability condition (447) takes the form

$$c_1 + \mu c_2 = 0 \qquad (449)$$

where

$$\mu = \frac{l_2}{l_1} \frac{I_1 \tau_1}{I_2 \tau_2} \qquad (450)$$

ϕ_2 can be expressed in terms of ϕ_1:

$$\phi_2 = \phi_1 \frac{l_2}{l_1} \sqrt{\frac{P_2}{P_1} \frac{I_1 \tau_1}{I_2 \tau_2}}$$

and by introducing the notation

$$\rho = \sqrt{\frac{P_2 l_2}{P_1 l_1}} \qquad (451)$$

this equation may be written

$$\phi_2 = \sqrt{\mu}\, \rho \phi_1 \qquad (452)$$

Equation (449) can be solved for ϕ_1 for given values of μ and ρ. The results are recorded in Fig. 129 in which the factor k, which determines the effective length of the compression member l_1, is plotted against μ for several values of ρ. It will be noted that the curves approach asymptotically the value $k = 1$ as μ becomes ∞. The relation between k and the variables μ and ρ presented by the curves in Fig. 129 can be expressed approximately by the algebraic formula

$$\left.\begin{array}{c} k = 0.700 + a\sqrt{\mu} - b\mu \\ a = 0.173 - 0.050\rho \qquad \text{and} \qquad b = 0.028 - 0.011\rho \end{array}\right\} \quad (453)$$

where μ and ρ are defined by Eqs. (450) and (451). Equations (453) are valid for $0 \le \rho \le 2$ and $0 \le \mu \le 4$.

If P_1 and P_2 in Eq. (451) are the axial forces under the design load, τ_1 and τ_2 in Eq. (450) are functions of the stresses $\nu P_1/A_1$ and $\nu P_2/A_2$. ν is the factor of safety used in designing the compression members, and A_1, A_2 are the cross-sectional areas of the members l_1 and l_2, respectively. The values of τ_1 and τ_2 must be taken from a table of the τ-values which shows $\tau = E_t/E$ as a function of the average stress P/A (Table 3 on page

55). Such a table can be used approximately for both compression and tension members. It is important to note that the restraint provided by the tension member primarily depends upon the ratio τ_1/τ_2. In some cases τ_2 will be far smaller than τ_1, and the ratio τ_1/τ_2 may become ∞ if the material has a well-defined yield point. This will happen when the stress P_2/A_2 in the tension member approaches the working stress, so that the value of $\sigma = \nu P_2/A_2$ becomes equal to the yield point or may lie beyond that point.[1] In such cases μ becomes ∞ and $k = 1$, indicating

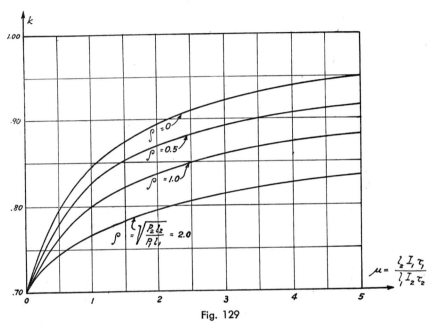

Fig. 129

that the tension member does not actually restrain the adjacent bar in compression. A marked restraining effect will occur only when the stress P_2/A_2 of the tension member lies appreciably below the permissible stress. Nevertheless in many cases the ratio τ_1/τ_2 may be sufficiently small, and Eqs. (453) will yield values of k well below unity.

For trusses made of aluminum alloy the conditions are more favorable, since τ_2, although becoming small, remains finite. But the restraining action of a tension member will be rather limited, except in cases where

---

[1] It must be kept in mind that the factor of safety ν for compression members, in general, is assumed greater than the factor of safety ν' which underlies the design of tension members. Thus, the bar under tension may already yield before the compression member reaches its critical load. The actual failure load of the structure is associated with ν. Although the ν'-fold design load causes yielding of the tension members, it actually does not incite collapse of the structure.

some reserve of strength is available when the adjacent compression member approaches its stability limit.

The procedure in checking the effective length of a compression member is simple. Determine first $\sigma_t = \nu P_2/A_2$. If σ_t is near the yield point σ_y or greater than σ_y, no further investigation is necessary, the effective length is equal to the theoretical length l_1. If τ_2 is not too small, say greater than 0.25, compute μ and ρ and then k from formula (453). kl_1 is the free length which may be used in redesigning the compression member.

70. Buckling of Web Members

Let us consider the web member ij in Fig. 130. In order to simplify the analysis as far as possible, we disregard any potential restraining

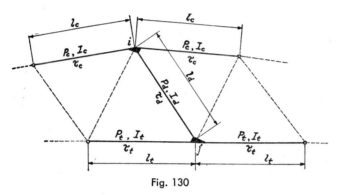

Fig. 130

effect of the adjacent two web members in tension and take account only of the rigid connection of the web member to the top and bottom chord members at i and j. The framework system to be investigated is indicated by full lines. We assume furthermore that the length l_c, the moments of inertia I_c, and the compressive forces P_c of the chord members which meet at i are equal and that the same is true for l_t, I_t, and P_t of the two chord members which join at j. P_t is assumed to be a tensile force.

We now apply Osgood's stability condition [Eq. (438)] to the simplified framework system indicated in Fig. 130. By introducing

$$c_{1i}' = c_{2i}' = c_c l_c', \qquad c_{1j}' = c_{2j}' = c_t l_t', \qquad c' = c_d l_d', \qquad s' = s_d l_d'$$

where c_c and c_t are functions of the stability factors ϕ_c and ϕ_t whereas c_d and s_d are functions of ϕ_d, we obtain first

$$\frac{4l_d'^2}{c_c l_c' c_t l_t'} (c_d^2 - s_d^2) + 2 \left(\frac{1}{c_c l_c'} + \frac{1}{c_t l_t'} \right) c_d l_d' + 1 = 0$$

and after rearrangement we arrive at the stability condition in the form

$$\left(c_c \frac{l_c'}{l_d'} + 2c_d\right)\left(c_t \frac{l_t'}{l_d'} + 2c_d\right) - 4s_d^2 = 0 \qquad (454)$$

Substituting the notations

$$\alpha = \frac{\phi_c}{\phi_d} = \frac{l_c}{l_d}\sqrt{\frac{P_c I_d \tau_d}{P_d I_c \tau_c}} \qquad (455a)$$

$$\beta = \frac{l_c'}{l_d'} = \frac{l_c I_d \tau_d}{l_d I_c \tau_c} \qquad (455b)$$

$$\gamma = c_t \frac{l_t'}{l_d'} = \frac{1}{\pi}\sqrt{\frac{P_d I_d \tau_d}{P_t I_t \tau_t}} \qquad (455c)$$

Eq. (454) can be written

$$[\beta c_c(\alpha\phi_d) + 2c_d(\phi_d)](\gamma + 2c_d(\phi_d)) - 4[s_d(\phi_d)]^2 = 0 \qquad (456)$$

where c_c, c_d, and s_d are now functions of ϕ_d and α, β, γ are parameters. Equation (456) can be solved for the unknown ϕ_d for given values of the parameters α, β, γ.

An approximation was made when deriving Eq. (455c). The value ϕ_t, pertaining to the tension members l_t, is far greater than π, and in the expression (398) for c_t the term coth ϕ_t can be replaced by unity. Thus $c_t = (\phi_t - 1)/\phi_t^2$ is obtained. For large values of ϕ_t this equation can be further simplified to $c_t = 1/\phi_t$. Expressing ϕ_t by ϕ_d,

$$\phi_t = \phi_d \frac{l_t}{l_d}\sqrt{\frac{P_t I_d \tau_d}{P_d I_t \tau_t}} \qquad (457)$$

Introducing this relation into $\gamma = c_t \dfrac{l_t'}{l_d'} = \dfrac{l_t'}{l_d'}\dfrac{1}{\phi_t}$, and then replacing φ_d by the constant value π, Eq. (455c) is obtained. ϕ_d is actually somewhat greater than π, and its smallest possible value, $\phi_d = \pi$, has been used. It must be emphasized that these simplifications tend to reduce the value of ϕ_d found from Eq. (456), so that the resulting value $k = \pi/\phi_d$ lies on the side of safety.

Table 18 gives the values of k which define the effective iength kl_d of the web member under consideration for a wide range of possible values of the parameters α, β, γ. The parameters α and β determine the influence of the compression chord upon the performance of the web member, whereas the value of γ determines the effect of the chord in tension. In applying Table 18 the value of the parameters α, β, γ is to be computed from the average values of l, I, and P of the two chord members which meet at A and B, respectively.

Inspection of Table 18 discloses that within the range of the parameters α, β, γ covered by the table the length factor k lies between 0.57 and 1.00.

TABLE 18. Length Factor k for Web Members in Trusses, Fig. 130
[The parameters α, β, and γ are defined by Eq. (455)]

β	γ						
	0.1	0.3	0.5	1.0	2.0	5.0	10
$\alpha = 0.5$							
0.2	0.57	0.60	0.61	0.66	0.69	0.71	0.72
0.6	0.61	0.64	0.67	0.70	0.73	0.76	0.77
1.0	0.63	0.67	0.69	0.73	0.76	0.79	0.80
2.0	0.66	0.70	0.73	0.77	0.81	0.84	0.85
5.0	0.70	0.74	0.77	0.82	0.86	0.90	0.91

β	γ						
	0.1	0.3	0.5	1.0	2.0	5.0	10
$\alpha = 0.6$							
0.2	0.62	0.64	0.65	0.68	0.71	0.73	0.74
0.6	0.65	0.68	0.69	0.73	0.75	0.78	0.79
1.0	0.67	0.70	0.72	0.75	0.78	0.81	0.82
2.0	0.69	0.72	0.75	0.79	0.82	0.85	0.86
5.0	0.71	0.75	0.78	0.83	0.87	0.90	0.92

β	γ						
	0.1	0.3	0.5	1.0	2.0	5.0	10
$\alpha = 0.7$							
0.2	0.70	0.71	0.72	0.73	0.75	0.76	0.77
0.6	0.71	0.73	0.74	0.76	0.79	0.81	0.81
1.0	0.72	0.74	0.76	0.78	0.81	0.83	0.84
2.0	0.72	0.75	0.77	0.81	0.84	0.87	0.88
5.0	0.73	0.77	0.80	0.84	0.88	0.91	0.93

β	γ						
	0.1	0.3	0.5	1.0	2.0	5.0	10
$\alpha = 0.8$							
0.2	0.79	0.80	0.81	0.81	0.82	0.82	0.83
0.6	0.78	0.80	0.81	0.82	0.84	0.85	0.86
1.0	0.78	0.79	0.81	0.83	0.85	0.87	0.88
2.0	0.76	0.79	0.81	0.84	0.87	0.90	0.91
5.0	0.75	0.79	0.82	0.85	0.89	0.93	0.94

β	γ						
	0.1	0.3	0.5	1.0	2.0	5.0	10
$\alpha = 0.9$							
0.2	0.89	0.88	0.89	0.90	0.91	0.91	0.91
0.6	0.86	0.87	0.88	0.89	0.91	0.92	0.92
1.0	0.85	0.86	0.87	0.89	0.91	0.93	0.93
2.0	0.82	0.86	0.86	0.89	0.91	0.94	0.95
5.0	0.79	0.82	0.84	0.88	0.92	0.95	0.96

β	γ					—	
	0.1	0.3	0.5	1.0	2.0		
$\alpha = 1.0$							
0.2	0.98	0.98	0.98	0.99	0.99		
0.6	0.95	0.96	0.97	0.97	0.98		
1.0	0.92	0.94	0.95	0.96	0.98		
2.0	0.88	0.91	0.92	0.94	0.96		
5.0	0.84	0.86	0.88	0.91	0.94		

No simple rule of design which takes into account the particular condition of restraint of an individual web member can be given. There is no other way than to design the web members tentatively with a free length equal to the distance between panel points and to check the effective values kl of the individual members with the aid of Table 18. The procedure in determining the parameters α, β, γ is essentially the same as that used in determining the parameters μ and ρ described in the preceding article.

Appreciable restraining effects upon the web members will be exerted by both the top and bottom chords when web and chord members do not simultaneously reach their maximum stresses. This will be the case when the maximum stress in the web member is due to a loading condition distinctly different from that which causes the greatest stresses in the chord members. This happens in bridge trusses, crane runways, and the like, where varying loading conditions in determining the maximum stresses must be considered. On the other hand, it becomes clear that no appreciable restraint is possible in trusses, where the maximum stresses on which the design of the individual members is based occur under one and the same loading condition. The web members of such trusses should be designed as columns having an effective length equal to the panel point distance.

71. Vertical Web Members in K-trusses

The effective length of the vertical web members in K-trusses for buckling *perpendicular* to the plane of the truss has often been ques-

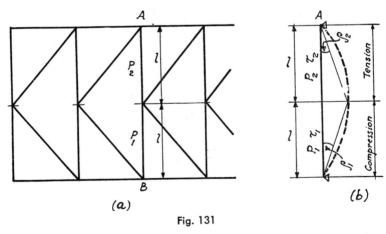

Fig. 131

tioned. In the case shown in Fig. 131a the upper half of the member AB is in tension, the lower half in compression. Put in its simplest form, the problem to be solved is that of a pin-ended member of length $2l$ under compression in one half and under tension in the other half of its length.

The moment of inertia I for buckling perpendicular to the plane of the truss is assumed to be the same in both portions of the member.

In terms of the notation shown in Fig. 131b the following stability equations can be set up:[1]

Three-moment Equation:

$$M\left(\frac{c_1}{\tau_1} + \frac{c_2}{\tau_2}\right)l - EI(\rho_1 - \rho_2) = 0 \tag{458}$$

Equilibrium Equations:

$$M - P_1 l \rho_1 - Ql = 0 \qquad \text{and} \qquad -M + P_2 l \rho_2 - Ql = 0 \tag{459}$$

Geometric Relation:

$$\rho_1 + \rho_2 = 0 \tag{460}$$

On eliminating Q, ρ_1, ρ_2 these four equations reduce to one, namely,

$$M\left[\frac{c_1}{\tau_1} + \frac{c_2}{\tau_2} - \frac{4EI}{l^2(P_1 - P_2)}\right] = 0$$

If M is to be different from zero, the expression within the brackets must vanish, and

$$\frac{c_1}{\tau_1} + \frac{c_2}{\tau_2} = \frac{4EI}{l^2(P_1 - P_2)}$$

represents the stability condition. With the notations

$$\left|\frac{P_2}{P_1}\right| = \alpha^2 \qquad \text{and} \qquad \frac{\tau_1}{\tau_2} = \beta^2 \tag{461}$$

in which P_1 is the compressive force, this equation can be written

$$c_1 + \beta^2 c_2 = \frac{4EI\tau_1}{l^2 P_1(1 - \alpha^2)} \tag{462}$$

where c_1 and c_2 are functions of

$$\phi_1 = l\sqrt{\frac{P_1}{EI\tau_1}} \qquad \text{and} \qquad \phi_2 = l\sqrt{\frac{P_2}{EI\tau_2}} = \alpha\beta\phi_1$$

If $P_1 > |P_2|$, then $\tau_1 < \tau_2$ and $\beta < 1$ in case of inelastic buckling. Assuming $\beta = 1$ leads to conservative results, which depend only on the ratio $\alpha^2 = |P_2/P_1|$. Under this simplifying assumption Eq. (462) has been solved for several values of α. The corresponding values of the length factor $k = \pi/\phi_1$ are compiled in the following Table 19. The effective length of the vertical is kL, where $L = 2l$ is the total length of the member.

[1] Equations (397), (403), and (404) in Chap. VI.

The values of k in Table 19 may be represented approximately by the simple relation

$$k = 0.73 - 0.23 \frac{P_2}{P_1} \qquad (463)$$

in which P_2 is the tensile force. If $P_2/P_1 > 1$, use $k = 0.5$.

TABLE 19. Length Factor k for Vertical Members of K-trusses, Fig. 131

P_2/P_1.......	0	0.2	0.4	0.6	0.8	1.0
k...........	0.73	0.67	0.62	0.57	0.53	0.50

Concluding Remarks. The foregoing discussion of the behavior of some types of compression members in trusses shows that a relatively simple analysis only is necessary to obtain insight into the performance of these members as parts of a rigid-frame structure. It is not within the scope of the preceding studies to treat all possible cases which may occur in various types of trusses used in engineering structures. The primary purpose has been to demonstrate the application of the four-moment equations to the group of stability problems which arise in the design of trusses and to show how the results can be interpreted suitably in order to supply the structural designer with rules and data for his routine work.

72. Buckling of Rectangular Rigid Frames

The problem of the stability of rectangular frames, in particular the investigation of the behavior of multistory frames, has been taken up relatively recently. Hertwig and Pohl[1] discussed the simple rectangular portal frame (Fig. 132) and showed that the antisymmetric buckling configuration (Fig. 132c) is associated with a far lower buckling load than the symmetric configuration (Fig. 132b). Under some simplifying assumptions Puwein[2] investigated the multistory frame having any number of bays and developed diagrams and approximate formulas for the determination of the effective length of the columns for symmetric and antisymmetric buckling of the frame structure. An instructive study of the single-bay portal frame and of one-bay multistory frames was made by Sievers,[3] who developed the buckling conditions by applying the energy method. He also studied the effect upon the critical load of the distortion caused by the axial forces of the columns.

[1] Hertwig, A., and K. Pohl, Die Stabilität des Brückenendrahmens, *Der Stahlbau*, Vol. 9, p. 129, 1936.
[2] Puwein, M. G., Die Knickfestigkeit des Stockwerkrahmens, *Der Stahlbau*, Vol. 9, p. 201, 1936.
[3] Sievers, H., Die Knickfestigkeit elastisch eingespannter Stäbe, *Der Stahlbau*, Vol. 13, p. 48, 1940.

Chwalla and Jokisch[1] applied the slope-deflection method to the study of multistory frames, developed the exact solution of the stability problem in a general form, and applied it to the investigation of single- and double-bay two-story frames. These authors also discussed the influence of longitudinal distortion of the columns.

In the papers mentioned above no account is taken of the presence of primary bending moments in the horizontal members of the frame due to transverse loading of these members. Chwalla[2] considered this problem and discussed the effect of transverse load on a single-bay portal frame but confined the investigation to cases where the stresses remain in the elastic range. Because of its primary significance the paper has already been discussed in Chap. VI.

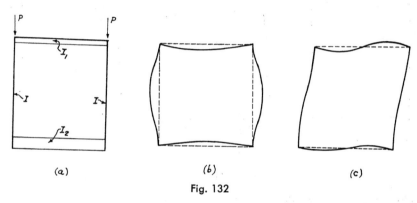

Fig. 132

In the subsequent articles some types of rigid-frame structures of practical importance will be investigated. The analysis is based on the analytical methods outlined in Art. 59 and 60 and does not take account of primary moments in the horizontal members. This effect can be discussed only in a somewhat vague manner, since at present, achievement in this special field is so limited that not more than a hope for future research work can be expressed.

73. Buckling of Single-bay Portal Frame, Hinged at Base

Symmetric Buckling. Figure 133a shows the frame and the assumed loading. Because of the symmetry of the buckling configuration (Fig. 133b), the additional moments M_1 at C and D are equal, and the bar rotations of all members are zero. The three-moment equation is

$$M_1(ch' + c_1l') + M_1s_1l' = 0$$

[1] Chwalla, E., and F. Jokisch, Über das ebene Knickproblem des Stockwerkrahmens, *Der Stahlbau*, Vol. 14, p. 33, 1941.

[2] Chwalla, *loc. cit.* on p. 227.

where the parameter c refers to the column and c_1 and s_1 to the horizontal member. After dividing by h' and substituting $h' = h/\tau$, $l' = Il/I_1$, the buckling condition is

$$c + \gamma(c_1 + s_1) = 0 \tag{464}$$

where

$$\gamma = \frac{l'}{h'} = \frac{Il\tau}{hI_1} \tag{465}$$

τ depends on the critical stress of the column. Since the axial load of the horizontal member is zero, $\phi_1 = 0$, we have $s_1 = \frac{1}{6}$ and $c_1 = \frac{1}{3}$.

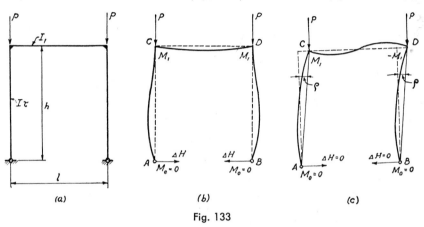

Fig. 133

Thus, Eq. (464) assumes the form

$$c + \frac{\gamma}{2} = 0 \tag{466}$$

where c is a transcendental function of the stability factor ϕ and defined by Eq. (394).

Table 20 shows the roots ϕ of Eq. (466) for various values of γ and also the length factor k which defines the effective length kh of the columns. Since the member CD restrains the columns, k is always smaller than unity.

Antisymmetric Buckling. The additional moments at C and D are M_1 and $-M_1$, as indicated in Fig. 133c. Since the bar rotation ρ is different from zero, two stability equations are required to determine the two unknown quantities M_1 and ρ. The three-moment equation reads:

$$M_1(ch' + c_1l') - M_1 s_1 l' - EI\rho = 0$$

The equilibrium equation (404) applied to the member AC is

$$M_1 = Ph\rho$$

since $M_0 = 0$ and $Q = \Delta H = 0$.

Eliminating M_1 from these two equations leads to

$$\rho[Ph(ch' + c_1l' - s_1l') - EI] = 0$$

The term inside the brackets, equated to zero, represents the stability condition. Upon dividing by Phh' we obtain

$$c + (c_1 - s_1)\frac{l'}{h'} - \frac{EI}{Phh'} = 0 \tag{467}$$

Substituting $\gamma = l'/h'$ [see Eq. (465)], introducing $c_1 - s_1 = \frac{1}{3} - \frac{1}{6} = \frac{1}{6}$, and noting that

$$\frac{EI}{Phh'} = \frac{EI\tau}{Ph^2} = \frac{1}{\phi^2}$$

the stability condition becomes

$$c + \frac{\gamma}{6} - \frac{1}{\phi^2} = 0 \tag{468}$$

Upon introducing $c = (1 - \phi \cot \phi)/\phi^2$ this equation finally assumes the form

$$\frac{\cot \phi}{\phi} - \frac{\gamma}{6} = 0 \tag{469}$$

The lower portion of Table 20 contains the values of φ computed from this equation and the corresponding values of k. ϕ is smaller than $\pi/2$ and approaches $\pi/2$ when γ approaches zero, i.e., when I_1 becomes infinitely large. The column can then be considered as fixed at the top, and it behaves like a column fixed at one end and free at the other.

Comparison of the lines which contain the k-values for symmetric and antisymmetric buckling reveals that the buckling load in the case of antisymmetric buckling is only a small fraction of the critical load associated with symmetric buckling. In designing a portal frame the far lower critical load which induces lateral buckling must be considered.

Results similar to those presented in Tables 20 and 21 were obtained in a different manner in investigations at Cornell University.[1]

TABLE 20.   Length Factor k for Single-bay Portal Frame, Hinged at Base, Fig. 133

$\gamma = \dfrac{lI\tau}{hI_1}$		0	0.1	0.2	0.5	1.0	5.0	∞
Symmetric buckling	ϕ/π....	1.430	1.366	1.315	1.219	1.143	1.038	1.000
	k.......	0.700	0.733	0.761	0.814	0.875	0.963	1.000
Antisymmetric buckling	ϕ/π....	0.500	0.492	0.483	0.461	0.430	0.296	
	k.......	2.00	2.03	2.07	2.17	2.33	3.38	

[1] Winter, G., P. T. Hsu, B. Koo, and M. H. Loh, Buckling of Trusses and Rigid Frames, *Cornell Univ. Eng. Expt. Sta. Bull.* 36, Ithaca, N.Y., 1948.

74. Buckling of Single-bay Portal Frame, Fixed at Base

Symmetric Buckling. In terms of the notation in Fig. 134a and b the following two equations determine the moments M_0 and M_1:

$$M_0 ch' + M_1 s_1 h' = 0$$
$$M_0 sh' + M_1 (ch' + c_1 l') + M_1 s_1 l' = 0$$

The determinant of the coefficients of these equations equated to zero yields, after substituting $c_1 + s_1 = \frac{1}{2}$ and $\gamma = l'/h' = lI\tau/hI_1$, the

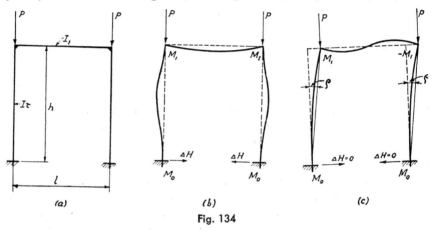

(a)   (b)   (c)

Fig. 134

stability condition

$$c\left(c + \frac{\gamma}{2}\right) - s^2 = 0 \tag{470}$$

The values of φ and the length factor k computed from Eq. (470) are shown in Table 21.

TABLE 21. Length Factor k for Single-bay Portal Frame, Fixed at Base, Fig. 134

$\gamma = \dfrac{lI\tau}{hI_1}$		0	0.1	0.2	0.5	1.0	5.0	∞
Symmetric buckling	ϕ/π....	2.000	1.908	1.833	1.696	1.597	1.470	1.430
	k......	0.500	0.524	0.545	0.590	0.626	0.680	0.700
Antisymmetric buckling	ϕ/π....	1.000	0.984	0.970	0.924	0.865	0.666	0.500
	k......	1.000	1.016	1.030	1.082	1.156	1.501	2.000

Antisymmetric Buckling. The antisymmetric buckling mode of the portal frame is illustrated by Fig. 134c. The three-moment equations now read:

$$M_0 ch' + M_1 sh' + EI\rho = 0$$
$$M_0 sh' + M_1 (ch' + c_1 l') - M_1 s_1 l' - EI\rho = 0$$

Noting that $Q = \Delta H = 0$ because of the antisymmetry, the equilibrium condition is

$$M_1 = M_0 + Ph\rho$$

Substituting ρ from the equilibrium equation in the three-moment equations, we obtain

$$M_0 ch' + M_1 sh' + \frac{EI}{Ph}(M_1 - M_0) = 0$$

$$M_0 sh' + M_1(ch' + c_1 l') - M_1 s_1 l' - \frac{EI}{Ph}(M_1 - M_0) = 0$$

After rearranging, these equations simplify to

$$M_0\left(c - \frac{1}{\phi^2}\right) + M_1\left(s + \frac{1}{\phi^2}\right) = 0$$

$$M_0\left(s + \frac{1}{\phi^2}\right) + M_1\left(c - \frac{1}{\phi^2} + \frac{\gamma}{6}\right) = 0$$

The determinant of their coefficients furnishes the stability condition

$$\left(c - \frac{1}{\phi^2}\right)\left(c - \frac{1}{\phi^2} + \frac{\gamma}{6}\right) - \left(s + \frac{1}{\phi^2}\right)^2 = 0 \qquad (471)$$

This equation can be further simplified by introducing the expressions (394) for c and s. The stability condition is finally obtained in the form

$$\phi \sin \phi \cos \phi \left(\frac{\cot \phi}{\phi} - \frac{\gamma}{6}\right) = 1 \qquad (472)$$

Table 21 gives the values of ϕ and k computed from this equation.

Inspection of Table 21 shows that k is considerably greater for antisymmetric buckling than for symmetric buckling. Thus, the critical load of the fixed portal frame is associated with the antisymmetric configuration.

75. Two-story Rectangular Frame, Fixed at Base (Fig. 135)

Antisymmetric Buckling. We begin with the more complex case of antisymmetric buckling in order to show the application of the method explained in Art. 60, which offers here some advantage in comparison with the method of the four-moment equations. The length and the moment of inertia of the vertical members are h and I, and those of the horizontal members l and I_1 (Fig. 135). The axial force in each column is P; that in the horizontal member is zero. The terminal moments M in the left half of the frame are shown in Fig. 135a. The joint rotations θ assigned to each joint and the bar rotations ρ are indicated in Fig. 135b for the antisymmetric buckling configuration. From this figure it is seen that, because of the assumed antisymmetric deformation, all joint rotations and bar rotations are clockwise rotations and therefore positive.

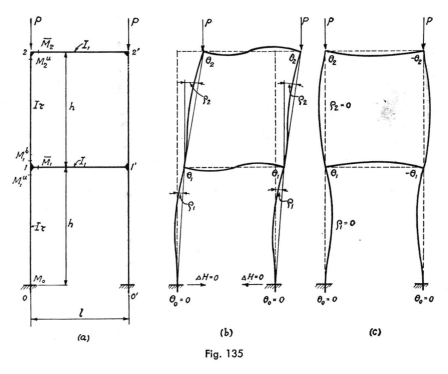

Fig. 135

We now apply Eqs. (409) which express the terminal moments of a member in terms of the angles θ and ρ to the two columns 0-1 and 1-2. Using the notation

$$\beta = \frac{EI\tau}{h} \tag{473}$$

we obtain the following equations:

Member 0-1:

$$M_0 = \beta[S\theta_1 - \rho_1(C + S)] \tag{474a}$$
$$M_1{}^u = -\beta[C\theta_1 - \rho_1(C + S)] \tag{474b}$$

Member 1-2:

$$M_1{}^b = \beta[C\theta_1 + S\theta_2 - \rho_2(C + S)] \tag{475a}$$
$$M_2{}^u = -\beta[S\theta_1 + C\theta_2 - \rho_2(C + S)] \tag{475b}$$

where C and S are functions of the stability factor ϕ of the columns, defined by Eqs. (408). Numerical values of C and S are contained in Table 14 on page 212.

For the horizontal members we have, by setting $\rho = 0$,

$$\bar{M}_1 = \frac{EI_1}{l}(C_1\theta_1 + S_1\theta_1)$$

$$\bar{M}_2 = \frac{EI_1}{l}(C_1\theta_2 + S_1\theta_2)$$

Since the stability factor of these members is zero, the values of the coefficients are $C_1 = 4$ and $S_1 = 2$. Hence these equations reduce to

$$\bar{M}_1 = \epsilon\theta_1 \tag{476}$$
$$M_2 = \epsilon\theta_2 \tag{477}$$

where

$$\epsilon = \frac{6EI_1}{l} \tag{478}$$

We consider the angles θ_1 and θ_2 and the angles ρ_1 and ρ_2 as the unknowns of the stability problem. There are two equations expressing the equilibrium of the moments acting at the joints 1 and 2. These joints are shown in Figs. 136a and 136b. From Fig. 136a we derive

$$M_1{}^u - M_1{}^b - M_1 = 0 \tag{479}$$

and from Fig. 136b

$$M_2{}^u - \bar{M}_2 = 0 \tag{480}$$

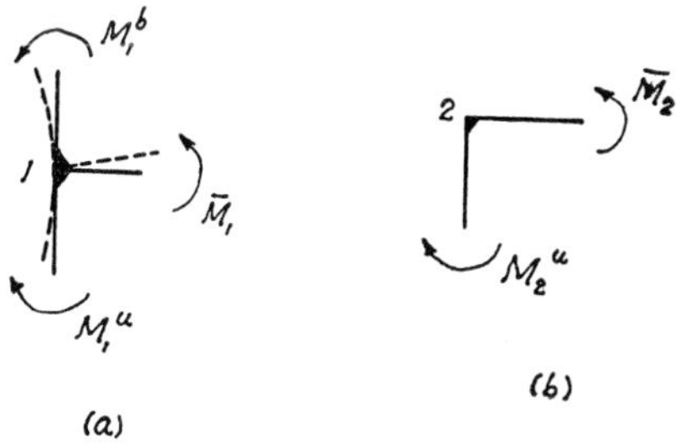

(a)

(b)

Fig. 136

Two more equations are obtained from the conditions of equilibrium of the members 0-1 and 1-2. Applying the equilibrium equations (404) and taking into account that the shearing force Q represented by the horizontal thrust ΔH is zero in both of the members, we obtain the following equations:

$$M_1{}^u = M_0 + Ph\rho_1 \quad \text{and} \quad M_2{}^u = M_1{}^b + Ph\rho_2 \tag{481}$$

Introducing the expressions for the moments [Eqs. (474) to (477)] into Eqs. (479) to (481), the following set of four equations in the unknowns θ_1, θ_2, ρ_1, ρ_2 is obtained:

$$\left.\begin{array}{l}
2C\theta_1 + S\theta_2 - (C + S)(\rho_1 - \rho_2) + \dfrac{\epsilon\theta_1}{\beta} = 0 \\[2mm]
S\theta_1 + C\theta_2 - (C + S)\rho_2 + \dfrac{\epsilon\theta_2}{\beta} = 0 \\[2mm]
(C + S)\theta_1 - 2(C + S)\rho_1 + \dfrac{Ph\rho_1}{\beta} = 0 \\[2mm]
(C + S)(\theta_1 + \theta_2) - 2(C + S)\rho_2 + \dfrac{Ph\rho_2}{\beta} = 0
\end{array}\right\} \tag{482}$$

The last two equations can be solved for ρ_1 and ρ_2:

$$\rho_1 = \delta\theta_1 \qquad \text{and} \qquad \rho_2 = \delta(\theta_1 + \theta_2) \qquad (483)$$

where

$$\delta = \frac{1}{2 - \dfrac{Ph}{\beta}\dfrac{1}{C+S}} \qquad (484)$$

Elimination of ρ_1 and ρ_2 from the first two Eqs. (482) leads to

$$\left. \begin{aligned} \theta_1\left[2C - 2\delta(C+S) + \frac{\epsilon}{\beta} \right] + \theta_2\left[S - \delta(C+S) \right] = 0 \\ \theta_1\left[S - \delta(C+S) \right] + \theta_2\left[C - \delta(C+S) + \frac{\epsilon}{\beta} \right] = 0 \end{aligned} \right\}$$

The expression ϵ/β in these equations can be simplified. Using Eqs. (473) and (478) we derive

$$\frac{\epsilon}{\beta} = \frac{6hI_1}{lI\tau} = \frac{6}{\gamma} \qquad (486)$$

where

$$\gamma = \frac{lI\tau}{hI_1} \qquad (487)$$

is the same parameter as encountered in Arts. 73 and 74 in the analysis of single-story frames.

Observing Eq. (486), the stability condition becomes

$$\left[2C - 2\delta(C+S) + \frac{6}{\gamma} \right]\left[C - \delta(C+S) + \frac{6}{\gamma} \right]$$
$$- [S - \delta(C+S)]^2 = 0 \qquad (488)$$

The expression for δ [Eq. (484)] can also be simplified. Using Eq. (473) gives

$$\frac{Ph}{\beta} = \frac{Ph^2}{EI\tau} = \frac{1}{\phi^2}$$

indicating that δ as defined by Eq. (484) is a function of ϕ alone. After introducing the values of C and S from Eqs. (408) and (394), δ assumes the simple form

$$\delta = \frac{1}{\phi}\tan\frac{\phi}{2} \qquad (489)$$

The buckling condition (488) therefore contains only one free parameter γ which depends on the given dimensions of the framework and can be solved by means of Table 14 of the C and S values. Table 22 shows the values of ϕ and k computed for several values of the parameter $\gamma = lI\tau/hI_1$.

TABLE 22.   Length Factor k for Two-story Rectangular Frame, Fig. 135

$\gamma = \dfrac{lI\tau}{hI_1}$		0	0.1	0.2	0.5	1.0	2.0	∞
Symmetric buckling	ϕ/π....	2.000	1.648	1.497	1.452	1.330	1.245	1.138
	k.......	0.500	0.507	0.668	0.689	0.753	0.803	0.879
Antisymmetric buckling	ϕ/π....	1.000	0.968	0.938	0.862	0.771	0.660	0.250
	k.......	1.000	1.033	1.065	1.160	1.310	1.515	4.000

Symmetric Buckling. This configuration is characterized by $\rho_1 = \rho_2 = 0$ (Fig. 135c). The angles θ are assumed as positive in the left half of the frame and, because of the assumed symmetry of the configuration, must be negative in the right half of the frame. The equations which correspond to Eqs. (474) to (477) now read:

$$\left.\begin{aligned}
M_0 &= \beta S\theta_1 &&\text{and} & M_1{}^u &= -\beta C\theta_1 \\
M_1{}^b &= \beta(C\theta_1 + S\theta_2) &&\text{and} & M_2{}^u &= -\beta(S\theta_1 + C\theta_2) \\
\bar{M}_1 &= \frac{EI_1}{l}(C\theta_1 - S\theta_1) = \epsilon'\theta_1 \\
\bar{M}_2 &= \frac{EI_1}{l}(C\theta_2 - S\theta_2) = \epsilon'\theta_2
\end{aligned}\right\} \qquad (490)$$

where

$$\epsilon' = \frac{2EI_1}{l} \qquad (491)$$

Introducing the expressions (490) into the equilibrium conditions (479) and (480), two stability equations are obtained:

$$\left.\begin{aligned}
\theta_1\left(2C + \frac{2}{\gamma}\right) + S\theta_2 &= 0 \\
S\theta_1 + \theta_2\left(C + \frac{2}{\gamma}\right) &= 0
\end{aligned}\right\} \qquad (492)$$

ϵ'/β can be expressed by the parameter γ:

$$\frac{\epsilon'}{\beta} = \frac{2hI_1}{lI\tau} = \frac{2}{\gamma}$$

and the stability condition is

$$\left(2C + \frac{2}{\gamma}\right)\left(C + \frac{2}{\gamma}\right) - S^2 = 0 \qquad (493)$$

ϕ and k-values derived from Eq. (493) are given in Table 22. The effective length of the columns is kh.

76. Multistory Rectangular Frames

Antisymmetric Buckling. In principle it is not difficult to apply the method used in the previous article to the framed structure shown in Fig. 137a. However, because of the high redundancy of the system, it would be an arduous task to evaluate the determinant if the axial loads

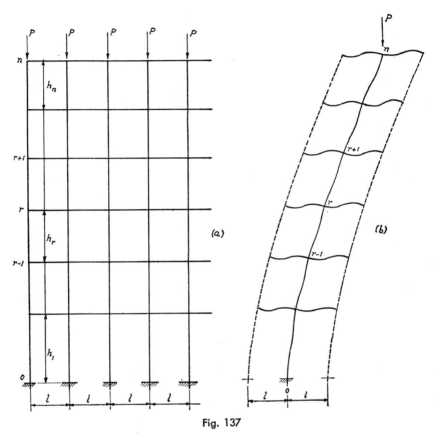

Fig. 137

and stiffnesses of the columns vary from story to story, as is actually the case in tier building frames. However, under certain simplifying assumptions a practicable solution can be found which is sufficiently general to enable us to discuss the influence upon stability of the number of stories and the effect of the ratio of column stiffness to the stiffness of the horizontal members framing into it. Although the assumptions which underlie the following analysis deviate from the conditions which prevail in real building frames, useful information of a general nature concerning the behavior of multistory frames can be obtained. The numerical results may serve for at least an approximate determination of the buckling load of actual structures.

We assume that the number of bays is large, so that the influence of the end bays on the behavior of a column in the interior of the framework can be neglected. We assume furthermore that the axial loads of all columns and the stiffness of all columns and beams are identical. It then suffices to consider the simplified system consisting of one column and the beams framing into it, as shown in the distorted state by full lines in Fig. 137b. In order to render the problem amenable to an analytical solution,

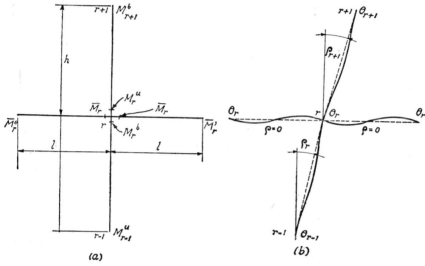

Fig. 138

we further assume that all stories have the same height h, which means that the stability factor $\phi = h \sqrt{P/EI\tau}$ is the same for all vertical members of the frame.

We consider the joint r at which four members of the frame meet (Fig. 138). With the notation indicated, Eqs. (409) furnish two equations for each member. All angles θ and ρ are assumed positive.

Member $r = 1, r$:

$$M_{r-1}^b = \beta[C\theta_{r-1} + S\theta_r - \rho_r(C + S)] \atop M_r^u = -\beta[S\theta_{r-1} + C\theta_r - \rho_r(C + S)] \Bigg\} \qquad (494)$$

Member $r, r + 1$:

$$M_r^b = \beta[C\theta_r + S\theta_{r+1} - \rho_{r+1}(C + S)] \atop M_{r+1}^u = -\beta[S\theta_r + C\theta_{r+1} - \rho_{r+1}(C + S)] \Bigg\} \qquad (495)$$

where $\beta = EI\tau/h$. C and S, depending only on ϕ, have the same value in all vertical members.

Members r, r' and r, r'':

$$\bar{M}_r = \frac{EI_1}{l}(4\theta_r + 2\theta_r) = \frac{6EI_1}{l}\theta_r = \epsilon\theta_r \tag{496}$$

With reference to Fig. 138, the equilibrium of the moments acting on joint r is expressed by

$$M_r{}^u - M_r{}^b - 2\bar{M}_r = 0 \tag{497}$$

whereas two supplementary equations are obtained from the condition of equilibrium of the members $r - 1$, r and r, $r + 1$:

$$\left.\begin{array}{l} M_r{}^u - M_{r-1}{}^b - Ph\rho_r = 0 \\ M_{r+1}{}^u - M_r{}^b - Ph\rho_{r+1} = 0 \end{array}\right\} \tag{498}$$

Substitution of the moments from Eqs. (494) and (495) furnishes the following expressions for ρ_r and ρ_{r+1}:

$$\left.\begin{array}{l} \rho_r = \dfrac{\theta_{r-1} + \theta_r}{2 - \dfrac{Ph}{\beta}\dfrac{1}{C + S}} = \delta(\theta_{r-1} + \theta_r) \\[3mm] \rho_{r+1} = \dfrac{\theta_r + \theta_{r+1}}{2 - \dfrac{Ph}{\beta}\dfrac{1}{C + S}} = \delta(\theta_r + \theta_{r+1}) \end{array}\right\} \tag{499}$$

Using Eqs. (499) for the elimination of ρ_r and ρ_{r+1} from Eqs. (494) and (495) and introducing the transformed expressions into the equilibrium condition (497), the following relation between three successive joint rotations θ is obtained:

$$\theta_{r-1} + 2\mu\theta_r + \theta_{r+1} = 0 \tag{500}$$

The parameter μ is given by

$$\mu = \frac{C - \delta(C + S) + \epsilon/\beta}{S - \delta(C + S)} = \frac{C - \delta(C + S) + 6/\gamma}{S - \delta(C + S)} \tag{501}$$

δ as defined by Eqs. (499) can be expressed in the form

$$\delta = \frac{1}{\phi}\tan\frac{\phi}{2}$$

[see Eq. (489)]. Because of the relation

$$\frac{\epsilon}{\beta} = \frac{6hI_1}{lI\tau} = \frac{6}{\gamma}$$

Eq. (500) contains only one free parameter, $\gamma = lI\tau/hI_1$. Equation (500) being valid for $r = 1, 2, \ldots, n - 1$, we have $n - 1$ equations of this type and we need two additional equations in order to complete the set of $n + 1$ equations necessary for the determination of the $n + 1$ joint rotations θ.

Under the assumption that the bases of the columns are fixed, one of these equations takes the simple form

$$\theta_0 = 0 \tag{502}$$

The other equation is obtained by applying the same procedure as outlined above to the top joint n. This leads to an equation

$$\theta_{n-1} + \mu'\theta_n = 0 \tag{503}$$

where μ' differs from μ in that $6/\gamma$ in Eq. (501) is replaced by $12/\gamma$. In order to simplify the following analysis, it is expedient to modify the boundary condition at the upper end [Eq. (503)] by replacing μ' by μ. The error involved becomes negligible if $n > 3$. Thus, the second boundary condition will be used in the form

$$\theta_{n-1} + \mu\theta_n = 0 \tag{503a}$$

We now consider Eq. (500) as a finite difference equation, the solution of which must satisfy the boundary conditions (502) and (503a). The solution of this finite difference equation of the second order is of the form[1]

$$\theta_r = A \sin r\omega + B \cos r\omega \tag{504}$$

the constants A and B to be determined from the boundary conditions. Introduction of $\sin r\omega$ or $\cos r\omega$ into Eq. (500) yields the characteristic equation

$$\cos \omega = -\mu \tag{505}$$

This equation determines the parameter ω. We further introduce the solution (504) into the boundary conditions, thus obtaining two homogenous, linear equations which define the constants A and B. The first of these two conditions gives $B = 0$, and the second condition leads to

$$A[\sin (n - 1)\omega + \mu \sin n\omega] = 0$$

from which the stability condition

$$\sin \omega \cos n\omega = 0$$

results. Vanishing of the first factor gives meaningless roots $\omega = 0$, π, 2π, . . . , because for these values $\theta_r = A \sin r\omega = 0$. The second factor leads to

$$\cos n\omega = 0$$

[1] A simple introduction to finite difference equations is contained in T. v. Kármán and M. A. Biot, "Mathematical Methods in Engineering," Chap. XI, McGraw-Hill Book Company, Inc., New York, 1940.

and

$$\omega = \frac{\pi}{2n}, \frac{3\pi}{2n}, \frac{5\pi}{2n}, \cdot \cdot \cdot \tag{506}$$

The first of these values is associated with the lowest buckling mode and with reference to Eqs. (501) and (505) gives the stability condition

$$\frac{C - \delta(C + S) + 6/\gamma}{S - \delta(C + S)} = - \cos \frac{\pi}{2n} \tag{507}$$

valid for $n > 3$.

C and S as well as δ are functions of ϕ, and Eq. (507) can be solved for any given value of n and γ, the latter value indicating the design characteristic of the idealized framework.

Figure 139 contains graphs of the length factor k which is plotted against the parameter $\gamma = lI\tau/hI_1$ for $n = 2, 3$, and 10. The curves for $n = 2$ and 3 were found directly by evaluating the determinant which defines the joint rotations θ. The curves begin at $\gamma = 0$ (rigid beams) with $k = 1$, and the effective length kh increases as the beam stiffness reduces. With increasing γ (diminishing stiffness of the horizontal members) the curves approach asymptotically the value $k = 2n$ indicating the effective length of a column of length nh, fixed at one end and free at the other one. A certain minimum stiffness of the horizontal member, therefore, is necessary to keep the length factor k within economic limits.

Multistory frames of the type here considered, independent of the number of bays, are highly susceptible to lateral buckling, and one purpose of the investigation was to show numerically the considerable reduction of buckling strength of the framework if horizontal displacement is not prevented by suitable structural means.

While the foregoing analysis leading to the diagram shown in Fig. 139 was based on the assumption of constant load P and constant moment of inertia I of the columns, it can be shown that Fig. 139 remains valid if the loads P in the columns and the moments of inertia I of columns and beams vary from story to story in the following manner:

1. The column load P_r in the rth story and the moment of inertia of the column I_r will vary in such a way that the ratio $P_r/I_r\tau$ is constant throughout the total height of the column.
2. The moment of inertia I_{1r} of the horizontal members on the rth level will vary in proportion to the average moment of inertia of the columns below and above; i.e., the ratio $I_{1r}/(I_r\tau + I_{r+1}\tau)$ will be constant.

Provided these two assumptions are satisfied and some minor numerical approximations made, an analysis leads again to Eq. (500), and Fig. 139 is therefore valid again. This is important because assumption 1 will be reasonably well satisfied in actual structures where the loads P and moments of inertia I increase from the roof down.   Assumption 2 is not consistent with the actual conditions in tier building frames.   To be on

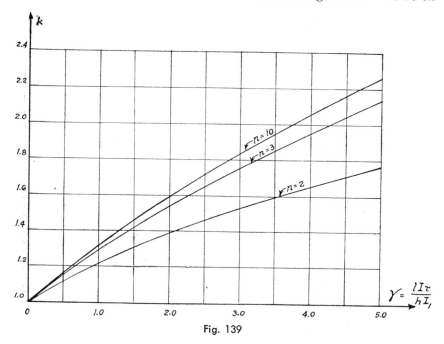

Fig. 139

the safe side the largest value of I/I_1 should be used for computing the parameter γ when applying Fig. 139.

Symmetric Buckling.   In order to show the considerable increase in buckling strength of a multistory frame, provided that the framework is laterally supported so that collapse in the antisymmetric buckling mode cannot occur, we consider a frame panel between the floors $r-1$ and r as shown in Fig. 140. For the sake of a simple analysis we assume again that I, I_1, and P are constant.   Under this condition the terminal moments at two consecutive joints deviate but slightly from each other, and without appreciable error it can be assumed that

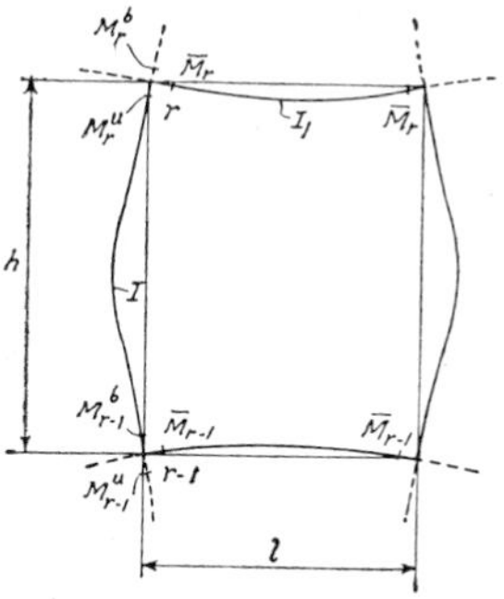

$$M_{r-1}{}^u = M_{r-1}{}^b = M_r{}^u = M_r{}^b \quad (508)$$

Fig. 140

Under this assumption one four-moment equation

$$M_{r-1}{}^b sh' + M_r{}^u ch' + \bar{M}_r c_1 l' + \bar{M}_r s_1 l' = 0 \quad (509)$$

suffices for arriving at the stability condition. Equation (508) together with the condition of equilibrium at joint r, namely,

$$2M_r{}^u = 2\bar{M}_r \qquad (510)$$

permit elimination of $M_{r-1}{}^b$ and $\bar{M}_r$ from Eq. (509), which assumes the form

$$M_r{}^u(sh' + ch' + c_1l' + s_1l') = 0$$

The expression within the parentheses equated to zero represents the stability condition,

$$s + c + (c_1 + s_1)\frac{l'}{h'} = s + c + \gamma/2 = 0 \qquad (511)$$

where $\gamma = lI\tau/hI_1$.

Table 23 gives values of ϕ and the corresponding length factor k for several values of γ.

TABLE 23. Length Factor k for Symmetrical Buckling of Multistory Rectangular Frames

γ	0	0.1	0.2	0.5	1.0	5.0	∞
ϕ/π.....	2.000	1.822	1.690	1.457	1.292	1.075	1.000
k.......	0.500	0.549	0.592	0.730	0.775	0.963	1.000

77. Effect of Primary Bending Moments on Buckling Strength of Rectangular Rigid Frames

So far it has been assumed that no primary bending moments due to transverse loading of the horizontal members are present in the framed structure prior to buckling. This, of course, does not conform with real conditions in building frames. At present no suitable method is available for determining the critical load of rectangular rigid frames which takes account of the influence of these bending moments on the stability of the structure. The general aspect of the problem has been discussed in Art. 62 of Chap. VI, and an account was given of one such problem solved by Chwalla. It may be recalled that his analytical investigation indicates that distortion of the framework prior to buckling, caused by the transverse loading of the horizontal members, reduces the buckling strength of the system only to a rather limited extent. However, Chwalla confined his study to stresses in columns and beams within the elastic region, and the gap in our knowledge of the performance of frames with transverse loaded members, stressed beyond the proportional limit, remains yet to be filled.

In conjunction with an extensive research program, designed primarily to clear up theoretically and by tests the principles of the method of plastic design as applied to rigidly jointed framework, Baker[1] and his associates in England have studied by means of small models the behavior of a strut as part of a simple framed structure.   Each of the models consisted of a stanchion with loaded beams, connected to it by rigid joints. Figure 141a shows the arrangement of the specimen with the strut bent by the beam loading in a single curvature.   Figure 141b represents the specimen in which the strut deflects in two half waves before buckling.

It is natural that the results obtained by a small number of tests, which are only the beginning of a comprehensive investigation into the complex buckling problem of framed structures within the plastic range, do not permit any conclusion of general nature concerning the effect of transverse

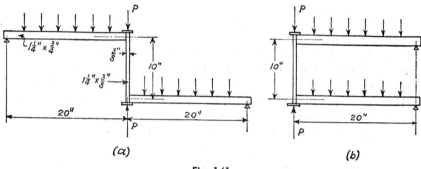

(a)   (b)

Fig. 141

loads when bending and buckling take place in the plastic region.   Many additional experiments will be necessary to obtain sufficient information about the influence of variations of those factors which determine the performance of an individual frame.   However, real success cannot be expected until the experimental research can be supplemented by the rational solution of the fundamental buckling problems outlined in Art. 62, page 222.   In view of its complexity, it appears questionable whether sufficient insight into the subject matter can be achieved without a guiding theory.

Additional References

Newmark, N. M., A Simple Approximation Formula for Effective End-fixity of Columns, *Jour. Aeronaut. Sci.*, Vol. 16, p. 116, 1949.
Wessman, H. E., and T. C. Kavanagh, End Restraints on Truss Members, *Trans. ASCE*, Vol. 115, p. 1135, 1950.

[1] Baker, J. F., A Review of Recent Investigations into the Behavior of Steel Frames in the Plastic Range, *Jour. Inst. Civil Engrs. (London)*, 1948–1949, p. 185.   Baker, J. F., and J. W. Roderick, The Behavior of Stanchions Bent in Single Curvature, 3d *Interim Rept., Trans. Inst. Welding*, Vol. 5, p. 97, 1942, and The Behavior of Stanchions Bent in Double Curvature, 5th *Interim Rept., Welding Research*, Vol. 2, No. 1, 1948.

CHAPTER VIII

STABILITY OF AXIALLY COMPRESSED BARS
ELASTICALLY SUPPORTED AT SPECIFIC POINTS

78. Introduction

The question of the lateral stability of the unbraced chords of the trusses or of the unbraced flanges of the girders in half-through bridges has long been a subject of great interest to the structural engineer. The development of the theory of framework stability actually started with various attempts to approach just this problem, and the early investigations of Zimmermann and Müller-Breslau at the beginning of this century bear witness to the importance which has been attached to the solution of this problem.

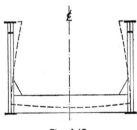

Fig. 142

The compression chord of a pony truss and the compression flange of a half-through girder represent members elastically supported in a horizontal plane by the vertical web members of the truss or by the web stiffeners of the girder, which form, together with the floor beams, rigid frames as shown in Fig. 142. The flexibility of the frame, in general, does not permit considering the chord as rigidly supported at the points of attachment to the frame. In the state of unstable equilibrium, when the chord deflects laterally, shearing forces occur which tend to displace the points of support. These displacements are of the same order of magnitude as the chord deflections, and their effect upon the failure load of the chord cannot be neglected.

Let us consider a bar hinged at both ends to rigid supports and having equally spaced elastic supports of equal stiffness between the end supports. If the elastic stiffness of these supports is sufficiently great, the bar will buckle in half waves of a length equal to the distance between two adjacent supports as illustrated by Fig. 143a. The points of inflection coincide with the points of support. The bar behaves like a bar on rigid supports. If, in turn, the supports are very flexible, it is possible that the entire chord will deflect in one half wave as shown in Fig. 143b.

For values of the elastic stiffness of the supports between these two limits, it can be concluded that the chord may buckle into a number of half waves greater than unity but smaller than the number of spans between the rigidly supported ends (Fig. 143c). The number of half waves increases with increasing stiffness of the supporting rigid frames. The length of the individual half waves which compose a certain buckling configuration will, in general, not be equal, even in the case of equally spaced supports.

It must be emphasized that the column need not be held by completely rigid intermediate supports in order that the critical buckling load is associated with displacements according to Fig. 143a. If a certain finite stiffness of the elastic supports is reached, the bar behaves like a bar on rigid supports and a further increase in the elastic stiffness of the supports has no effect on the failure load of the bar.

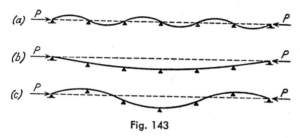

Fig. 143

The problem of the elastically supported bar was investigated first by Engesser,[1] who derived an approximate formula for the required stiffness of the elastic supports. Because of its extreme simplicity the formula is still in use in bridge design. Engesser's formula is based on the assumption that the bar, rigidly supported at both ends, rests on a continuous elastic medium and that the axial compressive force is constant over the entire length of the bar. Other cases with varying axial loads were treated later in a similar manner by Jasinski.[2]

The principles of an exact solution of the problem of stability of compression chords of half-through bridges were discussed by Zimmerman[3] and Müller-Breslau,[4] who arrived at the critical load by evaluating the denominator determinant of a system of linear equations. This method

[1] Engesser, F., Die Sicherung offener Brücken gegen Ausknicken, *Zentralblatt der Bauverwaltung*, 1884, p. 415; 1885, p. 93. See also F. Engesser, "Die Zusatzkräfte und Nebenspannungen eiserner Fachwerkbrücken," Vol. II, Berlin, 1893.

[2] Jasinski, F. S., La flexion des pièces comprimées, *Annales des ponts et chaussées*, 1894, 2d part, p. 233.

[3] Zimmermann, H., "Die Knickfestigkeit der Druckgurte offener Brücken," W. Ernst und Sohn, Berlin, 1910.

[4] Müller-Breslau, H., "Die graphische Statik der Baukonstruktionen," Vol. II.-2, A. Kröner, Leipzig, 1908.

has been refined and improved later by Ostenfeld[1] and Kriso.[2] However, all these methods are too involved to be applied to the analysis of any individual practical case.

By using finite difference equations an exact solution in a form conveniently applicable to routine design was given by Bleich.[3] It is valid for chords rigidly supported at the ends and supported elastically on equally spaced intermediate supports of equal rigidity. The analysis is based on the assumption of constant moment of inertia and constant axial compressive force over the entire length of the chord. An extension of the analysis involving the important case of elastic end supports was presented by Schweda,[4] who also succeeded in transforming the analytical results into a simple formula of design. In a recent paper the problems treated by Bleich and Schweda were discussed anew by Ratzersdorfer.[5]

For more involved cases, in which account must be taken of the varying rigidity and varying axial thrust of the bar or of the variation of the elastic stiffness of the supports, the energy method lends itself as an excellent means of developing methods of analysis of sufficient simplicity to meet the requirements of the structural engineer. Investigations along this line were made by Timoshenko,[6] who assumed the bar continuously supported, and by Kasarnowsky and Zetterholm,[7] who considered equidistant intermediate supports. A general analysis, utilizing all the possibilities of simplification inherent in the energy method, was presented by the author.[8] The method was especially devised for bars elastically supported at specific points, and its application is not limited by any restriction concerning the variation of the axial force, the rigidity of the bar, or the stiffness of the supports. The method applies to chords of single-span trusses as well as to the chords of continuous trusses.

Attempts have been made to apply the method of successive approximations discussed in Art. 27 of Chap. II to the investigation of the

[1] Ostenfeld, A., Die Seitensteifigkeit offener Brücken, *Beton und Eisen*, 1916, p. 123.

[2] Kriso, K., Die Knicksicherheit der Druckgurte offener Fachwerkbrücken, *Pubs. Intern. Assoc. Bridge and Structural Eng.*, Vol. III, p. 271, 1935.

[3] Bleich, F., Die Knickfestigkeit elastischer Stabverbindungen, *Der Eisenbau*, Vol. 10, 1919.

[4] Schweda, F., Die Bemessung des Endquerrahmens offener Brücken, *Der Bauingenieur*, Vol. 9, p. 535, 1928. See also *Sitzungsberichte der Akademie der Wissenschaften in Wien*, Vol. 137, Abt. IIa, p. 71, 1928.

[5] Ratzerdorfer, J., A Buckling Problem, The Case of an Elastically Supported Beam, *Aircraft Eng.*, 1945, p. 348.

[6] Timoshenko, S., Sur la stabilité des systèmes élastiques, *Annales des ponts et chaussés*, Fasc. III, IV, and V, 1913.

[7] Kasarnowsky, S., and D. Zetterholm, Zur Theorie der Seitensteifigkeit offener Fachwerkbrücken, *Der Bauingenieur*, Vol. 8, p. 760, 1927.

[8] Bleich, F., and H. Bleich, Beitrag zur Stabilitätsuntersuchung des punktweise elastisch gestützten Stabes, *Der Stahlbau*, Vol. 10, p. 17, 1937.

stability of elastically supported bars under varying axial load.[1] However, this method is practical only when the chord buckles in one or two half waves, which is the exception, and consequently the procedure has little practical significance.

Hrennikoff[2] investigated the effect of restraint against rotation of the chord about its longitudinal axis as a consequence of the rigid connection between the chord and the top end of the supporting web members. A problem closely related to the stability problem treated by Hrennikoff was discussed by Timoshenko,[3] namely, the buckling of a bar by torsion and flexure in an elastic medium.

Budiansky, Seide, and Weinberger[4] discussed recently the buckling load of a column restrained elastically at equally spaced intermediate points against deflection and against rotation in the plane of the deflection.

Charts for the computation of the buckling strength of the top chords of pony trusses of the type shown in Fig. 144 were computed by Kriso and Schibler[5] under simplifying assumptions concerning the design factors of the chord. The charts are valid for equal elastic stiffnesses

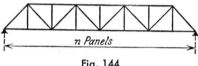

Fig. 144

of the supports, including the end supports, and were computed for trusses with $n = 4, 6, 8$, and 10 panels under the assumption that the compressive forces are those produced by a uniform load over the entire span.

The foregoing brief review of the theoretical research in the field of stability of chords of pony-truss bridges reveals that most of the actual stability problems which may arise in connection with the design of half-through bridges have been theoretically solved. It must be pointed out, however, that these theories do not furnish the answer to an auxiliary question which is not really a stability problem but nonetheless important to the designing engineer. While the theory furnishes the required stiffness of the elastic supports, it does not give the forces which act on the

[1] Keelhoff, M., La stabilité des membrures comprimées des ponts métalliques, *Annales des ponts et chaussées*, 1920, p. 193. Bazant, Z., Die Knicksicherheit der Druckgurte offener Brücken, *Pubs. Intern. Assoc. Bridge and Structural Eng.*, Vol. VII, p. 49, 1943–1944.

[2] Hrennikoff, A., Elastic Stability of a Pony Truss, *Pubs. Intern. Assoc. Bridge and Structural Eng.*, Vol. III, p. 192, 1935.

[3] Timoshenko, S., Theory of Bending, Torsion and Buckling of Thin-walled Members of Open Cross Section, *Jour. Franklin Inst.*, 1945, p. 348.

[4] Budiansky, B., P. Seide, and R. A. Weinberger, The Buckling of a Column on Equally Spaced Deflectional and Rotational Springs, *NACA Tech. Note* 1519, 1948.

[5] Schibler, W., Das Tragvermögen der Druckgurte offener Fachwerkbrücken mit parallelen Gurten, *Mitteilungen* 19, *Institut für Baustatik, Eidgenössische technische Hochschule, Zürich*, 1946.

posts of the stiffening cross frames. The magnitude of these forces is necessary to find stresses in posts and floor beams and to design their connections. No consideration has as yet been given to this problem, and no rational design formulas are known. The problem is somewhat similar to the one of designing built-up columns considered in Chap. V. The theory of elastic stability furnished formulas for the buckling load of the column, but a separate reasoning, not based on stability considerations, had to be used in Art. 55 to design lacing bars and batten plates.

A second question requiring study is the effect of the live-load deformation of the floor beams on the stability of the chord. If only a few of the floor beams carry live load, their deflection will result in lateral movements of the tops of the posts, which in turn impose deflections and stresses on the chord that may affect its stability. The magnitude of these additional stresses due to live load on the floor beams was studied by Schibler.[1]

The following articles will give a detailed account of the available theories which are considered suitable for the derivation of design formulas for the stability of unbraced bridge chords.

79. The Engesser Formula

We owe the first successful treatment of the stability problem with which this chapter is concerned to Engesser,[2] who developed an approximate formula valid under the following geometric and mechanical conditions:

1. The bar AB of length $L = nl$, loaded by the compressive force P, has rigid supports at the pin-connected ends and is elastically supported at the equally spaced intermediate supports (Fig. 145a).

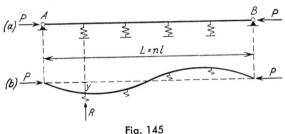

Fig. 145

2. The cross-sectional area A and the moment of inertia I are constant.
3. The reaction R at any elastic support (see Fig. 145b) is a linear function of the deflection y at this support, namely,

$$R = Cy \qquad (512)$$

[1] *Ibid.*
[2] Engesser, *loc. cit.* on p. 269.

in which C is the spring constant assumed to be the same for all intermediate points of support. C depends on the elastic stiffness of the supporting structure and may be defined as the force which produces the displacement $y = 1$ at the point of application, as illustrated by Fig. 146. C has the dimension of a force per unit length and may vary between 0 and ∞.

In Engesser's theory the simplifying assumption is made that the bar buckles between A and B (Fig. 145) in equal half waves of length v— which, in general, is not the case—and that the reactions R concentrated

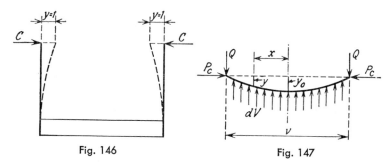

Fig. 146   Fig. 147

at the points of elastic support can be replaced by the continuously distributed elastic resistance dR defined by

$$dR = \frac{R}{l}\,dx = \frac{C}{l}\,y\,dx \qquad (513)$$

Figure 147 shows such a half wave of length v and the forces which act upon it, the elastic resistance dR, and the forces Q and P_c.

It is assumed that the deflection curve is a cosine curve

$$y = y_0 \cos \frac{\pi x}{v} \qquad (514)$$

the origin of the coordinate system x, y being at the mid-point of the length v.

The shear force Q is given by

$$Q = \int_{x=0}^{x=\frac{v}{2}} dR = \int_0^{\frac{v}{2}} \frac{C}{l} y_0 \cos \frac{\pi x}{v}\,dx = \frac{Cv}{\pi l} y_0 \qquad (515)$$

and the moment M_m at the center by

$$M_m = P_c y_0 - Q\frac{v}{2} + \int_0^{\frac{v}{2}} x\,dR$$

Applying the differential relation

$$E_t I y'' = -M*$$

to the point $x = 0$, we obtain

$$E_t I (y'')_{x=0} = -P_c y_0 + Q \frac{v}{2} \int_0^{\frac{v}{2}} x \, dR \tag{516}$$

With

$$Q \frac{v}{2} = \frac{Cv^2}{2\pi l} y_0 \qquad \text{and} \qquad \int_0^{\frac{v}{2}} x \, dR = \frac{Cy_0}{l}\left(\frac{v^2}{2\pi} - \frac{v^2}{\pi^2}\right)$$

and upon computing $[y'']_{x=0}$ from Eq. (514), we arrive at

$$P_c = \frac{\pi^2 E_t I}{v^2} + \frac{Cv^2}{\pi^2 l} \tag{517}$$

showing P_c as a function of the length v of the half wave for any given value of $E_t I$, l, and C. P_c will be a minimum when $\dfrac{dP_c}{dv} = 0$. This condition leads to

$$-\frac{2\pi^2 E_t I}{v^3} + \frac{2Cv}{\pi^2 l} = 0$$

from which the length of the half wave

$$v = \pi \sqrt[4]{\frac{E_t I l}{C}} \tag{518}$$

is derived. Using this value one obtains finally from Eq. (517) the required value C_{req} of the spring constant C necessary to ensure the carrying capacity $P_c = \nu P$ of the bar. The required value is

$$C_{\text{req}} = \frac{P_c{}^2 l}{4E_t I} \tag{519}$$

This is Engesser's formula. The supporting elastic structure must be designed so that its spring constant is equal to or greater than C_{req}.

Equation (519) contains the tangent-modulus E_t which depends on $\sigma_c = P_c/A$. In order to facilitate the use of Eq. (519) in routine design it is expedient to express P_c by means of the generalized Euler formula

$$P_c = \frac{\pi^2 E_t I}{(kl)^2} \tag{520}$$

which defines P_c as the failure load of a two-hinged column of length kl. The factor k must be greater than unity, since $k = 1$ corresponds to the

* By introducing the tangent-modulus E_t, Engesser's original analysis in which Young's modulus is used can be readily generalized.

limiting value $P_E = \pi^2 E_t I / l^2$, which cannot be exceeded. Equation (520) yields

$$E_t I = \frac{P_c (kl)^2}{\pi^2}$$

and substituting $E_t I$ from this equation in Eq. (519) finally gives

$$C_{\text{req}} = \frac{\pi^2}{4k^2} \frac{P_c}{l} \tag{521}$$

The slenderness ratio $\lambda = kl/r$ which corresponds to the critical stress $\sigma_c = P_c/A$ can be taken from the column curve of the material under consideration, giving $k = \lambda r/l$. The radius of gyration r in this equation is given by $\sqrt{I/A}$, in which I and A are defined at the outset of the discussion. Equation (521), therefore, is valid in the elastic and inelastic range of buckling.

The procedure in determining C_{req} is very simple. Multiply the design stress $\sigma = P/A$ of the bar by the factor of safety ν to obtain the critical stress $\sigma_c = \nu \sigma$. Read the slenderness ratio λ which corresponds to σ_c from the column curve, and compute $k = \lambda r/l$. Equation (521) finally gives C_{req}.

Engesser's formula is in good agreement with the exact solution for the bar with rigidly supported ends as long as the wavelength v is greater than $1.8l$, which will be shown in the following article. This limitation of the validity of the formula was already recognized by Engesser himself. The limiting length $v = 1.8l$ corresponds to a value of $k = 1.3$, and the formula can be applied when the flexural rigidity of the bar is sufficient to ensure stability as a two-hinged column of length $l_0 \geq 1.3l$.

Equations (519) and (521) apply only when the ends of the bar are rigidly supported, since the assumption of equal half waves between the rigid supports implies zero deflection at these points.

80. Exact Theory of the Elastically Supported Bar, General Solution

The general theory of the stability of frameworks presented in Art. 59 of Chap. VI will be used to obtain the stability equations for a straight bar supported elastically at the points 0, 1, 2, . . . , n. In this article we consider the general case illustrated by Fig. 148, in which the dimensions of each individual span and the axial forces vary from span to span. Subsequently, the case of constant l, I, and P will be considered in Arts. 81 and 82, where analytical solutions will be developed under the assumptions of unyielding end supports and elastic end supports, respectively.

The investigation of the framework represented by Fig. 148 by the analytical method outlined in Art. 59 leads to $n - 1$ three-moment equations at the supports 1, 2, . . . , $(n - 1)$ and n equilibrium equations for the n members of the column. These $2n - 1$ equations define the $n - 1$ moments M_r at the supports and the n bar rotations ρ_r, a total of $2n - 1$ unknowns.

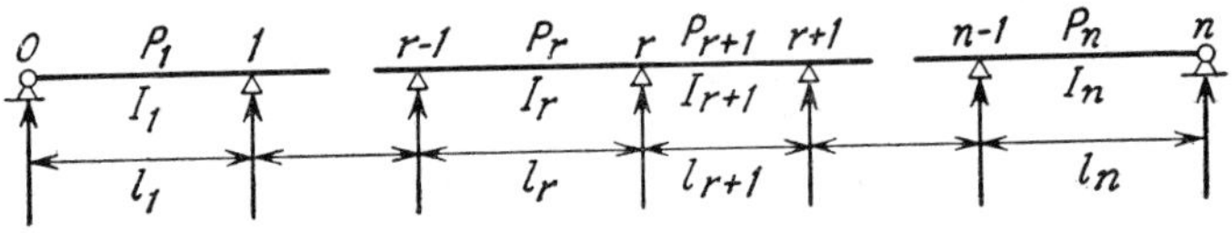

Fig. 148

Referring to Eqs. (397) and (404), we have one three-moment equation for each support $r = 1, 2, \ldots, (n - 1)$:

$$M_{r-1}s_rl_r' + M_r(c_rl_r' + c_{r+1}l_{r+1}') + M_{r+1}s_{r+1}l_{r+1}' - EI(\rho_r - \rho_{r+1}) = 0 \quad (522)$$

and one equilibrium condition for each span:

$$\frac{M_r - M_{r-1}}{l_r} - P_r\rho_r - Q_r = 0 \quad (523)$$

All notations are defined in Art. 59.

In order to eliminate the shear forces Q_k from the system of Eq. (523), we compute the difference of two successive equations:

$$\frac{M_r - M_{r-1}}{l_r} - \frac{M_{r+1} - M_r}{l_{r+1}} - P_r\rho_r + P_{r+1}\rho_{r+1} - Q_r + Q_{r+1} = 0 \quad (524)$$

Since

$$Q_{r+1} - Q_r = R_r$$

and

$$R_r = C_r y_r \quad (525)$$

in which C_r is the spring constant of the support r, Eq. (524) takes the form

$$\frac{M_r - M_{r-1}}{l_r} - \frac{M_{r+1} - M_r}{l_{r+1}} - P_r\rho_r + P_{r+1}\rho_{r+1} + C_r y_r = 0 \quad (526)$$

The bar rotations ρ_r can be expressed by the deflections y_r:

$$\rho_r = \frac{y_r - y_{r-1}}{l_r} \quad (527)$$

and upon introducing (527) into Eqs. (522) and (526) the following system of stability equations is obtained.

Three-moment Equations:

$$M_{r-1}s_rl_r' + M_r(c_rl_r' + c_{r+1}l_{r+1}') + M_{r+1}s_{r+1}l_{r+1}'$$
$$- EI\left[\frac{y_r - y_{r-1}}{l_r} - \frac{y_{r+1} - y_r}{l_{r+1}}\right] = 0 \quad (r = 1, 2, \ldots, n - 1) \quad (528)$$

with the boundary values $M_0 = 0$ and $M_n = 0$.

Equilibrium Conditions for Intermediate Points:

$$\frac{M_r - M_{r-1}}{l_r} - \frac{M_{r+1} - M_r}{l_{r+1}} - P_r \frac{y_r - y_{r-1}}{l_r} + P_{r+1} \frac{y_{r+1} - y_r}{l_{r+1}}$$
$$+ C_r y_r = 0 \qquad (r = 1, 2, \ldots, n-1) \qquad (529)$$

For the End Points 0 *and n:*

$$\left.\begin{array}{c} -\dfrac{M_1}{l_1} + P_1 \dfrac{y_1 - y_0}{l_1} + C_0 y_0 = 0 \\[2mm] -\dfrac{M_{n-1}}{l_n} - P_n \dfrac{y_n - y_{n-1}}{l_n} + C_n y_n = 0 \end{array}\right\} \qquad (530)$$

Equations (528) to (530) form the system of stability equations determining the $n-1$ unknown moments and the $n+1$ unknown displacements y. The determinant Δ of the coefficients of the system furnishes the stability condition $\Delta = 0$.

It is easily seen that the numerical computation becomes very cumbersome when a large number of elastic supports are involved. The solution of the stability equation $\Delta = 0$ by conventional methods is therefore not practicable, and other means of obtaining the critical load will be discussed in the following articles.

81. Bar with Rigidly Supported Ends[1]

We assume constant forces P, equal lengths l, equal moments of inertia I of the members, and equal spring constants C of the intermediate supports. Therefore, the functions c_r and s_r are identical in all members and we can omit the subscripts r. Since $l' = lI/I_r = l$, the three-moment equations (528) can be written in the simplified form

$$M_{r-1} + 2\frac{c}{s} M_r + M_{r+1} + \frac{E_t I}{sl^2}(y_{r-1} - 2y_r + y_{r+1}) = 0$$

By adding and subtracting $2M_r$ and introducing

$$\frac{c}{s} = \gamma \qquad \text{and} \qquad \frac{E_t I}{sl^2} = \vartheta \qquad (531)$$

we obtain

$$M_{r-1} - 2M_r + M_{r+1} + 2(\gamma + 1)M_r + \vartheta(y_{r-1} - 2y_r + y_{r+1}) = 0$$

With M_r and y_r considered as functions of the subscript r, the first three terms and the last term on the left-hand side of these equations represent the second difference of M_r and y_r. The system of equations above, therefore, can be regarded as a finite difference equation of the second

[1] Bleich, *loc. cit.* on p. 270.

order,[1] namely,

$$\Delta^2 M_r + 2(\gamma + 1)M_r + \vartheta\Delta^2 y_r = 0 \tag{532}$$

In a similar manner we transform the equilibrium equations (529). These equations, after multiplying by $-l$ and replacing P_r by νP, take the form

$$M_{r-1} - 2M_r + M_{r+1} - \nu P(y_{r-1} - 2y_r + y_{r+1}) - Cly_r = 0$$

or

$$\Delta^2 M_r - \nu P\Delta^2 y_r - Cly_r = 0 \tag{533}$$

Equations (532) and (533) form a system of two simultaneous finite difference equations which can be solved in a manner similar to the one used for the solution of differential equations with constant coefficients. We assume that the functions M_r and y_r have the form

$$M_r = A\xi^r \qquad \text{and} \qquad y_r = A\mu\xi^r \tag{534}$$

in which A is an arbitrary constant whereas ξ and μ are quantities the values of which are still to be determined. From Eqs. (534) we derive

$$\Delta^2 M_r = A\xi^r \frac{(\xi - 1)^2}{\xi} = A\xi^r z$$

$$\Delta^2 y_r = A\mu\xi^r \frac{(\xi - 1)^2}{\xi} = A\mu\xi^r z$$

where

$$z = \frac{(\xi - 1)^2}{\xi} \tag{535}$$

Introducing these expressions into Eqs. (532) and (533) furnishes the so-called characteristic equations

$$z + 2(\gamma + 1) + \vartheta\mu z = 0 \tag{536a}$$
$$z - \nu P\mu z - Cl\mu = 0 \tag{536b}$$

which determine ξ and μ. From Eq. (536b) we compute

$$\mu = \frac{z}{z\nu P + Cl} \tag{537}$$

and eliminating μ from Eq. (536a) leads to the following quadratic in z:

$$z^2 + z\frac{2(\gamma + 1)\nu P + Cl}{\vartheta + \nu P} + 2Cl\frac{\gamma + 1}{\vartheta + \nu P} = 0 \tag{538}$$

---

[1] A brief introduction into the theory of finite differences and finite difference equations is given in T. v. Kármán and M. A. Biot, "Mathematical Methods in Engineering," McGraw-Hill Book Company, Inc., New York, 1940. For a more extended study see F. Bleich and E. Melan, "Die gewöhnlichen und partiellen Differenzengleichungen der Baustatik," Julius Springer, Berlin, 1927.

This equation has two roots, z_1 and z_2, with which, according to Eq. (537), two values of μ, namely, μ_1 and μ_2, are associated.

Equation (535) leads to the quadratic equation

$$\xi^2 - \xi(z + 2) + 1 = 0 \tag{539}$$

that yields four roots, ξ_1, ξ_2 associated with z_1 and ξ_3, ξ_4 associated with z_2. This equation also indicates that $\xi_1\xi_2 = 1$ and $\xi_3\xi_4 = 1$. The general solution of the finite difference equations (532) and (533) therefore reads:

$$\left. \begin{aligned} M &= A_1\xi_1^r + A_2\xi_2^r + A_3\xi_3^r + A_4\xi_4^r \\ y &= A_1\mu_1\xi_1^r + A_2\mu_1\xi_2^r + A_3\mu_2\xi_3^r + A_4\mu_2\xi_4^r \end{aligned} \right\} \tag{540}$$

The arbitrary constants A_1 to A_4 are defined by the boundary condition of the problem, i.e.,

$$M_0 = 0, \qquad M_n = 0, \qquad y_0 = 0, \qquad y_n = 0 \tag{541}$$

which furnish the four linear and homogeneous equations

$$A_1 + A_2 + A_3 + A_4 = 0$$
$$A_1\mu_1 + A_2\mu_1 + A_3\mu_2 + A_4\mu_2 = 0$$
$$A_1\xi_1^n + A_2\xi_2^n + A_3\xi_3^n + A_4\xi_4^n = 0$$
$$A_1\mu_1\xi_1^n + A_2\mu_1\xi_2^n + A_3\mu_2\xi_3^n + A_4\mu_2\xi_4^n = 0$$

Finite values of A_1 to A_4 are possible only when the determinant Δ of the coefficients of this system of equations vanishes. The stability condition is

$$\Delta = (\mu_1 - \mu_2)^2(\xi_1^n - \xi_2^n)(\xi_3^n - \xi_4^n) = 0$$

which splits up into the three equations

$$\mu_1 - \mu_2 = 0, \qquad \xi_1^n - \xi_2^n = 0, \qquad \xi_3^n - \xi_4^n = 0 \tag{542}$$

The first of these three conditions leads only to the trivial case $M_r = 0$ and $y_r = 0$.[1] Considering that $\xi_1\xi_2 = \xi_3\xi_4 = 1$, the second and third conditions may be written

$$\xi_1^{2n} - 1 = 0 \quad \text{and} \quad \xi_3^{2n} - 1 = 0 \tag{543}$$

Both equations are identical, each of them being satisfied by the $2n$ roots

$$\xi = \cos p\,\frac{2\pi}{2n} \pm i \sin p\,\frac{2\pi}{2n} \qquad (p = 0, 1, 2, \ldots, n - 1) \tag{544}$$

From Eq. (539) we find $z + 2 = \xi + 1/\xi$, and on introducing ξ from Eq. (544)

$$z = 2\left(\cos \frac{p\pi}{n} - 1\right) \qquad (p = 0, 1, 2, \ldots, n - 1) \tag{545}$$

---

[1] See Bleich, loc. cit. on p. 270.

Solving Eq. (538) for Cl gives

$$Cl = -\frac{z(\vartheta + \nu P) + 2(\gamma + 1)\nu P}{1 + 2\frac{\gamma + 1}{z}}$$

and upon substituting the value of z we arrive at

$$Cl = -2\frac{\left(\cos\frac{p\pi}{n} - 1\right)(\vartheta + \nu P) + (\gamma + 1)\nu P}{1 + \frac{\gamma + 1}{\cos\frac{p\pi}{n} - 1}}$$

$$(p = 0, 1, 2, \ldots, n - 1) \quad (546)$$

This expression covers all possible buckling modes. The case $p = 0$ leads to $Cl = 0$ and can be omitted.

In order to obtain the final form of Eq. (546), we use Eqs. (531), and recalling that

$$\phi = l\sqrt{\frac{\nu P}{E_t I}}$$

we compute

$$\vartheta + \nu P = \nu P\left(1 + \frac{\vartheta}{\nu P}\right) = \nu P\left(1 + \frac{E_t I}{\nu P s l^2}\right) = \nu P\left(1 + \frac{1}{\phi^2 s}\right)$$

Since

$$s = \frac{1}{\phi^2}\left(\frac{\phi}{\sin\phi} - 1\right) \quad \text{and} \quad c = \frac{1}{\phi^2}(1 - \phi\cot\phi)$$

we have

$$\vartheta + \nu P = \nu P\frac{\phi}{\phi - \sin\phi}$$

We determine further

$$1 + \gamma = 1 + \frac{c}{s} = \frac{\phi(1 - \cos\phi)}{\phi - \sin\phi}$$

and obtain finally the following equation for C:

$$C = \frac{2\nu P}{l}\frac{\left(1 - \cos\frac{p\pi}{n}\right)a - b}{1 - \frac{b}{1 - \cos\frac{p\pi}{n}}} \quad (p = 1, 2, \ldots, n - 1) \quad (547)$$

where

$$a = \frac{\phi}{\phi - \sin\phi} \quad \text{and} \quad b = \frac{\phi(1 - \cos\phi)}{\phi - \sin\phi} \quad (548)$$

For a bar with n spans there are $n - 1$ different buckling configurations possible, and that value of p must be chosen which makes the spring constant C as computed from Eq. (547) a maximum. Thus the condition $\dfrac{dC}{dp}$ defines the value of C which is associated with the state of transition from stable to unstable equilibrium of the system under consideration. From this condition the value of

$$1 - \cos \frac{p\pi}{n} = b\left(1 \pm \sqrt{1 - \frac{1}{a}}\right) = \frac{\phi(1 - \cos \phi)}{\phi - \sin \phi}\left(1 \pm \sqrt{\frac{\sin \phi}{\phi}}\right) \quad (549)$$

can be derived. The maximum is associated with the minus sign in this expression.

Equation (547) in conjunction with (549) solves the problem and furnishes the value of the spring constant C necessary to ensure stability of the elastically supported bar of n members. The procedure in applying the two equations is as follows: After computing $\phi = l\sqrt{\nu P/E_t I}$, determine $1 - \cos(\pi p/n)$ from Eq. (549). In general, the value found will not coincide with one of the $n - 1$ possible values of $1 - \cos(p\pi/n)$, as p must be an integer. Choose those two values of $1 - \cos(p\pi/n)$ which are nearest to the one found from Eq. (549), and compute the corresponding two values of C from Eq. (547). The greater of these two values C must be used for the design of the elastic supports.

In order to eliminate the modulus E_t from the expression for φ we proceed in the same manner as in Art. 79. Substituting P_c from Eq. (520) in the expression for ϕ gives

$$\phi = \frac{\pi}{k} \quad (550)$$

where k can be determined from the column curve of the material under consideration, as explained at the end of Art. 79.

The displacement form of the buckled bar is

$$y_r = A \sin r\frac{p\pi}{n} \quad (551)$$

which gives the displacements at the supports, $r = 1, 2, \ldots, n - 1$. A is an arbitrary constant, and p is the integer which corresponds to the largest value of C as discussed previously.

Figure 149 shows $Cl/2\nu P$ plotted against ϕ for $n = 2, 4$, and 10. With increasing n the spring constant C rapidly approaches a limiting value C_∞, indicated by the dashed curve for $n = \infty$. Since C_∞ is always larger than any C_n, it seems to be logical to replace C_n by C_∞, at least for values $n > 6$, in which case the greatest difference amounts to not more than 1%. If $n = \infty$, the expression $1 - \cos(p\pi/n)$ may assume all values between

0 and 2, and Eq. (549) determines the exact value of $1 - \cos(p\pi/n)$ which corresponds to the largest value of C. The value $C_{max} = C_{req}$ for $n = \infty$ can be written in the form

$$C_{req} = \frac{2\nu P}{l} \frac{\phi(1 - \cos\phi)}{(\sqrt{\phi} + \sqrt{\sin\phi})^2} = \frac{2\nu P}{l}\Phi \qquad (552)$$

TABLE 24.   Values of Φ in Eq. (552)

$1/k$	Φ	$1/k$	Φ	$1/k$	Φ	$1/k$	Φ
0.30	0.111	0.50	0.309	0.70	0.614	0.90	1.102
0.32	0.126	0.52	0.335	0.72	0.652	0.91	1.138
0.34	0.142	0.54	0.361	0.74	0.692	0.92	1.177
0.36	0.160	0.56	0.388	0.76	0.734	0.93	1.219
0.38	0.179	0.58	0.417	0.78	0.777	0.94	1.264
0.40	0.198	0.60	0.447	0.80	0.822	0.95	1.316
0.42	0.218	0.62	0.478	0.82	0.870	0.96	1.375
0.44	0.239	0.64	0.510	0.84	0.921	0.97	1.444
0.46	0.261	0.66	0.544	0.86	0.976	0.98	1.530
0.48	0.285	0.68	0.578	0.88	1.036	0.99	1.652
						1.00	2.000

To facilitate the use of Eq. (552) for design purposes, Table 24 has been computed from which Φ can be read directly as a function of $\phi/\pi = 1/k$. The table is valid in the elastic and plastic range of buckling if k is determined from the column curve as described on page 275.

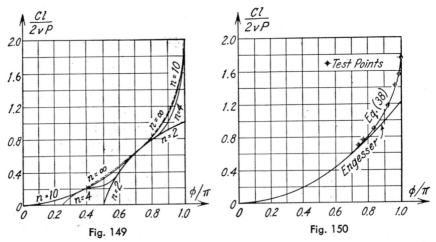

Fig. 149   Fig. 150

By introducing $\phi^2 = \nu P l^2 / E_t I$ the Engesser formula can be transformed into

$$C_{req} = \frac{2\nu P}{l} \frac{\phi^2}{8} \qquad (553)$$

permitting an easy comparison with Eq. (552). Both curves are drawn in Fig. 150. The Engesser curve coincides very well between $\phi = 0$ and $\phi = 0.7\pi$ but deviates substantially when ϕ approaches π. In 1918 Engesser[1] published the results of tests with elastically supported steel bars of rectangular cross section. He found good agreement between the tests results and his formula for values of $\phi < 0.7\pi$. In Fig. 150, therefore, only those test points are shown which correspond to values of $\phi > 0.7\pi$. The test points follow very closely the curve which illustrates Eq. (552).

The condition of constant force P is seldom satisfied in practice. In the top chord of a pony truss, for instance, P increases from the ends to the center of the truss; nevertheless in an economically designed truss the ratio $P/E_t I$ will be approximately constant. Thus, the function Φ which depends only on k may be considered sufficiently accurate if determined for the center portion of the chord, and the introduction of P_{max} into the factor $2\nu P/l$ of Eq. (552) will yield conservative results.

Both the Engesser formula and the exact Eqs. (547) and (552) have been developed under the assumption that the ends of the elastically supported bar are on unyielding supports. As far as the design of half-through bridges is concerned, this condition is actually not fulfilled, and the application of the above formulas to such cases leads to results which lie somewhat on the unsafe side. The Engesser formula is extensively used in European bridge design, with the expectation that the excess of safety obtained by computing C_{req} from P_{max} may offset the unfavorable effect of the flexibility of the end supports, which is far from being true. This state of affairs is not very satisfactory, especially in view of the fact that a design method exists which takes the elastic displacements of the ends of the chord into account. This method will be discussed in the following article.

82. Bar with Elastically Supported Ends[2]

In designing pony-truss bridges, as illustrated by Figs. 151, it would be difficult and also not economical to design the portal frame F_e at the ends of the bridge in such a manner that lateral displacement of the end points is entirely prevented. In most cases the stiffness of the rigid frames F_e is of the same order of magnitude as that of the intermediate frames, so that the effect of the displacements at the ends of the top chord cannot be neglected. If we denote the spring constant of the end supports by C_e and that of the intermediate supports by C, the problem to be solved thereafter can be put in the following form: The constant axial force

[1] Engesser, F., Versuche und Untersuchungen über den Knickwiderstand des seitlich gestützten Stabes, Der Eisenbau, Vol. 9, p. 28, 1918.

[2] Schweda, loc. cit. on p. 270.

νP which acts on the chord, its constant moment of inertia I, and the spring constant C of the intermediate supports are given; the required spring constant C_e of the end supports is to be determined. We assume that the number of spans is $2n$, an even number. Figure 152 shows the compression chord. The origin 0 is taken in the middle of the chord; the supports are numbered 0 to $-n$ in the left half and 0 to n in the right half of the chord. In order to take care of the influence of end diagonals in compression (Fig. 151b), we extend the system to be considered by adding two members of length d, subject to the compressive force νP_d and pin-connected at points $-n$ and $+n$, respectively.

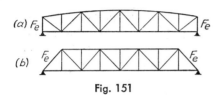

(a)

(b)

Fig. 151

The analysis follows essentially the pattern laid down in the previous article. The finite difference equations (532) and (533), the characteristic equations (536), and Eqs. (537) and (538) remain unchanged. The boundary conditions differ from the ones in the previous article. Two of these conditions indicate that the moments at the end points $\pm n$ must vanish. The other two boundary conditions follow from the equilibrium conditions [Eq. (530)] after adding a term $-\nu P_d l/d$ to allow for the end diagonals. The four boundary conditions are

$$\left. \begin{array}{c} M_n = 0 \qquad \text{and} \qquad M_{-n} = 0 \\[2mm] -M_{n-1} + \nu P y_{n-1} - \left(\nu P_d \dfrac{l}{d} + \nu P - C_e l \right) y_n = 0 \\[2mm] -M_{-(n-1)} + \nu P y_{-(n-1)} - \left(\nu P_d \dfrac{l}{d} + \nu P - C_e l \right) y_{-n} = 0 \end{array} \right\} \qquad (554)$$

The value of ξ in the expressions (534) in the foregoing article turned out to be complex, but the simple form of the boundary conditions (541)

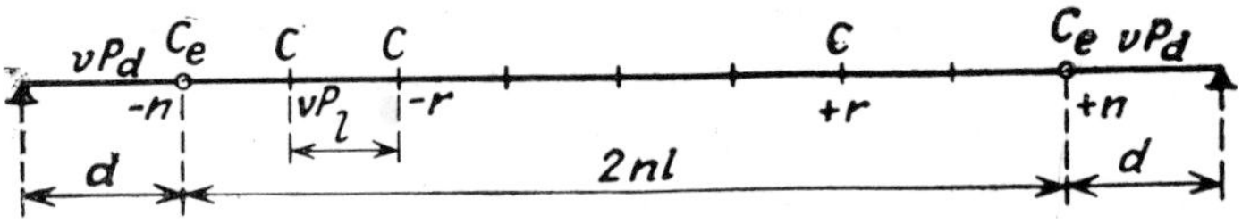

Fig. 152

rendered it possible to obtain the final result without any difficulty in a real form. In the present case it is expedient to assume the solutions of the two differential equations instead in the form

$$M = Ae^{ar} \qquad \text{and} \qquad y = A\mu e^{ar} \qquad (555)$$

where a is a constant to be determined.

The constants ξ and a are related, $\xi = e^a$, and eliminating ξ from Eq. (535) leads to

$$z = \frac{(\xi - 1)^2}{\xi} = 2(\cosh a - 1)$$

Equations (537) and (538) become

$$\mu = \frac{2(\cosh a - 1)}{2(\cosh a - 1)\nu P + Cl} \quad (556)$$

$$\cosh^2 a - \frac{4\vartheta + 2\nu P(1 - \gamma) - Cl}{2(\vartheta + \nu P)} \cosh a$$

$$+ \frac{2\vartheta - 2\gamma\nu P + Cl\gamma}{2(\vartheta + \nu P)} = 0 \quad (557)$$

Solving the last equation for a furnishes two roots $\cosh a_1$ and $\cosh a_2$, and since two values $\pm a$ correspond to each value of cosh, a total of four different roots a is obtained which correspond to the four roots ξ of Eq. (539). As the root of a quadratic cosh a has the form $\cosh a = v \pm \sqrt{v^2 - t}$, and assuming $v^2 - t < 0$ we can write

$$\cosh a = v \pm \sqrt{v^2 - t} = v \pm ui \quad (558)$$

where

$$\left.\begin{array}{l} u = \sqrt{t - v^2} \\[2mm] v = \frac{1}{2}\left[1 + \cos\phi - \frac{Cl}{2\nu P\phi}(\phi - \sin\phi)\right] \\[2mm] t = \left(1 - \frac{Cl}{2\nu P}\right)\cos\phi + \frac{Cl}{2\nu P\phi}\sin\phi \end{array}\right\} \quad (559)$$

To obtain the expressions for v and t Eqs. (531) were used.

We assumed $v^2 - t < 0$, an assumption which will be justified later on. From it follows that the two values $\cosh a_1$ and $\cosh a_2$ are conjugate complex, and since two roots $\pm a$ belong to each value $\cosh a$, we finally arrive at the four roots

$$\left.\begin{array}{llll} a_1 = \alpha + \beta i & \text{and} & a_3 = \alpha - \beta i \\ a_2 = -\alpha - \beta i & \text{and} & a_4 = -\alpha + \beta i \end{array}\right\} \quad (560)$$

According to Eq. (556) there will be two values μ_1 and μ_2 which are associated with a_1, a_2 and a_3, a_4, respectively.

In order to obtain the values of α and β we write

$$\cosh a = \cosh(\alpha + \beta i) = \cosh\alpha\cos\beta + i\sinh\alpha\sin\beta$$

and, with reference to Eq. (558),

$$v = \cosh\alpha\cos\beta \quad \text{and} \quad u = \sinh\alpha\sin\beta$$

Solving for cosh α and cos β, these two equations yield

$$\left. \begin{array}{l} 2 \cosh \alpha = \sqrt{(v + 1)^2 + u^2} + \sqrt{(v - 1)^2 + u^2} \\ 2 \cos \beta = \sqrt{(v + 1)^2 + u^2} - \sqrt{(v - 1)^2 + u^2} \end{array} \right\} \qquad (561)$$

defining α and β by the given design properties νP, ϕ and C. Substituting cosh $a = v \pm ui$ into Eq. (556) we obtain

$$\mu_{1,2} = \frac{p - Cl \pm qi}{\nu P(p \pm qi)} \qquad (562)$$

where

$$p = 2\nu P(v - 1) + Cl \qquad \text{and} \qquad q = 2\nu Pu \qquad (563)$$

The general solutions of the finite difference equations finally take the form

$$\begin{aligned} M_r = \; & A_1(p \cosh \alpha r \cos \beta r - q \sinh \alpha r \sin \beta r) \\ & + A_2 (p \sinh \alpha r \cos \beta r - q \cosh \alpha r \sin \beta r) \\ & + A_3 (q \cosh \alpha r \cos \beta r + p \sinh \alpha r \sin \beta r) \\ & + A_4 (q \sinh \alpha r \cos \beta r + p \cosh \alpha r \sin \beta r) \end{aligned} \qquad (564)$$

Introduction of these equations into the boundary conditions (554) leads to four equations in the unknowns A_1 to A_4, the determinant Δ of which must vanish. Because of the symmetry of the system the condition $\Delta = 0$ can be split into two separate equations:

$$\begin{aligned} \Delta_{1,2} = \; & \left(C_e l - \nu P - \nu P_d \frac{l}{d} \right) (\cosh 2\alpha n \pm \cos 2\beta n) \\ & + p[\sinh \alpha(2n - 1) \sin \beta \pm \sinh \alpha \sin \beta(2n - 1)] \\ & + q[\cosh \alpha(2n - 1) \cos \beta \pm \cosh \alpha \cos \beta(2n - 1)] = 0 \quad (565) \end{aligned}$$

Both determinants have the same form and differ only in the sign of some terms. Δ_1, associated with the plus signs, leads to the symmetric configurations, and Δ_2, associated with the minus signs, gives the antisymmetric buckling modes.

From these two equations the spring constant C_e can be directly determined, since the values α, β, p, and q can be computed from the design properties of the individual case. The larger of the values of C_e found from Eqs. (565) determines the required stiffness of the rigid frames F_e at the ends.

The spring constant C of the intermediate supports, of course, cannot be chosen arbitrarily, since C is limited by the value C_0 with rigid end supports, defined by Eq. (547). If the ends of the bar are elastically supported, then C must necessarily be larger than C_0. In designing, a value $C = cC_0$ must be selected where c is larger than unity. Assuming further that $k > 1.3$,[1] and in practice this will always be the case, it is

---

[1] It is assumed that the chord is designed for lateral buckling as a pin-ended column of length kl, in which l is the spacing of the supporting frames.

convenient to introduce $C = cC_0 = cC_E$, into Eqs. (565), C_E being the Engesser value according to Eq. (521). The required value of C_e can then be written in the form

$$C_e = \frac{\nu P_d}{d} + \Psi C_E \qquad (566)$$

where

$$C_E = \frac{\pi^2 \nu P}{4k^2 l}$$

The coefficient Ψ according to Schweda can be expressed

$$\Psi = \frac{4k^2}{\pi^2 c} \left(1 - \frac{1}{2u \cosh 2\alpha n \pm \cos 2\beta n} \left\{ m[\sinh \alpha(2n - 1) \sin \beta \right. \right.$$
$$\pm \sinh \alpha \sin \beta(2n - 1)] + 2u[\cosh \alpha(2n - 1) \cos \beta$$
$$\left. \left. \pm \cos \beta(2n - 1) \cosh \alpha] \right\} \right) \qquad (567)$$

where

$$m = 2(v - 2) + c \frac{\pi^2}{4k^2} \quad \text{and} \quad u = \sqrt{t - v^2}$$
$$v = \frac{1}{2} \left[1 + \cos \frac{\pi}{k} - c \frac{\pi}{8k} \left(\frac{\pi}{k} - \sin \frac{\pi}{k} \right) \right]$$
$$t = \left(1 - c \frac{\pi^2}{8k^2} \right) \cos \frac{\pi}{k} + c \frac{\pi}{8k} \sin \frac{\pi}{k}$$
$$\left. \right\} \qquad (567a)$$

Equations (567) define Ψ as a function of n, k, and c.

Using Eqs. (567a) it is easy to prove that the discriminant $v^2 - t$ of Eq. (557) is negative for values of $k > 1.2$ and $c > 1.1$, as was assumed when deriving Eq. (558). In practical cases k should be assumed not smaller than 1.3 and c not smaller than 1.2. Therefore, the formulas derived above cover the entire range of cases encountered in practical design.

Table 25 (pages 290–291) was computed by Schweda. For any given value of c and k and for $2n = 6, 8, 10, 12$ the value of Ψ can be read from the table, and the required magnitude of the spring constant C_e of the end supports can be computed by means of the simple formula (566).

Table 25 also permits the determination of the spring constant C in those cases where all the rigid frames which form the supports of the compression chord have the same elastic stiffness, including the end supports. This might occur in a truss as shown in Fig. 151a. In such cases $P_d = 0$ and $\Psi = 1$, and the value of c can be determined from Table 25. The procedure is very simple. From the design properties of the chord the value of k is first computed. Entering the table with this value of k, the column which contains $\Psi = 1$ indicates the value of c. The spring constant finally is

$$C = cC_E = c\,\frac{\pi^2 \nu P}{4kl^2} \tag{568}$$

In most cases two values of c will be obtained, corresponding to Ψ-values closely below and above unity. The actual value of c can be found by linear interpolation.

83. Stability of Chords for Varying Compressive Forces, Spans, Moments of Inertia, and Spring Constants

In this article we are concerned with the presentation of a practical method for solving the problem of elastically supported bars under general conditions concerning the loading, rigidity of the bar, and elastic stiffness of the supports. The standard solution of the problem which leads to a system of homogeneous linear equations has been discussed in Art. 80,

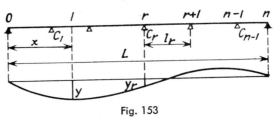

Fig. 153

but this method is not of much practical value because of the complexity of the numerical work connected with it in each individual case. It is also obvious that, in view of the variety of cases possible, neither formulas of design nor precalculated tables or diagrams which have to cover a wide range of various design factors can be prepared, even if it were possible to evaluate numerically the very complex stability condition derived by means of the above method. The task remains to develop a method which is sufficiently accurate to meet the requirements of the practical designer yet simple enough to keep the numerical work in any individual case within reasonable limits.

The Ritz method, extensively discussed in Chap. II, renders it possible to approach the problem with some prospect of success. A method of design will be presented in this article which takes into account the variability of P, I, l, and C and which permits the determination of the required spring constants without excessive labor.[1]

Let us consider a bar of length L, pin-connected to rigid supports at both ends (Fig. 153).[2] The variable moment of inertia is I_x, and the

---

[1] Bleich, F., and H. Bleich, Beitrag zur Stabilitätsuntersuchung des punktweise elastisch gestützten Stabes, *Der Stahlbau*, Vol. 18, p. 17, 1937.

[2] The original paper also considers the cases of free or elastically supported ends.

variable axial force at the instant of buckling P_x.   The spring constants are C_1, C_2, . . . , C_{n-1}.   The potential energy U of the system is

$$U = \frac{1}{2} \int_0^L D_x y''^2 \, dx + \frac{\mu}{2} \sum_{r=1}^{n-1} C_r y_r^2 - \frac{1}{2} \int_0^L P_x y'^2 \, dx \qquad (569)$$

where $D_x = E_t I_x$.   The first two terms on the right-hand side represent the elastic energy accumulated in the bar and in the supporting structure. It is assumed that D_x and P_x are given numerically as functions of x and also that all spring constants C_r are known. P_x is the design force multiplied by the factor of safety ν.

The factor μ is a free parameter, considered as the unknown quantity of the stability problem.   If μ is found to be equal to or smaller than unity, the assumed stiffnesses of the supporting frames, expressed by the spring constants C_r, are sufficient to ensure stability of the chord. $\mu > 1$ indicates that the supporting frames are too flexible and that the moments of inertia of the chord members or the rigidity of the frames must be increased.

The Ritz method approximates the deflection y by a series

$$y = \sum_{i=1}^{p} a_i \varphi_i \qquad (570)$$

where φ_i are the so-called coordinate functions.   Introducing this expression into Eq. (569), the parameter μ can be determined from the conditions

$$\frac{\partial U}{\partial a_i} = 0 \qquad (i = 1, 2, \ldots, p) \qquad (571)$$

The special feature of the method outlined below is the use of a set of coordinate functions φ_i which are the characteristic functions of an auxiliary minimum problem, the solution of which already takes into account the variability of D_x and P_x of the given main problem.   For this purpose we consider the characteristic solutions of a minimum problem defined by the integral

$$\bar{U} = \frac{1}{2} \int_0^L D_x \varphi''^2 \, dx - \frac{1}{2}\lambda \int_0^L P_x \varphi'^2 \, dx \qquad (572)$$

assuming that the boundary conditions of the auxiliary problems are the same as those of the main problem.   Applying the theorem of stationary potential energy,[1] the condition $\delta \bar{U} = 0$ furnishes, upon performing the

[1] See Art. 23.

TABLE 25.   Factor Ψ in Eq. (566)

	k	c							
		1.2	1.3	1.4	1.5	1.6	1.7	1.8	1.9
$2n = 6$	1.2	1.00	0.78	0.65					
	1.3	1.25	0.93	0.75					
	1.4	1.41	1.04	0.84					
	1.5	1.39	1.06	0.87					
	1.6	1.35	1.10	0.94	0.82				
	1.7	1.65	1.30	1.09	0.94				
	1.8	2.01	1.54	1.25	1.06	0.94			
	1.9	2.41	1.77	1.40	1.18	1.03	0.90		
	2.0	2.79	1.97	1.55	1.29	1.11	0.97	0.85	
	2.1	2.98	2.12	1.64	1.36	1.17	1.02	0.90	
	2.2	2.93	2.10	1.66	1.38	1.19	1.04	0.94	
	2.3	2.69	1.97	1.60	1.35	1.17	1.04	0.94	0.85
	2.4	2.27	1.76	1.48	1.27	1.12	1.00	0.91	0.83
	2.5	1.99	1.71	1.48	1.32	1.17	1.06	0.96	0.89

	k	c							
		1.2	1.3	1.4	1.5	1.6	1.7	1.8	1.9
$2n = 8$	1.2	0.93	0.74	0.62					
	1.3	1.12	0.86	0.71					
	1.4	1.27	0.96	0.80					
	1.5	1.32	1.01	0.85					
	1.6	1.42	1.12	0.94	0.81				
	1.7	1.69	1.28	1.06	0.90				
	1.8	1.96	1.44	1.17	0.99	0.87			
	1.9	2.07	1.54	1.24	1.06	0.92			
	2.0	2.04	1.54	1.26	1.08	0.95	0.85		
	2.1	1.85	1.47	1.25	1.08	0.96	0.87		
	2.2	2.08	1.66	1.39	1.20	1.05	0.94	0.85	
	2.3	2.43	1.89	1.55	1.32	1.16	1.03	0.92	
	2.4	2.83	2.13	1.73	1.46	1.26	1.11	1.00	0.90
	2.5	3.25	2.37	1.90	1.58	1.36	1.20	1.07	0.97

variation, the differential equation of the buckling problem of a straight bar, having variable axial loading P_x and variable stiffness I_x, namely,

$$(D_x\varphi'')'' + \lambda(P_x\varphi')' = 0 \tag{573}$$

We assume that the characteristic values λ_i and the characteristic solutions φ_i $(i = 1, 2, \ldots)$ of the differential equation (573) are known. They form a complete system of orthogonal functions and will serve as

TABLE 25. Factor Ψ in Eq. (566). (Continued)

	k	c							
		1.2	1.3	1.4	1.5	1.6	1.7	1.8	1.9
$2n = 10$	1.2	0.99	0.75	0.63					
	1.3	1.06	0.83	0.70					
	1.4	1.21	0.93	0.78					
	1.5	1.26	1.00	0.84					
	1.6	1.43	1.11	0.93	0.81				
	1.7	1.64	1.24	1.03	0.88				
	1.8	1.74	1.32	1.09	0.94	0.83			
	1.9	1.72	1.34	1.13	0.98	0.87			
	2.0	1.85	1.46	1.22	1.05	0.93	0.83		
	2.1	2.14	1.63	1.34	1.14	1.00	0.89		
	2.2	2.42	1.80	1.45	1.23	1.07	0.95	0.86	
	2.3	2.66	1.92	1.55	1.34	1.14	1.01	0.91	
	2.4	2.74	1.99	1.61	1.36	1.18	1.05	0.94	0.86
	2.5	2.65	2.00	1.63	1.39	1.21	1.08	0.97	0.89

	k	c							
		1.2	1.3	1.4	1.5	1.6	1.7	1.8	1.9
$2n = 12$	1.2	0.97	0.74	0.62					
	1.3	1.06	0.82	0.69					
	1.4	1.17	0.92	0.77					
	1.5	1.25	0.99	0.84					
	1.6	1.41	1.10	0.93	0.80				
	1.7	1.54	1.19	1.00	0.87				
	1.8	1.60	1.26	1.06	0.92	0.82			
	1.9	1.73	1.35	1.12	0.98	0.87			
	2.0	1.96	1.49	1.22	1.05	0.93	0.83		
	2.1	2.12	1.60	1.30	1.12	0.99	0.88		
	2.2	2.17	1.65	1.37	1.17	1.03	0.92	0.84	
	2.3	2.12	1.66	1.40	1.20	1.06	0.95	0.87	
	2.4	2.28	1.78	1.48	1.27	1.12	1.00	0.91	0.82
	2.5	2.57	1.94	1.60	1.36	1.19	1.06	0.96	0.87

the coordinate functions φ_i for the approximate solution (570) of the given problem. In comparison with any other system of coordinate functions which could be chosen for the approximate solution of the problem, we obtain the benefit that the orthogonality relations of the functions φ_i will substantially simplify the following analytical procedure.

The orthogonality relations which ensue from Eq. (573) are

$$\int_0^L P_x\varphi_i{}'\varphi_k{}'\,dx = 0 \qquad \text{and} \qquad \int_0^L D_x\varphi_i{}''\varphi_k{}''\,dx = 0 \qquad \text{if } i \neq k \qquad (574)$$

Furthermore there is the relation

$$\int_0^L D_x\varphi_i''^2 \, dx - \lambda_i \int_0^L P_x\varphi_i'^2 \, dx = 0 \tag{575}$$

which is also of importance for the subsequent analysis.[1]

We now turn to the actual problem under consideration. Introducing the series (570) into the energy expression (569) we obtain

$$U = \frac{1}{2}\int_0^L D_x \left(\sum_{i=1}^p a_i\varphi_i''\right)^2 dx - \frac{1}{2}\int_0^L P_x \left(\sum_{i=1}^p a_i\varphi_i'\right)^2 dx$$
$$+ \frac{\mu}{2}\sum_{r=1}^{n-1} C_r\left(\sum_{i=1}^p a_i\varphi_{ir}\right)^2 \tag{576}$$

where φ_{ir} is the value of φ_i at support r.

Expanding the squares in the above equation we find

$$U = \frac{1}{2}\sum_{i=1}^p a_i^2 \left[\int_0^L D_x\varphi_i''^2 \, dx - \int_0^L P_x\varphi_i'^2 \, dx\right]$$
$$+ \frac{\mu}{2}\sum_{i=1}^p \sum_{j=1}^p a_i a_j \sum_{r=1}^{n-1} C_r\varphi_{ir}\varphi_{jr} \tag{577}$$

observing that the cross products in the first two terms on the right side of Eq. (576) vanish because of the orthogonality relations (574). We derive from Eq. (575)

$$\tfrac{1}{2}\sum_{i=1}^p a_i^2 \left[\int_0^L D_x\varphi_i''^2 \, dx - \lambda_i \int_0^L P_x\varphi_i'^2 \, dx\right] = 0$$

and subtracting this expression from Eq. (577) leads to

$$U = \frac{1}{2}\sum_{i=1}^p a_i^2(\lambda_i - 1)\int_0^L P_x\varphi_i'^2 \, dx + \frac{\mu}{2}\sum_{i=1}^p \sum_{j=1}^p a_i a_j \sum_{r=1}^{n-1} C_r\varphi_{ir}\varphi_{jr} \tag{578}$$

With the notation

$$N_i = (\lambda_i - 1)\int_0^L P_x\varphi_i'^2 \, dx \tag{579a}$$

$$\alpha_{ij} = \sum_{r=1}^{n-1} C_r\varphi_{ir}\varphi_{jr} \tag{579b}$$

[1] Equations (574) and (575) can be derived from Eq. (573) in a similar manner as Eq. (75) in Art. 22 was obtained.

U assumes the form

$$U = \frac{1}{2} \sum_{i=1}^{p} a_i^2 N_i + \frac{\mu}{2} \sum_{i=1}^{p} \sum_{j=1}^{p} a_i a_j \alpha_{ij} \tag{580}$$

The coefficients α_{ij} can be found by multiplying the ordinates of the φ_i curve at the points 1, 2, 3, . . . , $(r-1)$ with the corresponding ordinates of the φ_j-curve, then multiplying by the corresponding C_r, and finally adding the products. The coefficients are symmetric, $\alpha_{ij} = \alpha_{ji}$.

The stability conditions [Eqs. (571)] finally furnish p linear equations determining the coefficients a_i, namely,

$$\left. \begin{aligned} \left(\alpha_{11} + \frac{N_1}{\mu}\right) a_1 + \alpha_{12} a_2 + \alpha_{13} a_3 + \cdots &= 0 \\ \alpha_{21} a_1 + \left(\alpha_{22} + \frac{N_2}{\mu}\right) a_2 + \alpha_{23} a_3 + \cdots &= 0 \\ \alpha_{31} a_1 + \alpha_{32} a_2 + \left(\alpha_{33} + \frac{N_3}{\mu}\right) a_3 + \cdots &= 0 \\ \cdots\cdots\cdots\cdots\cdots\cdots\cdots\cdots\cdots\cdots\cdots\cdots \end{aligned} \right\} \tag{581}$$

The determinant Δ of the coefficients of this system of equations must vanish if values of the coefficients a_i different from zero are to exist. This condition, $\Delta = 0$, leads to an equation of the pth degree in μ, and the largest root μ of this equation defines the critical value μ_c. The system is stable for the loads P_x if μ_c is equal to or smaller than unity.

In the majority of cases a two- or three-term series (570) suffices to obtain the value of μ_c sufficiently accurately; thus the determinant of Eq. (581) reduces to a determinant of second or third order which can be easily evaluated. However, since a bar elastically supported at $n+1$ points may buckle in 1, 2, . . . , n half waves, there is at first no clue for the selection of the appropriate functions φ from the infinite number of characteristic functions obtained from the solution of the auxiliary problem. In order to obtain an indication about the shape of the buckling curve, it is advisable to determine the length v of the half wave from the Engesser formula (518)

$$v = \pi \sqrt[4]{\frac{D_x l}{C}}$$

applying this equation for the center and quarter points of the bar. Thus it is possible to estimate the number of half waves of the actual buckling curve and to select accordingly a group of successive coordinate functions φ_i such that their combination will lead to a curve of the expected number of half waves. In cases where the structure is symmetric and the forces P_x are symmetrically distributed, the buckling modes are either symmetric or antisymmetric. Then a combination of two or three consecutive symmetric or antisymmetric modes, respectively, suffices to find the critical value of μ with acceptable accuracy. However, it is frequently necessary to try two sequences, say φ_3, φ_5 and φ_5, φ_7, to obtain the maximum value of μ associated with a symmetric mode and to try the sequences φ_2, φ_4 and φ_4, φ_6 to obtain the maximum value of μ associated with an antisymmetric buckling mode.

The method is particularly convenient in cases where the buckling modes of the auxiliary problem are already known, as in cases where I_x and P_x are constant or can be considered approximately constant, whereas the spring constants C_r vary substantially along the bar. Examples are shown in Fig. 154a and b. The elastic support supplied by the cross frames in the planes of the vertical members varies considerably with the length of the verticals. The polygonally shaped, elastically supported chord can be replaced without substantial error by a straight chord restrained by supports with the spring constants C_r of the given bridge system. The effect of the variation of the C_r upon μ is so dominant that the influence of variations of the force P_x or of the moment of inertia I_x becomes comparatively insignificant.

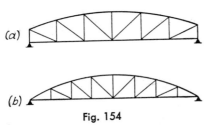

(a)

(b)

Fig. 154

In cases where variations of P_x and I_x are to be considered, the buckling modes of a two-hinged column of length L having the varying moment of inertia I_x and a varying axial load P_x must be determined. By using the Ritz method the solution of the auxiliary problem, i.e., the determination of a number of modes and of the corresponding characteristic values λ, can be obtained without too much labor. These approximate solutions of the auxiliary problem by the Ritz method also satisfy strictly the conditions of orthogonality, which form such an integral part in the development of the method outlined in this article.

84. Torsional Effects upon the Buckling Strength of the Compressed Chords of Pony Trusses

In the previous articles the stability of elastically supported bars was investigated without taking into account the actual shape of the cross section; we simply assumed that the bar possesses a flexural rigidity E_tI which, besides the elastic stiffness of the supports, defines the critical load of the compressed bar. However, in many cases the cross section of the chord consists of open thin-walled sections having only one axis of symmetry, and in the deflected state of buckling the bending of the chord will be accompanied by twisting. Thus, the problem of the elastically supported bar becomes a problem of buckling by torsion and flexure. It has been shown in Chap. III that the actual failure load of columns having sections of the type referred to may be less than the critical load predicted by the generalized Euler formula. On the other hand, the rigid connection between chord and supporting structure counteracts the twisting of the chord. It seems necessary, therefore, to investigate the effect that torsion may have upon the buckling load of chords of pony trusses. To clarify the interaction between chord and supports and to judge the effect of the rigid, moment-resisting attachment of the chord members to the tops of the verticals (Fig. 155a), the investigation will be extended to the case where the supporting structure restrains the chord against horizontal displacement as well as against rotation about its longitudinal axis.

The purpose of the following study is not to develop a more or less exact design method, but to obtain insight into the influence of the twisting of the cross sections on the buckling strength in cases where the torsional rigidity of the section is small. For this reason the analysis will be simplified by assuming that the reaction of the supports can be replaced by a uniformly distributed reaction, as was done in deriving the Engesser formula. We consider a bar of length $L = nl$ (l is the spacing

Fig. 155

of the supports), of constant flexural and torsional rigidity, hinged at both ends to rigid supports, and continuously restrained against lateral displacement and rotation. The bar is acted on by a constant compressive force P. We assume furthermore that the cross section of the bar has one axis of symmetry and is of a type common in bridge design, as indicated in Figs. 155b and 155c. The y-axis is the axis of symmetry.

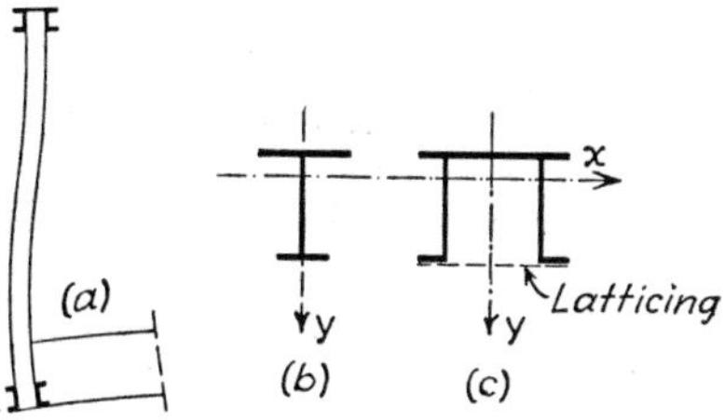

The theorem of stationary potential energy requires that

$$U = V + U_w = \text{stationary} \qquad (582)$$

where U is the entire potential energy, V the change in elastic potential of the entire system, i.e., of the bar and the supporting structure when the system passes from stable to unstable equilibrium, and U_w the change of the potential energy of the external forces during the transition. V consists of two parts V_1 and V_2. V_1 is the strain energy accumulated in the bent and twisted bar; V_2 the elastic energy of the deflected supporting structure.

V_1 is given by Eq. (235) of Chap. III, *i.e.*,

$$V_1 = \frac{\tau}{2} \int_0^L (EI_y u''^2 + EI_x v''^2 + E\Gamma\beta''^2 + GK\beta'^2)\, dz$$

where u, v are the displacements of the center of shear in the direction x and y, respectively, and β is the rotation of the cross section. I_x and

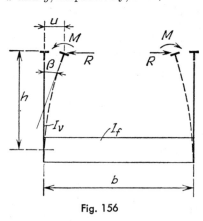

Fig. 156

I_y are the moments of inertia with respect to the x- and y-axes through the centroid, GK is the torsional rigidity, and Γ is a geometric constant of the cross section defined in Art. 38 of Chap. III. A column having a cross section with one axis of symmetry may buckle in the direction of this axis without twisting, or it may buckle at right angle to it by torsion and flexure. In the latter case, which is of interest here, the distortion is described by the displacement u and the rotation β only, and we are therefore allowed to drop the term which depends on v in the expression for V_1:

$$V_1 = \frac{\tau}{2} \int_0^L (EI_y u''^2 + E\Gamma\beta''^2 + GK\beta'^2)\, dz \qquad (583)$$

In order to derive the expression for the strain energy V_2 we consider the rigid frame, shown in Fig. 156, consisting of the floor beam and the

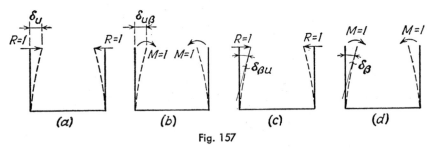

Fig. 157

two vertical members having the moments of inertia I_f and I_v, respectively. Since the chord is assumed rigidly attached to the top of the verticals, there will be a horizontal force R and a moment M acting on the chord. The reactions R and M, applied to the frame in opposite directions, produce the deflection u and the rotation β of the top of the vertical. With reference to Fig. 157 the following displacements and rotations of the tops of the vertical members will be defined:

δ_u = the horizontal displacement due to $R = 1$ applied to the tops of both vertical members (Fig. 157a)

$\delta_{u\beta} = \delta_{\beta u}$ = the horizontal displacement due to $M = 1$ (Fig. 157b) and rotation due to $R = 1$ (Fig. 157c), respectively

δ_β = the rotation due to $M = 1$ (Fig. 157d)

These displacements and rotations are given by the following equations:

$$\left. \delta_u = \frac{h^3}{3EI_v} + \frac{h^2 b}{2EI_f} \qquad \text{and} \qquad \delta_\beta = \frac{h}{EI_v} + \frac{b}{2EI_f} \atop \delta_{u\beta} = \delta_{\beta u} = \frac{h^2}{2EI_v} + \frac{bh}{2EI_f} \right\} \tag{584}$$

The strain energy $\bar{V}_2$ accumulated in one rigid frame is equal to the work done by the reactions R and M. Therefore

$$\bar{V}_2 = \tfrac{1}{2}(Ru + M\beta) \tag{585}$$

According to the definition of δ_u, δ_β, $\delta_{u\beta}$, $\delta_{\beta u}$ given above we may write

$$u = R\delta_u + M\delta_{u\beta} \qquad \text{and} \qquad \beta = R\delta_{\beta u} + M\delta_\beta$$

Solution of these equations for R and M yields the relations

$$R = \frac{u\delta_\beta - \beta\delta_{u\beta}}{\delta_u\delta_\beta - \delta_{u\beta}{}^2} \qquad \text{and} \qquad M = \frac{\beta\delta_u - u\delta_{u\beta}}{\delta_u\delta_\beta - \delta_{u\beta}{}^2}$$

Thus, we obtain from Eq. (585) the following expression for the total strain energy V_2, assuming that the reactions R and M are uniformly distributed over the spacing l of the rigid frames:

$$V_2 = \frac{1}{2l} \int_0^L (C_1 u^2 - 2C_2 u\beta + C_3 \beta^2)\, dz \tag{586}$$

The coefficients C_1, C_2, and C_3 are defined by

$$C_1 = \frac{\delta_\beta}{\delta_u\delta_\beta - \delta_{u\beta}{}^2}, \qquad C_2 = \frac{\delta_{u\beta}}{\delta_u\delta_\beta - \delta_{u\beta}{}^2}, \qquad C_3 = \frac{\delta_u}{\delta_u\delta_\beta - \delta_{u\beta}{}^2} \tag{587}$$

They express, by virtue of Eqs. (584), the elastic behavior of the supporting rigid frame.

Under the assumption that the bar is axially loaded by the force P, Eq. (242) in Chap. III expresses the change U_w in the potential energy of the external forces. For $v = 0$ and $P = A\sigma$, this equation reads:

$$U_w = \frac{P}{2} \int_0^L \left(u'^2 + 2y_0 u'\beta' + \frac{I_p}{A} \beta'^2 \right) dz \tag{588}$$

where y_0 is the distance of the center of shear from the centroid of the cross section under consideration and I_p the polar moment of inertia of the cross section with reference to the center of shear.

The total potential energy U is given by the sum of the parts [Eqs. (583), (586), and (588)], and the condition of Eq. (582) requires

$$\delta U = \delta(V + U_w) = \delta \left[\frac{\tau}{2} \int_0^L (EI_y u''^2 + E\Gamma \beta''^2 + GK\beta'^2)\, dz \right.$$
$$+ \frac{1}{2l} \int_0^L (C_1 u^2 - 2C_2 u\beta + C_3 \beta^2)\, dz - \frac{P}{2} \int_0^L \left(u'^2 + 2y_0 u'\beta' \right.$$
$$\left. \left. + \frac{I_p}{A} \beta'^2 \right) dz \right] = 0 \quad (589)$$

According to the rules of the calculus of variations we obtain the following two Eulerian equations:[1]

$$\left. \begin{array}{l} EI_y \tau u^{IV} + Pu'' + Py_0\beta'' + \dfrac{C_1}{l} u - \dfrac{C_2}{l} \beta = 0 \\[2mm] Py_0 u'' + E\Gamma\tau\beta^{IV} + \left(P\dfrac{I_p}{A} - GK\tau \right)\beta'' - \dfrac{C_2}{l} u + \dfrac{C_3}{l} \beta = 0 \end{array} \right\} \quad (590)$$

For the case of the above-stated boundary conditions the solutions u and β of these two homogeneous differential equations are of the form

$$u = A_1 \sin \frac{i\pi z}{L} \quad \text{and} \quad \beta = A_2 \sin \frac{i\pi z}{L} \quad (591)$$

where A_1 and A_2 are constants and $i = 1, 2, 3, \ldots$. Introducing these expressions into Eqs. (590), two linear equations for the constants A_1 and A_2 are obtained:

$$\left. \begin{array}{l} \left(\dfrac{i^4\pi^4}{L^4} EI_y\tau - P\dfrac{i^2\pi^2}{L^2} + \dfrac{C_1}{l} \right) A_1 - \left(\dfrac{i^2\pi^2}{L^2} Py_0 + \dfrac{C_2}{l} \right) A_2 = 0 \\[3mm] -\left(\dfrac{i^2\pi^2}{L^2} Py_0 + \dfrac{C_2}{l} \right) A_1 + \left[\dfrac{i^4\pi^4}{L^4} E\Gamma\tau - \dfrac{i^2\pi^2}{L^2} \left(P\dfrac{I_p}{A} - GK\tau \right) \right. \\[3mm] \left. \left. + \dfrac{C_3}{l} \right] A_2 = 0 \right. \end{array} \right\} \quad (592)$$

Finite solutions A_1 and A_2 exist only if the determinant Δ of the coefficients vanishes. $\Delta = 0$ therefore defines the limit of stability from which the critical load P_c or any parameter which defines the stiffness of the supporting rigid frames can be derived.

We introduce the notation

$$P_i = i^2 \frac{\pi^2 EI_y\tau}{L^2} \quad \text{and} \quad \mu_i = \frac{C_1}{l} \frac{L^2}{i^2\pi^2} \frac{1}{P_i} \quad (593)$$

where τ depends upon $\sigma_c = P_c/A$. After dividing all terms by $i^2\pi^2 P_i/L^2$ the stability condition takes the form

[1] See Art. 31 in Chap. II.

$$
\begin{vmatrix}
1 - \dfrac{P_c}{P_i} + \mu_i & -\dfrac{P_c}{P_i} y_0 - \dfrac{C_2}{C_1} \mu_i \\[2ex]
-\dfrac{P_c}{P_i} y_0 - \dfrac{C_2}{C_1} \mu_i & \dfrac{\Gamma}{I_y} - \dfrac{P_c}{P_i}\dfrac{I_p}{A} + \dfrac{L^2}{i^2\pi^2}\dfrac{GK}{EI_y} + \dfrac{C_3}{C_1} \mu_i
\end{vmatrix} = 0 \qquad (594)
$$

In this equation P is replaced by P_c, indicating the critical load $P_c = \nu P$, where P is the design load and ν the factor of safety. Equation (594) permits the determination of the critical load P_c or the computation of the parameter μ_i which determines the stiffness of the supporting rigid frames. We prefer to consider μ_i as the unknown, and upon expanding the determinant (594), we obtain

$$
\left[\frac{C_3}{C_1} - \left(\frac{C_2}{C_1}\right)^2 \right] \mu_i{}^2 - \left[\left(\frac{P_c}{P_i} - 1\right)\frac{C_3}{C_1} - Z + \frac{2P_c y_0}{P_i}\frac{C_2}{C_1} \right] \mu_i
$$
$$
- \left(\frac{P_c}{P_i} - 1\right) Z - \left(\frac{P_c}{P_i}\right)^2 y_0{}^2 = 0 \quad (595)
$$

where

$$
Z = \frac{\Gamma}{I_y} - \frac{P_c}{P_i}\frac{I_p}{A} + \frac{L^2}{i^2\pi^2}\frac{GK}{EI_y} \tag{596}
$$

Assuming successively $i = 1, 2, 3, \ldots$, where i is the number of half waves of the buckling configuration, Eq. (595) furnishes a series of values of the parameter μ_i. Introducing these values μ_i into Eqs. (593), a series of values C_1 is obtained, the largest of which defines the required stiffness of the elastic supports. By means of Eqs. (584) and (587) the required value of the moment of inertia I_v of the supporting vertical members can be computed if I_f for the floor beam is considered a given design property of the structure.

Equation (595) may also serve to determine the value of μ_i when no moments can be transmitted from the vertical members to the chord, an assumption which underlies the analysis in the previous articles. Since the spring constants C_2 and C_3 are zero, we obtain for μ_i

$$
\mu_i = \left(\frac{P_c}{P_i} - 1\right) + \left(\frac{P_c}{P_i}\right)^2 \frac{y_0{}^2}{Z}
$$

Expressing μ_i by C_1 according to Eq. (593) we arrive at

$$
C_1 = \frac{i^2\pi^2 l}{L^2}\left[(P_c - P_i) + P_i\left(\frac{P_c}{P_i}\right)^2 \frac{y_0{}^2}{Z} \right] \tag{597}
$$

in which that value of $i = 1, 2, \ldots$ has to be chosen which makes C_1 a maximum.

If the chord has two axes of symmetry, the center of shear coincides with the centroid, $y_0 = 0$, and Eq. (597) reduces to

$$
C_1 = \frac{i^2\pi^2 l}{L^2}(P_c - P_i) \tag{598}
$$

The second term in Eq. (597) indicates the effect of torsion, which is always present if the section has only one axis of symmetry. Since $y_0{}^2$ and Z are positive, it follows that the required spring constant C_1 for sections with one axis of symmetry is larger than for sections with two axes of symmetry.

Comparative computations disclose that the effect of torsion is considerable in the case of open chord sections of the type indicated by Fig. 155b, especially for buckling in the inelastic range. Disregarding this effect would lead to an unsafe design of the rigid frames which support the chord against lateral buckling. However, the freedom to twist is substantially reduced when the chords are rigidly attached to the tops of the vertical members, as is actually the case in a properly designed bridge structure. Comparison of the results obtained from Eq. (595), which takes into account the effect of torsion as well as the influence of the rigid connection between chord and supporting members, with the results computed from Eq. (597) shows that the unfavorable effect of torsion is offset to some extent by the above-mentioned connections. Nevertheless, numerical investigations reveal that Eq. (595) always leads to values of the required spring constant which are 10 to 20% greater than those obtained from Eq. (598), which gives the value of the spring constant when the chord is considered as elastically restrained only against lateral displacements.

Top chords having box sections of the type illustrated by Fig. 155c exhibit a completely different behavior. Owing to the great torsional rigidity of this type of section, twisting of the chord is negligible and the stiff connection between the chords and the top of the vertical members diminishes the distortion of the frames substantially when the chords deflect. The result is that the required flexural rigidity of the vertical members becomes considerably less than that computed from a method which neglects the rigid attachment of the chords to the supporting frames.

We conclude by restating the findings of this article: The usual methods of computing the necessary stiffness of rigid frames which support the chords of a pony-truss bridge overestimate the carrying capacity of the chord in case of open sections but underestimate the carrying capacity considerably in the case of closed box sections.

Additional References

Chwalla, E., Die Seitensteifigkeit offener Parallel- und Trapezträgerbrücken, *Der Bauingenieur*, Vol. 10, p. 443, 1929.

Klemperer, W. B., and H. B. Gibbons, Über die Knickfestigkeit eines auf elastischen Zwischenstützen gelagerten Balkens, *Zeitschrift für angewandte Mathematik und Mechanik*, Vol. 13, p. 251, 1933.

Tu, Shou-Ngo, Columns with Equal Spaced Elastic Supports, *Jour. Aeronaut. Sci.*, Vol. 11, p. 67, 1944.

Lazard, A., Flambement en milieu élastique discontinu, *Annales des ponts et chaussées*, Vol. 116, p. 289, 1946.

Ratzersdorfer, J., A Buckling Problem. The Case of a Beam Resting on a Continuous Elastic Foundation with Concentrated Elastic End Supports, *Aircraft Eng.*, Vol. 18, 1946.

Lazard, A., Compte rendu d'essais sur la flambage d'une tige posée sur supports élastiques équidistants, *Annales de l'institut technique du bâtiment et des travaux publics*, No. 88, 1949.

Schibler, W., Stabilität der Druckgurte offener Brücken unter Berücksichtigung der Plastizität der Querträger, *Pubs. Intern. Assoc. Bridge and Structural Eng.*, Vol. 9, p. 452, 1949.

CHAPTER IX

LOCAL BUCKLING OF PLATE ELEMENTS OF COLUMNS

85. Introduction

In the investigation of the condition of instability of columns in the preceding chapters we have considered the column as a whole, *i.e.*, as a prismatic strut having flexural and torsional rigidity, without considering the possibility of any change in the shape of the cross section and its effect upon the carrying capacity of the column. As a rule, however, the compression members of metal structures consist of plate elements. It is therefore conceivable that, even before the inception of instability of the kind which we have hitherto discussed and which involves integral failure of the column (primary failure), the plates of which the columns are built up will reach a state of unstable equilibrium and buckle locally, so that premature failure of the entire column characterized by a distortion of the cross section will occur. Hence, considerations concerning the stability of the plate elements enter into column design. However, it is not necessary in each individual case to undertake a tedious investigation of the condition for the occurrence of local buckling. The theory discussed hereafter serves the double purpose of demonstrating the fundamental laws which control the behavior of compressed plates under the various conditions of restraint to which the plate elements of a column are subject and of providing the basis for reliable rules for the required thickness of plates for practical purposes.

Local failure of plate elements of columns represents only a particular case of plate instability. In the design of metal structures we are confronted with a great number of questions as to the instability of plates under loading conditions different from those in structural members under axial compressive loading. The thin webs of plate girders may prove unstable under the action of combined longitudinal and shear stresses. Since ships are essentially an assembly of plates under various loading conditions, we encounter in the design of ship plating under compression similar problems of instability as in column design. However, the special character of the ship structure and the particular loading conditions encountered in the design of ships lead to a series of special problems in the field of plate instability. A number of plate problems arising in stiffener reinforced shell structures, of importance in aircraft design, have been successfully attacked by analysts and investigators in this field, and their papers constitute important steps toward the solution of problems of plate instability. The results of these studies have significance for the development of methods for the design of ship plating.

This chapter will deal with rectangular plates under uniformly distributed compressive loading on two opposite edges, the governing problem in the design of axially loaded compression members. In recent times the theory set forth in this chapter attained significance in the design of towers of suspension bridges, where potential local instability of stiffened plates under edge compression plays a primary role in the proportioning of the plate elements of such towers. Chapter X will be concerned with the effect of stiffeners reinforcing the plates in the direction of the compressive stresses which act upon the plates. Chapter XI will be devoted to the investigation of the stability of webs of plate girders, and Chap. XII to the discussion of stability problems in the design of ship plating.

The history of the theory of the stability of plates under edge compression goes back to 1891, when Bryan[1] presented the analysis for a rectangular plate simply supported on all its edges and acted upon on two opposite sides by a uniformly distributed compressive load in the plane of the plate. Bryan was not only the first to treat the stability problem of plates, but the importance of his classic paper lies in the fact that he was the first to apply the energy criterion of stability to the solution of a buckling problem. This method later proved a powerful tool for the investigation of those problems of elastic stability which could not be solved by conventional methods because of the difficulty of the mathematical treatment.

More than fifteen years later, the problem of buckling of rectangular plates was taken up anew by Timoshenko and Reissner. Credit for the most extensive treatment of the buckling problems of rectangular plates belongs to Timoshenko,[2] who discussed in a series of papers the stability of plates under various conditions of support at the two edges parallel to the acting compressive forces and showed the application of the theory to the investigation of the plate elements of steel columns. Independent

[1] Bryan, G. H., On the Stability of a Plane Plate under Thrusts in Its Own Plane with Application on the "Buckling" of the Sides of a Ship, *Proc. London Math. Soc.*, 1891, p. 54.

[2] Timoshenko, S., Einige Stabilitätsprobleme der Elasticitätstheorie, *Zeitschrift für Mathematik und Physik*, 1910, p. 337; Sur la stabilité des systèmes élastiques, *Annales des ponts et chaussées*, 1913, Fasc. III, IV, and V. The earliest paper appeared in Russian, *Bull. Polytech. Inst. Kiev*, 1907.

of Timoshenko, Reissner[1] presented in 1909 the solution for the edge-compressed rectangular plate with two clamped edges and for plates having one edge clamped and the other one free.

In 1924 the author[2] made an attempt to extend the theory of flat-plate stability into the inelastic range by considering the plate as nonisotropic and by introducing tentatively a variable modulus of elasticity into the basic differential equation upon which the solution for elastic buckling is based.

Attempts to formulate a rational theory of stability of plates beyond the elastic limit, based upon modern failure theories, were made by Roš and Eichinger,[3] Bijlaard,[4] and Ilyushin.[5] The results of Roš's and Eichinger's and of Ilyushin's theories do not show good agreement with experiments. In a later paper Bijlaard[6] shows agreement between his theory and tests by Kollbrunner on plates supported on all four sides. Using Ilyushin's general relations Stowell[7] recently succeeded in developing a rational theory of inelastic buckling which apparently leads to theoretical results in good agreement with the observations made in the laboratory.

Credit for the first extensive analysis of the stability of plate assemblies belongs to Lundquist, Stowell, and Schuette,[8] who applied the moment distribution method to the stability of structures composed of plates. The local instability of columns of symmetric rectangular section and of channel- and Z-sections was studied by Lundquist and Stowell.[9]

In order to study the behavior of plates in the elastic and inelastic range of buckling, tests on a large scale on edge-compressed plates were

[1] Reissner, H., Über die Knicksicherheit ebener Bleche, *Zentralblatt der Bauverwaltung*, 1909, p. 93.

[2] Bleich, F., "Theorie und Berechnung der eisernen Brücken," Julius Springer, Berlin, 1924.

[3] Roš, M., and A. Eichinger, *Final Rept. 1st Congr., Intern. Assoc. Bridge and Structural Eng.*, Paris, 1932, p. 144.

[4] Bijlaard, P. P., Theory of the Plastic Stability of Thin Plates, *Pubs. Intern. Assoc. Bridge and Structural Eng.*, Vol. VI, p. 45, 1940–1941.

[5] Ilyushin, A. A., The Elasto-plastic Stability of Plates. Translation in *NACA Tech. Mem.* 1188.

[6] Bijlaard, P. P., Some Contributions to the Theory of Elastic and Plastic Stability, *Pubs. Intern. Assoc. Bridge and Structural Eng.*, Vol. VIII, p. 17, 1947.

[7] Stowell, E. Z., A Unified Theory of Plastic Buckling of Columns and Plates, *NACA Tech. Note* 1556, 1948.

[8] Lundquist, E. E., E. Z. Stowell, and E. H. Schuette, Principles of Moment Distribution Applied to Stability of Structures Composed of Bars or Plates, *NACA Wartime Rept.* L-326.

[9] Lundquist, E. E., Local Instability of Symmetrical Rectangular Tubes, *NACA Tech. Note* 686, 1939. Stowell, E. Z., and E. E. Lundquist, Local Instability of Columns with Channel, and Rectangular Tube Sections, *NACA Tech. Note* 743, 1939.

conducted in Zürich by Kollbrunner[1] who published reports of his investigations in 1935 and 1946. Extensive tests to clarify the problem of the behavior of plates buckling beyond the elastic limit were made at the Langley Structures Research Laboratory, Langley Field, Va.[2]

In comparison with the theory of stability of columns, the problem of the stability of plates is further complicated by the fact that the critical buckling load may be different from the ultimate load which the plate can carry. While the buckling load is for practical purposes the largest load any column can carry, plates may be able to sustain in the buckled state ultimate loads exceeding the buckling load noticeably. The differences between buckling and ultimate loads become important only for very thin plates and for materials with low modulus of elasticity, like aluminum alloys. The determination of the ultimate load of plates is not a stability problem and will not be considered in this chapter. However, the question has been given considerable attention by aeronautical engineers and will be considered in Chap. X, Art. 103, and in Chap. XII, Arts. 120 to 126, in connection with the design of stiffened sheet and of ship plating, respectively.

The following is a presentation of the stability problem of rectangular plates compressed in one direction by a uniformly distributed load in the plane of the plate and its application to the design of thin-walled compression members. The problem will be treated in a general manner comprising the elastic and plastic regions of buckling and the entire range of possible conditions of support at the unloaded edges.

86. The Fundamental Differential Equation of the Plate Problem

We consider a flat plate which is loaded on the two edges b parallel to the y-axis by the uniformly distributed load $t\sigma_x$ where t is the plate thickness (Fig. 158a). We assume these edges to be simply supported so that the plate can rotate freely about them.[3] The edges parallel to the x-axis (edges a) may be supported in various ways:

Case I: The plate is elastically restrained on both edges. This case includes as limiting cases simply supported or clamped edges.

---

[1] Kollbrunner, C. F., Das Ausbeulen des auf Druck beanspruchten freistehenden Winkels, *Mitteilungen 4, Institut für Baustatik, Eidgenössische Technische Hochschule, Zurich*, 1935, and Das Ausbeulen der auf einseitigen, gleichmässig verteilten Druck beanspruchten Platten im elastischen und plastischen Bereich, *Mitteilungen 17, Institut für Baustatik, Eidgenössische Technische Hochschule, Zurich*, 1946.

[2] Heimerl, G. J., Determination of Plate Compressive Strength, *NACA Tech. Note 1480*, 1947.

[3] Clamping the loaded edges has little effect on the critical load of long plates such as occur in columns. The influence of the type of support at the edges parallel to the direction of loading is decisive. The effect of restraining the loaded edges of short plates will be considered in Art. 116.

Case II: One edge a is elastically restrained; the other is free.   This case likewise includes the two limiting conditions in which the supported edge is free to rotate or is clamped.

Figure 158b shows typical longitudinal sections of the buckled plates, and Fig. 158c cross sections for each case of support.   In plates supported on both edges (Case I), buckling occurs in one or more half waves depending upon the ratio a/b.   In Case II, where one edge of the plate is free, it will buckle in one half wave when it is free to rotate at the supported edge but in one or more half waves if elasticaly restrained or clamped.

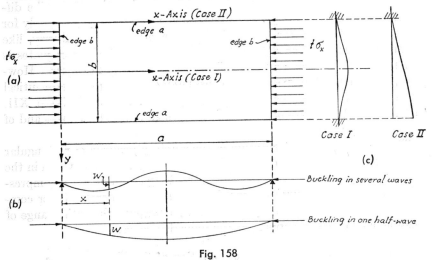

Fig. 158

The following investigation is based upon the fundamental differential equation for the deflection w of a thin flat plate under the action of forces in its middle plane.   This equation is derived under the assumption that the deflection w is small compared with the thickness t of the plate.   The equation reads:[1]

$$\frac{EI}{1-\nu^2}\left(\frac{\partial^4 w}{\partial x^4} + 2\frac{\partial^4 w}{\partial x^2\,\partial y^2} + \frac{\partial^4 w}{\partial y^4}\right) + t\left(\sigma_x\frac{\partial^2 w}{\partial x^2} + \sigma_y\frac{\partial^2 w}{\partial y^2} + 2\tau_{xy}\frac{\partial^2 w}{\partial x\,\partial y}\right) = 0 \quad (599)$$

σ_x and σ_y are the normal stresses in the direction of the x- or y-axis, respectively, and τ_{xy} is the shear stress in a section perpendicular to the plane of the plate cut parallel to the x- or y-axis.   These stresses are due to forces acting along the boundary of the plate and will be considered as given functions of x and y.   The variations which

[1] We owe this equation to St. Venant.   For its derivation see S. Timoshenko, "Theory of Elastic Stability," p. 302, McGraw-Hill Book Company, Inc., New York, 1936.

the stresses σ_x, σ_y, and τ_{xy} undergo when the plate is bent are disregarded. $I = t^3/12$ is the moment of inertia of the cross-sectional area of a strip of plating of unit width and thickness t. ν is Poisson's ratio, assumed $\nu = 0.3$.

If only a uniformly distributed compressive load at the edges b is considered, as indicated in Fig. 158a, the stress σ_x becomes a constant and σ_y and τ_{xy} vanish. The differential equation for the displacement w then assumes the simplified form

$$\frac{EI}{1 - \nu^2} \left(\frac{\partial^4 w}{\partial x^4} + 2 \frac{\partial^4 w}{\partial x^2 \, \partial y^2} + \frac{\partial^4 w}{\partial y^4} \right) + \sigma_x t \frac{\partial^2 w}{\partial x^2} = 0 \qquad (600)$$

This equation is a homogeneous differential equation and plays the same role in the theory of instability of plates as the homogeneous differential equation

$$EI \frac{d^2 y}{dx^2} + Py = 0$$

in the theory of columns. Analogous to the findings in the column theory, solutions w of Eq. (600) exist only for certain values σ_c (characteristic values) of the parameter σ_x. Such a solution describes the shape of an unstable, deflected equilibrium form of the plate associated with the corresponding characteristic value σ_c. If the parameter σ_x is different from the characteristic values, Eq. (600) is satisfied only by the solution $w = 0$. Assuming that σ_x gradually increases from zero to the lowest characteristic value of σ_x, we arrive at a point where, beside the plane equilibrium form $w = 0$, a deflected but unstable form of equilibrium is possible. This bifurcation of the equilibrium position indicates that the critical value of σ_x, i.e., the buckling load, has been reached. Mathematically speaking, the determination of σ_c is the determination of the characteristic values of the parameter σ_x in Eq. (600).

In its present form the above differential equation is valid only within the range of Hooke's law and has yet to be adapted when σ_x exceeds the proportional limit. Based on a widely accepted plasticity hypothesis, Ilyushin and Stowell have derived differential equations for this case, which will be presented in the next article. However, their results are too complicated for the derivation of design rules, and the further analysis in this and the later chapters is based on the following approximation introduced by the author.[1] It is natural to assume that, when σ_x exceeds the proportional limit, the tangent-modulus E_t will be effective in the x-direction while in the y-direction Young's modulus E remains valid because $\sigma_y = 0$. We thus assume anisotropic behavior of the plate when the critical stress σ_c lies above the elastic limit, meaning that stretching

[1] Bleich, *op. cit.* on p. 304.

the flat plate beyond the proportional limit in the direction of the x-axis does not noticeably affect the elastic properties in the direction of the y-axis. This point of view was challenged by some investigators[1] who pointed out that plastic deformation of the material is isotropic and that stretching the plate beyond the elastic limit in one direction produces yielding in all other directions. If the plate remains isotropic, Young's modulus E in Eq. (600) should be replaced merely by a reduced plate modulus $\bar{E}$ which lies very close to Kármán's reduced modulus. However, a great number of tests on angle specimens of various aluminum alloys and medium and high-tensile steels, as well as experiments on edge-compressed plates under various conditions of support along the unloaded edges, showed good agreement with the predictions of the author's two-modulus concept when buckling occurs above the proportional limit.[2] It is also important to point out that the author's differential equation (601) can be interpreted as an approximation of the result of Stowell's theory.

We now return to Eq. (600). If the deflection w is not a function of y, the second and third terms within the parentheses equal zero, and the remaining expression is

$$\frac{EI}{1 - \nu^2}\frac{\partial^4 w}{\partial x^4} + \sigma_x t\frac{\partial^2 w}{\partial x^2} = 0$$

This is the differential equation of the elastic curve of a bent bar under axial load $\sigma_x t$, wherein the factor $1/1 - \nu^2$ expresses the effect of lateral contraction of the plates. The first term corresponds to the bending of strips parallel to the x-axis. Since these strips of plating are stressed by the longitudinal force $\sigma_x t$, the factor $E\tau$ must be substituted for E when σ_x exceeds the proportional limit. We assume that $\tau = E_t/E$, where E_t is the tangent-modulus, in accordance with the conclusions in Chap. I. Thus the first term within the parentheses of Eq. (600) will read

$$\tau\frac{\partial^4 w}{\partial x^4}$$

In the same manner, the third term within the parentheses may be taken as the bending term arising from the bending of the strips of plating running parallel to the y-axis. Since $\sigma_y = 0$, these strips are free of stresses, with the exception of small normal stresses due to bending, E retains its value and the third term will remain

$$\frac{\partial^4 w}{\partial y^4}$$

[1] Roš, M., and A. Eichinger, *Final Rept. 1st Congr. Intern. Assoc. Bridge and Structural Eng.*, Paris, 1932, p. 144.

[2] Kollbrunner, *loc. cit.* on p. 305.

The middle term in the parentheses, finally, is associated with the distortion of a square plate element due to the twisting moments acting on that element. Since the different elastic-plastic characteristics in the direction of the two axes x and y affect this term, we take this circumstance into account by introducing a coefficient which we expect to have a mean value between 1 and τ. We select somewhat arbitrarily the value $\sqrt{\tau}$ and obtain for the second term within the parentheses

$$\sqrt{\tau}\,\frac{\partial^4 w}{\partial x^2\,\partial y^2}$$

Equation (600) assumes the generalized form

$$D\left(\tau\,\frac{\partial^4 w}{\partial x^4} + 2\,\sqrt{\tau}\,\frac{\partial^4 w}{\partial x^2\,\partial y^2} + \frac{\partial^4 w}{\partial y^4}\right) + \sigma_x t\,\frac{\partial^2 w}{\partial x^2} = 0 \tag{601}$$

where

$$D = \frac{EI}{1 - \nu^2}$$

It has been tacitly assumed that Poisson's ratio ν remains independent of σ_x. The influence of ν is very small, since this quantity apparently varies but slightly.

The boundary conditions for the differential equation (601) are obtained from the conditions of support of the plate. For this purpose the expressions[1] for moments M and shears Q must also be modified by introducing coefficients τ or $\sqrt{\tau}$ in a similar manner. The appropriate expressions for the moments are

$$\left.\begin{aligned}
M_x &= -D\left(\tau\,\frac{\partial^2 w}{\partial x^2} + \nu\,\sqrt{\tau}\,\frac{\partial^2 w}{\partial y^2}\right) \\
M_y &= -D\left(\nu\,\sqrt{\tau}\,\frac{\partial^2 w}{\partial x^2} + \frac{\partial^2 w}{\partial y^2}\right) \\
M_{xy} &= -M_{yx} = D\,\sqrt{\tau}\,(1 - \nu)\,\frac{\partial^2 w}{\partial x\,\partial y}
\end{aligned}\right\} \tag{602}$$

The shear forces are

$$\left.\begin{aligned}
Q_x &= -D\,\frac{\partial}{\partial x}\left(\tau\,\frac{\partial^2 w}{\partial x^2} + \sqrt{\tau}\,\frac{\partial^2 w}{\partial y^2}\right) \\
Q_y &= -D\,\frac{\partial}{\partial y}\left(\sqrt{\tau}\,\frac{\partial^2 w}{\partial x^2} + \frac{\partial^2 w}{\partial y^2}\right)
\end{aligned}\right\} \tag{603}$$

The plate theory based upon the generalized equation (601) must be regarded as a semirational theory which can find its justification only by comparison of the theoretical predictions with the results of tests. It will

[1] Timoshenko, S., "Theory of Plates and Shells," p. 88, McGraw-Hill Book Company, Inc., New York, 1940.

be demonstrated in Art. 95 that experiments confirm the hypothesis of nonisotropic behavior of the plate when stressed in one direction beyond the elastic limit and that the above assumptions lead to theoretical values of σ_c which agree rather well with the observed data provided that τ is determined according to the tangent-modulus theory.

The assumption of Roš and Eichinger that the plate remains isotropic even when σ_x exceeds the proportional limit simplifies the differential equation (601) considerably. With reference to the discussion on page 308, Eq. (601) takes the form

$$D\tau \left(\frac{\partial^4 w}{\partial x^4} + 2 \frac{\partial^4 w}{\partial x^2 \, \partial y^2} + \frac{\partial^4 w}{\partial y^4} \right) + \sigma_x t \frac{\partial^2 w}{\partial x^2} = 0 \tag{604}$$

Roš and Eichinger proposed $\tau = \bar{E}/E$, using Kármán's double-modulus theory which was generally accepted at the time. Based on the conclusions of Chap. I it appears that $\tau = E_t/E$ should rather be used, leading to a very simple buckling theory of plates. If Eq. (604) were used, the theoretical results derived under the assumption of perfectly elastic behavior of the plate could be applied in the inelastic range by replacing E by the tangent-modulus E_t. As shown in Art. 95, the test results speak against Eq. (604), whether Kármán's double modulus or the tangent-modulus is used, and we shall base the further analysis in this chapter on the slightly more complicated Eq. (601).

87. The Stability Theories of Ilyushin and Stowell

Ilyushin[1] based his solution of the plastic buckling problem on the concept that in the incipient state of buckling a certain zone on the concave side of the deflected plate is in a plastic state of deformation whereas the other part of the plate behaves elastically, i.e., unloading takes place on the convex side of the bent plate. To arrive at the equilibrium condition of a plate element in the plastic zone, he introduces in his analysis the plasticity hypothesis developed by Huber, Mises, and Hencky, which implies isotropy of the material in the plastic state.[2] Ilyushin assumes the material to be incompressible and takes Poisson's ratio $\nu = 0.5$. Adoption of the principle of unloading on the convex side, as visualized in the double-modulus theory of column stability, and assumption of a constant value of $\nu = 0.5$ may explain that the predictions of Ilyushin's theory do not show satisfactory agreement with test results.

Stowell[3] improved and simplified Ilyushin's theory by basing it on

[1] Ilyushin, loc. cit. on p. 304.
[2] This theory assumes that the energy of shear distortion at failure due to combined stresses equals the value of the energy of shear distortion for simple tension.
[3] Stowell, loc. cit. on p. 304.

Shanley's conception that in a uniformly loaded compression member, when stressed beyond the elastic limit, buckling and increase in load proceed simultaneously, so that no strain reversal occurs in any part of the member. Stowell also takes Poisson's ratio equal to 0.5, but the effect of any error of ν is partially eliminated by the following device used in the computation of the critical stress σ_c. To find σ_c the critical stress computed for elastic buckling must be multiplied by a factor η to give the critical stress for the plastic case. The values of η are obtained by dividing the critical stress found for the plate in the plastic range by the critical stress computed on the assumption of perfect elasticity but with $\nu = 0.5$ instead of $\nu = 0.3$. The ratio η of these two critical stresses may be considered as being only slightly affected by any error in the ν-value.

In his paper Stowell follows Ilyushin's mathematical concept in its essential features. It suffices, therefore, to give an outline of Stowell's analysis. In the case of a two-dimensional state of stress defined by the normal stresses σ_x and σ_y and the shear stress τ_{xy}, the intensities of stress and strain, σ_i and e_i, are defined by the plasticity hypothesis of Huber, Mises, and Hencky:

$$\left.\begin{array}{l} \sigma_i = \sqrt{\sigma_x{}^2 + \sigma_y{}^2 - \sigma_x\sigma_y + 3\tau_{xy}{}^2} \\[2mm] e_i = \dfrac{2}{\sqrt{3}} \sqrt{\epsilon_x{}^2 + \epsilon_y{}^2 + \epsilon_x\epsilon_y - \dfrac{\gamma^2}{4}} \end{array}\right\} \tag{605}$$

σ_i may be considered as an equivalent tensile stress producing the same strain e_i as the combined stresses σ_x, σ_y, and τ. The intensity of stress σ_i is for any given material a uniquely defined function of the intensity of strain e_i if σ_i increases in magnitude with e_i (loading condition). If σ_i decreases (unloading condition), the relation between σ_i and e_i becomes linear. For the loading condition we may therefore write

$$\sigma_i = \omega(e_i)$$

ω is called the plasticity function. Because of the assumed isotropy of the material in the plastic range, the following basic relations between stress and strain must hold:

$$\frac{\sigma_x - \nu\sigma_y}{\epsilon_x} = \frac{\sigma_i}{e_i} = \frac{\omega(e_i)}{e_i}, \qquad \frac{\sigma_y - \nu\sigma_x}{\epsilon_y} = \frac{\sigma_i}{e_i} = \frac{\omega(e_i)}{e_i},$$

$$\frac{\tau_{xy}}{2(1 + \nu)\gamma} = \frac{\sigma_i}{e_i} = \frac{\omega(e_i)}{e_i} \tag{606}$$

ϵ_x, ϵ_y are the strains in the x- and y-direction, respectively, and γ is the shear strain.

The plasticity function $\omega(e_i)$ is defined by the stress-strain diagram of the material under consideration. Accordingly, $\omega(e_i)/e_i$ is identical with the secant modulus E_s of the material, because $\sigma_i/e_i = E_s$. Substituting $\mathfrak{p} = \frac{1}{2}$ and $\omega(e_i)/e_i = E_s$, Eqs. (606) become

$$\epsilon_x = \frac{\sigma_x - \sigma_y/2}{E_s} = \frac{S_x}{E_s}, \qquad \epsilon_y = \frac{\sigma_y - \sigma_x/2}{E_s} = \frac{S_y}{E_s}, \qquad \gamma = \frac{3\tau_{xy}}{E_s} \qquad (607)$$

where $S_x = \sigma_x - \sigma_y/2$, $S_y = \sigma_y - \sigma_x/2$. We may also write

$$\sigma_x = \frac{4}{3}\left(S_x + \frac{1}{2}S_y\right), \qquad \sigma_y = \frac{4}{3}\left(S_y + \frac{1}{2}S_x\right), \qquad \tau_{xy} = \frac{E_s}{3}\gamma \qquad (608)$$

When buckling occurs, the slight distortion of the plate gives rise to a variation of the strains ϵ_x, ϵ_y, and γ. The variations $\delta\epsilon_x$, $\delta\epsilon_y$, and $\delta\gamma$ will arise partly from variations of the middle surface strains (membrane stresses), partly from strains due to bending. Since small deflections are assumed, the strain variations of the middle surface strains are small quantities of a higher order, and their effect on the bending of the plate can be neglected. The strains due to bending vary linearly with the distance z from the middle surface and are proportional to the change in curvature $\delta\chi_1$, $\delta\chi_2$ in the directions x and y and to the change in twist $\delta\chi_3$. Thus

$$\delta\epsilon_x = -z\,\delta\chi_1, \qquad \delta\epsilon_y = -z\,\delta\chi_2, \qquad \delta\gamma = 2z\,\delta\chi_3 \qquad (609)$$

The minus sign is chosen to comply with the sign convention on which the equilibrium condition [Eq. (615)] is based.

Observing that in the equation

$$S_x = \epsilon_x E_s$$

E_s is a function of e_i, the variation of S_x becomes

$$\delta S_x = E_s\,\delta\epsilon_x + \epsilon_x\,\delta E_s = E_s\,\delta\epsilon_x + \epsilon_x\delta\frac{\sigma_i}{e_i}$$

$$= E_s\,\delta\epsilon_x - \frac{\epsilon_x}{e_i}\left(\frac{\sigma_i}{e_i} - \frac{d\sigma_i}{de_i}\right)\delta e_i \qquad (610)$$

As the stresses σ_x, σ_y, τ_{xy} due to the external forces do not vary, the work done by the internal forces when the plate passes from its plane form to the deflected form is

$$\sigma_i\,\delta e_i = \sigma_x\,\delta\epsilon_x + \sigma_y\,\delta\epsilon_y + 2\tau_{xy}\,\delta\gamma$$

and after substituting Eqs. (609)

$$\delta e_i = -\frac{z}{\sigma_i}(\sigma_x\,\delta\chi_1 + \sigma_y\,\delta\chi_2 + 2\tau_{xy}\,\delta\chi_3)$$

Introducing this expression into Eq. (610) furnishes

$$\delta S_x = E_s\,\delta\epsilon_x + \frac{\epsilon_x}{\sigma_i e_i}\left(\frac{\sigma_i}{e_i} - \frac{d\sigma_i}{de_i}\right) z(\sigma_x\,\delta\chi_1 + \sigma_y\,\delta\chi_2 + 2\tau_{xy}\,\delta\chi_3)$$

and after replacing σ_i/e_i by E_s, $\dfrac{d\sigma_i}{de_i}$ by the tangent-modulus E_t, and using the first Eq. (609),

$$\delta S_x = -E_s z\,\delta\chi_1 + \frac{\epsilon_x}{\sigma_i e_i}(E_s - E_t)z(\sigma_x\,\delta\chi_1 + \sigma_y\,\delta\chi_2 + 2\tau_{xy}\,\delta v_x) \quad (611a)$$

In a similar way we obtain

$$\delta S_y = -E_s z\,\delta\chi_2 + \frac{\epsilon_y}{\sigma_i e_i}(E_s - E_t)z(\sigma_x\,\delta\chi_1 + \sigma_y\,\delta\chi_2 + 2\tau_{xy}\,\delta\chi_3) \quad (611b)$$

$$\delta\tau_{xy} = -\frac{2}{3}E_s z\,\delta\chi_3 + \frac{\gamma}{3\sigma_i e_i}(E_s - E_t)z(\sigma_x\,\delta\chi_1 + \sigma_y\,\delta\chi_2 + 2\tau_{xy}\,\delta\chi_3) \quad (611c)$$

The stresses $\delta\sigma_x$, $\delta\sigma_y$, and $\delta\tau_{xy}$ which act on the sides of a rectangular element of thickness t have resulting couples δM_x, δM_y, and δM_{xy}:

$$\delta M_x = \int_{-\frac{t}{2}}^{\frac{t}{2}} \delta\sigma_x z\,dz, \qquad \delta M_y = \int_{-\frac{t}{2}}^{\frac{t}{2}} \delta\sigma_y z\,dz, \qquad \delta M_{xy} = \int_{-\frac{t}{2}}^{\frac{t}{2}} \delta\tau_{xy} z\,dz \quad (612)$$

Substituting σ_x from Eqs. (608) we find

$$\delta M_x = \tfrac{4}{3}\int_{-\frac{t}{2}}^{\frac{t}{2}} (\delta S_x + \tfrac{1}{2}\delta S_y)z\,dz$$

Equations (610) furnish

$$\delta S_x z = -\left[E_s\,\delta\chi_1 - \frac{\epsilon_x}{\sigma_i e_i}(E_s - E_t)(\sigma_x\,\delta\chi_1 + \sigma_y\,\delta\chi_2 + 2\tau_{xy}\,\delta\chi_3)\right]z^2$$

$$\frac{1}{2}\delta S_y z = -\frac{1}{2}\left[E_s\,\delta\chi_2 - \frac{\epsilon_y}{\sigma_i e_i}(E_s - E_t)(\sigma_x\,\delta\chi_1 + \sigma_y\,\delta\chi_2 + 2\tau_{xy}\,\delta\chi_3)\right]z^2$$

and therefore

$$\delta M_x = \frac{4}{3}\frac{E_s t^3}{12}\left[-(\delta\chi_1 + \frac{1}{2}\delta\chi_2) + \frac{\epsilon_x + \epsilon_y/2}{\sigma_i e_i}\left(1 - \frac{E_t}{E_s}\right)(\sigma_x\,\delta\chi_1 \right.$$

$$\left. + \sigma_y\,\delta\chi_2 + 2\tau_{xy}\,\delta\chi_3)\right]$$

Using Eqs. (607) to express ϵ_x and ϵ_y by σ_x, σ_y and τ_{xy} finally results in

$$\delta M_x = -D'\left[\left(1 - \frac{3}{4}\kappa\frac{\sigma_x^2}{\sigma_i^2}\right)\delta\chi_1 + \frac{1}{2}\left(1 - \frac{3}{2}\kappa\frac{\sigma_x\sigma_y}{\sigma_i^2}\right)\delta\chi_2 - \frac{3}{2}\kappa\frac{\sigma_x\tau_{xy}}{\sigma_i^2}\delta\chi_3\right]$$

$$(613a)$$

where

$$D' = \frac{E_s t_3}{9} \qquad \text{and} \qquad \kappa = 1 - \frac{E_t}{E_s}. \tag{614}$$

Similarly,

$$\delta M_y = -D' \left[\left(1 - \frac{3}{4} \kappa \frac{\sigma_y}{\sigma_i^2}\right) \delta\chi_2 + \frac{1}{2}\left(1 - \frac{3}{2} \kappa \frac{\sigma_x \sigma_y}{\sigma_i^2}\right) \delta\chi_2 - \frac{3}{2} \kappa \frac{\sigma_x \tau_{xy}}{\sigma_i^2} \delta\chi_2 \right] \tag{613b}$$

$$\delta M_{xy} = -\frac{D'}{2} \left[\left(1 - \kappa \frac{3\tau^2}{\sigma_i^2}\right) \delta\chi_3 - \frac{3}{2} \kappa \left(\frac{\sigma_x \tau_{xy}}{\sigma_i^2} \delta\chi_1 + \frac{\sigma_y \tau_{xy}}{\sigma_i^2} \delta\chi_2\right) \right] \tag{613c}$$

If w is the bending deflection of the plate perpendicular to its plane, the equation of equilibrium of an element of the plate can be written[1]

$$\frac{\partial^2(\delta M_x)}{\partial x^2} + 2\frac{\partial^2(\delta M_{xy})}{\partial x\,\partial y} + \frac{\partial^2(\delta M_y)}{\partial y^2} - t\left(\sigma_x \frac{\partial^2 w}{\partial x^2} + \sigma_y \frac{\partial^2 w}{\partial y^2} + 2\tau_{xy} \frac{\partial^2 w}{\partial x\,\partial y}\right) = 0$$

in which the forces $\sigma_x t$, $\sigma_y t$, and $\tau_{xy} t$ are considered as given. σ_x and σ_y are assumed positive for compression. $\frac{\partial^2 w}{\partial x^2}$, $\frac{\partial^2 w}{\partial y^2}$ are the changes in curvature denoted previously by $\delta\chi_1$ and $\delta\chi_2$, and $\frac{\partial^2 w}{\partial x\,\partial y}$ is the change in twist denoted by $\delta\chi_3$.

In the case of a rectangular plate loaded on two opposite sides by uniformly distributed forces $\sigma_x t$ the above equation becomes

$$\frac{\partial^2(\delta M_x)}{\partial x^2} + 2\frac{\partial^2(\delta M_{xy})}{\partial x\,\partial y} + \frac{\partial^2(\delta M_y)}{\partial y^2} - t\sigma_x \frac{\partial^2 w}{\partial x^2} = 0 \tag{615}$$

Expressing the quantities $\delta\chi_1$, $\delta\chi_2$, and $\delta\chi_3$ in Eqs. (613) by w and introducing $\sigma_y = \tau_{xy} = 0$ give

$$\frac{\partial^2(\delta M_x)}{\partial x^2} = -D'\left[\left(1 - \frac{3}{4}\kappa\frac{\sigma_x^2}{\sigma_i^2}\right)\frac{\partial^4 w}{\partial x^4} + \frac{1}{2}\frac{\partial^4 w}{\partial x^2 \partial y^2}\right]$$

$$\frac{\partial^2(\delta M_y)}{\partial y^2} = -D'\left(\frac{\partial^4 w}{\partial y^4} + \frac{1}{2}\frac{\partial^4 w}{\partial x^2\,\partial y^2}\right)$$

$$\frac{\partial^2(\delta M_{xy})}{\partial x\,\partial y} = -\frac{D'}{2}\left(\frac{\partial^4 w}{\partial x^2\,\partial y^2}\right)$$

and Eq. (615) becomes

$$D'\left[\left(1 - \frac{3}{4}\kappa\frac{\sigma_x^2}{\sigma_i^2}\right)\frac{\partial^4 w}{\partial x^4} + 2\frac{\partial^4 w}{\partial x^2\,\partial y^2} + \frac{\partial^4 w}{\partial y^4}\right] + t\sigma_x \frac{\partial^2 w}{\partial x^2} = 0$$

As $\sigma_y = \tau_{xy} = 0$, Eq. (605) furnishes $\sigma_i = \sigma_x$, and the final result is

$$D'\left[\left(1 - \frac{3}{4}\kappa\right)\frac{\partial^4 w}{\partial x^4} + 2\frac{\partial^4 w}{\partial x^2\,\partial y^2} + \frac{\partial^4 w}{\partial y^4}\right] + t\sigma_x \frac{\partial^2 w}{\partial x^2} = 0 \tag{616}$$

[1] Timoshenko, S., "Theory of Elastic Stability," p. 305.

In contrast to Eq. (601) in which the elastic-plastic properties of the material are represented by one parameter τ, Eq. (616) contains two parameters, the secant-modulus and the tangent-modulus [see Eqs. (614)]. As a result the analysis based on this equation becomes extremely involved. The relationship between the results based on Stowell's differential equation (616) and on the simplified Eq. (601) are discussed in Art. 95.

88. General Solution of the Differential Equation (601)

The solution of the partial differential equation (601) must satisfy the boundary conditions on all four edges. At the moment we consider only those on the loaded edges b; the other two edges will be considered later (see Fig. 158). The conditions of simple support on the edges b require that the displacement w and the moments M_x at the edges $x = 0$, $x = a$ vanish. With reference to Eqs. (602) we have

$$w = 0$$

$$M_x = -D\left(\tau\frac{\partial^2 w}{\partial x^2} + \nu\sqrt{\tau}\frac{\partial^2 w}{\partial y^2}\right) = 0$$

Since, by assumption, the edges $x = 0$, $x = a$ remain straight, $\dfrac{\partial^2 w}{\partial y^2}$ must be zero, and the boundary conditions become

$$w = 0 \qquad \text{and} \qquad \frac{\partial^2 w}{\partial x^2} = 0 \tag{617}$$

The differential equation (601) and the boundary conditions (617) are satisfied by the expression

$$w = Y \sin\frac{n\pi x}{a} \qquad (n = 1, 2, 3, \ldots) \tag{618}$$

where Y is a function of y yet to be determined. Upon introducing this expression into the differential equation (601) and canceling $\sin n\pi x/a$ we obtain the ordinary differential equation of the fourth order

$$\frac{d^4 Y}{dy^4} - 2\sqrt{\tau}\left(\frac{n\pi}{a}\right)^2\frac{d^2 Y}{dy^2} + \left[\tau\left(\frac{n\pi}{a}\right)^4 - \frac{\sigma_c t}{D}\left(\frac{n\pi}{a}\right)^2\right]Y = 0$$

In this equation σ_x is replaced by σ_c, the unknown critical longitudinal stress at which the plate buckles. Introducing the notation

$$\mu^2 = \frac{\sigma_c t}{D\tau}\left(\frac{a}{n\pi}\right)^2 \tag{619}$$

the above differential equation assumes the form

$$\frac{d^4 Y}{dy^4} - 2\sqrt{\tau}\left(\frac{n\pi}{a}\right)^2\frac{d^2 Y}{dy^2} + \tau\left(\frac{n\pi}{a}\right)^4(1 - \mu^2)Y = 0 \tag{620}$$

This differential equation determines the parameter μ which by virtue of Eq. (619) leads to the formula for the critical stress

$$\sigma_c = \left(\frac{n\pi}{a}\right)^2 \frac{D\tau}{t} \mu^2 \qquad (621)$$

The general solution of Eq. (620) is

$$Y = C_1 \cosh \kappa_1 y + C_2 \sinh \kappa_1 y + C_3 \cos \kappa_2 y + C_4 \sin \kappa_2 y \qquad (622)$$

where κ_1 and κ_2 are defined by

$$\kappa_1 = \frac{n\pi}{a} \sqrt[4]{\tau} \sqrt{\mu+1} \qquad \text{and} \qquad \kappa_2 = \frac{n\pi}{a} \sqrt[4]{\tau} \sqrt{\mu-1} \qquad (623)$$

Thus the general solution of equation (601), represented by Eq. (618), finally takes the form

$$w = \sin \frac{n\pi x}{a} (C_1 \cosh \kappa_1 y + C_2 \sinh \kappa_1 y + C_3 \cos \kappa_2 y + C_4 \sin \kappa_2 y) \qquad (624)$$

The constants C_1 to C_4 are to be determined such that the boundary condition at the two edges a will be satisfied. Special cases of these boundary conditions will be considered in the following articles.

89. Case I, Plate Simply Supported at Edges b, Elastically Restrained at Edges a

The origin of the coordinates x, y is assumed to be at the mid-point of the left edge of the plate as indicated in Fig. 158. If we assume equal elastic restraint on both unloaded edges, the deflection w corresponding to the smallest value of σ_c is a symmetric function of y, and the terms $C_2 \sinh \kappa_1 y$ and $C_4 \sin \kappa_2 y$ in Eq. (624) vanish. This equation reads therefore

$$w = \sin \frac{n\pi x}{a} (C_1 \cosh \kappa_1 y + C_3 \cos \kappa_2 y) \qquad (625)$$

To determine the constants C_1 and C_3 we use the boundary conditions at the unloaded edges a, namely,

$$[w]_{y = \pm \frac{b}{2}} = 0 \qquad (626a)$$

$$\varphi = \bar{\varphi} \qquad (626b)$$

The first condition expresses the fact that the edges $y = \pm b/2$ remain straight when the plate buckles. The second equation is a condition of continuity which indicates that the angle of rotation φ at the edge of the buckling plate is equal to the angle of rotation $\bar{\varphi}$ of the adjoining restraining plate which is assumed to be rigidly connected (Fig. 159).

In order to be able to introduce the solution (625) into the boundary condition (626b) it is necessary to express φ and $\bar{\varphi}$ in terms of the deflection w. The bending moment M_y per unit length that occurs along the edge when the plates distort is assumed proportional to the angle $\bar{\varphi}$. This elastic restraint can be expressed

$$M_y = -\bar{\zeta}\bar{\varphi} \qquad (627)$$

where $\bar{\zeta}$ is a factor or proportionality depending upon the dimensions

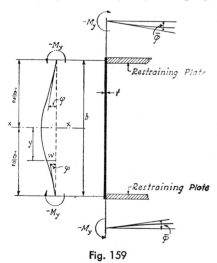

Fig. 159

of the restraining structure, assumed constant along the edge. The moment M_y, on the other hand, is according to Eq. (602)

$$M_y = -D\left[\frac{\partial^2 w}{\partial y^2} + \nu \sqrt{\bar{\tau}}\frac{\partial^2 w}{\partial x^2}\right]_{y=\pm\frac{b}{2}}$$

Since $\dfrac{\partial^2 w}{\partial x^2} = 0$ everywhere along the edges a, this equation reduces to

$$M_y = -D\left[\frac{\partial^2 w}{\partial y^2}\right]_{y=\pm\frac{b}{2}}$$

Substitution into Eq. (627) furnishes

$$\bar{\varphi} = \frac{D}{\bar{\zeta}}\left[\frac{\partial^2 w}{\partial y^2}\right]_{y=\pm\frac{b}{2}}$$

Since $\varphi = \pm\left[\dfrac{\partial w}{\partial y}\right]_{y=\pm\frac{b}{2}}$, the boundary condition (626b) takes the form

$$\left[\frac{\partial w}{\partial y} \pm \frac{D}{\bar{\zeta}}\frac{\partial^2 w}{\partial y^2}\right]_{y=\pm\frac{b}{2}} = 0$$

$D/\bar{\zeta}$ has the dimension of length, and it is advantageous to write this equation

$$\left[\frac{\partial w}{\partial y} \pm \frac{b}{2} \zeta \frac{\partial^2 w}{\partial y^2}\right]_{y = \pm \frac{b}{2}} = 0 \tag{628}$$

where ζ is defined by

$$\zeta = \frac{2}{b} \frac{D}{\bar{\zeta}} \tag{629}$$

ζ is a dimensionless number, which is assumed constant along the edges a. It is a function of the dimensions of the buckling and restraining plates and will be referred to as the *coefficient of restraint*. Its determination will be discussed later. It may be noted that theoretically ζ can assume values from 0 to ∞. When $\zeta = 0$, the plate is completely fixed at the edges a, and when $\zeta = \infty$, it is free to rotate about these edges.

Introducing the solution (625) into the boundary conditions (626a) and (628) yields two equations:

$$C_1 \cosh \kappa_1 \frac{b}{2} + C_3 \cos \kappa_2 \frac{b}{2} = 0$$

$$\left(C_1 \kappa_1 \sinh \kappa_1 \frac{b}{2} - C_3 \kappa_2 \sin \kappa_2 \frac{b}{2}\right) + \zeta \frac{b}{2}\left(C_1 \kappa_1{}^2 \cosh \kappa_1 \frac{b}{2}\right.$$

$$\left. - C_3 \kappa_2{}^2 \cos \kappa_2 \frac{b}{2}\right) = 0$$

These are homogeneous linear equations, and nonzero values for C_1 and C_3 result only when the determinant Δ of this system of equations vanishes. Therefore, $\Delta = 0$ is the buckling criterion which leads to the stability condition

$$\kappa_1 \tanh \kappa_1 \frac{b}{2} + \kappa_2 \tan \kappa_2 \frac{b}{2} + \zeta \frac{b}{2}(\kappa_1{}^2 + \kappa_2{}^2) = 0$$

Introducing the aspect ratio $\alpha = a/b$ into Eqs. (621) and (623), these equations take the form

$$\sigma_c = \frac{1}{b^2}\left(\frac{n\pi}{\alpha}\right)^2 \frac{D\tau}{t} \mu^2 \tag{630}$$

$$\kappa_1 \frac{b}{2} = \frac{n\pi}{2\alpha} \sqrt[4]{\tau} \sqrt{\mu + 1} \quad \text{and} \quad \kappa_2 \frac{b}{2} = \frac{n\pi}{2\alpha} \sqrt[4]{\tau} \sqrt{\mu - 1} \tag{631}$$

and the above stability condition becomes

$$\sqrt{\mu + 1} \tanh\left(\frac{\pi}{2}\sqrt{\mu + 1}\,\frac{n\sqrt[4]{\tau}}{\alpha}\right) + \sqrt{\mu - 1} \tan\left(\frac{\pi}{2}\sqrt{\mu - 1}\,\frac{n\sqrt[4]{\tau}}{\alpha}\right)$$

$$+ \pi\zeta\mu\,\frac{n\sqrt[4]{\tau}}{\alpha} = 0 \tag{632}$$

This transcendental equation defines the relation between the parameter μ and the ratio $n\sqrt[4]{\tau}/\alpha$. If we compute μ from this equation for a given value of $n\sqrt[4]{\tau}/\alpha$, the determination of σ_c by means of Eq. (630) is relatively simple. However, before discussing the general equation (632), a special case will be subjected to closer study in order to comprehend the nature of the problem more easily.

Introducing $\zeta = \infty$ into Eq. (632) we obtain the stability condition for a plate simply supported along the edges:[1]

$$\tan\left(\frac{\pi}{2}\sqrt{\mu - 1}\,\frac{n\sqrt[4]{\tau}}{\alpha}\right) = -\infty$$

The smallest root satisfying this equation is

$$\frac{\pi}{2}\sqrt{\mu - 1}\,\frac{n\sqrt[4]{\tau}}{\alpha} = \frac{\pi}{2}$$

and

$$\mu^2 = \left[\left(\frac{\alpha}{n\sqrt[4]{\tau}}\right)^2 + 1\right]^2 \tag{633}$$

Referring to Eq. (630) and substituting $D = \dfrac{Et^3}{12(1-\nu^2)}$, we arrive at

$$\sigma_c = \frac{\pi^2 E \sqrt{\tau}}{12(1-\nu^2)}\left(\frac{t}{b}\right)^2\left(\frac{\alpha}{n\sqrt[4]{\tau}} + \frac{n\sqrt[4]{\tau}}{\alpha}\right)^2 \tag{634}$$

The only unknown in Eq. (634) remaining to be found is n, which indicates the number of half waves in which the plate buckles in the x-direction. To find this number of half waves for a given aspect ratio α we proceed as follows: For sufficiently short plates, i.e., for small values of α, buckling will occur in one half wave. Above a certain ratio α two half waves will be formed. For the limiting ratio at which there is the transition from one state of equilibrium to the other, i.e., when both cases are equally possible at the same buckling stress σ_c, Eq. (634) will yield the same value of σ_c whether we introduce $n = 1$ or $n = 2$. In the same way it will be possible to determine the limiting value of α for buckling in two or three half waves. In general we find the limiting ratio $\bar{\alpha}$ at which either n or $n + 1$ half waves can occur from the equation

$$\frac{\bar{\alpha}}{n\sqrt[4]{\tau}} + \frac{n\sqrt[4]{\tau}}{\bar{\alpha}} = \frac{\bar{\alpha}}{(n+1)\sqrt[4]{\tau}} + \frac{(n+1)\sqrt[4]{\tau}}{\bar{\alpha}}$$

It follows that

$$\bar{\alpha} = \sqrt[4]{\tau}\sqrt{n(n+1)}$$

For $n = 1, 2, 3, \ldots$ we have $\bar{\alpha}/\sqrt[4]{\tau} = \sqrt{2}, \sqrt{6}, \sqrt{12}, \ldots$

[1] To obtain this equation it is essential to remember that the function tanh assumes values only between $+1$ and -1.

In the elastic range when $\tau = 1$, the number of half waves becomes
independent of the nature of the material.   When buckling occurs above
the elastic limit, the characteristics of the material affect the number of
half waves considerably.   In the elastic range buckling occurs in one
half wave up to $a = 1.414b$, and from $a = 1.414b$ to $a = 2.449b$ in two
half waves.   For long plates the length of the half waves approaches the
width b.   If the elastic limit is exceeded, the limiting ratios approach

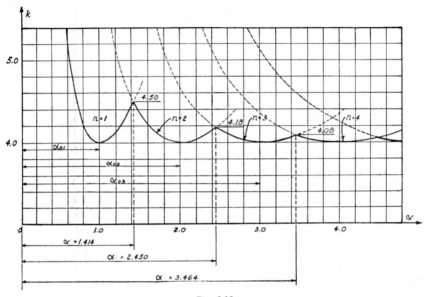

Fig. 160

each other more closely, since $\tau < 1$, and the waves become shorter the
higher the critical stress σ_c.[1]   For long plates the length of the half waves
approaches $b \sqrt[4]{\tau}$.

If $\tau = 1$, Eq. (634) takes the form

$$\sigma_c = \frac{\pi^2 E}{12(1 - \nu^2)} \left(\frac{t}{b}\right)^2 \left(\frac{\alpha}{n} + \frac{n}{\alpha}\right)^2 = \frac{\pi^2 E}{12(1 - \nu^2)} \left(\frac{t}{b}\right)^2 k$$

The factor k indicates the dependence of σ_c on the aspect ratio α.
$k = (\alpha/n + n/\alpha)^2$ determines a sequence of curves, shown in Fig. 160,
which correspond to buckling in 1, 2, 3, . . . half waves depending upon
the ratio α.   It is seen that the curves for $n = 2, 3, . . .$ can be readily
obtained from the curve for $n = 1$ by multiplying the abscissa by 2, 3,

[1] It may be noted that according to the isotropic concept the number of half waves
would be independent of τ and remains the same if buckling occurs below or above the
propotional limit.

etc., and keeping the ordinate unchanged. The fully drawn parts of these curves determine finally the dependence of σ_c on the aspect ratio α.

For each number of half waves there is an aspect ratio α at which k, and therefore σ_c, assumes a minimum value. The lowest points of the curves lie at $\alpha = 1, 2, 3, \ldots$. The minimum values of the individual branches of the curve are equal throughout, and with increasing plate length a the difference between the value of k corresponding to the actual plate length and the minimum value of k decreases. As only long, narrow plates need be considered in connection with columns, we can base the design on the minimum value of k which is constant for all length-width ratios α, thus greatly simplifying the analysis. Similar conditions apply when $\tau < 1$, i.e., when the elastic limit is exceeded.

The value of α which yields the minimum stress σ_c can be determined from the condition $\dfrac{\partial \sigma_c}{\partial \alpha} = 0$ and is[1]

$$\alpha_0 = n \sqrt[4]{\tau}$$

Introducing α_0 into Eq. (633) we obtain the critical stress of a long, simply supported plate

$$\text{Min } \sigma_c = \frac{\pi^2 E \sqrt{\tau}}{3(1 - \nu^2)} \left(\frac{t}{b}\right)^2 \tag{635}$$

or using $\nu = 0.3$

$$\text{Min } \sigma_c = 3.615 E \sqrt{\tau} \left(\frac{t}{b}\right)^2 \tag{635a}$$

For $\tau = 1$ this is Bryan's formula.

Returning now to the discussion of the general buckling condition (632) for elastically restrained plates, we find that the transcendental form in which μ depends upon $\alpha/n\sqrt[4]{\tau}$ is inconvenient for applications. In the case of the simply supported plate just considered in detail we have found an algebraic expression [Eq. (633)] for μ^2, namely,

$$\mu^2 = 1 + 2 \left(\frac{\alpha}{n \sqrt[4]{\tau}}\right)^2 + \left(\frac{\alpha}{n \sqrt[4]{\tau}}\right)^4$$

It is possible to express the relationship between μ^2 and $\alpha/n\sqrt[4]{\tau}$ defined by Eq. (632) approximately by a similar algebraic expression. With an error of less than 1%, the values μ^2 can be computed from

$$\mu^2 = 1 + p \left(\frac{\alpha}{n \sqrt[4]{\tau}}\right)^2 + q \left(\frac{\alpha}{n \sqrt[4]{\tau}}\right)^4 \tag{636}$$

where p and q are factors depending on the coefficient of restraint ζ.

---

[1] In determining α_0, τ is assumed to be independent of σ_c, which, strictly speaking, is not correct. However, when $n > 1$, the influence upon α_0 of the assumed independence of the factor τ from σ_c is extremely small.

p and q were computed for various values of ζ from the exact stability condition (632). Figure 161 shows p and q plotted against ζ.[1]

Substituting the expression (636) into Eq. (630) and introducing $D = Et^3/12(1 - \nu^2)$ and $a = \alpha b$, the following equation for σ_c, valid for all possible values of elastic restraint, is obtained:

$$\sigma_c = \frac{\pi^2 E \sqrt{\tau}}{12(1 - \nu^2)} \left(\frac{t}{b}\right)^2 \left[\left(\frac{n \sqrt[4]{\tau}}{\alpha}\right)^2 + p + q \left(\frac{\alpha}{n \sqrt[4]{\tau}}\right)^2\right] \quad (637)$$

Introducing the notation

$$k = \left(\frac{n \sqrt[4]{\tau}}{\alpha}\right)^2 + p + q \left(\frac{\alpha}{n \sqrt[4]{\tau}}\right)^2 \quad (638)$$

the equation for σ_c assumes the conventional form

$$\sigma_c = \frac{\pi^2 E \sqrt{\tau}}{12(1 - \nu^2)} \left(\frac{t}{b}\right)^2 k \quad (638a)$$

where k is a nondimensional coefficient that depends on the aspect ratio α of the plate, on the conditions of support at the unloaded edges, and on the value of τ.

Based on the same reasoning as for the simply supported plate, we find the limiting ratio $\bar{\alpha}$ at which either n or $n + 1$ half waves can exist:

$$\bar{\alpha} = \sqrt[4]{\frac{\tau}{q}} \sqrt{n(n + 1)} \quad (639)$$

q is found to lie between 1 and 5. For $q = 1$ (simple support at the edges a) $\bar{\alpha} = \sqrt[4]{\tau} \sqrt{n(n + 1)}$, as derived above, and for $q = 5$ (both edges fully fixed), $\bar{\alpha} = 0.668 \sqrt[4]{\tau} \sqrt{n(n + 1)}$. The half waves are appreciably shortened by clamping. The value α_0 for which σ_c reaches a minimum and upon which the design of long plates can be based is found from the condition $\dfrac{\partial \sigma_c}{\partial \alpha} = 0$, namely,

$$\alpha_0 = n \sqrt[4]{\frac{\tau}{q}}$$

Substituting α_0 in Eq. (637) we arrive at

$$\text{Min } \sigma_c = \frac{\pi^2 E \sqrt{\tau}}{12(1 - \nu)^2} \left(\frac{t}{b}\right)^2 (p + 2 \sqrt{q}) = \frac{\pi^2 E \sqrt{\tau}}{12(1 - \nu^2)} \left(\frac{t}{b}\right)^2 k \quad (640)$$

[1] The coefficients p and q were first introduced into the analysis by the author; see Bleich, *op. cit.* on p. 304. The advantage achieved by the introduction of the p- and q-diagram is that a pair of curves suffices to determine the coefficient k for any value ζ. Otherwise a chart showing a family of k-curves for various values of ζ between 0 and ∞ would be necessary to find the values of the coefficient k.

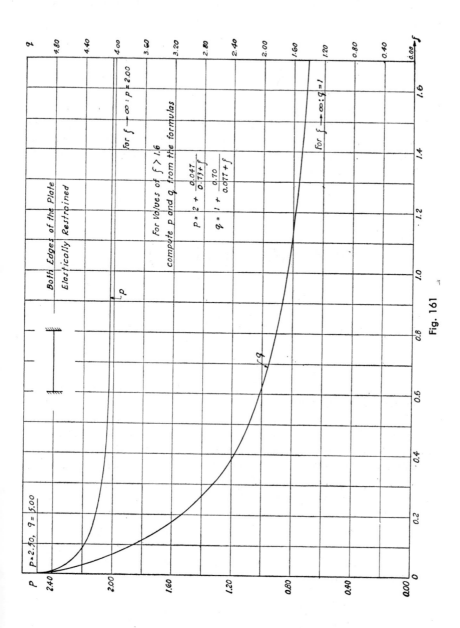

Fig. 161

an expression independent of n, and valid for columns of any length. The plate coefficient

$$k = p + 2\sqrt{q} \tag{641}$$

becomes independent of τ. This is important because it permits the use of precalculated tables and charts for the coefficient k which are applicable in the elastic and inelastic ranges of buckling.

It is interesting to compare the results obtained above with those obtained from the differential equation (604), which is based upon the isotropic concept. The most significant formulas are easily derived from Eqs. (634), (637), and (639) by replacing $\sqrt{\tau}$ by τ and $\sqrt[4]{\tau}$ by unity. In this way we obtain from Eq. (631)

$$\kappa_1 \frac{b}{2} = \frac{n\pi}{2\alpha}\sqrt{\mu + 1} \quad \text{and} \quad \kappa_2 \frac{b}{2} = \frac{n\pi}{2\alpha}\sqrt{\mu - 1} \tag{631a}$$

from Eq. (634)

$$\sigma_c = \frac{\pi^2 E\tau}{12(1 - \nu^2)} \left(\frac{t}{b}\right)^2 \left(\frac{\alpha}{n} + \frac{n}{\alpha}\right)^2 \tag{634a}$$

from Eq. (637)

$$\sigma_c = \frac{\pi^2 E\tau}{12(1 - \nu^2)} \left(\frac{t}{b}\right)^2 \left[\left(\frac{n}{\alpha}\right)^2 + p + q\left(\frac{\alpha}{n}\right)^2\right] \tag{637a}$$

and from Eq. (639)

$$\bar{\alpha} = \sqrt[4]{\frac{1}{q}} \sqrt{n(n + 1)} \tag{639a}$$

τ is always smaller than $\sqrt{\tau}$; hence σ_c computed from Eq. (634a) or (637a) lies below the value of σ_c derived from Eq. (634) or (637). However, the actual difference between these values is far smaller than the ratio $\tau/\sqrt{\tau}$ may indicate, since τ itself is a function of σ_c, and this fact tends to reduce the difference between the σ_c-values derived from the two differential equations (601) and (604). Comparative computations show that the difference for steel or aluminum alloy barely exceeds 10% when σ_c is close to the yield point for small ratios b/t. The difference diminishes when σ_c decreases with increasing ratio b/t. Equations (634a) and (637a) therefore furnish approximate but conservative values of the critical stress σ_c, and the use of the simpler differential equation (604) can be justified in cases where the effect upon the economy of the structure is less important and a far-reaching simplification of the design method is feasible.

Equation (604) has special importance for plates of small aspect ratio, when $\alpha < 1$. The values σ_c derived from Eq. (637a) approach with decreasing α the values of σ_c computed from the original Eq. (637). This fact is readily understood because the bending stresses in the y-direction and the shear stresses diminish rapidly when α decreases and finally vanish when α approaches zero. In this limiting case the plate behaves as a column of length equal to the length a of the plate, and the critical stress σ_c becomes proportional to τ.

A comparison of Eqs. (639) and (639a), which determine the number of half waves in which the plate buckles, indicates that the two theories lead to values α which deviate markedly from each other when applied to long plates if σ_c approaches the neighborhood of the yield point and τ becomes small. The tests reported in Art. 95 agree with Eq. (639) and therefore support the validity of the nonisotropic concept which underlies the differential equation (601).

So far it has been assumed that equal restraint exists at both unloaded edges. In studying the effect of unequal restraint on the unloaded edges of a plate the following approximate method has been recommended by Lundquist and Stowell:[1] The method outlined above for equal restraint on both unloaded edges is applied, first using the coefficient of restraint ζ_1 of one side to find a plate coefficient k_1 from Eq. (641) and then using the other value ζ_2 to find a plate coefficient k_2. The mean value $k = (k_1 + k_2)/2$ represents a fairly good approximation of the exact value of k and can be introduced into Eq. (638a) to obtain the critical stress of the plate under consideration. Lundquist and Stowell gave a comparison of the approximate and accurate values of k for a number of cases and showed that the differences amount, in the worst cases, only to a few per cent of the exact value.

When σ_c lies above the proportional limit, it is advisable to compute a value of σ_c which corresponds to k_1 and then the value of σ_c corresponding to k_2 and to average the two values of σ_c.

90. Case II, Plate Simply Supported at Edges b, Elastically Restrained at One Edge a, and Free at Other Edge a

It is convenient to use the following system of coordinates x, y: The x-axis coincides with the supported edge a, and the y-axis is drawn through the left edge of the plate as indicated in Fig. 158. There is no symmetry with respect to the x-axis, and we must use the general solution of the differential equation (624):

$$w = \sin \frac{n\pi x}{a} (C_1 \cosh \kappa_1 y + C_2 \sinh \kappa_1 y + C_3 \cos \kappa_2 y$$

$$+ C_4 \sin \kappa_2 y) \quad (642)$$

κ_1 and κ_2 are defined by Eqs. (623).

The boundary conditions which determine the four constants C_1 to C_4

[1] Lundquist, E., and E. Z. Stowell, Critical Compressive Stress for Flat Rectangular Plates Supported along All Edges and Elastically Restrained against Rotation along the Unloaded Edges, *NACA Tech. Note* 733, 1942.

are

$$\text{For } y = 0: \quad w = 0 \quad \text{and} \quad \varphi = \bar{\varphi} \qquad (643a)$$
$$\text{For } y = b: \quad M_y = 0 \quad \text{and} \quad Q_y = 0 \qquad (643b)$$

where Q_y is the transverse shear at the free edge. Equations (643a) are identical with Eqs. (626) above, since the same boundary conditions

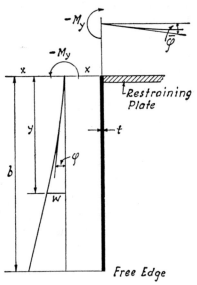

Fig. 162

prevail in Cases I and II at the restrained edge (Fig. 162). Similar reasoning as in Case I leads therefore to the equation

$$\left[\frac{\partial w}{\partial y} - \frac{b}{2} \zeta \frac{\partial^2 w}{\partial y^2} \right]_{y=0} = 0 \qquad (644)$$

which corresponds to Eq. (628). For M_y and Q_y we have the expressions (602), and Eqs. (643b) become

$$\left. \begin{aligned} M_y &= -D \left[\frac{\partial^2 w}{\partial y^2} + \nu \sqrt{\tau} \frac{\partial^2 w}{\partial x^2} \right]_{y=b} = 0 \\ Q_y &= -D \frac{\partial}{\partial y} \left[\frac{\partial^2 w}{\partial y^2} + (2 - \nu) \sqrt{\tau} \frac{\partial^2 w}{\partial x^2} \right]_{y=b} = 0 \end{aligned} \right\} \qquad (645)$$

Substitution of the solution (642) into the boundary conditions for $y = 0$ yields the relations

$$C_1 + C_3 = 0$$
$$C_2 \kappa_1 + C_4 \kappa_2 - \zeta \frac{b}{2} (C_1 \kappa_1{}^2 - C_3 \kappa_2{}^2) = 0$$

and we obtain

$$C_1 = -C_3$$

$$C_2 = C_4 \frac{\kappa_2}{\kappa_1} - C_3 \zeta \frac{b}{2} \frac{\kappa_1{}^2 + \kappa_2{}^2}{\kappa_1}$$

Using these expressions Eq. (642) becomes

$$w = \sin \frac{2\pi x}{a} \left[C_3 \left(\cos \kappa_2 y - \cosh \kappa_1 y - \zeta \frac{b}{2} \frac{\kappa_1{}^2 + \kappa_2{}^2}{\kappa_1} \sinh \kappa_1 y \right) \right.$$
$$\left. + C_4 \left(\sin \kappa_2 y - \frac{\kappa_2}{\kappa_1} \sinh \kappa_1 y \right) \right]$$

Introducing this equation into the two boundary conditions (645) leads to two equations:

$$C_3 (r \cos \kappa_2 b + t \cosh \kappa_1 b + ht \sinh \kappa_1 b) + C_4 \left(r \sin \kappa_2 b \right.$$
$$\left. + t \frac{\kappa_2}{\kappa_1} \sinh \kappa_1 b \right) = 0$$

$$C_3 \left(t \frac{\kappa_2}{\kappa_1} \sin \kappa_2 b - r \sinh \kappa_1 b - hr \cosh \kappa_1 b \right) - C_4 \left(t \frac{\kappa_2}{\kappa_1} \cos \kappa_2 b \right.$$
$$\left. + r \frac{\kappa_2}{\kappa_1} \cosh \kappa_1 b \right) = 0$$

where r, t, and h are defined by

$$r = \kappa_2{}^2 + \nu \sqrt{\tau} \left(\frac{n\pi}{a} \right)^2 = \kappa_1{}^2 - (2 - \nu) \sqrt{\tau} \left(\frac{n\pi}{a} \right)^2$$

$$t = \kappa_1{}^2 - \nu \sqrt{\tau} \left(\frac{n\pi}{a} \right)^2 = \kappa_2{}^2 + (2 - \nu) \sqrt{\tau} \left(\frac{n\pi}{a} \right)^2$$

$$h = \zeta \frac{b}{2} \frac{\kappa_1{}^2 + \kappa_2{}^2}{\kappa_1}$$

The condition $\Delta = 0$ yields finally the buckling condition

$$\frac{2rt}{\cosh \kappa_1 b \cos \kappa_2 b} + r^2 + t^2 - \frac{r^2 \kappa_1{}^2 - t^2 \kappa_2{}^2}{\kappa_1 \kappa_2} \tanh \kappa_1 b \tan \kappa_2 b$$
$$+ h \left(t^2 \tanh \kappa_1 b - r^2 \frac{\kappa_1}{\kappa_2} \tan \kappa_2 b \right) = 0 \quad (646)$$

Similarly[1] as in Case I the critical stress σ_c can be expressed in the form

$$\sigma_c = \frac{\pi^2 E}{12(1 - \nu^2)} \frac{\sqrt{\tau}}{} \left(\frac{t}{b} \right)^2 \left[\left(\frac{n \sqrt[4]{\tau}}{\alpha} \right)^2 + p + q \left(\frac{\alpha}{n \sqrt[4]{\tau}} \right)^2 \right] \quad (647)$$

[1] The critical stress σ_c is defined as a function of μ [Eq. (630)], and κ_1, κ_2, r, and t can be expressed by μ as follows:

$$\kappa_1 b = \frac{n\pi}{\alpha} \sqrt[4]{\tau} \sqrt{\mu + 1} \quad \text{and} \quad \kappa_2 b = \frac{n\pi}{\alpha} \sqrt[4]{\tau} \sqrt{\mu - 1}$$

$$r = \frac{1}{b^2} \left(\frac{n\pi}{\alpha} \right)^2 \sqrt{\tau} (\mu - 1 + \nu) \quad \text{and} \quad t = \frac{1}{b^2} \left(\frac{n\pi}{\alpha} \right)^2 \sqrt{\tau} (\mu + 1 - \nu)$$

Equation (646) is then a relation between μ and $\alpha / n \sqrt[4]{\tau}$ and can be approximated by an expression of the form (636).

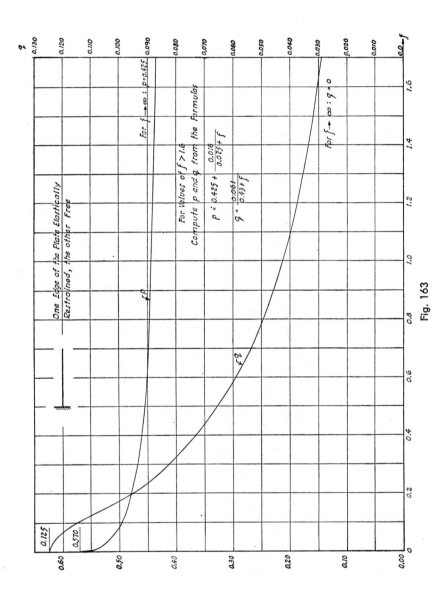

Fig. 163

Making use of the notation (638) this equation can be written in the condensed form

$$\sigma_c = \frac{\pi^2 E}{12(1 - \nu^2)} \sqrt{\tau} \left(\frac{t}{b}\right)^2 k \tag{648}$$

The parameters p and q in this equation are dependent upon the coefficient of restraint ζ. They have been computed from Eq. (646) and are plotted in Fig. 163 versus ζ.

By the same reasoning as in Case I we derive the limiting aspect ratio $\bar{\alpha}$ at which either n or $n + 1$ half waves can exist; i.e.,

$$\bar{\alpha} = \sqrt[4]{\frac{\tau}{q}} \sqrt{n(n + 1)} \tag{649}$$

The ratio α_0 corresponding to the minimum value of σ_c is

$$\alpha_0 = n \sqrt[4]{\frac{\tau}{q}} \tag{650}$$

and thus

$$\text{Min } \sigma_c = \frac{\pi^2 E}{12(1 - \nu^2)} \sqrt{\tau} \left(\frac{t}{b}\right)^2 (p + 2\sqrt{q}) = \frac{\pi^2 E}{12(1 - \nu^2)} \sqrt{\tau} \left(\frac{t}{b}\right)^2 k \tag{651}$$

where the plate coefficient k is independent of τ and has the value

$$k = p + 2\sqrt{q}$$

It may be noted that Eqs. (637) and (647) have the same form but differ in the numerical values of p and q.

It follows from Eq. (650) that with decreasing elastic restraint α_0 will constantly increase, since q will decrease steadily. In the limiting case of a simply supported edge, $q = 0$, the ratio α_0 will be infinite, indicating that the plate always buckles in one half wave. With increasing α_0 the critical stress, min σ_c, decreases and asymptotically approaches the value

$$\text{Min } \sigma_c = \frac{\pi^2 E}{12(1 - \nu^2)} \sqrt{\tau} \left(\frac{t}{b}\right)^2 p \tag{652}$$

If one edge a of the plate is free to rotate, the plate will bulge in one half wave, regardless of its length. However, no matter how great the length of the plate, the value of the critical stress will not decrease below the value given by Eq. (652). If one side of the plate is elastically built in, Eq. (649) indicates that several half waves will form if the length of the plate is sufficiently great.

The stability conditions (632) and (646) for Cases I and II have recently been evaluated very exactly by Lundquist and Stowell[1] for various values

[1] Lundquist, E., and E. Z. Stowell, Critical Compressive Stress for Flat Rectangular Plates Supported along All Edges and Elastically Restrained against Rotation along the Unloaded Edges, *NACA Tech. Note* 733, 1942, and Critical Compressive Stress for Outstanding Flanges, *NACA Tech. Note* 734, 1942.

of ζ between 0 and ∞. Lundquist and Stowell use a different restraint coefficient $\epsilon = 2/\zeta$. The values of the plate coefficient k in Eqs. (640) and (651) are presented in Lundquist and Stowell's papers by charts and tables. Comparison shows that the p- and q-curves in Figs. 161 and 163 yield k-values with an error of less than 1%.

91. Critical Stresses and Lengths of Half Waves for Simply Supported and Fully Fixed Plates

In the following articles and chapters we shall have occasion to refer to limiting cases where the plate is simply supported, $\zeta = \infty$, or fixed,

TABLE 26. Coefficients k and β in Eqs. (653)

Case	Description of support at the unloaded edges		k	β
1	Both edges simply supported		4.00	1.000
2	One edge simply supported, the other fixed		5.42	0.800
3	Both edges fixed		6.97	0.668
4	One edge simply supported, the other free		0.425	*
5	One edge fixed, the other free		1.277	1.680

* λ is always equal to the length a of the plate.

$\zeta = 0$, on the unloaded edges. Table 26 shows the plate coefficient k and the numerical value of the factor β for the computation of the critical stress σ_c and of the half wavelength λ:

$$\sigma_c = \frac{\pi^2 E \sqrt{\tau}}{12(1 - \nu^2)} \left(\frac{t}{b}\right)^2 k \quad \text{and} \quad \lambda = \beta b \sqrt[4]{\tau} \qquad (653)$$

The numerical values in Table 26 apply to long plates only.

92. Determination of the Coefficient of Restraint

In the study of rectangular plates in the previous articles a coefficient of restraint ζ was introduced, and it now remains to show how this coefficient can be determined in each individual case. At the outset of Art. 89 we assumed proportionality between the edge moment M_y and the angle of rotation $\bar{\varphi}$ and stated that the factor of proportionality depends on the dimensions of the restraining structure. As far as plate elements

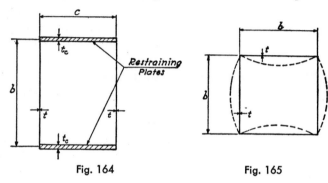

Fig. 164   **Fig. 165**

of the columns are concerned which we shall consider in this article, we must add that the factor of proportionality also depends on the compressive stresses acting on the supporting structural elements. The bending and twisting of the restraining plates in Fig. 164, for example, is determined not only by the effect of the elastic interaction between the web plates and the restraining elements but also by the longitudinal compressive forces acting on the restraining plates. The heavier the restraining plates, the smaller will be the effect of the compressive stresses. This effect takes on practical significance when the ratio b/t of the buckling plates and the ratio c/t_c of the restraining plates approach the same value. In the limiting case, when both plates buckle simultaneously, there is no restraining effect and each element behaves as a plate having simply supported unloaded edges.

An example is represented by the box section shown in Fig. 165. If only one pair of plates were stressed by longitudinal compressive forces, the second pair would be able to exert some restraining influence owing to their inherent rigidity. But if all four sides are under uniform compression, as is the case with columns, both pairs of plates enter the state of unstable equilibrium simultaneously and neither pair is able to support the other. The plates behave as though they were supported without restraining moments at the edges.   In reality it is not the single plate which becomes unstable, but the whole assembly of plates enters a state of instability characterized by the beginning of distortion of the column cross section.

The exact solution of this problem, of course, is feasible by considering the stability of the entire plate assembly.   The general solution [Eq. (624)] can be applied to any combination of plates, but such a procedure ultimately leads to very lengthy mathematical derivations which are difficult to evaluate for practical use.

Lundquist and Stowell[1] derived the exact solution for rectangular tubes having double-symmetric cross sections and for columns having I-, Z-, and U-sections and published charts showing the values of the plate coefficient k as a function of b/c for values of $t/t_c = 0.5$, 1, and 2.   Hartmann[2] discussed the stability of T-sections and applied his analysis, developed under some simplifying assumptions, to a single numerical example.   He called attention to the fact that the torsional resistance of the flange contributes considerably to the elastic restraint of the web.

Applying the principles of the moment distribution method to the stability of structures built up of long plates under longitudinal compressive loads Lundquist, Stowell, and Schuette[3] succeeded in deriving a suitable method for the solution of problems concerning the stability of plate assemblies.   The procedure devised by these authors is based upon the principles of James's method of moment distribution for members under axial loads.[4]   These authors develop a procedure for calculating the critical value of the plate coefficient k and give the derivation of the involved expressions for carry-over and stiffness factors.   A different method for the direct solution of the problem of local instability of plate assemblies will be demonstrated in Chap. XII in connection with the investigation of the hull structure of ships.   This method is based upon the principle of the four-moment equation for frameworks and offers special advantages for the investigation of the cellular structures used in ship design.

The derivation of exact solutions for the stability problems of various types of plate assemblies is extremely cumbersome, and the preparation

---

[1] Lundquist, E. E., Local Instability of Symmetrical Rectangular Tubes, *NACA Tech. Note* 686, 1939.   Stowell, E. Z., and E. E. Lundquist, Local Instability of Columns with I-, Z-, Channel-, and Rectangular-tube Sections, *NACA Tech. Note* 743, 1939.

[2] Hartmann, F., Die Berechnung von T-Gurten auf Ausbeulung, *Der Stahlbau*, Vol. 7, 1934.

[3] Lundquist, E. E., E. Z. Stowell, and E. Schuette, Principles of Moment Distribution Applied to Stability of Structures Composed of Bars or Plates, *NACA Wartime Rept.* L-326.

[4] See Art. 61.

of charts for use in practical design is an arduous and time-consuming task. However, columns in structural design are composed of few plate elements and usually have two axes of symmetry. As far as such columns are concerned, it is feasible to derive approximate formulas for the restraint coefficient ζ which determines the plate coefficient k. In order to arrive at a practical method for the determination of ζ, which renders the results capable of straightforward application to routine calculation, it is even considered permissible to sacrifice accuracy, provided the results of the approximation remain on the side of safety. Being in possession of the exact solution of many of the special problems of local instability in columns, we are able to check the simplified design formulas as to the degree of their accuracy.

Fortunately the effect of the compressive stresses upon the distortion of the restraining plate or plates in the example (Fig. 164) diminishes very rapidly with increasing difference between the ratios b/t and c/t_c, so that the effect of compressive stresses in the restraining elements can be accounted for by a suitable factor which in the limiting case, when b/t becomes equal to c/t_c, furnishes the correct value of ζ. In the subsequent discussion we first assume the coefficient ζ as independent of the longitudinal stresses σ_c in the restraining elements and finally show how we can take care, approximately at least, of the effect of the compressive stress in the restraining structure.

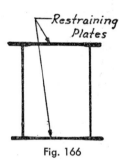

Fig. 166

We shall now determine the coefficients of restraint ζ for the webs and flanges of a number of practically important sections. The findings will be utilized in Art. 94 to give simple design rules for these column sections based on the results of Arts. 89 and 90. The following investigations are based upon these assumptions:

1. No primary buckling of the entire plate assembly takes place prior to the occurrence of local instability in the plates.
2. The edges where the plates join remain straight and do not distort before local failure takes place.

Box Sections. We begin with the box section shown in Fig. 164.[1] When the cross section distorts, each of the restraining plates of width c is acted upon on both unloaded edges by moments M_y per unit length, equal in magnitude and distribution as indicated in Fig. 167. We infer from Eq. (624) that M_y must be proportional to $\sin (n\pi x/a)$ where a

---

[1] Riveted or welded box sections commonly used may have a form as shown in Fig. 166. The restraining effect of the outstanding parts of the cover plates is comparatively small and is disregarded.

is the length of the plate and $\lambda = a/n$ the length of a half wave. The distribution of M_y along the edges a is sinusoidal as illustrated by Fig. 167. The restraining plate is bulged alternately upward and downward, and the lines n-n in this figure are nodal lines. Each panel between two such straight nodal lines therefore represents a plate simply supported on all four edges and loaded symmetrically on two opposite edges by the

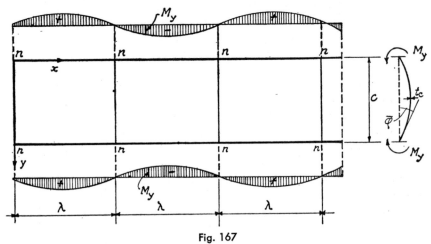

Fig. 167

variable moment M_y per unit length. For this special loading condition and under the assumption that no compressive forces are acting on the restraining plate, it is possible to develop the following expression for the angle of rotation $\bar{\varphi}$ as function of M_y:[1]

[1] The deflection $\bar{w}$ of the restraining plate can be determined from the differential equation (601). Due to the assumption $\sigma_x = 0$ the last term of this equation vanishes, but we allow for the effect of the anisotropy produced by compressive stresses σ_x above the proportional limit by retaining the coefficients τ and $\sqrt{\tau}$ in the first two terms of the differential equation. For the loading condition considered here

$$M_y = C \sin \frac{\pi x}{l},$$

the deflection $\bar{w}$ can be expressed in the general form

$$\bar{w} = \left(C_1 \sinh \frac{\sqrt[4]{\tau}\,\pi y}{\lambda} + C_2 \cosh \frac{\sqrt[4]{\tau}\,\pi y}{\lambda} + C_3 y \sinh \frac{\sqrt[4]{\tau}\,\pi y}{\lambda} + C_4 y \cosh \frac{\sqrt[4]{\tau}\,\pi y}{\lambda} \right)$$

in which C_1 to C_4 are constants which are defined by the given boundary conditions. When the four sides of the plate are simply supported, the expression for $\bar{w}$ becomes

$$\bar{w} = \frac{c\lambda}{2\pi D' \sinh (\sqrt[4]{\tau}\,\pi y/\lambda)} \left[\frac{y}{c} \cosh \frac{\sqrt[4]{\tau}\,\pi (y-c)}{\lambda} + \left(1 - \frac{y}{c} \right) \cosh \frac{\sqrt[4]{\tau}\,\pi y}{\lambda} \right.$$
$$\left. - \frac{\sinh (\sqrt[4]{\tau}\,\pi y/\lambda) + \sinh \dfrac{\sqrt[4]{\tau}\,\pi (y-c)}{\lambda}}{\sinh (\sqrt[4]{\tau}\,\pi y/\lambda)} \right] M_y$$

Using $\bar{\varphi} = \left(\dfrac{\partial \bar{w}}{\partial y} \right)_{y=c}$ leads to Eq. (654.)

$$\bar{\varphi} = -\frac{\lambda}{2\sqrt[4]{\tau}D'}\frac{1}{\pi}\tanh\frac{\sqrt[4]{\tau}\pi c}{2\lambda}\left[1 + \frac{\sqrt[4]{\tau}\pi c/\lambda}{\sinh(\sqrt[4]{\tau}\pi c/\lambda)}\right]M_y$$

$$= -\frac{\lambda}{2\sqrt[4]{\tau}D'}\rho_1\left(\frac{\sqrt[4]{\tau}c}{\lambda}\right)M_y \quad (654)$$

The transcendental term ρ_1 defined by this equation is independent of x, indicating that the ratio of the moment M_y to the rotation $\bar{\varphi}$ is constant along the edge, as assumed in Eq. (627). c and t_c are the width and the thickness of the restraining plate, $D' = Et_c^3/12(1 - \nu^2)$ the flexural

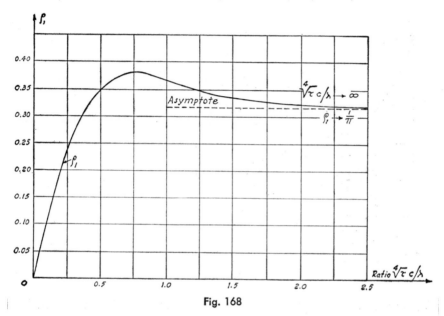

Fig. 168

rigidity of the restraining plate, and λ the length of the half wave of the buckling plate.

The length λ of the half wave lies between $0.668\sqrt[4]{\tau}\,b$ for clamped edges and $\sqrt[4]{\tau}\,b$ for freely supported edges, where b is the width of the web plate.[1] For the sake of simplification we assume $\lambda = \sqrt[4]{\tau}\,b$ independent of the degree of fixity at the edges of the web plate. The error involved in this assumption is small and lies on the safe side because an increase of the wave length λ always decreases the effective restraint. Introducing this value for λ into Eq. (654) we have $\sqrt[4]{\tau}\,c/\lambda = c/b$, and

$$\bar{\varphi} = -\frac{b}{2D'}\rho_1\left(\frac{c}{b}\right)M_y \quad (655)$$

In Fig. 168 ρ_1 is plotted as a function of $\sqrt[4]{\tau}\,c/\lambda$. The curve begins

[1] See Cases 1 and 3 in Table 26 on p. 330.

with $\rho_1 = 0$ at $\sqrt[4]{\tau}\,c/\lambda = 0$, reaches a maximum value $\rho_1 = 0.386$ at $\sqrt[4]{\tau}\,c/\lambda = 0.764$, and approaches $1/\pi$ asymptotically. Since $(b/2D')$ $\rho_1(c/b)$ represents the factor $1/\bar{\zeta}$ in Eq. (627), the coefficient ζ as defined by Eq. (629) becomes

$$\zeta = \frac{2}{b}\frac{D}{\bar{\zeta}} = \frac{2D}{b}\frac{b}{2D'}\,\rho_1\left(\frac{c}{b}\right) = \frac{t^3}{t_c{}^3}\,\rho_1\left(\frac{c}{b}\right) \tag{656}$$

Thus far we have neglected the effect of the longitudinal stress σ_x on the stiffness of the restraining plate. It is now necessary to adapt Eq.

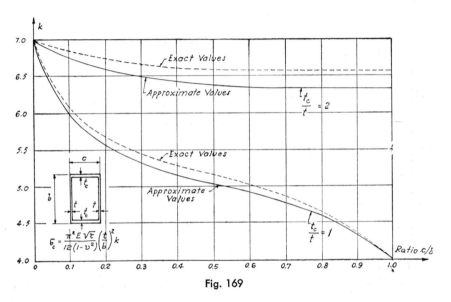

Fig. 169

(656) to include this effect, which can be done approximately by multiplying expression (656) by the factor

$$r = \frac{1}{1 - (t^2c^2/t_c{}^2b^2)} \tag{657}$$

This expression exactly satisfies the conditions which control the limiting cases. r and therefore ζ become infinite when $t/b = t_c/c$, in which case both plates are simply supported without restraint. When, owing to high rigidity of the restraining members, $t^2c^2/t_c{}^2b^2$ is very small, r approaches unity, which is correct, as in this case no modification of Eq. (656) is required. Introducing the expression r as a factor in Eq. (656) finally leads to

$$\zeta = \frac{t^3}{t_c{}^3}\frac{\rho_1(c/b)}{1 - (t^2c^2/t_c{}^2b^2)} \tag{658}$$

This equation applies when $tc/t_cb \leq 1$.

Computing, in any given case, the value of ζ with the aid of the diagram for ρ_1 in Fig. 168, the values of the parameters p and q can be read from Fig. 161. This permits computation of the factor $k = p + 2\sqrt{q}$ required to determine σ_c from Eq. (640).

Figure 169 shows the application of the method outlined above. The values of k have been plotted for $t_c/t = 1$ and $t_c/t = 2$ for ratios c/b between zero and unity. The dashed curves in Fig. 169 show the results of the exact computation of the stability condition of the box section,

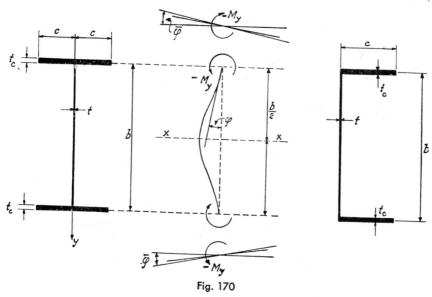

Fig. 170

taken from the chart in Lundquist's paper.[1] Both solid curves give somewhat smaller values of k than indicated by the exact solution; the approximate results therefore lie on the safe side. The maximum deviations between the exact and approximate values of k amount to 2% of the exact value for $t_c/t = 1$ and about 5% for $t_c/t = 2$. These deviations are mainly a consequence of the simplification made by assuming the length of the half waves $\lambda = \sqrt[4]{\tau}\,b$. This explains the larger difference in case of the stronger restraint $t_c/t = 2$.

Web Plates in I- and Channel-sections. We now turn to I- and channel-sections where the web plate is equally restrained on two sides by the flanges. Inspection of Fig. 170 shows that in the case of an I-section each of the flanges is acted on along its center line by a torque M_y. By the same reasoning as before we conclude that M_y varies with $\sin(n\pi x/a)$, having the half wavelength $\lambda = a/n$. The investigation of

[1] Lundquist, *loc. cit.* on p. 332.

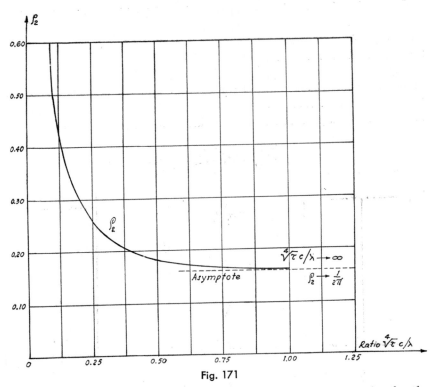

Fig. 171

this loading condition of the flange leads to the following equation for the angle of rotation:[1]

$$\bar{\varphi} = - \frac{\lambda}{2\sqrt[4]{\tau}\,D'} \frac{1}{2\pi} \frac{3\cosh^2(\sqrt[4]{\tau}\,\pi c/\lambda) + \sqrt[4]{\tau}\,\pi^2 c^2/\lambda^2 + 1}{\sqrt[4]{\tau}\,\pi c/\lambda + 3\sinh(\sqrt[4]{\tau}\,\pi c/\lambda)\,\cosh(\sqrt[4]{\tau}\,\pi c/\lambda)} M_y$$

$$= - \frac{\lambda}{2\sqrt[4]{\tau}\,D'} \rho_2 \left(\frac{\sqrt[4]{\tau}\,c}{\lambda} \right) M_y \quad (659)$$

Assuming $\lambda = \sqrt[4]{\tau}\,b$ as before, we may write

$$\bar{\varphi} = \frac{-b}{2D'} \rho_2 \left(\frac{c}{b} \right) M_y \quad (660)$$

The function ρ_2 is shown in Fig. 171. Referring to Eqs. (627) and (629) we obtain in the same manner as before

$$\zeta = \frac{t^3}{t_c{}^3} \rho_2 \left(\frac{c}{b} \right) \quad (661)$$

[1] This equation was derived from the general solution given in the footnote on p. 334. The deflection $\bar{w}$ and angle of rotation $\bar{\varphi}$ were determined for one-half of the flange, representing a plate simply supported on three sides and free on the fourth side, acted on by the moment $M_y/2$ along the supported long side.

In order to take care of the effect of the compressive stresses in the flanges, this expression must be multiplied by the factor

$$r = \frac{1}{1 - 9.4(t^2c^2/t_c{}^2b^2)} \qquad (662)$$

This factor was determined in such manner that it becomes infinite if the flange and the web as simply supported plates buckle at the same stress. According to cases 1 and 4 in Table 26 this will occur if $4(t/b)^2 = 0.425(t_c/c)^2$ or, after division, $9.4t^2c^2/b^2t_c{}^2 = 1$. Upon introducing r into Eq. (661) the final expression for ζ for webs of I-beams is

$$\zeta = \frac{t^3}{t_c{}^3} \frac{\rho_2(c/b)}{1 - 9.4t^2c^2/t_c{}^2b^2} \qquad (663)$$

This equation applies when $9.4t^2c^2/t_c{}^2b^2 \leq 1$.

It is readily seen that for channel-sections (Fig. 170) the restraining effect of the flanges is half of the effect of the flanges in an I-section. Therefore ζ assumes a value twice as great as given by Eq. (663). We have therefore for channel-sections

$$\zeta = 2\frac{t^3}{t_c{}^3} \frac{\rho_2(c/b)}{1 - 9.4t^2c^2/t_c{}^2b^2} \qquad (664)$$

When the term $9.4t^2c^2/t_c{}^2b^2$ becomes greater than unity, the implication is that the web is no longer restrained by the flange but that the flange is the weaker plate which is restrained by the web. This case will be treated in the following paragraph.

Outstanding Flanges of Channel- and Z-sections. The outstanding flanges of some types of cross sections represent plates of high aspect ratio α which are supported on three edges and free on one long side. Such conditions of support have been considered as Case II in Art. 90.

We first study the restraint provided by the web plate to the two outstanding flanges of the cross section shown in Fig. 172a. The web plate is affected along the unloaded edges by the moments M_y in the same manner as previously discussed for the box section. However, the half wavelength of the buckled flange now lies between $1.68 \sqrt[4]{\tau} b$ and the full length a of the plate.[1] We obtain a conservative but simple result if we assume the wavelength $\lambda = \infty$, and introducing this value into Eq. (654) we obtain

$$\bar{\varphi} = -\frac{c}{2D'} M_y$$

and finally

$$\zeta = \frac{D}{D'} \frac{c}{b} = \frac{t^3 c}{t_c{}^3 b} \qquad (665)$$

[1] See cases 4 and 5 in Table 26.

In the same manner as before we can take care of the effect of the compressive stresses in the restraining web plate by introducing a factor r similar to expression (662) but observing that the limiting case $\zeta = \infty$ requires that $(0.425/4)(t^2c^2/t_c^2b^2) = 1$. We have therefore for channel-sections

$$\zeta = \frac{t^3}{t_c^3} \frac{c}{b} \frac{1}{1 - 0.106 t^2 c^2 / t_c^2 b^2} \tag{666}$$

valid for $0.106 t^2 c^2 / t_c^2 b^2 \le 1$. This equation is also applicable to Z-sections (Fig. 172b).

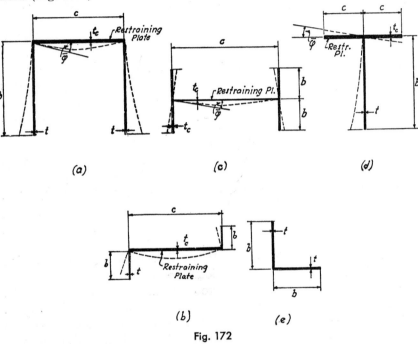

(a)   (c)   (d)

(b)   (e)

Fig. 172

Outstanding Flanges of I-sections. In the case of I-sections (Fig. 172c) where the web is assumed to restrain the flanges, we have

$$\bar{\varphi} = \frac{c}{D'} M_y$$

and the coefficient of restraint ζ for the outstanding flanges assumes the value

$$\zeta = 2 \frac{t^3}{t_c^3} \frac{c}{b} \frac{1}{1 - 0.106 (t^2 c^2 / t_c^2 b^2)} \tag{667}$$

The charts published by Stowell and Lundquist[1] for the coefficient k

[1] Stowell and Lundquist, *loc. cit.* on p. 332.

of channel- and I-sections afford the opportunity to check the accuracy of the expressions just developed for ζ for flange and web buckling of such sections. Equations (663) and (667) have been used to determine the coefficients k for I-sections for the two ratios $t_w/t_f = 1$ and $t_w/t_f = 0.5$,

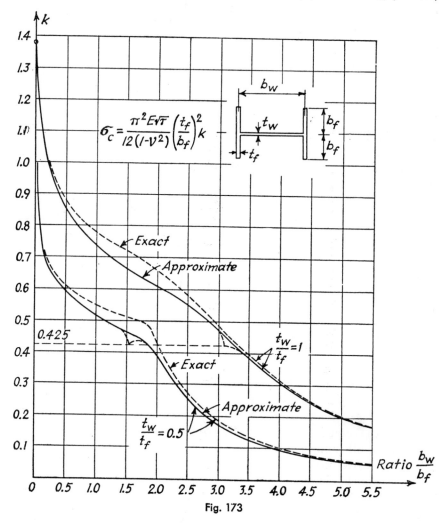

Fig. 173

where t_w and t_f are the thickness of web and flange, respectively. The values of k are plotted in Fig. 173 versus the ratio b_w/b_f. The solid curves are computed from Eqs. (663) and (666); the dashed lines are the exact k-curves given by Stowell and Lundquist. Inspection shows that the approximate formulas for ζ lead to k-curves which conform fairly well with the exact diagrams and that the above-outlined method leads, for practical purposes at least, to sufficiently accurate and conservative values of k.

Webs of T-sections. The web is a plate supported and elastically restrained against rotation along one edge and free on the other one. The flange is acted on along its center line by a twisting moment M_y varying with $\sin(\pi x/\lambda)$, where λ is the length of the half waves of the bulged web plate. λ lies between $1.68 \sqrt[4]{\tau}\, b$ and the total length of the plate.[1] The angle of rotation $\bar{\varphi}$ in Fig. 172d is given by Eq. (659).

Tentative computations indicate that even in case of thin and small flanges within the conventional range in steel construction the restraining effect of the flange is considerable and that the length of the half waves into which the web buckles does not exceed appreciably the value $2\sqrt[4]{\tau}\, b$, where b is the width of the web plate. Using $\lambda = 2\sqrt[4]{\tau}\, b$ and assuming $c/b = \frac{1}{5}$ as an extreme ratio, Eq. (659) yields for $\sqrt[4]{\tau}\, c/\lambda = c/2b = \frac{1}{10}$ the value $\rho_2 = 0.53 \doteq \frac{1}{2}$, and proceeding in the same manner as before we obtain

$$\zeta = \frac{t^3}{t_c^3} \tag{668}$$

This equation indicates that the value of ζ depends principally on the ratio t/t_c.

The effect of the compressive stress acting on the restraining flange can be taken into account by multiplying this expression by the factor r defined by Eq. (657). Thus we arrive finally at

$$\zeta = \frac{t^3/t_c^3}{1 - (t^2 c^2/t_c^2 b^2)} \tag{669}$$

valid for $t/t_c \leq 1$ and $c/b \leq 1$.

Outstanding Legs of Angles. It is readily conceived that each leg of an angle (Fig. 172e) behaves like a plate simply supported on three sides and free on the fourth side. Since both legs, assumed of equal width, arrive at the same instant at the state of buckling, neither of the legs can restrain the other one, and the coefficient of restraint ζ therefore is infinite. For long angles the plate coefficient k approaches the value 0.425.[2] Both angle legs buckle in one half wave.

In case of unequal angles a certain restraining effect upon the wider leg is exerted by the smaller one. An exact solution of the stability problem of unequal angles undertaken by the author shows that for long angles the plate coefficient k approaches the value 0.504 for the leg ratio 2 to 3 and 0.568 for the ratio 1 to 2. The above values of k pertain to the wider leg and therefore must be used in the formula for σ_c together

---

[1] See cases 4 and 5 in Table 26.
[2] See case 1 in Table 26.

with the slenderness ratio b/t of the wider leg. Independent of the length of the angle, the legs buckle in one half wave.

93. Determination of the Critical Stress in the Inelastic Range of Buckling

It has been demonstrated in this chapter that the critical stress σ_c of long rectangular plates, loaded longitudinally by compressive forces in the plane of the plates, may be computed from the formula

$$\sigma_c = \frac{\pi^2 E \sqrt{\tau}}{12(1 - \nu^2)} \left(\frac{t}{b}\right)^2 k$$

where k is independent of τ. In the elastic range of buckling, when $\tau = 1$, the critical stress σ_c can be directly computed from this equation. However, in the inelastic range τ, which depends on σ_c, is an unknown quantity at the outset of the computation, and a method of trial and error would be necessary to determine σ_c. This can be avoided by writing the above equation in the form

$$\frac{\sigma_c}{\sqrt{\tau}} = \frac{\pi^2 E}{12(1 - \nu^2)} \left(\frac{t}{b}\right)^2 k \tag{670}$$

Determining $\sigma_c/\sqrt{\tau}$ from this equation the corresponding value of σ_c can be found from a precalculated table of the values σ_c as function of $\sigma_c/\sqrt{\tau}$. Such a table can be computed from the τ-values for the material under consideration. Tables 27 and 28 are examples of such tables.

TABLE 27. Determination of the Critical Stress σ_c for Steel, Kips/In.^{2}
($\sigma_p = 25$ kips/in.^{2}, $\sigma_y = 33$ kips/in.^{2})

$\sigma_c/\sqrt{\tau}$	σ_c	$\sigma_c/\sqrt{\tau}$	σ_c	$\sigma_c/\sqrt{\tau}$	σ_c
25.0	25.00	35.0	28.37	120.0	32.55
25.5	25.23	36.0	28.59	140.0	32.66
26.0	25.46	37.0	28.79	160.0	32.73
26.5	25.68	38.0	28.98	180.0	32.79
27.0	25.89	39.0	29.16	200.0	32.84
27.5	26.10	40.0	29.33	250.0	32.89
28.0	26.29	45.0	30.03	300.0	32.93
28.5	26.48	50.0	30.55	400.0	32.96
29.0	26.66	55.0	30.95	500.0	32.98
29.5	26.83	60.0	31.26		
30.0	27.00	70.0	31.70		
31.0	27.31	80.0	32.00		
32.0	27.60	90.0	32.20		
33.0	27.87	100.0	32.35		
34.0	28.13				

The values τ on which these tables are based were computed by means of Eq. (64), Chap. I. Table 27 applies to steel having a proportional limit $\sigma_p = 25$ kips/in.^{2} and a yield point $\sigma_y = 33$ kips/in.^{2}, while Table 28 applies for $\sigma_p = 34$ kips/in.^{2}, $\sigma_y = 45$ kips/in.^{2}.*

TABLE 28.   Determination of the Critical Stress σ_c for Steel, Kips/In.^{2}
($\sigma_p = 34$ kips/in.^{2}, $\sigma_y = 45$ kips/in.^{2})

$\sigma_c/\sqrt{\tau}$	σ_c	$\sigma_c/\sqrt{\tau}$	σ_c	$\sigma_c/\sqrt{\tau}$	σ_c
34.0	34.00	46.0	38.24	100.0	43.38
34.5	34.24	47.0	38.48	110.0	43.65
35.0	34.47	48.0	38.71	120.0	43.85
35.5	34.70	49.0	38.93	130.0	44.02
36.0	34.92	50.0	39.14	140.0	44.15
36.5	35.13				
		52.0	39.53	150.0	44.26
37.0	35.34	54.0	39.88	200.0	44.58
37.5	35.54	56.0	40.21	250.0	44.71
38.0	35.74	58.0	40.50	300.0	44.81
38.5	35.93	60.0	40.76		
39.0	36.12			400.0	44.89
39.5	36.30	65.0	41.34	500.0	44.93
		70.0	41.80	600.0	44.95
40.0	36.47	75.0	42.20		
41.0	36.81	80.0	42.54		
42.0	37.13	85.0	42.79		
43.0	37.43	90.0	43.01		
44.0	37.71	95.0	43.21		
45.0	37.98				

94. Design Formulas for the Required Thickness of Plate Elements of Columns

To prevent premature failure of compression members by local buckling, the cross section should be selected so that the individual plates offer the same or larger resistance to local buckling as the whole member presents to primary column buckling. Therefore, the critical stress σ_c which results in local instability must be equal to or larger than the critical stress at which the column of slenderness ratio l/r buckles as a whole. This can be expressed by the equation

$$\frac{\pi^2 E \tau}{(l/r)^2} \leq \frac{\pi^2 E \sqrt{\tau}}{12(1 - \nu^2)} \left(\frac{t}{b}\right)^2 k$$

* The properties were selected to apply for medium and high-tensile steel, respectively, according to U.S. Navy Department Specification 48S5f, Nov. 15, 1945.

from which we obtain the design criterion

$$\frac{b}{t} \leq \frac{\sqrt{k}}{2\sqrt{3(1-\nu^2)}\sqrt{\tau}} \frac{l}{r} = \frac{0.303\ l}{\sqrt[4]{\tau}\ r}\sqrt{k} \tag{671}$$

This equation indicates the important fact that the permissible ratio of plate width b to plate thickness t increases with the slenderness ratio of the column. In slender columns, therefore, thinner walls can be used than in short columns.

Denoting the term $(0.303/\sqrt[4]{\tau})\ (l/r)$ in Eq. (671) by C, we obtain

$$\frac{b}{t} \leq C\sqrt{k} \tag{672}$$

The coefficient C is a function of the slenderness ratio l/r only, as τ depends for a given material on the critical stress σ_c, which in turn is a function of l/r defined by the column curve. It is therefore possible to obtain a diagram representing C from the column curve for any material. Above the proportional limit, these C-diagrams can be approximated by algebraic expressions of the type

$$C = a\sqrt{\frac{l}{r}} - b \tag{673}$$

where a and b are constants depending on the shape of the column curve of the material under consideration.

Based on Eq. (64) for the values of τ, the expression (673) for steel,[1] having a proportional limit $\sigma_p = 25$ kips/in.[2] and a yield point $\sigma_y = 33$ kips/in.[2], becomes

$$\left.\begin{array}{ll} 20 < \dfrac{l}{r} < 108: & C = 3.37\sqrt{\dfrac{l}{r}} - 2.30 \\[2ex] \dfrac{l}{r} > 108: & C = 0.303\,\dfrac{l}{r} \end{array}\right\} \tag{673a}$$

and for $\sigma_p = 34$ kips/in.[2], $\sigma_y = 45$ kips/in.[2]

$$\left.\begin{array}{ll} 20 < \dfrac{l}{r} < 93: & C = 3.17\sqrt{\dfrac{l}{r}} - 2.40 \\[2ex] \dfrac{l}{r} > 93: & C = 0.303\,\dfrac{l}{r} \end{array}\right\} \tag{673b}$$

To obtain the permissible ratio b/t from Eq. (672), the plate factor k must first be determined, which can be done by means of the diagrams in Figs. 161 and 163 presented in Arts. 89 and 90. To apply the results of these articles, the values of the coefficient of restraint ζ derived in Art. 92 must be used. While the procedure of computing the plate factor k,

[1] See the footnote on p. 344.

TABLE 29.　Design Formulas for the Required Plate Thickness of Elements of Columns
[For coefficient C see Eqs. (673a) and (673b)]

Type of cross section	Coefficient of restraint ζ	$\sqrt{k}$	Required plate thickness
Web plates of box section	$\zeta = \dfrac{t^3}{t_c{}^3}\,\dfrac{0.38}{1 - \dfrac{t^2}{t_c{}^2}\dfrac{c^2}{d^2}}$ valid for: $\dfrac{tc}{t_c d} \leq 1$	$2 + \dfrac{2}{10\zeta + 3}$	$d/t \leq C\sqrt{k}$
Web plate in I-section	$\zeta = \dfrac{t^3}{t_f{}^3}\,\dfrac{0.16 + 0.0056(d/c)^2}{1 - 9.4\dfrac{t^2}{t_f{}^2}\dfrac{c^2}{d^2}}$ valid for: $9.4\dfrac{t^2 c^2}{t_f{}^2 d^2} \leq 1$	$2 + \dfrac{2}{10\zeta + 3}$	$d/t \leq C\sqrt{k}$
Flanges of I-section	$\zeta = 2\dfrac{t_f{}^3 d}{t^3 c}\,\dfrac{1}{1 - 0.106\dfrac{t_f{}^2 d^2}{t^2 c^2}}$ valid for: $9.4\dfrac{t^2 c^2}{t_f{}^2 d^2} \geq 1$	$0.65 + \dfrac{2}{3\zeta + 4}$	$c/t_f \leq C\sqrt{k}$
Web plate of T-section	$\zeta = \dfrac{t^3}{t_c{}^3}\,\dfrac{1}{1 - 0.106\dfrac{t^2}{t_c{}^2}\dfrac{c^2}{d^2}}$ valid for: $0.106\dfrac{t^2 c^2}{t_c{}^2 d^2} \leq 1$	$0.65 + \dfrac{2}{3\zeta + 4}$	$d/t \leq C\sqrt{k}$

TABLE 29. Design Formulas for the Required Plate Thickness of Elements of Columns (Continued)

Type of cross section	Coefficient of restraint ζ	$\sqrt{k}$	Required plate thickness
Web plate in channel-section	$\zeta = 2\dfrac{t^3}{t_c{}^3}\dfrac{0.16 + 0.0056(d/c)^2}{1 - 9.4\dfrac{t^2}{t_f{}^2}\dfrac{c^2}{d^2}}$ valid for: $9.4\dfrac{t^2c^2}{t_f{}^2d^2} \leq 1$	$2 + \dfrac{2}{10\zeta + 3}$	$d/t \leq C\sqrt{k}$
Flanges of channel-section	$\zeta = \dfrac{t_f{}^3 d}{t^3 c}\dfrac{1}{1 - 0.106\dfrac{t_f{}^2}{t^2}\dfrac{d^2}{d^2}}$ valid for: $9.4\dfrac{t^2c^2}{t_f{}^2d^2} \geq 1$	$0.65 + \dfrac{2}{3\zeta + 4}$	$c/t \leq C\sqrt{k}$
Web plates of U-section*	$\zeta = \dfrac{t^3}{t_c{}^3}\dfrac{c}{d}\dfrac{1}{1 - 0.106\dfrac{t^2}{t_c{}^2}\dfrac{c^2}{d^2}}$ valid for: $9.4\dfrac{t_c{}^2d^2}{t^2c^2} \geq 1$	$0.65 + \dfrac{2}{3\zeta + 4}$	$d/t \leq C\sqrt{k}$
Angle-sections			$b_1/b = 1:\ b/t \leq 0.652C$ $b_1/b = \frac{2}{3}:\ b/t \leq 0.711C$ $b_1/b = \frac{1}{2}:\ b/t \leq 0.754C$
Cruciform-section			$b/t \leq 0.652C$

* The formula given does not apply if the lower edges of the webs are connected by lacing bars.

from Eqs. (641) and (652), $k = p + 2\sqrt{q}$, is not really difficult, it can be simplified further by expressing $\sqrt{k}$ approximately as an algebraic function of ζ as follows: from Eq. (641) and Fig. 161 for the boundary conditions of Case I,

$$\sqrt{k} = 2 + \frac{2}{10\zeta + 3} \tag{674}$$

and from Eq. (652) and Fig. 163 for the boundary conditions of Case II,

$$\sqrt{k} = 0.65 + \frac{2}{3\zeta + 4} \tag{675}$$

These expressions have no theoretical basis but were obtained by plotting the values of $\sqrt{k}$ as functions of ζ and selecting the above expressions to approximate these plots.

The coefficients ζ occurring in Eqs. (674) and (675) have been determined in Art. 92 for a number of sections and are compiled in Table 29 for practical use. The values of ζ as determined in Art. 92 were in some cases functions of coefficient $\rho_1(c/b)$ or $\rho_2(c/b)$ defined in Figs. 168 and 171. As in practical cases c/b varies for each section only within a limited range, these coefficients were replaced in Table 29 either by a constant or by a simple algebraic expression.

Tables of design factors for various sections similar to Table 29 were previously derived by the author and also by Bijlaard.[1]

95. Buckling Tests on Plates

Swiss Buckling Tests. Kollbrunner's[2] buckling tests, already mentioned, were made with the chief purpose of checking the theory of long edge-compressed rectangular plates over the entire elastic and inelastic range. More than 500 angles of steel and aluminum alloy of various cross-sectional dimensions and lengths and 349 plates of aluminum alloy under various conditions of support at the unloaded edges were tested. The tests were conducted on angles, because each leg of an angle acts as a plate simply supported at one edge and free on the other edge, and compared with other experimental arrangements, there was the least possibility of an unintentional restraint on the supported edge. Figure 174 shows a test diagram where buckling occurred below the proportional limit, except for two specimens. For all aspect ratios α, the test points agree very well with the theoretical stability curve derived from Eq. (647), using $\tau = 1$ and $p = 0.425$, $q = 0$, as read from the diagram in Fig. 164 for $\zeta = \infty$.

---

[1] Bleich, *op. cit.* on p. 304. Bijlaard, *loc. cit.* on p. 304.
[2] Kollbrunner, *loc. cit.* on p. 305.

Kollbrunner based his computation of the critical stresses σ_c upon values τ_r derived from stress-strain diagrams according to the double-modulus concept. He found that the observed values of σ_c showed a tendency to remain somewhat below those computed. In order to obtain better agreement between theory and experiment, he suggested replacing $\sqrt{\tau}$ in Eqs. (637) and (647) by $(\tau_r + \sqrt{\tau_r})/2$.

However, using the tangent-modulus concept on which the presentation of this chapter is based, we obtain good agreement between theory and

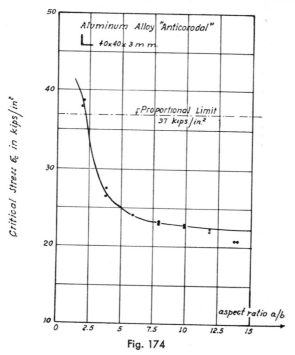

Fig. 174

tests without the arbitrary change from $\sqrt{\tau}$ to $(\tau + \sqrt{\tau})/2$. This was borne out by a series of comparative computations. As an example for the agreement between observed and calculated values of the critical stress, see Fig. 175. It represents a typical test diagram of a plate buckling in the inelastic range. Curve 1 shows the value of the critical stress σ_c plotted versus the aspect ratio a/b, derived from Eq. (647) by using the tangent-modulus in determining τ. Curve 2 was computed on the basis of assuming isotropic behavior of the plate in the plastic range (Roš-Brunner theory). The agreement between the test points and curve 1 is satisfactory, whereas curve 2 lies distinctly below the measured values. The values of $\tau = E_t/E$ as derived from the stress-strain diagram given in Kollbrunner's report are listed in Fig. 175.

In his tests on plates of aluminum alloy Kollbrunner studied four types of support along the unloaded edges, namely, one edge fixed, the other one free; both edges simply supported; one edge fixed, the other one simply supported; and both edges fixed.[1]   There are only a few series of these tests where the critical stress exceeded the proportional limit, but these can serve for a comparison between the tests and the theoretical predictions in the inelastic range.   Data from these series are given in

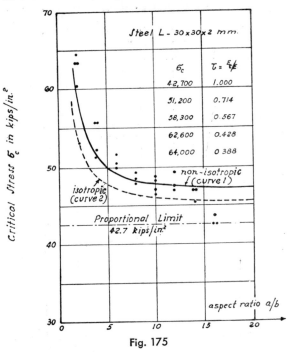

Fig. 175

Table 30, which also shows the values of σ_c computed from Eq. (640) by using the tangent-modulus E_t for the determination of τ.   In the last two columns the observed and computed numbers of half waves are given.

The agreement between the measured and computed stresses is as good as can be expected in tests where the critical stresses lie above the elastic limit.   The calculated and observed number of half waves is in strict agreement only in the case where the plates were simply supported at the unloaded edges.   In the two other series, where one or two edges were fixed, the computed number of half waves lies distinctly above the observed number.   This might be due to the fact that the edges actually were not completely fixed.   A computation of stresses and numbers of half waves under the assumption that the restraint of the specimens was

[1] The modulus of elasticity of the material was $E = 10,200$ kips/in.[2], and the proportional limit was $\sigma_p = 28$ kips/in.[2]

TABLE 30. Comparison of Kollbrunner's Tests and Theoretical Results

Specimen	Length-width ratio	Observed average critical stress of three tests, kips/in.²	Average	Critical stress computed from Eq. (640), kips/in.²	Difference, %	No. of half waves	
						Observed	Computed from Eq. (639)
0.079 in. 2.44 in. $b/t = 31$	3.23	30.2	30.1	30.3	0.7	3	4
	4.84	29.8				5	5
	6.45	29.9				7	7
	8.17	30.6				9	9
0.079 in. 2.09 in. $b/t = 26.5$	3.77	39.7	38.8	38.3 (37.8)	1.3 (2.6)	6	7 (6)
	5.76	38.3				8	10 (9)
	7.55	38.3				11	13 (12)
	9.44	39.1				14	16 (14)
0.079 in. 1.74 in. $b/t = 22$	4.55	40.7	41.7	42.8 (42.4)	2.6 (1.7)	9	10 (9)
	6.82	41.8				13	17 (14)
	9.10	42.8				18	24 (19)
	11.35	42.8				24	29 (24)

slightly elastic, corresponding to a value $\zeta = 0.12$ of the coefficient of restraint, leads to values of the stresses only a few tenths of a kip below the stresses computed with $\zeta = 0$. However, the computed number of half waves reduces considerably and agrees well with the observed data. The results for $\zeta = 0.12$ are shown in Table 30 in parentheses.

This series of careful tests on plates made it possible to compare the predictions of Ilyushin's plate theory in the inelastic range with the observed critical stress.[1] Comparison of the test series in Table 30 for simply supported and clamped plates showed that the results obtained from Ilyushin's theory lead to values of the critical stress which lie definitely above the observed values. The tests indicate that the plates failed at critical stresses considerably below those predicted by Ilyushin's theory. A comparison of these tests with Stowell's theory reported in Art. 87 has not been made, but this theory does necessarily give lower critical stresses than Ilyushin's and can be expected to be in better agreement with the tests.

American Buckling Tests. Local buckling has been investigated by Gerard[2] with the purpose of clarifying the question of the effective modulus E_e which should be applied in plate design. The ratio $\eta = E_e/E$ represents the nondimensional factor by which the critical stress σ_c computed for elastic buckling must be multiplied to obtain the critical stress when σ_c lies above the elastic limit. Gerard suggested the use of the secant modulus E_s and assumed $\eta = E_s/E$. Starting from the plate formula in the elastic range, which may be written in the condensed form

$$\frac{\sigma_c}{E} = K \left(\frac{t}{b} \right)^2$$

he reasoned in the following manner: σ_c/E is the critical strain ϵ_c at which buckling occurs. Assuming general validity of the equation

$$\epsilon_c = K \left(\frac{t}{b} \right)^2$$

in the elastic and inelastic range leads to

$$\frac{\sigma_c}{E_s} = K \left(\frac{t}{b} \right)^2 \tag{676}$$

for the inelastic case, presuming that critical stress and critical strain are implicitly related by the stress-strain diagram of the material.

[1] Kollbrunner, C. F., and G. Herrmann, Stabilität der Platten im plastischen Bereich, Theorie von A. Ilyushin mit Vergleichswerten von durchgeführten Versuchen, *Mitteilungen* 20, *Institut für Baustatik, Eidgenössische Technische Hochschule, Zurich,* 1947.

[2] Gerard, G., Secant Modulus Method for Determining Plate Instability above the Proportional Limit, *Jour. Aeronaut. Sci.,* Vol. 13, p. 38, 1946.

Gerard found good agreement between his test results and the values of σ_c computed from Eq. (676). However, the tests made on channel- and Z-sections included only flange buckling, and the objection can be made that Eq. (676) cannot have general validity, for it contradicts the theory of column buckling which is controlled by the tangent-modulus. It therefore remains questionable whether Eq. (676) applies to buckling of plates supported on both unloaded edges.

Stowell's theory discussed in Art. 87 explains the situation. His theoretical investigation reveals that in cases of plate buckling the effective modulus is in the vicinity of the secant-modulus. η assumes the value E_s/E in the case of a long hinged flange which buckles by twisting but is distinctly smaller when the flange is clamped along one side or when the plate is supported along both unloaded edges. In these cases η is a function of E_s and E_t. Table 31 shows the formulas for η for long plates under various boundary conditions and for columns. Numerical values for η have been computed from a stress-strain curve for extruded alumi-

TABLE 31

Type of plate	η	Curve in Fig. 176
Long flange, one unloaded edge simply supported	$\dfrac{E_s}{E}$	A
Long flange, one unloaded edge clamped	$\dfrac{E_s}{E}\left(0.428 + 0.572\sqrt{\dfrac{1}{4} + \dfrac{3}{4}\dfrac{E_t}{E}}\right)$	B
Long plates, both unloaded edges simply supported	$\dfrac{E_s}{E}\left(\dfrac{1}{2} + \dfrac{1}{2}\sqrt{\dfrac{1}{4} + \dfrac{3}{4}\dfrac{E_t}{E}}\right)$	C
Long plates, both unloaded edges clamped	$\dfrac{E_s}{E}\left(0.352 + 0.648\sqrt{\dfrac{1}{4} + \dfrac{3}{4}\dfrac{E_t}{E}}\right)$	D
Columns	$\dfrac{E_t}{E}$	G

num alloy and are plotted in Fig. 176. Inspection shows that except for flanges having no restraint along the supported edge (curve A) the η-curves lie very close together, curves B, C, and D. Finally curve G represents the values of $\eta = E_t/E$ for columns, which agrees with the tangent-modulus theory.

Extensive tests have been made at the Langley Memorial Aeronautical Laboratory, Langley Field, Va., in order to clarify the question of the effective modulus which has to be applied in the field of plate instability. The outcome of these tests confirms Stowell's theory of plastic buckling, in particular the prediction that long flanges which twist without appreciable bending require the secant modulus as effective modulus.[1]

It is of interest to compare the η-values given by the curves A to D in Fig. 176 with the value $\eta = \sqrt{E_t/E}$ for long plates derived from the approximate theory of plates based on the differential equation (601). From the G-curve in Fig. 176 the values $\sqrt{E_t/E}$ were easily computed, and they are plotted as a dashed curve in this figure. The inference is that this curve, which is independent of the boundary condition along the

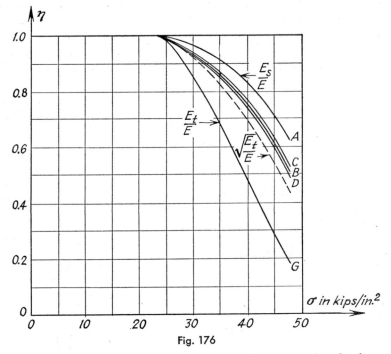

Fig. 176

unloaded edges, may be considered as a limiting curve for the factor η, furnishing conservative values of the critical stress.

96. Summary and Concluding Remarks

The theory of local instability of thin walls of columns may be considered as well established. It is based on the theory of the stability of rectangular plates, acted on by compressive forces distributed uniformly over two opposite edges. This theory is confirmed by various tests in the elastic and inelastic range. The solution of the plate problem for the two fundamental cases, given in Arts. 89 and 90, and the approximate methods developed in Art. 92 for the determination of the coefficient of

[1] Heimerl, G. J., Determination of Plate Compressive Strength, *NACA Tech. Note* 1480, 1947.

restraint ζ rendered it feasible to develop the rational design formulas collected in Table 29. These design formulas define the required thickness ratio of the thin walls of a column as a function of the slenderness ratio l/r of the column. These formulas may replace the rules of thumb of many specifications now in use in structural design.

In closing this chapter an important fact concerning the behavior of plates after reaching the limit of stability must be discussed. An ideal column will collapse when the critical column load is reached and no higher load than the critical load can be carried. However, when the critical stress at which plate buckling begins lies sufficiently below the yield point, the load on plates may be considerably increased beyond the critical load, causing only moderate increase of deflection, until the ultimate strength of the plate is reached. This state of deformation at stresses higher than the critical stresses of the plate is accompanied by a redistribution of the compressive stresses over the cross section—these stresses are no longer uniformly distributed. As far as the design of columns in bridges and buildings is concerned, it would be incorrect to take advantage of the fact that the ultimate strength of plates lies often definitely beyond the critical stress. Column formulas for primary buckling are based upon the assumption that the stresses are uniformly distributed over the cross section until the ultimate strength of the column is reached. Any change in the stress distribution reduces the carrying capacity of the column because parts of the cross section would no longer be fully effective. Consequently the plate elements must be designed in such manner that no distortion of the cross section due to local buckling can occur before the column as a whole reaches its primary buckling strength.

A somewhat different approach is used in aircraft design, particularly in the design of stiffened sheet panels, where much thinner plates are used than in conventional steel construction and where the low value of E for aluminum or magnesium alloy increases the importance of local buckling. By introducing the concept of the effective width of thin plates, only a part of the cross section is considered effective for primary strength of the structure. It is therefore permissible to stress the plate elements above the buckling stresses for local buckling, as the reduction in strength of the primary structure has been allowed for.

The difference between the approaches in conventional steel design and in aircraft design is, of course, not arbitrary. If the effective width concept of aircraft design were applied to the design of a heavy steel column, it would be found that economy lies with a section where the effective width of all plates is 100%, which means that the plates must not buckle before the critical load for the entire column is reached. For lightly loaded columns of thin metal, on the other hand, the effective width concept is appropriate. The behavior of plates above the buckling stress and the effective width concept are discussed further in Chaps. X and XII.

Additional References

Rode, H., Beiträge zur Theorie der Knickerscheinungen, *Der Eisenbau*, Vol. 7, p. 217, 1916.

Schwerin, E., Über die Knicksicherheit ebener Bleche bei exzentrischer Randbelastung, *Zeitschrift für angewandte Mathematik und Mechanik*, Vol. 3, p. 422, 1923.

Timoshenko, S., Stability and Strength of Thin-walled Constructions, *Proc. 3d Intern. Cong. Applied Mechanics*, Vol. 3, p. 1, Stockholm, 1930.

Bleich, F., Die Stabilität dünner Wände gedrückter Stäbe, *Prelim. Pubs. 1st Cong. Intern. Assoc. Bridge and Structural Eng.*, Paris, 1932, p. 130.

Schleicher, F., Stabilität leicht gekrümmter Rechteckplatten, *Intern. Assoc. Bridge and Structural Eng. Pubs.*, Vol. 1, p. 433, 1932.

Sezawa, K., Das Ausknicken von allseitig befestigten und gedrückten Rechteckplatten, *Zeitschrift für angewandte Mathematik und Mechanik*, Vol. 12, p. 227, 1932.

Sattler, K., Beitrag zur Knicktheorie dünner Platten, *Mitteilungen aus den Forschungsanstalten des Gutehoffnungshütte-Konzerns*, Vol. 3, p. 257, 1935.

Heck, O. S., and H. Ebner, Methods and Formulas for Calculating the Strength of Plate and Shell Structures as Used in Aircraft Design. Translation in *NACA Tech. Mem.* 785, 1936.

Kaufmann, W., Über unelastisches Knicken rechteckiger Platten, *Ingenieur-Archiv*, Vol. 7, p. 156, 1936.

Iguchi, S., Allgemeine Lösung der Knickaufgabe für rechteckige Platten, *Ingenieur-Archiv*, Vol. 7, p. 207, 1936.

Lundquist, E. E., Local Instability of Centrally Loaded Columns of Channel-section and Z-section, *NACA Tech. Note* 722, 1939.

Hill, H. N., Chart for Critical Compressive Stress of Flat Rectangular Plates, *NACA Tech. Note* 773, 1940.

Moisseiff, L. S., and F. Lienhard, Theory of Elastic Stability Applied to Structural Design, *Trans. ASCE*, Vol. 106, p. 1052, 1941.

Lundquist, E. E., and E. Z. Stowell, Restraint Provided a Flat Rectangular Plate by Sturdy Stiffener along the Edges of the Plate, *NACA Tech. Note* 735, 1942.

Kroll, W. D., Tables of Stiffness and Carry-over Factor for Flat Rectangular Plates under Compression, *NACA Wartime Rept.* L-398, 1943.

Kroll, W. D., G. P. Fisher, and G. J. Heimerl, Charts for Calculation of the Critical Stress for Local Instability of Columns with I-, Z-, Channel-, and Rectangular-tube Section, *NACA Wartime Rept.* L-429, 1943.

Hoff, N. J., Note on Inelastic Buckling, *Jour. Aeronaut. Sci.*, Vol. 11, p. 163, 1944.

Reissner, E., Buckling of Plates with Intermediate Rigid Supports, *Jour. Aeronaut. Sci.*, Vol. 12, p. 375, 1945.

Budiansky, B., and P. C. Hu, The Lagrangian Multiplier Method of Finding Upper and Lower Limits to Critical Stresses of Clamped Plates, *NACA Tech. Note* 1103, 1946.

Hu, P. C., E. E. Lundquist, and S. B. Batdorf, Effects of Small Deviations from Flatness on Effective Width and Buckling of Plates in Compression, *NACA Tech. Note* 1124, 1946.

Pflüger, A., Zum Beulproblem der anisotropen Rechteckplatte, *Ingenieur-Archiv*, Vol. 16, p. 111, 1947.

Houbolt, J. C., and E. Z. Stowell, Critical Stress of Plate Columns, *NACA Tech. Note* 2163, 1950.

CHAPTER X

RECTANGULAR PLATES WITH LONGITUDINAL STIFFENERS

97. Introduction

A longitudinally compressed rectangular plate of large aspect ratio $\alpha = a/b$, supported on all four edges, will buckle in several half waves with a length between $0.668 \sqrt[4]{\tau}\, b$ and $\sqrt[4]{\tau}\, b$ according to the degree of restraint along the unloaded sides a of the plate.[1] It is obvious that reinforcing the plate by transverse stiffeners will have little effect upon the buckling strength of the plate unless these are spaced very closely. The critical compressive stress of the plate will be increased to any considerable extent only if the distance between transverse stiffeners is far smaller than the width of the plate, thus forcing it to buckle in waves much shorter than those of the unstiffened plate.

A more economical construction is frequently obtained by introducing one or more longitudinal stiffeners. These stiffeners not only carry a portion of the compressive load but subdivide the plate into smaller panels, thus increasing considerably the critical stress at which the plate will buckle.

The important problem of the stability of rectangular plates supported on all four edges and reinforced with stiffeners, and especially the problem of minimum rigidity of these stiffeners required to restrict buckling in a stiffened plate to the plating between the stiffening ribs, was considered first by Timoshenko. Applying his energy method, he obtained approximate solutions for rectangular plates having longitudinal or transverse stiffening ribs under various loading conditions.[2] To Timoshenko we also owe the first numerical tables for the design of stiffened plates.

An exact solution of the problem of longitudinally or transversely stiffened plates, acted on by uniformly distributed stresses on two opposite edges, was published by Lokshin.[3] He derived the stability condi-

---

[1] See Table 26 on p. 330.

[2] Timoshenko, S., Über die Stabilität versteifter Platten, *Der Eisenbau*, 1921, p. 147.

[3] Lokshin, A. S., On the Calculation of Plates with Ribs, *Jour. Applied Math. and Mechanics*, Vol. 2, Moscow, p. 225, 1935 (in Russian).

tions for plates having any number of equidistant stiffeners. Later, Barbré[1] investigated the effect of longitudinal stiffeners in two particular cases, namely, one rib in the middle of the plate, and two ribs dividing the width of the plate into three equal panels. He gave numerical tables and charts for the design of the stiffeners. The mathematical treatment was based upon the differential equation (600) of Chap. IX. Barbré discussed simply supported plates as well as plates clamped at the unloaded edges. A general treatment of the stability problem of plates with longitudinal or transverse stiffeners was presented later in an extensive paper by the same author.[2] Lokshin as well as Barbré studied the stability of stiffened plates only in the elastic range.

Melan[3] presented in 1930 an analysis of rectangular plates supported on both long sides by elastic ribs. An extensive investigation of the same problem was published later by Rendulic.[4] This problem was also studied by Miles,[5] who extended his investigation to plates with an elastic rib on one unloaded edge while the other edge is simply supported or fully fixed. In all the above-mentioned papers it was assumed that the plate is free to rotate along the supported edges, which requires that the ribs do not resist twisting during buckling of the plate.

The effect of torsional rigidity of the supporting elastic flanges or ribs was discussed first by Chwalla,[6] who showed the considerable influence of this torsional rigidity upon the critical stress of the plate. The case of a plate simply supported but free to rotate on one long side and supported on the other long side by an elastic flange which resists lateral deflection and twisting was treated by Windenburg.[7]

All the papers mentioned so far were concerned with the critical buckling load of the plate and stiffener combination. It was already mentioned in the previous chapter that for very thin plates such combinations may be able to support ultimate loads considerably above the load for local buckling of the plate. It should be emphasized, however, that the

---

[1] Barbré, R., Beulspannungen in Rechteckplatten mit Längssteifen bei gleichmässiger Druckbeanspruchung, *Der Bauingenieur*, Vol. 17, p. 268, 1936.

[2] Barbré, R., Stabilität gleichmässig gedrückter Rechteckplatten mit Längs- oder Quersteifen, *Ingenieur-Archiv*, Vol. 8, p. 117, 1937.

[3] Melan, E., Über die Stabilität von Stäben, welche aus einem mit Randwinkeln verstärkten Blech bestehen, *Proc. 3d Intern. Congr. Applied Mechanics*, Vol. 3, p. 59, 1930.

[4] Rendulic, L., Über die Stabilität von Stäben, welche aus einem mit Randwinkeln verstärkten Bleche bestehen, *Ingenieur-Archiv*, Vol. 3, p. 447, 1932.

[5] Miles, A. J., Stability of Rectangular Plates Elastically Supported at the Edges, *Jour. Applied Mechanics*, Vol. 3, p. A-47, 1936.

[6] Chwalla, E., Das allgemeine Stabilitätsproblem der gedrückten, durch Randwinkel verstärkten Platte, *Ingenieur-Archiv*, Vol. 5, p. 54, 1934.

[7] Windenburg, D. F., The Elastic Stability of Tee Stiffeners, U.S. Experimental Model Basin, Rept. 457, 1938.

problem of finding the ultimate load is distinctly different from that of finding the buckling load, and the two must not be confused. The question of the ultimate load of stiffened sheet is of great importance in aircraft design and has been given considerable attention. While the behavior of individual unstiffened rectangular plate panels above the buckling stress has been analyzed,[1] the equivalent problem for the stiffened sheet is too complex a problem for mathematical treatment. Based on experimental evidence Lundquist[2] concluded that a good approximation can be obtained by including an effective portion of the sheet into the cross section of the stiffener.

The bulk of this chapter will be devoted to theories concerning the buckling load of the stiffened plates; the question of ultimate strength will be discussed only in Art. 103. The theory of stiffened plates presented will be used to obtain simple design rules for the required rigidity of stiffeners in order that plate and stiffener combinations will develop specified critical buckling stresses. Since the stiffeners carry the same compressive stresses as the plate, they may be considered as columns, and we shall also consider the question of the stability of the stiffeners themselves, which must be designed with due regard to the additional possibility of torsional or local failure.

The solutions of the various buckling problems considered in the following articles can be obtained through an extension of the theory of plates discussed in the previous chapter. The theory and its mathematical framework are rather involved, and the mathematical treatment becomes particularly tedious when the stiffeners are not equally spaced. In the following article the method will be demonstrated in the case of one longitudinal stiffener on the center line of the plate. Other cases will be discussed briefly in Arts. 99 and 100. Elastically supported plates will be considered in Art. 101, and Art. 102 will deal with the special problem of local instability of the stiffeners. The question of the ultimate strength of stiffened sheet will be discussed in Art. 103.

98. Simply Supported Plates Having One Stiffener on Center Line

Consider a rectangular plate of length a, width b, and thickness t, which is reinforced by a longitudinal stiffener on the center line (see Fig. 177a). The area of the cross section of the stiffener is A, and its moment of inertia I. It is assumed that the center line of the stiffener lies in the middle plane of the plate, and the moment of inertia I therefore refers to the axis of the stiffener in this plane. The torsional rigidity

---

[1] See Chap. XII.

[2] Lundquist, E. E., Comparison of Three Methods for Calculating the Compressive Strength of Flat and Slightly Curved Sheets and Stiffener Combination, *NACA Tech. Note* 455.

of the stiffener is regarded as small and will be neglected; only the flexural rigidity of the stiffener perpendicular to the plane of the plate is being considered. We select a system of coordinates x, y having its origin O in the center of the left edge of the plate. The plate is loaded by a uniformly distributed load σt acting on the edges $x = 0$ and $x = a$. The stiffener is assumed welded or riveted to the plate and having the same compressive stress σ as the plate.

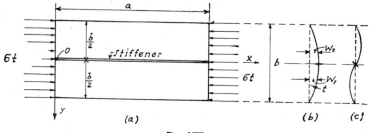

Fig. 177

We introduce the following notation:

$$\gamma = \frac{EI}{Db} = \frac{12(1 - \nu^2)I}{bt^3} \tag{677}$$

$$\delta = \frac{A}{bt} \tag{678}$$

The coefficient γ is the ratio of the flexural rigidity of the stiffener to that of the plate of width b, and δ is the ratio of the cross-sectional area of the stiffener to the area bt of the plate.

Because of the symmetry of the plate stiffener system the displacement of the buckled system will be one of the following two types: (1) a symmetric configuration with deflected stiffener (Fig. 177b), (2) an antisymmetric configuration where the stiffener remains straight (Fig. 177c). The buckled plate has in the latter case a nodal line coinciding with the axis of the stiffener, and each half of the plate behaves as plate of length a and width $b/2$, simply supported on all four edges. No bending moment is carried over from one half of the plate to the other half because the deflection surface has a line of inflection at the nodal line. The buckling load of the plate stiffener system reaches in this case its maximum value.

The antisymmetric displacement form (Fig. 177c) will occur when the rigidity ratio γ is larger than a certain value γ_0. It is important to note that the critical stress for antisymmetric buckling does not depend on γ, but it is the critical stress for a simply supported plate of width $b/2$. For values of γ below γ_0, the symmetric displacement form in which the stiffener deflects with the plate will occur. At the ratio γ_0 both configurations are equally possible. Accordingly, we can limit the investigation to the study of symmetric buckling for values $\gamma < \gamma_0$ and to the determination of the limiting value γ_0 which corresponds to the minimum value of the flexural rigidity of the stiffening rib which just guarantees antisymmetric buckling of the system. The largest possible value of the critical stress σ_c of the system for a given ratio b/t is associated with the antisymmetric configuration, and the knowledge of γ_0 permits the selection of an economical structure in which local buckling of the plate and primary buckling of the plate stiffener system occur simultaneously.[1]

No general method for handling the problem in the entire range of stresses below and above the proportional limit is available, but Timoshenko's and Barbré's theories can be extended into the inelastic range. There is no fundamental difficulty in solving the problem considered here by starting from the generalized differential equation (601) of inelastic buckling developed in the previous chapter. However, the analytical solution of the problem becomes such an involved function of the characteristic of the material, $\tau = E_t/E$, that a numerical evaluation of the analytical results becomes too laborious.

As pointed out above, the unknown of the problem considered here is the quantity γ from which the required value of the moment of inertia I of the stiffener can be computed. In order to arrive at a suitable design method for the stiffening rib, equally applicable in the elastic and inelastic range of buckling, the simpler differential equation (604) provides a basis for an approximate analysis. This equation leads to values of γ which are theoretically exact when the critical stress is below the proportional limit[2] but are only approximate if it is above the proportional limit.

We investigate on this basis the symmetric configuration of the buckled plate in order to derive the condition of instability, which will contain the ratios γ and δ as parameters. For the deflection of the buckled plate Eq. (622) in Chap. IX applies:

$$w_1 = \sin \frac{n\pi x}{a} (C_1 \cosh \kappa_1 y + C_2 \sinh \kappa_1 y + C_3 \cos \kappa_2 y$$

$$+ C_4 \sin \kappa_2 y) \quad (679)$$

where w_1 denotes the deflections of the lower half of the plate, $y \geq 0$. A similar expression for the deflection w_2 of the other half of the plate is not needed because of the symmetry. κ_1 and κ_2 are given by Eqs. (631a):

$$\kappa_1 \frac{b}{2} = \frac{n\pi}{2\alpha} \sqrt{\mu + 1} \quad \text{and} \quad \kappa_2 \frac{b}{2} = \frac{n\pi}{2\alpha} \sqrt{\mu - 1} \quad (680)$$

---

[1] A structure in which local buckling of the plate and primary buckling of the entire system occur at the same stress is not necessarily the most economical if the design is based on ultimate load instead of on buckling load.

[2] Equations (601) and (604) become identical if $\tau = 1$.

where $\alpha = a/b$. The value μ follows from Eq. (630):

$$\mu = b\frac{\alpha}{n\pi}\sqrt{\frac{\sigma_c t}{D_\tau}} \tag{681}$$

The four constants C_1 to C_4 in Eq. (679) will be determined from the following boundary conditions:

$$\text{For } y = +\frac{b}{2}: \qquad w_1 = 0 \tag{681a}$$

$$\frac{\partial^2 w_1}{\partial y^2} = 0 \tag{681b}$$

$$\text{For } y = 0: \qquad \frac{\partial w_1}{\partial y} = 0 \tag{681c}$$

$$Q_1 - Q_2 = q \tag{681d}$$

By Q_1 and Q_2 we denote the shearing forces per unit length in the plates adjacent to the stiffener (see Fig. 178). Condition (681d) expresses the fact that the difference of the shearing forces equals the load q which

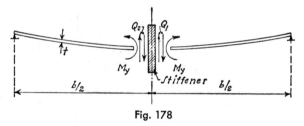

Fig. 178

must be carried by the stiffener. Taking account of the axial load $\sigma_c A$ in the stiffener, the differential equation for its deflection w is

$$EI_\tau \frac{\partial^4 w}{\partial x^4} + \sigma_c A \frac{\partial^2 w}{\partial x^2} = q \tag{682}$$

The expression for difference $Q_1 - Q_2$ is

$$Q_1 - Q_2 = q = -D_\tau \frac{\partial}{\partial y}\left[\frac{\partial^2 w_1}{\partial y^2} + (2-\nu)\frac{\partial^2 w_1}{\partial x^2} - \frac{\partial^2 w_2}{\partial y^2} - (2-\nu)\frac{\partial^2 w_2}{\partial x^2}\right]_{y=0}$$

Because of the symmetry we have the relations

$$\left[\frac{\partial^2 w_1}{\partial x^2} = \frac{\partial^2 w_2}{\partial x^2}\right]_{y=0} \qquad \text{and} \qquad \left[\frac{\partial^3 w_1}{\partial y^3} = -\frac{\partial^3 w_2}{\partial y^3}\right]_{y=0}$$

and therefore

$$q = -2D_\tau\left[\frac{\partial^3 w_1}{\partial y^3}\right]_{y=0} \tag{683}$$

The deflection w of the stiffener and the deflection w_1 of the plate and their derivatives for $y = 0$ must be alike:

$$w = [w_1]_{y=0}, \qquad \frac{\partial w}{\partial x} = \left[\frac{\partial w_1}{\partial x}\right]_{y=0}, \qquad \text{etc.},$$

and Eqs. (682) and (683) lead to the final form of the boundary condition (681d):

$$\left[2\,\frac{\partial^3 w_1}{\partial y^3} + \gamma b\,\frac{\partial^4 w_1}{\partial x^4} + \delta\,\frac{\sigma_c bt}{D\tau}\,\frac{\partial^2 w_1}{\partial x^2}\right]_{y=0} = 0 \qquad (684)$$

Introducing the solution (679) into the boundary conditions (681a) to (681c) and (684), we arrive at the following four homogeneous equations for the constants C_1 to C_4.

$$C_1 \cosh\frac{\kappa_1 b}{2} + C_2 \sinh\frac{\kappa_1 b}{2} + C_3 \cos\frac{\kappa_2 b}{2} + C_4 \sin\frac{\kappa_2 b}{2} = 0$$

$$\kappa_1{}^2\left(C_1 \cosh\frac{\kappa_1 b}{2} + C_2 \sinh\frac{\kappa_1 b}{2}\right) - \kappa_2{}^2\left(C_3 \cos\frac{\kappa_2 b}{2} + C_4 \sin\frac{\kappa_2 b}{2}\right) = 0$$

$$\kappa_1 C_2 + \kappa_2 C_4 = 0$$

$$2(\kappa_1{}^3 C_2 - \kappa_2{}^3 C_4) + \left(\frac{\gamma}{b^3}\,\frac{n^4\pi^4}{\alpha^4} - \delta\,\frac{\sigma_c t}{Db\tau}\,\frac{n^2\pi^2}{\alpha^2}\right)(C_1 + C_3) = 0$$

The determinant of this system of equations furnishes the stability condition for the symmetric mode of buckling:

$$\left(\frac{1}{\kappa_1}\tanh\frac{\kappa_1 b}{2} - \frac{1}{\kappa_2}\tan\frac{\kappa_2 b}{2}\right)\left(\frac{\gamma}{b^3}\,\frac{n^4\pi^4}{\alpha^4} - \delta\,\frac{\sigma_c t}{Db\tau}\,\frac{n^2\pi^2}{\alpha^2}\right) - 2(\kappa_1{}^2 + \kappa_2{}^2) = 0 \qquad (685)$$

This equation will now be utilized for the determination of the limiting ratio γ_0. As stated above, γ_0 defines the flexural rigidity of the rib at which the symmetric and the antisymmetric configurations of the buckled plate are equally possible. In the antisymmetric configuration each panel of the plate behaves like a simply supported plate of width $b/2$, and the critical stress found in Chap. IX for this case will apply. Equation (685) having been derived from the differential equation (604) based on the isotropic concept, we must use the value of σ_c for the simply supported plate derived on the same basis, $i.e.$, Eq. (634a). To allow for the difference in symbols used, we must replace b, α, and n in Eq. (634a) by $b/2$, 2α, and n_1, respectively, and obtain

$$\sigma_c = \frac{\pi^2 E\tau}{12(1 - \nu^2)}\left(\frac{2\alpha}{n_1} + \frac{n_1}{2\alpha}\right)^2\left(\frac{2t}{b}\right)^2 = \frac{4\pi^2 D\tau}{b^2 t}\left(\frac{2\alpha}{n_1} + \frac{n_1}{2\alpha}\right)^2 \qquad (686)$$

n_1 is the number of half waves for antisymmetric buckling, which is likely to be different from the number n of half waves for symmetric buckling, which occurs in Eq. (685).

Solving the stability condition (685) for γ and introducing the expression (686) for σ_c, we arrive at the limiting value γ_0:

$$\gamma_0 = \frac{8}{\pi^2} \frac{\left(\frac{2\alpha}{n_1} + \frac{n_1}{2\alpha}\right)\left(\frac{\alpha}{n}\right)^3}{\frac{1}{\kappa_1 b}\tanh\frac{\kappa_1 b}{2} - \frac{1}{\kappa_2 b}\tan\frac{\kappa_2 b}{2}} + 4\left(\frac{\alpha}{n}\right)^2\left(\frac{2\alpha}{n_1} + \frac{n_1}{2\alpha}\right)^2 \delta \quad (687)$$

Substituting the value of σ_c from Eq. (686) into Eq. (681) gives

$$\mu = \frac{2\alpha}{n}\left(\frac{2\alpha}{n_1} + \frac{n_1}{2\alpha}\right) \quad (688)$$

and Eqs. (680) furnish the following expressions for the coefficients κ_1 and κ_2:

$$\left.\begin{aligned}
\kappa_1 &= \frac{n\pi}{b\alpha}\sqrt{\frac{2\alpha}{n}\left(\frac{2\alpha}{n_1} + \frac{n_1}{2\alpha}\right) + 1} \\
\kappa_2 &= \frac{n\pi}{b\alpha}\sqrt{\frac{2\alpha}{n}\left(\frac{2\alpha}{n_1} + \frac{n_1}{2\alpha}\right) - 1}
\end{aligned}\right\} \quad (689)$$

γ_0 is a function of the ratio $\alpha = a/b$ and of the ratio δ. In Fig. 179, γ_0 is plotted versus α for various values of δ.[1] Each diagram is composed of a sequence of curves which correspond to the number of half waves $n = 1, 2, 3, \ldots$. Again, these curves are not smooth lines but consist of curved sections pertaining to the number of half waves $n_1 = 1, 2, 3, \ldots$. The vertices of the individual branches of any one curve have nearly the same ordinate γ_0. These ordinates very rapidly approach the limiting value which corresponds to $\alpha = \infty$. This limiting value is somewhat smaller than the value $\gamma_{0\,\text{max}}$ of the first branch.

Equation (687) can be greatly simplified and made independent of n_1 by the following reasoning. For integral values, $2\alpha = 1, 2, 3, \ldots$, the number n_1 of half waves is 2α, and the term $(2\alpha/n_1 + n_1/2\alpha)$ assumes the value 2. For values of $\alpha > 1$ this term is close to the value 2, even for nonintegral values of 2α, and we can introduce $(2\alpha/n_1 + n_1/2\alpha) = 2$ into Eq. (687). We obtain in this manner for $\alpha \geq 1$

$$\gamma_0 = \frac{(16/\pi^2)(\alpha/n)^3}{\frac{1}{\kappa_1 b}\tanh\frac{\kappa_1 b}{2} + \frac{1}{\kappa_2 b}\tan\frac{\kappa_2 b}{2}} + 16\left(\frac{\alpha}{n}\right)^2\delta \quad (690)$$

in which the coefficients κ are defined by

$$\kappa_{1,2} = \frac{n\pi}{b\alpha}\sqrt{\frac{4\alpha}{n} \pm 1} \quad (691)$$

[1] The diagram is taken from Barbré's paper of 1936.

γ_0 now is represented by smooth curves, indicated for $\delta = 0$ by the dashed line in the diagram (Fig. 179). It is apparent that the error of basing the computation on the simplified Eq. (690) is negligible.

In order to obtain a simple design formula it is convenient to replace the transcendental expression (690) by algebraic expressions. This can be done, as indicated in Fig. 180 for the case $\delta = 0.10$, by replacing the

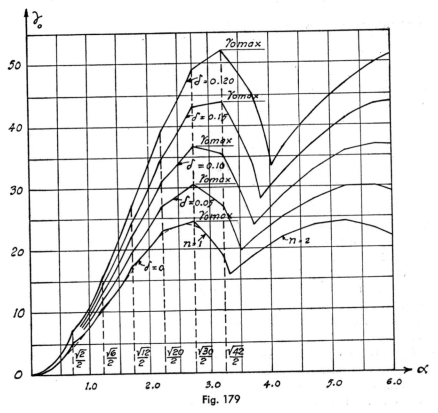

Fig. 179

γ_0-diagram by a curve A for small values of α and by a horizontal line on the level of $\gamma_{0\ max}$ for large values of α. The following approximate rule was derived by the author:

Compute γ_0 from the formula

$$\gamma_0 = 11.4\alpha + (1.25 + 16\delta)\alpha^2 - 5.4\sqrt{\alpha} \qquad (692)$$

If γ_0 becomes greater than $\gamma_{0\ max}$ given by

$$\gamma_{0\ max} = 24.4 + 112\delta(1 + \delta) \qquad (692a)$$

it must be replaced by $\gamma_{0\ max}$. The above formulas are valid for $0 \le \delta \le 0.20$.

The required moment of inertia I_0 of the stiffener follows from Eq. (677):

$$I_0 = \frac{bt^3}{12(1 - \nu^2)} \gamma_0 = 0.092bt^3\gamma_0 \qquad (693)$$

Equations (687) and (690) are independent of the modulus of elasticity and of the ratio τ. These equations and the design formulas (692) and (693) are therefore valid for all kinds of metal and in the elastic and inelastic range.

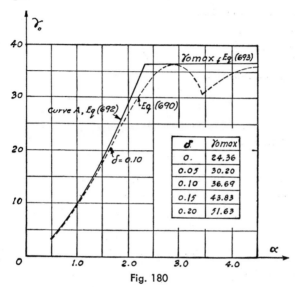

Fig. 180

δ	γ_{0max}
0.	24.36
0.05	30.20
0.10	36.69
0.15	43.83
0.20	51.63

If the moment of inertia I of the stiffener is larger than the value I_0 given by Eq. (693), each panel of the plate will buckle as a simply supported plate at a critical stress which is independent of the value of I. The value of this critical stress can be found from Eq. (635a) and can be written

$$\frac{\sigma_c}{\sqrt{\tau}} = 14.46E \left(\frac{t}{b}\right)^2 \qquad (694)$$

Any increase of I above the value I_0 does not increase the buckling strength of the stiffened plate,[1] the critical stress remaining at the value given by Eq. (694).

To find σ_c in the inelastic range compute $\sigma_c/\sqrt{\tau}$ from Eq. (694) and read the corresponding value of σ_c from Tables 27 and 28 on pages 343 and 344.

Equation (685) can also be utilized to determine the required moment

[1] An increase of I above I_0 will, however, increase the ultimate strength of the stiffened plate (see Art. 103).

of inertia I of the stiffener in order that the stiffened plate will buckle at a given critical stress σ_c smaller than that given by Eq. (694). The value of I required for this purpose is naturally smaller than I_0. In such a case the stiffened plate will buckle in a symmetric configuration and the stability condition (685) applies. We substitute into this equation

$$\frac{\sigma_c t}{D\tau} = \frac{n^2\pi^2}{b^2\alpha^2}\mu^2 \quad \text{and} \quad 2(\kappa_1{}^2 + \kappa_2{}^2) = 4\frac{n^2\pi^2}{b^2\alpha^2}\mu$$

derived from Eqs. (680) and (681), and obtain

$$\left(\frac{1}{b\kappa_1}\tanh\frac{b\kappa_1}{2} - \frac{1}{b\kappa_2}\tan\frac{b\kappa_2}{2}\right)(\gamma - \delta\mu^2) - \frac{4\alpha^2}{n^2\pi^2}\mu = 0$$

Introducing the notation

$$\Phi = \frac{(4\alpha^2/n^2\pi^2)\mu}{\dfrac{1}{b\kappa_1}\tanh\dfrac{b\kappa_1}{2} - \dfrac{1}{b\kappa_2}\tan\dfrac{b\kappa_2}{2}} \tag{695}$$

the required value of γ is

$$\gamma = \Phi + \delta\mu^2 \tag{696}$$

The critical stress σ_c for which we intend to design the stiffened panel will correspond to a certain plate factor k which can be found from[1]

$$\sigma_c = \frac{\pi^2 E\tau}{12(1 - \nu^2)}\left(\frac{t}{b}\right)^2 k \tag{697}$$

This plate factor and the factor μ are related, $k = (n/\alpha)^2\mu^2$, and Eq. (696) becomes finally

$$\gamma = \Phi + \left(\frac{\alpha}{n}\right)^2 k\delta \tag{698}$$

According to Eqs. (680) κ_1 and κ_2 are functions of μ, and Eq. (695) defines a relationship between the variables α, Φ, and k. Figure 181 contains diagrams giving the values of k as function of α for various values of Φ. The curves have branches for $n = 1, 2, \ldots$, the controlling ones being indicated by solid lines. The diagrams are suitable to determine the value of Φ if α and k are given.

In the above derivation we have used the isotropic concept, and Eq. (697) is therefore conservative, as was outlined at the end of Art. 89. In order to be consistent with the plate theories used in other parts of this book it is suggested to use, instead of Eq. (697), the relation

$$\sigma_c = \frac{\pi^2 E\sqrt{\tau}}{12(1 - \nu^2)}\left(\frac{t}{b}\right)^2 k \tag{699}$$

[1] The factor τ, and not $\sqrt{\tau}$, occurs in this equation because we use the isotropic concept based on Eq. (604).

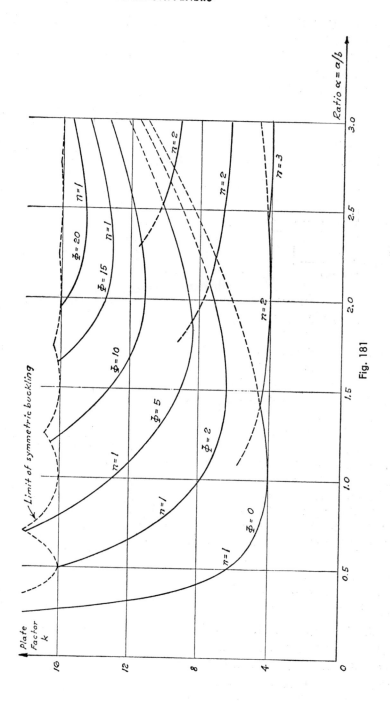

Fig. 181

and assume that the values of Φ remain as given by Fig. 181. This procedure is slightly on the unsafe side.

The method of finding the required value of I is therefore as follows: Use the given value of σ_c to determine k from Eq. (699),[1] find Φ from Fig. 181, compute γ from Eq. (698) and, finally, I from

$$I = \frac{bt^3}{12(1 - \nu^2)} \gamma = 0.092bt^3\gamma \tag{700}$$

At the outset we have assumed that the centroidal axis of the stiffener coincides with the middle plane of the plate. However, in actual struc-

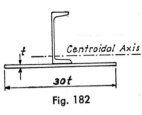

Fig. 182

tures the stiffeners are frequently welded or riveted to one side of the plate only. This results in a considerable increase in the flexural rigidity of the stiffener, since the adjacent zones of the plate take part in the bending of the deflected stiffener. In computing the moment of inertia I it is recommended to include in the effective section of the stiffener a strip of plate having the width $30t$ and compute the moment of inertia I about an axis through the centroid of the resulting section (see Fig. 182).

Chwalla[2] investigated analytically the effective width of the plate in the case of a flat bar stiffener welded to a plate subjected to shearing stresses. He found that a consid-erable portion of the plate rein-forces the stiffener. Compared with Chwalla's findings for this particu-lar case the rule given above is conservative.

The case of rectangular plates clamped at both unloaded edges and having one center stiffener was also investigated by Barbré. He found that, in spite of the increased value of the critical stress, clamped edges reduce considerably the value of γ_0

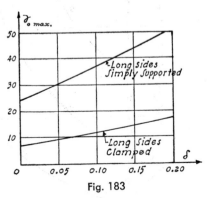

Fig. 183

necessary to secure a nodal line of the buckled plate along the stiffener. Figure 183 shows for comparison the values $\gamma_{0\,max}$ of plates having simply supported edges and those for plates with two fixed edges.

99. Simply Supported Plates Having Two Equidistant Stiffeners

The case of two stiffeners subdividing the plate into three equal panels (Fig. 184) can be treated in the same manner as demonstrated in the

[1] Table 3 on p. 55 may be used to find the value of τ.

[2] Chwalla, E., Theorie der einseitig angeordneten Stegblechsteife, *Der Bauingenieur*, Vol. 10, 1937.

previous article. The limiting values γ_0 of the stiffness ratio γ at which buckling in three half waves occurs were determined by Barbré, and the result is shown in Fig. 185, where γ_0 is plotted versus the aspect ratio α for $\delta = 0, 0.05, 0.10, 0.15, 0.20.$

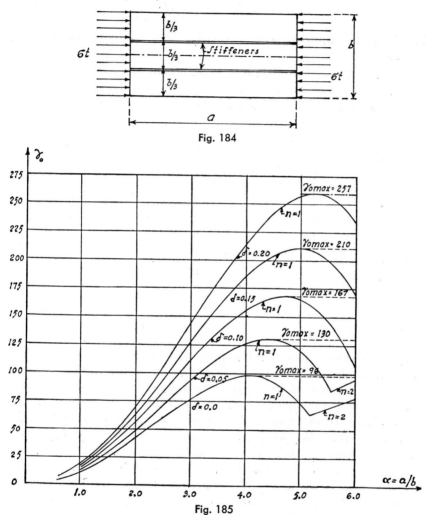

Fig. 184

Fig. 185

The transcendental curves can be approximated by algebraic functions in order to arrive at simple design formulas for γ_0. The following formulas for plates with two stiffeners are suggested:

$$\gamma_0 = 14.5 \sqrt{\alpha^3} + 36\alpha^2\delta \qquad (701)$$

where γ_0 shall not exceed the limiting value

$$\gamma_{0 \; max} = 96 + 610\delta + 975\delta^2 \qquad (701a)$$

valid for $0 < \delta < 0.20$.   The minimum value of I is given by Eq. (693), and the critical stress of the stiffened plate is

$$\sigma_c = 32.5E \ \sqrt{\tau} \left(\frac{t}{b}\right)^2 \tag{702}$$

100. Simply Supported Plates Having One Stiffener Eccentrically Located

The mathematical procedure in investigating the effect of an eccentrically located longitudinal stiffener is similar to that demonstrated in Art. 98 but becomes more involved.[1]   Owing to the effect of the stiffener,

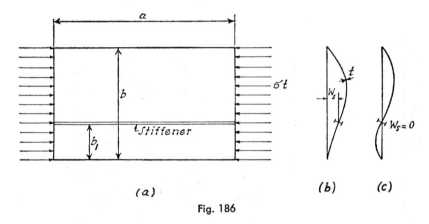

Fig. 186

the plate buckles as shown in Fig. 186b.   The deflection w_s of the axis of the stiffener decreases with increasing rigidity of the rib and becomes zero as the moment of inertia of the rib approaches infinity, in which case the axis of the stiffener forms a nodal line in the buckled surface of the plate.   In this respect the behavior of the eccentrically stiffened plate differs from the previously discussed cases where straight nodal lines occur when a certain finite limiting value of the moment of inertia I of the rib is reached.   From the practical angle such a limiting value of I also exists in the case of an eccentrically located rib, but this value of I is not sharply defined.   The critical stress σ_c increases at first rapidly with increasing I, until a point is reached where increase of I does not result in any substantial increase of the critical stress σ_c.

If b_1/b is a proper fraction l/r, where r is an integer, the stability condition assumes the form

[1] The theory was developed by Barbré, Stabilität gleichmässig gedrückter Rechteckplatten mit Längs- oder Quersteifen, *Ingenieur-Archiv*, Vol. 8, p. 117, 1937.

$$\left(\frac{\alpha}{n\pi}\right)^4 \left(\frac{b}{b_1}\right)^3 (\bar{\kappa}_1{}^2 + \bar{\kappa}_2{}^2)$$

$$- \Phi \left[\frac{\sinh \bar{\kappa}_1 \sinh (r-1)\bar{\kappa}_1}{\bar{\kappa}_1 \sinh r\bar{\kappa}_1} - \frac{\sin \bar{\kappa}_2 \sin (r-1)\bar{\kappa}_2}{\bar{\kappa}_2 \sin r\bar{\kappa}_2}\right] = 0 \quad (703)$$

$\bar{\kappa}_1$, $\bar{\kappa}_2$, and Φ are nondimensional quantities given by the following equations as functions of the unknown μ:

$$\bar{\kappa}_{1,2} = \frac{n\pi}{\alpha}\frac{b_1}{b}\sqrt{\mu \pm 1} \quad (704)$$

$$\Phi = \gamma - \mu^2 \delta \quad (705)$$

α is the aspect ratio a/b, and γ and δ are defined by Eqs. (677) and (678). For given values of γ and δ Eq. (703) can be solved for μ, and the critical stress σ_c of the reinforced plate is

$$\frac{\sigma_c}{\sqrt{\tau}} = \frac{\pi^2 E}{12(1-\nu^2)}\left(\frac{t}{b}\right)^2 k \quad (706)$$

where $k = (n/\alpha)^2\mu^2$. To find σ_c in the inelastic range compute $\sigma_c/\sqrt{\tau}$ from Eq. (706) and read the corresponding value of σ_c from Tables 27 and 28 on pages 343 and 344.

Equation (703) was derived by Barbré under the assumption of elastic behavior of plate and stiffener. But reasoning in the same manner as in Art. 98, it may be considered valid in the elastic and inelastic range. Since this equation is independent of E, it applies for any metal provided that stiffener and plate are of the same material.

Figure 187 represents k-curves for the case $b_1/b = \frac{1}{3}$, plotted versus the ratio α for the values $\Phi = 5, 10, 20,$ and ∞. This diagram corresponds to Fig. 181 for the plate with one stiffener at the center. Φ, defined by Eq. (705), indicates the rigidity of the stiffener. The fully drawn curve for $\Phi = \infty$ consists of branches corresponding to the number of half waves $n = 1, 2, \ldots$ into which the plate buckles and gives the value of k if the plate is rigidly supported by the stiffener. The curves for $\Phi = 10$ and 20 each have two minima as indicated in Fig. 187 for the branches, $n = 1$. In the case $\Phi = 10$ both minima define decisive parts of the diagram, but with increasing Φ only the left minimum remains decisive, as can be seen on the curve for $\Phi = 20$. Focusing attention to the minimum values in the region of $\alpha = 0.6$ it will be seen that, for values of $\Phi = 10$ and over, the k-values approach with increasing Φ the lowest point on the curve $\Phi = \infty$. Between $\Phi = 20$ and $\Phi = \infty$ k increases only from 10.42 to 10.58. We may, therefore, consider $\Phi = 20$ as the upper limit of the stiffness parameter Φ and assume that this value determines stiffener dimensions which guarantee a straight nodal line

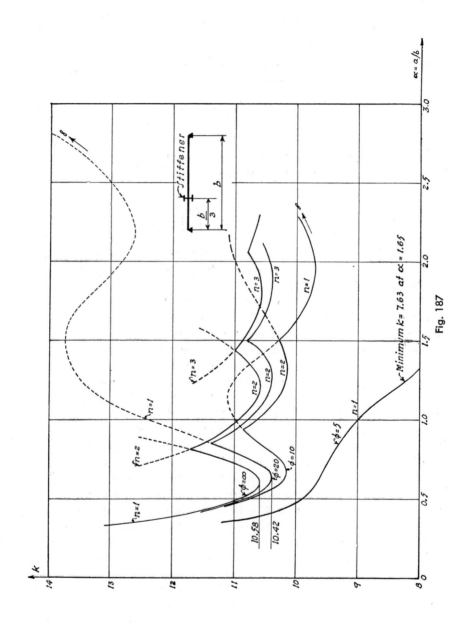

Fig. 187

along the stiffener axis. By this reasoning we arrive at a criterion for the stiffness parameter Φ required to obtain the full buckling strength of the plate.

Substituting $\mu^2 = k(\alpha/n)^2$ in Eq. (705) we obtain with reference to Eqs. (677) and (678)

$$12(1 - \nu^2)\frac{I}{bt^3} - k\left(\frac{\alpha}{n}\right)^2\frac{A}{bt} = \Phi$$

Upon introducing $\Phi = 20$, $k = 10.42$, $\alpha = 0.64$, and $n = 1$, the criterion which determines the moment of inertia I of the stiffener reads

$$10.92\frac{I}{bt^3} - 4.27\frac{A}{bt} = 20$$

from which

$$I = 1.85bt^3 + 0.4At^2 \tag{707}$$

is derived. This equation is applicable for values $\alpha \leq 1$. b and t are the given dimensions of the plate. Using an assumed value of A/bt the moment of inertia I can be quickly computed and if necessary corrected by a second step.

The value of k which corresponds to the assumed value $\Phi = 20$ is $k = 10.42$. Therefore, the critical stress of the stiffened plate is given by

$$\frac{\sigma_c}{\sqrt{\tau}} = \frac{10.42\pi^2 E}{12(1 - \nu^2)}\left(\frac{t}{b}\right)^2 = 9.4E\left(\frac{t}{b}\right)^2 \tag{708}$$

To find σ_c in the inelastic range compute $\sigma_c/\sqrt{\tau}$ from Eq. (708) and read the corresponding value of σ_c from Tables 27 and 28 on pages 343 and 344.

101. Rectangular Plates Elastically Supported at the Unloaded Edges

In order to obtain insight into the behavior of plates which are supported on one or both sides by elastic ribs, the problem of the rectangular plate shown in Fig. 188 is discussed. The plate of width b and thickness t represented in this figure carries uniformly distributed load on two opposite edges. One unloaded edge is simply supported; the other edge rests upon an elastic rib having the moment of inertia I and the cross-sectional area A. It is assumed that the resistance of the rib against twisting is zero and that the rib is under the same compressive stress as the plate.

Starting from Eq. (679) the following condition of stability was derived by Miles:[1]

$$\sqrt{\mu - 1}(\mu + 1 - \nu)^2 \cot \kappa_2 - \sqrt{\mu + 1}(\mu - 1 + \nu)^2 \coth \kappa_1$$
$$+ 2\frac{n\pi}{\alpha}\mu\Phi = 0 \tag{709}$$

---

[1] Miles, *loc. cit.* p. 359.

where

$$\kappa_1 = \frac{n\pi}{\alpha}\sqrt{\mu+1} \quad \text{and} \quad \kappa_2 = \frac{n\pi}{\alpha}\sqrt{\mu-1} \tag{710}$$

$$\Phi = \frac{EI}{bD} - \frac{A}{bt}\mu^2 \tag{711}$$

The plate factor is $k = (n/\alpha)^2\mu^2$. Determining for given values of α and Φ the smallest root μ of Eq. (709), the critical stress σ_c of the plate is

$$\frac{\sigma_c}{\sqrt{\tau}} = \frac{\pi^2 E}{12(1-\nu^2)}\left(\frac{t}{b}\right)^2 k \tag{712}$$

To find σ_c in the inelastic range compute $\sigma_c/\sqrt{\tau}$ from Eq. (712) and read the corresponding value of σ_c from Tables 27 and 28 on pages 343 and 344.

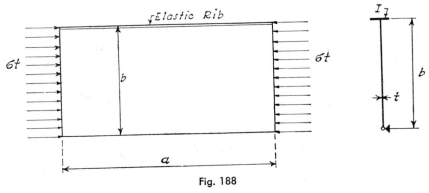

Fig. 188

Figure 189 contains the k-diagrams for several values of Φ, but for the sake of clarity only the diagram $\Phi = 20$ is completely shown, involving curves for $n = 1, 2, 3, \ldots$. The first branches $n = 1$ of all the diagrams for finite values of Φ show a minimum in the neighborhood of $\alpha = 1$, followed by a maximum, after which the ordinates decrease continuously. For very large values α the coefficient k approaches the value $k = 0.425$, which is the coefficient k of a plate simply supported on three sides and free on the fourth side. From the complete diagram $\Phi = 20$ it is seen that for small values of α the plate buckles in one, two, or more half waves until its length reaches the value $a = b\alpha_i$ (see Fig. 189). At this length the plate suddenly changes its displacement form; rib and plate buckle in one half wave. For not too small values of Φ, say $\Phi = 20$, the point of change may be replaced, without any appreciable error, by the point of intersection of the k-curve with the horizontal line $k = 4$. Thus for each value of Φ, which expresses the rigidity of the elastic rib, a limiting length $a = b\alpha_i$ is defined. Below this length the plate develops its maximum buckling strength; above this length the value of k and

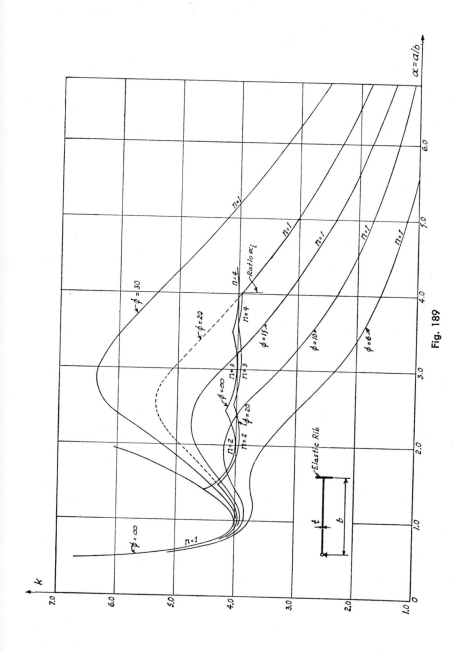

Fig. 189

therefore σ_c decrease rapidly with increasing length. The abscissa α_i of the point of intersection can be approximately computed from

$$1.29(\alpha_i - 0.41)^2 + 5.15 = \Phi \qquad (713)$$

where Φ is a function of I and A.

In designing the plate and rib two criteria must be observed. (1) To secure maximum strength of the plate, which requires that it act as a plate simply supported on the unloaded edges, it is necessary that $\Phi \geq 20$.[1] I and A must therefore satisfy the condition

$$\frac{12(1 - \nu^2)}{bt^3} I - \frac{A}{bt} \mu^2 \geq 20$$

derived from Eq. (711).

Introducing $\mu^2 = k(\alpha/n)^2$ and assuming $\alpha/n = 1$ and $k = 4$, we obtain

$$\frac{I}{bt^3} \geq 1.85 + 2.73 \frac{A}{bt} \qquad (714)$$

(2) The second criterion requires that Φ be chosen so that the given length of the plate is equal to or smaller than $\alpha_i b$, where α_i is determined by Eq. (713). For $\alpha = \alpha_i$ the coefficient k has the value 4, and because of $n = 1$, $\mu^2 = k(\alpha/n)^2 = 4\alpha^2$, we have

$$\Phi = \frac{10.92I}{bt^3} - \frac{4A}{bt} \alpha^2$$

Replacing Φ in Eq. (713) by this expression and using $\alpha_i = \alpha$ furnishes

$$\frac{I}{bt^3} = 1.18(\alpha - 0.41)^2 + 0.47 + 0.43 \frac{A}{bt} \alpha^2 \qquad (715)$$

This equation gives a second value for the moment of inertia of the rib. The larger of the two values of I found from Eqs. (714) and (715) must be used.

The stability condition becomes more involved than Eq. (709) when the torsional rigidity of the rib is taken into account. This case has been discussed by Windenburg.[2] The mathematical investigation shows that the torsional rigidity does not affect the essential features of the behavior of the plate. A certain aspect ratio α_i exists, now depending on the flexural and torsional rigidity of the elastic rib, below which the plate buckles in half waves shorter than the width b and above which plate and stiffener deflect in one half wave.

[1] The value $\Phi = 20$ has been chosen somewhat arbitrarily. The corresponding value of k deviates only 1% from the value $k = 4$ for $\Phi = \infty$ and may be replaced without any appreciable error by $k = 4$.

[2] Windenburg, loc. cit. on p. 359.

In Fig. 190 the k-curve is shown for $\Phi = 20$ and $C/Db = 2$, where C is the torsional rigidity of the rib.[1] Comparison with the corresponding k-curve for $\Phi = 20$ in Fig. 189 reveals the similarity of the curves. The rigid connection between plate and rib produces a shortening of the half waves in which the plate buckles, increases the critical stress σ_c, but decreases the aspect ratio α_i above which the structure buckles in a single half wave. The problem is of importance for the discussion of the

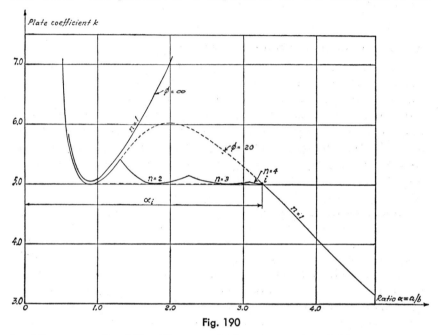

Fig. 190

buckling strength of T-stiffeners, which will be studied in the following section.

In closing it may be pointed out that the two cases of elastically supported plates discussed above are typical for a group of problems for which one condition of stability covers simultaneously primary and local buckling. The ratio α_i defines a certain length $a = b\alpha_i$ above which an unstable state of equilibrium occurs without distortion of the cross section, thus indicating primary buckling of the plate rib system. The implication is that, for a length smaller than $a = b\alpha_i$, the plate can be considered as rigidly supported and, possibly, elastically restrained by the rib, while the entire plate rib system behaves as a column (primary buckling) when the length $a = b\alpha_i$ is exceeded.

In the case where the plate is restrained by the rib, the system may be considered as a T-section hinged along the toe of the web. The primary

[1] This diagram was derived from Windenburg's paper.

stability of this type of column has been discussed in Art. 43 of Chap. III. The results derived from the plate theory and those determined by the theory of Chap. III are not quite identical because of differences in the basic assumptions. For practical purposes it is preferable to investigate the primary stability of T-sections according to the theory of Chap. III because of the simplicity of the computation as compared with the complicated numerical procedure of solving plate problems. The theory in Chap. III gives more conservative results than the more accurate plate theory.

102. Local Instability of Flat-bar and T-stiffeners

In the previous articles we have studied the effect of stiffeners upon the buckling strength of plates with the purpose of determining the moment of inertia of the stiffener required to develop the desired buckling strength of the plate. However, adequate moment of inertia is not sufficient to assure the stability of the stiffener itself. Primary failure of the stiffener by torsional buckling is possible and must be avoided. This problem was studied in Chap. III. In addition, the possibility of local failure due to instability of the plate elements of the stiffener must be considered, which will be done in this article.

Flat-bar Stiffeners. A flat-bar stiffener is a plate of great aspect ratio α_s supported on three edges and free on the fourth edge. If we consider the stiffened plate in its distorted form in the state of buckling (Fig. 191) and assume the most unfavorable condition—that the stiffener becomes unstable under the same compressive stress which causes buckling of the plate—it is clear that the plate has no restraining effect upon the stiffener. The plate buckles in bulges alternately up and down, the half wavelength being approximately equal to $b\sqrt[4]{\tau}$. The stiffener therefore behaves like a plate of aspect ratio $\alpha_s = b\sqrt[4]{\tau}/b_s$, simply supported along one edge, where b_s is the depth of the stiffener. The critical stress of the stiffener is according to Table 26, case 4,

$$\frac{\sigma_c}{\sqrt{\tau}} = 0.425 \frac{\pi^2 E}{12(1 - \nu^2)} \left(\frac{t_s}{b_s}\right)^2 \tag{716}$$

To find σ_c in the inelastic range compute $\sigma_c/\sqrt{\tau}$ from Eq. (716) and read the corresponding value of σ_c from Tables 27 and 28 on pages 343 and 344.

T-stiffeners. T-stiffeners present a more complex problem. Similar considerations as before make it advisable to assume that the toe of the web of the stiffener is attached to the plate in such a manner that no bending moments act between web and plate. This assumption makes it possible to solve the problem of local instability of the T-stiffener loaded by uniform compressive forces.

The web of the T-stiffener is a plate supported elastically on one unloaded edge by the flange and hinged along the other edge to the plate (Fig. 192). Web and flange are assumed rigidly connected. The stability of such a plate combination was discussed in the previous article, and it was found that, if the stiffener is designed to be safe against torsional buckling (primary buckling), the web may be regarded as a plate hinged on one unloaded edge and elastically restrained by the flange on the opposite edge.

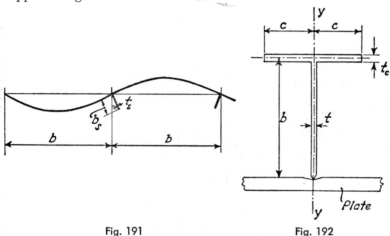

Fig. 191   Fig. 192

We determine the plate factor k from the analysis in Chap. IX. Because the web is restrained to a different degree at the toe and at the root, we make use of the approximate method suggested for such a case on page 325. According to this method the plate factor k is the average, $k = (k_1 + k_2)/2$, of the plate factors k_1 and k_2 if the plate were simply supported or elastically restrained at both edges, respectively. We know $k_1 = 4$. To compute k_2 we need the coefficient of restraint, which is according to Eq. (663)

$$\zeta = \frac{t^3}{t_c^3} \frac{\rho_2(c/b)}{1 - 9.4t^2c^2/t_c^2b^2} \tag{717}$$

The value of $\rho_2(c/b)$ can be taken from the diagram in Fig. 171. With the value of ζ computed from Eq. (717) the diagrams in Fig. 161 furnish values of p and q, from which $k_2 = p + 2\sqrt{q}$ can be computed. Since $k_1 = 4$ we finally have

$$k = 2 + \frac{k_2}{2} \tag{718}$$

The critical stress σ_c of the web plate is given by

$$\sigma_c = \frac{\pi^2 E \sqrt{\tau}}{12(1 - \nu^2)} \left(\frac{t}{b}\right)^2 k \tag{719}$$

The procedure outlined above was used to determine the values of the plate factor k shown in Table 32. k is given as function of the ratios c/b and t_c/t (Fig. 192).

TABLE 32. Plate Factors k for the Web of T-stiffeners, Eq. (719)

t_c/t	Ratio c/b							
	0.15	0.20	0.25	0.30	0.35	0.40	0.45	0.50
1.00	4.52	4.49	4.42	4.22				
1.05	4.58	4.55	4.50	4.34				
1.10	4.63	4.62	4.58	4.45	4.10			
1.15	4.68	4.68	4.66	4.54	4.29			
1.20	4.74	4.74	4.73	4.63	4.44			
1.25	4.79	4.80	4.79	4.72	4.55	4.12		
1.30	4.82	4.84	4.84	4.79	4.66	4.36		
1.35	4.86	4.88	4.88	4.85	4.75	4.51		
1.40	4.90	4.92	4.93	4.90	4.82	4.65	4.14	
1.45	4.94	4.96	4.97	4.95	4.88	4.75	4.41	
1.50	4.97	4.99	5.01	4.99	4.94	4.85	4.59	
1.60	5.03	5.05	5.06	5.05	5.03	4.97	4.84	4.46
1.70	5.06	5.10	5.11	5.11	5.09	5.05	4.99	4.81
1.80	5.11	5.14	5.15	5.15	5.14	5.11	5.06	4.99
1.90	5.15	5.17	5.19	5.19	5.18	5.17	5.14	5.06
2.00	5.17	5.19	5.21	5.21	5.21	5.21	5.18	5.14

The restraining effect of the web on the flange, in general, is small and can be disregarded. The flange can be considered as a plate simply supported by the web along one edge and free on the other one. The critical stress obtained from Table 26 is

$$\frac{\sigma_c}{\sqrt{\tau}} = 0.425 \frac{\pi^2 E}{12(1 - \nu^2)} \left(\frac{t_c}{c}\right)^2 \tag{720}$$

To find σ_c in the inelastic range compute $\sigma_c/\sqrt{\tau}$ from Eq. (719) or (720) and read the corresponding value of σ_c from Tables 27 and 28 on pages 343 and 344.

103. Ultimate Strength of Stiffened Sheet Panels

The investigations in Arts. 98 to 101 were aimed at determining the moment of inertia of the stiffeners required to obtain a given buckling load equal to the design load. We considered both primary buckling of the plate stiffener system and local buckling of the plate between stiffeners. The primary buckling load was in all cases lower than or, at the most, equal to the local buckling load, and the buckling load was therefore equal to the ultimate load which the stiffened plates could carry.

In aircraft construction stiffened sheet is frequently used in such a manner that local buckling of the sheet occurs at loads considerably below primary buckling of the entire system.   As was pointed out at the end of Chap. IX, such local buckling need not mean collapse of the structure but results in redistribution of the stresses.   The structure is capable of sustaining a larger ultimate load, which will be the primary buckling load of the stiffened sheet.   Obviously, this primary buckling load will be affected somehow by the fact that the sheet buckled locally at a lower load.

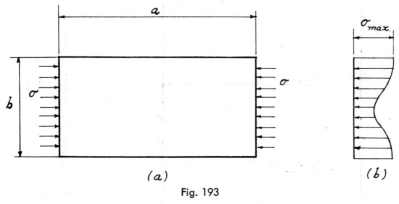

(a)   (b)

Fig. 193

To obtain an insight into the action of stiffened, thin sheet we start by considering an individual rectangular panel simply supported on all edges (Fig. 193a).   For small loads the stresses will be equally distributed until the critical load of the panel is reached.   If the load is increased above the critical, the panel will buckle.   If the load is applied in such a manner that the loaded edge remains straight in the plane of the plate, the center portions of the plate will have less compressive strain than the portions near the edges because of the larger deflections in the center of the plate.   The stress distribution will therefore be as shown in Fig. 193b.   Continuing the loading, the plate will reach its carrying capacity when σ_{max} near the edge reaches the yield point.   For the individual panel the ultimate load P_u can be expressed in terms of an effective width b_e, $P_u = t b_e \sigma_y$.   Theoretical and experimental investigations to determine b_e are reported in Chap. XII.

The behavior of a stiffened panel is somewhat similar, but the question of the stability of the stiffeners enters.   If the stiffeners are sufficiently rigid the plate will buckle between stiffeners, and the stress distribution will be as shown in Fig. 194.   The stresses in the stiffeners and adjacent parts of the sheet will be higher than in the portion between stiffeners.

The maximum stress at failure will, however, not reach the yield point; the stiffened panel will fail when the stress in the stiffeners reaches the critical value σ_c for primary buckling of the stiffeners.

Based on tests by Schuman and Back[1] it was observed by Gall[2] that the strength of stiffened sheet may be approximately computed as the sum of the strength of the stiffeners and of the individual sheet panels. Lundquist[3] showed subsequently that more accurate values are obtained by including the effective area of the sheet in the section of the stiffener

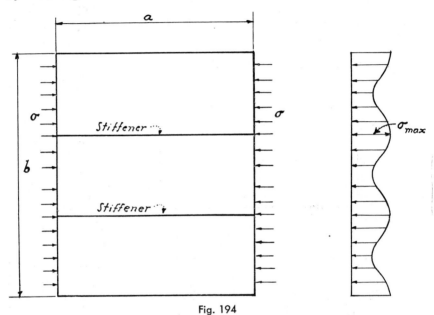

Fig. 194

and obtaining the critical load of the resulting column section. This method fits the behavior of the stiffened plate described in the previous paragraph.

The theoretical derivations of the effective width presented in Chap. XII do not apply when the stresses are above the elastic limit or when they are many times larger than σ_c. Based on experiments the effective width can be expressed in the form

$$b_e = Ct\sqrt{\frac{E}{\sigma}} \tag{721}$$

where σ is the stress in the stiffener and C is a coefficient which is a func-

[1] Schuman and Back, *loc. cit.* on p. 478.

[2] Gall, H. W., Compressive Strength of Stiffened Sheet Panels, Thesis, 1930, reported by J. S. Newell, The Strength of Aluminum Alloy Sheets, *Airway Age*, 1930.

[3] Lundquist, *loc. cit.* on p. 360.

tion of the ratio $(t/b)\sqrt{E/\sigma}$. Values of the coefficient C have been determined from tests, and different curves for C were obtained depending whether σ was close to or distinctly below the yield point.[1] These tests indicate that C in Eq. (721) is considerably larger than in the otherwise similar Eq. (921) for the ultimate strength of simply supported plates,

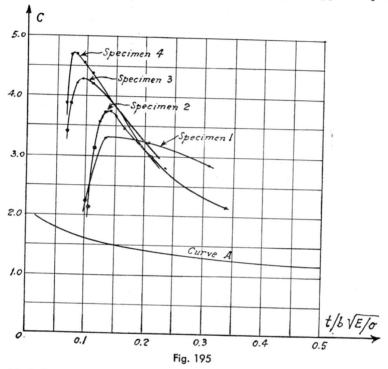

Fig. 195

provided the stress σ does not exceed the proportional limit. Figure 195 indicates values of C in Eq. (721) found from tests on four specimens and also a curve, marked A, for the values of C in Eq. (921) determined from tests on the ultimate strength of simply supported plates. The values of C are far above curve A, except for small values of $(t/b)\sqrt{E/\sigma}$ where the stress σ in the specimens exceeded the proportional limit.

[1] Sechler, E. E., Stress Distribution in Stiffened Panels under Compression, *Jour. Aeronaut. Sci.*, 1937, p. 320.

CHAPTER XI

STABILITY OF WEB PLATES OF GIRDERS

104. Introduction

Owing to the fact that one of the principal stresses in web plates of girders in bending is a compressive stress, the possibility of the occurrence of an unstable state of equilibrium in the web plates must be considered. Therefore, the conventional design of webs with regard to the allowable shearing stresses should be supplemented by an investigation of the stability of the webs.

The basic problem may be illustrated by Fig. 196. A rectangular plate of length a, width b, and thickness t, supported at the four edges, is subjected to uniformly distributed shearing forces $\tau_{xy}t$ along all edges

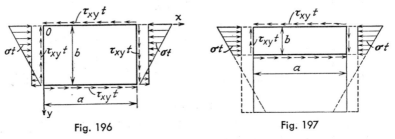

Fig. 196   Fig. 197

and in addition is loaded on the edges $x = 0$ and $x = a$ by longitudinal forces $\sigma_x t$, linearly distributed along these edges. The stress distribution shown in Fig. 196 represents the most general case which would occur in a web panel of a girder between two rigid stiffeners when an axial thrust acts beside the longitudinal bending moment, as is the case in web plates of arch ribs. A similar loading condition occurs when the web is reinforced by a longitudinal stiffener, in addition to the vertical stiffeners, as shown in Fig. 197, and the stability of the web plate between top chord and longitudinal stiffeners is to be investigated.

The above-described loading condition represents, of course, an idealized case, since the shear stresses are actually parabolically distributed along the edges $x = 0$ and $x = a$ and vary also along the edges $y = 0$ and $y = b$. The assumption that the stresses σ_x are constant between $x = 0$

and $x = a$ is a further simplification, since these stresses vary along the girder with the bending moment. However, to permit a solution of the buckling problem without undue complication of the analysis, the simplification of the loading condition is the first step necessary in dealing with the stability of web plates in girders. The error of basing the investigation on a simplified loading condition will be small if average values of σ_x and τ_{xy} are used.

The web plates of deep girders are in general too thin to develop a sufficiently high buckling strength for an economical design of the web without resorting to stiffeners. Therefore, longitudinal or transverse stiffeners or a combination of both play an important role in the design of web plates. The necessity of using stiffened plates is responsible for the rather involved theoretical and experimental research into the problem of stiffened plates under combined shearing and bending stresses.

The first group of stability problems to be discussed in this chapter will concern the determination of the critical stress of unstiffened web plates under various loading conditions and various conditions of support at the edges. In the second part of the chapter we shall be concerned with the effect of longitudinal and transverse stiffeners on the buckling strength of plates under shearing and bending stresses.

Pioneers in the field of unstiffened web plates were Boobnoff and Timoshenko. Boobnoff[1] investigated the simply supported rectangular plate under combined bending and compressive stresses acting in the plane of the plate on two opposite edges. Timoshenko[2] was the first to present a practical solution of the stability problem of rectangular plates in shear by applying the energy method, which proved an excellent tool in solving a problem that could not be solved directly as a characteristic value problem. He applied the energy method also to the determination of the critical stress of simply supported rectangular plates under bending and compressive stresses and extended the investigation to the case of combined shearing and pure bending stresses.[3]

An account will be given first of the further development of the theory of plates in shear. An exact solution for the infinitely long plate acted on at its long sides by shearing stresses was presented by Southwell and Skan,[4] who treated simply supported and clamped plates. A thorough

[1] Boobnoff, J., "Theory of Structure of Ships," Vol. 2, p. 515, St. Petersburg, 1914 (in Russian).

[2] Timoshenko, S., Stability of Rectangular Plates with Stiffeners, *Mem. Inst. Engs. Ways of Commun.*, Vol. 89, p. 23, 1915 (in Russian); Über die Stabilität versteifter Platten, *Der Eisenbau*, Vol. 12, p. 147, 1921.

[3] Timoshenko, S., Stability of the Webs of Plate Girders, *Engineering*, Vol. 238, p. 207, 1935.

[4] Skan, S. W., and R. V. Southwell, On the Stability under Shearing Forces of a Flat Elastic Strip, *Proc. Roy. Soc. (London)*, Series A, Vol. 105, p. 582, 1924.

investigation concerning the accuracy of Timoshenko's results for simply supported plates was made by Bergmann and Reissner[1] and by Seydel,[2] who gave improved values of the plate factor k. Stein and Neff[3] determined the critical shear stresses more accurately than previous authors by considering symmetric and antisymmetric buckling configurations. Buckling stresses of clamped rectangular plates in shear were obtained by Moheit[4] and by Budiansky and Connor.[5] The last two authors obtained rather accurate values of the critical stress. The case of infinitely long clamped plates divided into square panels by rigid intermediate supports was recently investigated by Budiansky, Connor, and Stein.[6] Stowell[7] examined infinitely long plates in shear having equal elastic restraints against rotation along the parallel edges.

Buckling under nonuniformly distributed compressive stresses acting on two opposite sides of the plate was considered by Nölke,[8] who treated clamped plates.

Plates under combined bending and shearing stresses were studied by Stein,[9] who gave tables showing the interaction between the critical longitudinal stresses σ_c and the critical shear stresses τ_c. Stein's paper was published at about the same time as Timoshenko's paper on the same subject. Papers by Batdorf and Stein[10] and by Stowell and Schwartz[11] are devoted to the problem of plates under combined shear and uniform longitudinal stress.

[1] Bergmann, S., and H. Reissner, Über die Knickung von rechteckigen Platten bei Schubbeanspruchung, *Zeitschrift für Flugtechnik und Motorluftschiffahrt*, Vol. 23, p. 6, 1932.

[2] Seydel, E., Über das Ausbeulen von rechteckigen isotropen oder orthogonal-anisotropen Platten bei Schubbeanspruchung, *Ingenieur-Archiv*, Vol. 4, p. 169, 1933.

[3] Stein, M., and J. Neff, Buckling Stress of Simply Supported Rectangular Flat Plates in Shear, *NACA Tech. Note* 1222, 1947.

[4] Moheit, W., Schubbeulung rechteckiger Platten mit eingespannten Rändern, Thesis, Technische Hochschule Darmstadt, Leipzig, 1939.

[5] Budiansky, B., and R. W. Connor, Buckling Stresses of Clamped Rectangular Flat Plates in Shear, *NACA Tech. Note* 1559, 1948.

[6] Budiansky, B., R. W. Connor, and M. Stein, Buckling in Shear of Continuous Flat Plates, *NACA Tech. Note* 1565, 1948.

[7] Stowell, E. Z., Critical Shear Stresses for an Infinitely Long Plate with Equal Elastic Restraints against Rotation along the Parallel Edges, *NACA Wartime Rept.* L-476.

[8] Nölke, K., Biegungsbeulung der Rechteckplatte mit eingespannten Längsrändern, *Der Bauingenieur*, Vol. 17, p. 111, 1936, and *Ingenieur-Archiv*, Vol. 8, p. 403, 1937.

[9] Stein, O., Die Stabilität der Blechträgerstehbleche im zweiachsigen Spannungszustand, *Der Stahlbau*, Vol. 7, p. 57, 1934.

[10] Batdorf, S. B., and M. Stein, Critical Combinations of Shear and Direct Stress for Simply Supported Rectangular Flat Plates, *NACA Tech. Note* 1223, 1947.

[11] Stowell, E. Z., and E. B. Schwartz, Critical Stresses for an Infinitely Long Plate with Elastically Restrained Edges under Combined Shear and Direct Stress, *NACA Wartime Rept.* L-340.

The problem of stiffened web plates was studied by Timoshenko[1] in his papers of 1915 and 1921. Various problems concerning the performance of web plates with stiffeners have been studied by Schmieden,[2] Seydel,[3] Chwalla,[4] and Denke.[5] Exact solutions for infinitely long, simply supported plates with transverse stiffeners have been presented recently by Stein and Fralich.[6]

In addition to these theoretical investigations concerning the stability of web plates of girders which have been carried out over more than two decades, experimental work has been done in recent years. The laboratory investigations were made to verify the theoretical results and to observe the actual behavior of web plates in real structures in which the loading conditions and the conditions of support along the edges may deviate substantially from the idealized conditions upon which the mathematical analysis is based. Some of these tests were made with the special purpose of disclosing the performance of plates after buckling and to determine the ultimate strength of web plates under conditions which prevail in actual structures.

The behavior of web plates of girders subjected to bending moments has been investigated experimentally by Gabor[7] and by Bergman and Wästlund.[8] Plates under the action of shearing forces and under combined bending and shearing forces have been studied experimentally by Moheit,[9] Godfrey and Lyse,[10] Moore,[11] and Bergman and Wästlund.

[1] Timoshenko, S., Stability of Rectangular Plates with Stiffeners, *Mem. Inst. Engrs. Ways of Commun.*, Vol. 89, p. 23, 1915 (in Russian); Uber die Stabilitat versteifter Platten, *Der Eisenbau*, Vol. 12, p. 147, 1921.

[2] Schmieden, C., Das Ausknicken versteifter Bleche unter Schubbeanspruchung, *Zeitschrift für Flugtechnik und Motorluftschiffahrt*, Vol. 21, p. 61, 1930.

[3] Seydel, E., Beitrag zur Frage des Ausbeulens versteifter Platten unter Schubbeanspruchung, *Jahrbuch Deutscher Verein für Luftfahrt-Forschung*, 1930, p. 235. Translation in *NACA Tech Mem.* 602, 1931.

[4] Chwalla, E., Beitrag zur Stabilitätstheorie des Stegbleches vollwandiger Träger, *Der Stahlbau*, Vol. 9, p. 161, 1936; Die Bemessung der waagerecht ausgesteiften Stegbleche vollwandiger Träger, *Prelim. Rept.* 2d Cong. *Intern. Assoc. Bridge and Structural Eng.*, Berlin, 1936, p. 957.

[5] Denke, P. H., Analysis and Design of Stiffened Shear Webs, *Jour. Aeronaut. Sci.* Vol. 17, p. 217, 1950.

[6] Stein, M., and R. W. Fralich, Critical Shear Stress of Infinitely Long, Simply Supported Plate with Transverse Stiffeners, *NACA Tech. Note* 1851, 1949.

[7] Gabor, E., Beulversuche an Modellträgern aus Stahl, *Die Bautechnik*, Vol. 22, p. 6, 1944.

[8] Wästlund, G., and S. G. A. Bergman, Buckling of Webs in Deep Steel I-Girders, *Pubs. Intern. Assoc. Bridge and Structural Eng.*, Vol. 8, p. 291, 1947.

[9] Moheit, *op. cit.* on p. 388.

[10] Godfrey, H. J., and I. Lyse, Investigation of Web Buckling in Steel Beams, *Trans. ASCE*, Vol. 100, p. 675, 1935.

[11] Moore, R. L., Observations on the Behavior of Aluminum Alloy Test Girders, *Trans. ASCE*, Vol. 112, p. 901, 1947.

All the theoretical papers quoted consider stability in the elastic range only. For practical applications, particularly in the design of structural steel and of ships, the extension of the theory to inelastic buckling is essential. In the following articles the author has attempted to present the results of all these theories for elastic buckling in such a manner that they are applicable to inelastic buckling also.

105. Buckling of Rectangular Plates in Shear

Simply Supported Plates. A rectangular plate of length a, width b, and thickness t, simply supported along all four edges, is subjected to uniformly distributed shear forces $\tau_{xy}t$ along the edges (Fig. 198). Since an exact solution of the buckling problem for a plate of finite length a based on the fundamental differential equation (599) is not known, an approximate solution using the theorem of stationary potential energy will be derived. For the time being only elastic buckling is considered.

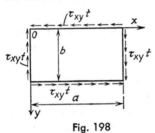

Fig. 198

We start from the principle of stationary potential energy[1]

$$V + U_w = \text{stationary} \qquad (722)$$

in which V is the strain energy of bending of the plate and U_w the change of the potential energy of the external forces when the plate passes from its plane form to the deflected shape.

The following notation will be used:

x and y = coordinates with respect to the origin O in the middle plane of the plate, Fig. 198

w = the deflection of the plate in the state of buckling

$D = \dfrac{Et^3}{12(1 - \nu^2)}$ = the flexural rigidity of the plate. Since elastic buckling of the plate is assumed, E is Young's modulus

The strain energy V is given by the double integral[2]

$$V = \frac{D}{2} \int_0^a \int_0^b \left\{ \left(\frac{\partial^2 w}{\partial x^2} + \frac{\partial^2 w}{\partial y^2} \right)^2 - 2(1 - \nu) \left[\frac{\partial^2 w}{\partial x^2} \frac{\partial^2 w}{\partial y^2} - \left(\frac{\partial^2 w}{\partial x\,\partial y} \right)^2 \right] \right\} dx\,dy \qquad (723)$$

[1] Equation (82), Chap. II.
[2] Timoshenko, S., "Theory of Elastic Stability," p. 307, McGraw-Hill Book Company, Inc., New York, 1936.

When the edges are simply supported or clamped, the term

$$\frac{\partial^2 w}{\partial x^2}\frac{\partial^2 w}{\partial y^2} - \left(\frac{\partial^2 w}{\partial x\, \partial y}\right)^2$$

in Eq. (723) does not contribute to the variation δV of the strain energy V and therefore does not influence[1] the extremum condition (722). In computing V this term can be omitted, and expression (723) becomes

$$V = \frac{D}{2}\int_0^a \int_0^b \left(\frac{\partial^2 w}{\partial x^2} + \frac{\partial^2 w}{\partial y^2}\right)^2 dx\, dy \tag{724}$$

The change U_w of the potential energy equals the negative value of the work done by the uniformly distributed shear stresses $\tau_{xy}t$ and is expressed by

$$U_w = -\tau_{xy}t \int_0^a \int_0^b \frac{\partial w}{\partial x}\frac{\partial w}{\partial y} dx\, dy \tag{725}$$

Using the Ritz method we express the displacement w in terms of appropriately chosen coordinate functions which satisfy the given boundary conditions:

$$w = \sum_{i=1}^n \sum_{j=1}^n f_{ij} \sin\frac{i\pi x}{a}\sin\frac{j\pi y}{b} \tag{726}$$

and substitute this expansion into Eqs. (724) and (725).

We compute

$$\frac{\partial^2 w}{\partial x^2} = -\frac{\pi^2}{a^2}\sum_{i=1}^n \sum_{j=1}^n f_{ij}i^2 \sin\frac{i\pi x}{a}\sin\frac{j\pi y}{b}$$

$$\frac{\partial^2 w}{\partial y^2} = -\frac{\pi^2}{b^2}\sum_{i=1}^n \sum_{j=1}^n f_{ij}j^2 \sin\frac{i\pi x}{a}\sin\frac{j\pi y}{b}$$

Substituting these two expressions into Eq. (724) we find that the integrals of the cross products vanish because of the orthogonality relations between the coordinate functions of the expansion (726). We obtain

$$V = \frac{\pi^4}{8}Dab \sum_{i=1}^n \sum_{j=1}^n f_{ij}^2 \left(\frac{i^2}{a^2} + \frac{j^2}{b^2}\right)^2 \tag{727}$$

[1] See the discussion of Eq. (168) in Chap. II.

In order to find U_w we determine

$$\frac{\partial w}{\partial x} = \frac{\pi}{a} \sum_{i=1}^{n} \sum_{j=1}^{n} f_{ij} i \cos \frac{i\pi x}{a} \sin \frac{j\pi y}{b}$$

$$\frac{\partial w}{\partial y} = \frac{\pi}{b} \sum_{i=1}^{n} \sum_{j=1}^{n} f_{ij} j \sin \frac{i\pi x}{a} \cos \frac{j\pi y}{b}$$

and

$$\frac{\partial w}{\partial x}\frac{\partial w}{\partial y} = \frac{\pi^2}{ab} \sum_{\substack{i=1 \\ i'=1}}^{n} \sum_{\substack{j=1 \\ j'=1}}^{n} f_{ij} f_{i'j'} i j' \cos \frac{i\pi x}{a} \sin \frac{i'\pi x}{a} \sin \frac{j\pi y}{b} \cos \frac{j'\pi y}{b}$$

where i, i', j, and j' assume all the values 1, 2, . . . , n. Taking into account that

If $m + k$ is an even number: $\displaystyle\int_0^l \sin \frac{m\pi z}{l} \cos \frac{k\pi z}{l}\, dz = 0$

and

If $m + k$ is an odd number: $\displaystyle\int_0^l \sin \frac{m\pi z}{l} \cos \frac{k\pi z}{l}\, dz = \frac{2l}{\pi}\frac{m}{m^2 - k^2}$

the following expression for U_w is obtained:

$$U_w = -4\tau_{xy} l \sum_{\substack{i=1 \\ i'=1}}^{n} \sum_{\substack{j=1 \\ j'=1}}^{n} f_{ij} f_{i'j'} \frac{i j i' j'}{(i^2 - i'^2)(j'^2 - j^2)} \tag{728}$$

In this equation i, i', j, and j' do not assume all values from 1 to n, but only those values for which both $i + i'$ and $j + j'$ are odd numbers.

In this presentation we limit the number of terms of the expansion (726) to four, by assuming $n = 2$. i, j, i', and j' can therefore have the values 1 or 2 only. Equation (728) will have four terms because only the following combinations of values i, j, i', and j' satisfy the condition that $i + i'$ and $j + j'$ are odd:

i	j	i'	j'
1	1	2	2
1	2	2	1
2	1	1	2
2	2	1	1

With the notation $\alpha = a/b$ the expression for the entire potential energy $V + U_w$ becomes

$$V + U_w = \frac{\pi^4}{8} \frac{D}{\alpha^3 b^2} \left[f_{11}{}^2(1 + \alpha^2)^2 + f_{12}{}^2(1 + 4\alpha^2)^2 + f_{21}{}^2(4 + \alpha^2)^2 \right.$$

$$\left. + f_{22}{}^2(4 + 4\alpha^2)^2 \right] + 8\tau_{xy}t \left(\frac{4}{9} f_{11}f_{22} - \frac{4}{9} f_{12}f_{21} \right) \quad (729)$$

Applying Eq. (722) we find stationary values of Eq. (729) by differentiation with respect to the variables f_{11}, f_{12}, f_{21} and f_{22} and obtain the following set of four linear equations:

$$\left. \begin{array}{l} B(1 + \alpha^2)^2 f_{11} \qquad\qquad\qquad\qquad + \tfrac{4}{9}\tau_{xy}f_{22} = 0 \\ \qquad B(1+4\alpha^2)^2 f_{12} \quad -\tfrac{4}{9}\tau_{xy}f_{21} \qquad\qquad = 0 \\ \qquad -\tfrac{4}{9}\tau_{xy}f_{12}+B(4+\alpha^2)^2 f_{21} \qquad\qquad = 0 \\ \tfrac{4}{9}\tau_{xy}f_{11} \qquad\qquad\qquad\qquad + B(4 + 4\alpha^2)^2 f_{22} = 0 \end{array} \right\} \quad (730)$$

where

$$B = \frac{\pi^4}{32} \frac{D}{\alpha^3 b^2 t} \quad (731)$$

The four linear and homogeneous equations (730) have solutions $f_{11} = f_{12} = \cdots \, 0$ unless the determinant Δ of their coefficients vanishes. $\Delta = 0$ is therefore the stability condition. Expansion of this determinant Δ leads to an equation of the fourth degree in the unknown τ_{xy}, which has four roots:

$$\left. \begin{array}{l} \tau_{1,2} = \pm\tfrac{9}{4}B(1 + \alpha^2)(4 + 4\alpha^2) \\ \tau_{3,4} = \pm\tfrac{9}{4}B(1 + 4\alpha^2)(4 + \alpha^2) \end{array} \right\} \quad (732)$$

The occurrence of plate instability does not depend on the sense of the shear stress, and the smallest absolute value of τ_{xy}, given by $\tau_{1,2}$, indicates the critical stress τ_c. Using Eq. (731) the critical value τ_c of the shear stress τ_{xy} becomes

$$\tau_c = \frac{9}{32} \frac{\pi^4 E}{12(1 - \nu^2)} \left(\frac{t}{b} \right)^2 \frac{(1 + \alpha^2)^2}{\alpha^3}$$

This equation has the typical form of the expression for the critical stress of rectangular plates, i.e.,

$$\tau_c = \frac{\pi^2 E}{12(1 - \nu^2)} \left(\frac{t}{b} \right)^2 k \quad (733)$$

where k is the plate factor

$$k = \frac{9\pi^2}{32} \frac{(1 + \alpha^2)^2}{\alpha^3} \quad (734)$$

k depends on the aspect ratio α.

The value of k given by Eq. (734) differs for $\alpha = 1$ by about 15% from the correct value, and this difference is even larger for $\alpha > 1$. A far greater number of terms of the expansion (726) than used above is necessary to obtain satisfactory approximations. Using a larger value of n

Timoshenko derived for various aspect ratios α values of k which are close to the correct values, at least for ratios $\alpha < 2.5$.

The exact value, $k = 5.34$, for $\alpha = \infty$ was determined by Skan and Southwell.[1] Careful computations were made by Bergmann and Reissner[2] and later by Seydel[3] using large numbers of coordinate functions in order to approach the exact values of k as far as possible.   Seydel deter-

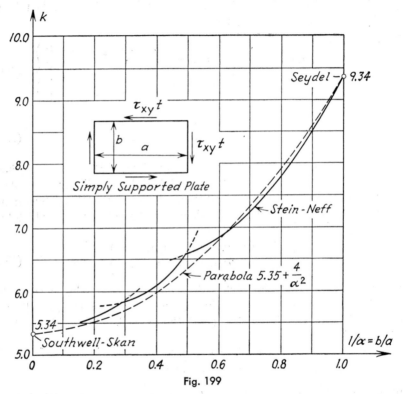

Fig. 199

mined the value $k = 9.34$ for $\alpha = 1$ very exactly.   The best values of k available for other ratios are contained in a recent paper by Stein and Neff[4] and were derived from a tenth-order determinant, considering both symmetric and antisymmetric buckling configurations.   The data given by Stein and Neff are shown in Fig. 199, where the k-values are plotted versus $1/\alpha$.   The shape of this curve suggests its replacement by a parabola connecting $k = 5.34$ for $1/\alpha = 0$ (Southwell and Skan) with $k = 9.34$ for $1/\alpha = 1$ (Seydel).   This parabola is indicated in Fig. 199,

[1] Skan and Southwell, *loc. cit.* on p. 387.
[2] Bergmann and Reissner, *loc. cit.* on p. 388.
[3] Seydel, *loc. cit.* on p. 388.
[4] Stein and Neff, *loc. cit.* on p. 388.

and it is seen that it approximates the theoretical curves quite well.   A simple formula for design purposes,

$$k = 5.34 + \frac{4}{\alpha^2} \qquad \text{(valid for } \alpha > 1\text{)} \qquad (735)$$

is thus obtained.   It is not necessary to derive a formula for k if $\alpha < 1$ because in analyzing a plate panel a may always be selected as the larger dimension, as illustrated by Fig. 200.

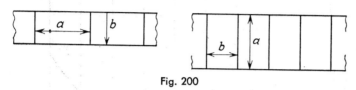

Fig. 200

Plates Clamped at All Four Edges.   This problem has also been considered by Southwell and Skan,[1] who gave the exact solution for the infinitely long plate $k = 8.98$.   By means of the Ritz method Cox[2] investigated plates of several aspect ratios.   Iguchi[3] used a series method to obtain approximate solutions for rectangular plates.   The results obtained by these authors differ substantially for some ratios of α from the more accurate values determined by Budiansky and Connor.[4]   These authors applied the Lagrangian multiplier method[5] to compute upper and lower limits for the buckling stress and thus succeeded in determining the plate factors k with satisfactory accuracy.   The maximum error amounts to 1.25%.   The k-values computed by Budiansky and Connor are presented in Fig. 201 as a function of $1/\alpha$.   Similar to the case of simply supported edges the plate factor k can be approximated by the parabola

$$k = 8.98 + \frac{5.60}{\alpha^2} \qquad (736)$$

which follows the theoretical curve rather well.

Plates Clamped at the Long Edges Only.   Plates clamped at the two longer edges but free to rotate at the two other edges have been studied

[1] Skan and Southwell, *loc. cit.* on p. 387.

[2] Cox, H. L., Summary of the Present State of Knowledge Regarding Sheet Metal Construction, *R.&M.* No. 1553, 1933.

[3] Iguchi, S., Die Knickung der rechteckigen Platte durch Schubkräfte, *Ingenieur-Archiv*, Vol. 9, p. 1, 1938.

[4] Budiansky and Connor, *loc. cit.* on p. 388.   Budiansky, B., Pai C. Hu, and R. W. Connor, Notes on the Lagrangian Multiplier Method in Elastic Stability Analysis, *NACA Tech. Note* 1558, 1947.

[5] See Chap. II, Art. 26.

by Leggett[1] and Iguchi.[2]   Leggett gave the solution for the square plate; Iguchi investigated plates within the entire range $1 \leq \alpha \leq \infty$.   Table 33 shows the values of k as given by Iguchi.   The degree of approximation

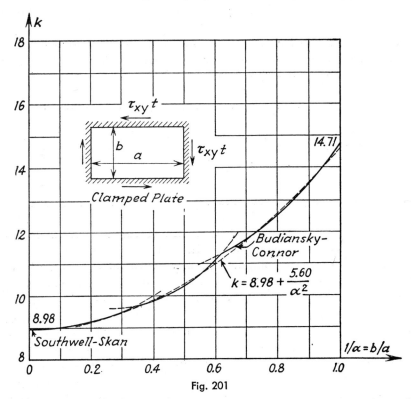

Fig. 201

of the k-values in this table is not known, except for $\alpha = \infty$, where the value given is close to Southwell and Skan's exact value, $k = 8.98$.

TABLE 33.   Plate Factors k for Plates in Shear, Clamped along the Two Long Edges

α........	1.0	1.5	2.0	2.5	3.0	∞
k........	12.28	11.12	10.21	9.81	9.61	8.99

Critical Shearing Stresses in the Inelastic Range.   The previously discussed solutions of the buckling problem of web plates in shear have been derived under the assumption that the plates behave perfectly elastic.   It is now necessary to adapt the plate formulas obtained to

---

[1] Leggett, D. M. A., The Buckling of a Square Panel under Shear When One Pair of Opposite Edges Is Clamped, *R.&M.* No. 1991, 1941.

[2] Iguchi, *loc. cit.* on p. 395.

allow for the effect of plasticity on the critical stress τ_c when this stress lies above the proportional limit in shear.

The basic differential equation (601) for inelastic buckling of plates in longitudinal compression was derived in Chap. IX from the hypothesis that the plate apparently behaves nonisotropically when buckling occurs above the proportional limit. It was assumed that in the direction of the acting compressive stresses σ_x a reduced modulus of elasticity will be effective, whereas at right angles to it Young's modulus remains valid.

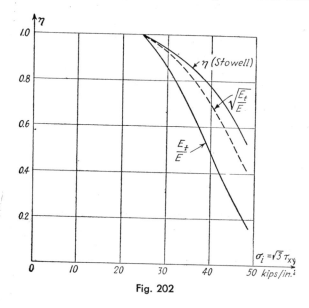

Fig. 202

Quite different conditions exist, however, in a plate in pure shear. The principal stresses corresponding to a state of pure shear, $\sigma_1 = -\sigma_2 = \tau_{xy}$, are alike, and it appears that isotropic behavior of the plate in the elastic range of buckling is a reasonable assumption. The implication is that the formulas derived above are valid in the elastic and inelastic range provided that in the inelastic range Young's modulus is replaced by an appropriate reduced modulus E_r. With $\eta = E_r/E$ the plate formula (733) assumes the generalized form

$$\tau_c = \frac{\pi^2 E \eta}{12(1 - \nu^2)} \left(\frac{t}{b}\right)^2 k \tag{737}$$

where $\eta = 1$ when the critical stress τ_c is below the proportional limit, and $\eta < 1$ when τ_c is above this limit. k is the plate factor derived above for elastic buckling and given by Eqs. (735) and (736) or Table 33, depending on the conditions of support

In a recent paper Stowell[1] applied his unified theory of plastic buckling to determine for plates in shear the plasticity factor η as function of the tangent-modulus E_t and of the secant-modulus E_s. Figure 202 is taken from Stowell's paper and presents η plotted versus the intensity of stress $\sigma_i = \sqrt{3}\tau_{xy}$.[2] The diagram was computed for an infinitely long plate of 24 ST aluminum alloy in uniform shear. It was found that η is nearly independent of the degree of restraint at the long edges of the plate and the values apply for both simply supported and clamped edges. Figure 202 also shows the curves E_t/E and $\sqrt{E_t/E}$. Comparison of the η-curve with $\sqrt{E_t/E}$-curve discloses that $\sqrt{\tau} = \sqrt{E_t/E}$ may be considered a fair approximation for η, giving values of the critical shear stress τ_c which are on the side of safety. By using $\eta = \sqrt{\tau}$, the advantage is obtained that the same plasticity factor $\sqrt{\tau}$ applies both for plates in shear and for plates in uniform longitudinal compression.[3]

Substituting the relationships $\sigma_i = \sqrt{3}\tau_c$ and $\eta = \sqrt{\tau}$, Eq. (737) can be written[4]

$$\frac{\sigma_i}{\sqrt{\tau}} = \frac{\pi^2 \sqrt{3}E}{12(1 - \nu^2)} \left(\frac{t}{b}\right)^2 k \tag{738}$$

To find the critical shear stress τ_c compute $\sigma_i/\sqrt{\tau}$ from Eq. (738), whereupon the corresponding value σ_i can be read from a table showing the stress σ as a function of $\sigma/\sqrt{\tau}$. Such tables were already used in Art. 93 in connection with the buckling of compressed plates (see Tables 27 and 28). From this critical value σ_i the critical shear stress is finally computed:

$$\tau_c = \sigma_i/\sqrt{3} \tag{739}$$

[1] Stowell, E. Z., Critical Shear Stresses of an Infinitely Long Plate in the Plastic Region, *NACA Tech. Note* 1681, 1948. See also the discussion of Stowell's theory in Art. 87 of Chap. IX.

[2] According to the plasticity hypothesis of Huber, Mises, and Hencky, the intensity of stress for plane stress distribution is given by

$$\sigma_i = \sqrt{\sigma_x^2 + \sigma_y^2 - \sigma_x\sigma_y + 3\tau_{xy}^2}$$

which becomes $\sigma_i = \sqrt{3}\,\tau_{xy}$ when $\sigma_x = \sigma_y = 0$. For readers not familiar with plasticity theories it might be added that σ_i is of the nature of the reduced stress used in the elementary theory of structures. Therefore, if for a certain combination of stresses, σ_x, σ_y, and τ_{xy}, the intensity of stress σ_i is equal to the yield point in uniaxial tension, it is assumed that this very combination of stresses just produces yielding in the material.

[3] See Chap. IX.

[4] It should be noted that τ_{xy} and τ_c designate shearing stresses while τ is the non-dimensional ratio $\tau = E_t/E$.

Equation (738) is valid in the elastic and inelastic range. When $\sigma_i/\sqrt{\tau} \leq \sigma_p$ (proportional limit), $\sqrt{\tau} = 1$, and Eqs. (738) and (739) lead to the same result as Eq. (733).

106. Buckling of Web Plates Due to Nonuniform Longitudinal Stresses

Simply Supported Plates. Figure 203 indicates the loading condition which will be investigated in this article. Counting σ positive when compression, the magnitude of the stress σ at a distance y from the upper edge of the plate can be expressed by the linear relationship

$$\sigma = \sigma_1 \left(1 - \frac{\xi y}{b}\right) \quad \text{and} \quad \xi = \frac{\sigma_1 - \sigma_2}{\sigma_1} \tag{740}$$

$\xi = 0$ corresponds to a uniformly distributed compressive stress, $\xi = 2$ indicates pure bending, and $0 < \xi < 2$ indicates combined bending and compression.

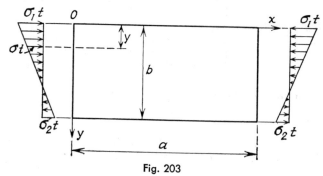

Fig. 203

A plate in longitudinal compression buckles in the longitudinal direction in equal half waves with straight nodal lines perpendicular to the x-axis. Thus, each buckle represents a plate simply supported on its four edges which can be investigated as an independent unit. We assume, therefore, the following expansion for the deflection w:

$$w = \sin \frac{\pi x}{a} \sum_{i=1}^{n} f_i \sin \frac{i\pi y}{b} \tag{741}$$

The strain energy V is found from Eq. (724)

$$V = \frac{\pi^4}{8} Dab \sum_{i=1}^{n} f_i^2 \left(\frac{1}{a^2} + \frac{i^2}{b^2}\right)^2 \tag{742}$$

The change in the potential energy of the external forces is given by

$$U_w = \frac{\sigma_1 t}{2} \int_0^a \int_0^b \left(1 - \xi \frac{y}{b}\right) \left(\frac{\partial w}{\partial x}\right)^2 dx \, dy \tag{743}$$

To evaluate this integral we compute

$$\left(\frac{\partial w}{\partial x}\right)^2 = \frac{\pi^2}{a^2} \cos^2 \frac{\pi x}{a} \sum_{i=1, j=1}^{n} f_i f_j \sin \frac{i \pi y}{b} \sin \frac{j \pi y}{b}$$

where i and j assume all values from 1 to n. Substituting this expression into Eq. (743) and integrating give

$$U_w = \frac{\pi^2 \sigma_1 t}{8} \frac{b}{a} \sum_{i=1}^{n} f_i^2 - \frac{\sigma_1 t}{4} \xi \frac{\pi^2}{ab} \left[\frac{b^2}{4} \sum_{i=1}^{n} f_i^2 - \frac{8b^2}{\pi^2} \sum_{i=1}^{n} \sum_{j=1}^{n} \frac{ij f_i f_j}{(i^2 - j^2)^2} \right] \quad (744)$$

where i assumes all values 1 to n, while j can have such values only that $i + j$ becomes an odd number. In performing the integrations leading to Eq. (744) the following formula was used:

$$\int_0^b y \sin \frac{i \pi y}{b} \sin \frac{j \pi y}{b} \, dy = \begin{cases} \dfrac{b^2}{4} & \text{if } i = j \\ 0 & \text{if } i + j \text{ is an even number} \\ -\dfrac{4b^2}{\pi^2} \dfrac{ij}{(i^2 - j^2)^2} & \text{if } i + j \text{ is an odd number} \end{cases}$$

The extremum conditions $\dfrac{\partial(V + U_w)}{\partial f_i} = 0$, $(i = 1, 2, \ldots, n)$ form

a system of n equations

$$\left[(1 + i^2 \alpha^2)^2 - \alpha^2 k \left(1 - \frac{\xi}{2} \right) \right] f_i - \frac{8}{\pi^2} \xi \alpha^2 k \sum_j \frac{ij f_j}{(i^2 - j^2)^2} = 0$$

$$(i = 1, 2, \ldots, n) \quad (745)$$

where $\alpha = a/b$ and $k = \sigma_1 b^2 t / \pi^2 D$. The summation $\sum_j$ is to extend only

to those numbers j which satisfy the condition that $i + j$ is an odd number. Nonvanishing solutions for the unknowns f_i exist only if the determinant Δ of the coefficients of Eqs. (745) vanish. This condition, $\Delta = 0$, can be used to determine the value of the plate factor k.

Timoshenko, who derived Eq. (745), first used three equations for the computation of k in the case of pure bending $\xi = 2$, two equations for values $\xi < 2$ and obtained k-values of sufficient accuracy. The critical value σ_{1c} of the compressive fiber stress σ_1 is finally

$$\sigma_{1c} = \frac{\pi^2 E}{12(1 - \nu^2)} \left(\frac{t}{b}\right)^2 k \quad (746)$$

Table 34 gives the plate factor k for a number of values of the coefficient ξ and of the ratio α. Inspection of the table reveals that there is a minimum value of k in each line, which occurs at $\alpha = \frac{2}{3}$ for $\xi = 2$ and

WEB PLATES OF GIRDERS

at $\alpha = 1$ when $\xi = 0$. A very long plate, therefore, buckles in half waves of length $\lambda = 2b/3$ in case of pure bending. The wavelength increases as ξ decreases and approaches the limiting value $\lambda = b$ in the case of uniform compressive load. The minimum value of α applies to long plates and

TABLE 34. Plate Factors k in Eq. (746) for Simply Supported Plates in Nonuniform Longitudinal Compression

Type of stress distribution	α							
	0.4	0.5	0.6	0.667	0.75	0.8	1.0	1.5
$\sigma_2 = -\sigma_1$	29.1	25.6	24.1	23.9	24.1	24.4	25.6	24.1
$\sigma_2 = -2\sigma_1/3$	23.6	....	17.7	....	15.7	16.4	16.9	15.7
$\sigma_2 = -\sigma_1/3$	18.7	....	12.9	....	11.5	11.2	11.0	11.5
$\sigma_2 = 0$	15.1	....	9.7	....	8.4	8.1	7.8	8.4
$\sigma_2 = \sigma_1/3$	10.8	....	7.1	....	6.1	6.0	5.8	6.1
$\sigma_2 = \sigma_1$	8.4	....	5.2	....	4.3	4.2	4.0	4.3

can be used in routine design for all plates having an aspect ratio α exceeding λ/b.

Plates Clamped along the Longitudinal Edges. This problem was treated by Nölke,[1] who obtained the solution by the Ritz method, using the following expansion:[2]

[1] Nölke, *loc. cit.* p. 388.

[2] The paper uses a double sum which reduces to the expression (747) when, reasoning in the same manner as in the case of simply supported plates, only buckling in one half wave is considered.

$$w = \sin \frac{\pi x}{a} \sum_{i=1}^{n} f_i \left[\left(\cos \frac{p_i y}{b} - \cosh \frac{p_i y}{b} \right) (\sin p_i - \sinh p_i) \right.$$
$$\left. - \left(\sin \frac{p_i y}{b} - \sinh \frac{p_i y}{b} \right) (\cos p_i - \cosh p_i) \right] \quad (747)$$

where the coefficients p_i are the roots of the transcendental equation

$$\cos p_i \cosh p_i = 1 \qquad (747a)$$

The expressions in parenthesis in Eq. (747) form a complete set of orthogonal functions if the coefficients p_i are determined from Eq. (747a). These expressions are the normal modes of vibration of a bar of length b clamped at both ends and satisfy the boundary conditions $\frac{dw}{dy} = 0$ for $y = 0$ and $y = b$.

Table 35 gives the values of the plate factor k computed by Nölke for two loading conditions. The convergence of the k-values was checked carefully by Nölke, and they may be considered good approximations. The first line in Table 35 was computed from a fifth-order determinant; the second line from a third-order one. Minimum values of k occur at $\alpha = 0.47$ and 0.65, giving the length of half waves in infinitely long plates $\lambda = 0.47b$ and $\lambda = 0.65b$, respectively.

TABLE 35. Plate Factors k in Eq. (746) for Plates in Nonuniform Longitudinal Compression, Clamped at the Longitudinal Edges

Type of stress distribution	α						
	0.4	0.47	0.5	0.6	0.65	0.7	0.8
$\sigma_2 = -\sigma_1$	42.7	39.6	39.7	41.8	....	45.8	
$\sigma_2 = 0$	17.7	....	14.8	13.7	13.6	13.7	14.3

Critical Stresses in the Inelastic Range. For plates in uniform longitudinal compression the value $\eta = \sqrt{\tau}$ has been obtained for the plasticity factor in Chap. IX. It is obvious that with increasing nonuniformity of the stress distribution the effect of the plasticity of the material on the critical stress σ_{1c} will decrease and that the plasticity factor η for nonuniform distribution of the stresses σ must be larger than $\sqrt{\tau}$. No investigation has been made hitherto to determine the relationship between η and the distribution of the stress σ. No better result being available, it is recommended to use $\eta = \sqrt{\tau}$, leading to conservative values of the critical stress. The value of σ_{1c} can be determined by computing

$$\frac{\sigma_{1c}}{\sqrt{\tau}} = \frac{\pi^2 E}{12(1 - \nu^2)} \left(\frac{t}{b}\right)^2 k \tag{748}$$

and finally obtaining the corresponding value of σ_{1c} from a table, as explained in Art. 93.

107. Simply Supported Plates under Combined Shear and Uniformly Distributed Longitudinal Stresses

The stresses in the web plates of girders are a combination of shearing stresses τ_{xy} and longitudinal stresses σ. It is important to consider the

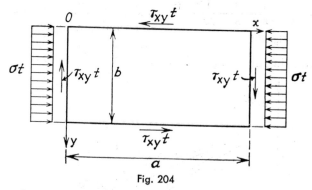

Fig. 204

effect of such a combination of stresses on the stability of the web. Approximate solutions of the problem are known for two limiting cases: (1) The longitudinal stresses σ are uniformly distributed over the cross section of the web, which case will be considered in this article; (2) the stresses σ are pure bending stresses, which case will be considered in the following article. The mathematical treatment according to the Ritz method does not differ essentially from that discussed in the two preceding articles. The expression for the potential energy of the external forces is the sum of the expressions given by Eqs. (725) and (743). The solution is obtained by assuming the deflection w in the form of the double Fourier expansion [Eq. (726)]. Since the mathematical analysis does not offer any new aspect, the following discussion will be confined to the presentation of results.

We consider a plate acted on by shearing stresses τ_{xy} and uniform compressive stresses σ as illustrated by Fig. 204.

It is obvious that the buckling stress σ_c which a plate of given aspect ratio α can carry will depend upon the magnitude of the shearing stress τ_{xy} present in the plate and will increase when τ_{xy} decreases. In turn, focusing attention on the critical shearing stress τ_c its critical value will be higher when the compressive stress σ decreases.

Using a tenth-order determinant Batdorf and Stein[1] obtained the critical stress combinations for the case of shear and simultaneous longitudinal or transverse compressive stresses. They developed interaction curves from which the critical value of one stress can be obtained when a given value of the other stress is present.[2] The interaction between σ_c and τ_c can be expressed conveniently by introducing the ratios $\sigma_c/\sigma_c^{\,0}$ and $\tau_c/\tau_c^{\,0}$, where $\tau_c^{\,0}$ is the critical stress in pure shear and $\sigma_c^{\,0}$ the critical stress in pure compression. In plotting the ratio $\tau_c/\tau_c^{\,0}$ versus the

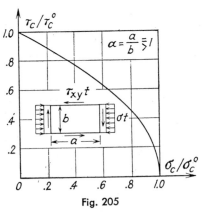

Fig. 205

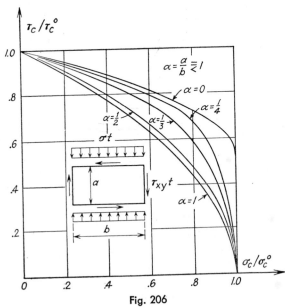

Fig. 206

ratio $\sigma_c/\sigma_c^{\,0}$, as shown in Fig. 205, an interaction curve is obtained. Batdorf and Stein found that for ratios $\alpha \geq 1$ the curve between $\sigma_c/\sigma_c^{\,0} = 0$ and 1

[1] Batdorf and Stein, *loc. cit.* on p. 388.

[2] Such interaction curves were first computed by E. Chwalla, Beitrag zur Stabilitätstheorie des Stegbleches vollwandiger Träger, *Der Stahlbau*, 1936, p. 161.

can be approximated by the parabola

$$\left(\frac{\tau_c}{\tau_c^\circ}\right)^2 + \frac{\sigma_c}{\sigma_c^\circ} = 1 \tag{749}$$

For values of $\alpha < 1$ the interaction curves computed by Batdorf and Stein are shown in Fig. 206. These curves, except that for $\alpha = \frac{1}{2}$, deviate substantially from the parabola for $\alpha = 1$. The curve $\alpha = 0$ for the infinitely long plate in transverse compression was determined by Stowell and Schwartz.[1]

Design Formulas for Long Plates, $\alpha \geq 1$. The simple relationship (749) suggests the development of a formula of design for the buckling strength of a plate in combined shear and uniform compression for $\alpha \geq 1$. We proceed in the following manner: If σ and τ_{xy} are the given stresses in the plate panel under consideration and if their ratio is

$$\beta = \frac{\sigma}{\tau_{xy}} = \frac{\sigma_c}{\tau_c} \tag{750}$$

we obtain from Eq. (749) by substituting $\sigma_c = \beta\tau_c$

$$\left(\frac{\tau_c}{\tau_c^\circ}\right)^2 + \beta\frac{\tau_c}{\tau_c^\circ}\frac{\tau_c^\circ}{\sigma_c^\circ} = 1 \tag{751}$$

Solving for τ_c this equation yields two roots, the smaller one being

$$\tau_c = \frac{\beta}{2}\sigma_c^\circ\kappa^2\left(-1 + \sqrt{1 + \frac{4}{\beta^2\kappa^2}}\right) \tag{752}$$

where $\kappa = \tau_c^\circ/\sigma_c^\circ$. The values of σ_c° and τ_c° are

$$\sigma_c^\circ = \frac{4\pi^2 E}{12(1 - \nu^2)}\left(\frac{t}{b}\right)^2$$

$$\tau_c^\circ = \frac{\pi^2 E}{12(1 - \nu^2)}\left(\frac{t}{b}\right)^2\left(5.34 + \frac{4}{\alpha^2}\right)$$

whence

$$\kappa = \frac{5.34 + 4/\alpha^2}{4} = \frac{4}{3} + \frac{1}{\alpha^2} \tag{753}$$

The ratio κ depends only on the aspect ratio $\alpha = a/b > 1$. Substituting the value of σ_c° into Eq. (752) we obtain

$$\tau_c = \frac{\pi^2 E}{12(1 - \nu^2)}\left(\frac{t}{b}\right)^2 2\beta\kappa^2\left(-1 + \sqrt{1 + \frac{4}{\beta^2\kappa^2}}\right) \tag{754a}$$

$$\sigma_c = \beta\tau_c \tag{754b}$$

These equations are valid in the elastic range of buckling only.

[1] Stowell and Schwartz, *loc. cit.* on p. 388.

Critical Stresses, τ_c and σ_c in the Inelastic Range. In the case of combined shear and longitudinal stress the plasticity factor $\eta = \sqrt{\tau}$ is assumed to depend on the stress intensity[1]

$$\sigma_i = \sqrt{\sigma_c^2 + 3\tau_c^2}$$

Introducing the value of the stress ratio $\beta = \sigma_c/\tau_c$, the following relations are obtained:

$$\sigma_i = \tau_c \sqrt{\beta^2 + 3} \qquad \text{and} \qquad \sigma_i = \sigma_c \sqrt{1 + \frac{3}{\beta^2}} \qquad (755)$$

In order to extend Eq. (754a) into the plastic region, we replace E by $E \sqrt{\tau}$, and expressing τ_c by σ_i we obtain

$$\frac{\sigma_i}{\sqrt{\tau}} = \frac{\pi^2 E}{12(1 - \nu^2)} \left(\frac{t}{b}\right)^2 2\kappa^2 \beta \sqrt{\beta^2 + 3} \left(-1 + \sqrt{1 + \frac{4}{\beta^2 \kappa^2}}\right) \qquad (756)$$

where κ is given by Eq. (753). After computing the value of $\sigma_i/\sqrt{\tau}$ the value of σ_i can be obtained from the tables in Art. 93, and the critical stresses are

$$\tau_c = \frac{\sigma_i}{\sqrt{\beta^2 + 3}} \qquad \text{and} \qquad \sigma_c = \frac{\beta \sigma_i}{\sqrt{\beta^2 + 3}} \qquad (757)$$

Equations (756) and (757) apply in the elastic and inelastic range. When $\sigma_i/\sqrt{\tau} \lessgtr \sigma_p$ (proportional limit), $\sqrt{\tau} = 1$, and these equations agree with Eqs. (754).

Design Formulas for Short Plates, $\frac{1}{2} < \alpha < 1$. Assuming that Eq. (749) can be considered a fair approximation of the interaction curve for plates with an aspect ratio between $\frac{1}{2}$ and 1, Eq. (752) remains valid. For wide plates, $\alpha < 1$, we have

$$\sigma_c{}^\circ = \frac{\pi^2 E}{12(1 - \nu^2)} \left(\frac{t}{b}\right)^2 \left(\alpha + \frac{1}{\alpha}\right)^2$$

$$\tau_c{}^\circ = \frac{\pi^2 E}{12(1 - \nu^2)} \left(\frac{t}{b}\right)^2 \left(4 + \frac{5.34}{\alpha^2}\right)^*$$

Therefore,

$$\kappa = \frac{\tau_c{}^\circ}{\sigma_c{}^\circ} = \frac{4\alpha^2 + 5.34}{(\alpha^2 + 1)^2} \qquad (758)$$

Expressing $\sigma_c{}^\circ$ in Eq. (752) by the above expression gives

$$\tau_c = \frac{\pi^2 E}{12(1 - \nu^2)} \left(\frac{t}{b}\right)^2 \left(\alpha + \frac{1}{\alpha}\right)^2 \kappa^2 \frac{\beta}{2} \left(-1 + \sqrt{1 + \frac{4}{\beta^2 \kappa^2}}\right) \Bigg\} \quad (759)$$

$$\sigma_c = \beta \tau_c$$

These equations are valid in the elastic range of buckling only.

[1] See footnote 2 on p. 398.
* This equation follows from Eqs. (733) and (735) by interchanging the dimensions a and b.

Critical Stresses in the Inelastic Range. By the same reasoning which led to Eq. (756) we now obtain

$$\frac{\sigma_i}{\sqrt{\tau}} = \frac{\pi^2 E}{12(1 - \nu^2)} \left(\frac{t}{b}\right)^2 \left(\alpha + \frac{1}{\alpha}\right)^2 \kappa^2 \frac{\beta}{2} \sqrt{\beta^2 + 3} \left(-1 + \sqrt{1 + \frac{4}{\beta^2 \kappa^2}}\right)$$

(760)

where κ is defined by Eq. (758). After determining σ_i the critical stresses are

$$\tau_c = \frac{\sigma_i}{\sqrt{\beta^2 + 3}} \quad \text{and} \quad \sigma_c = \frac{\beta \sigma_i}{\sqrt{\beta^2 + 3}} \quad (761)$$

Equations (760) and (761) are valid in the elastic and inelastic range of buckling.

108. Simply Supported Plates under Combined Shear and Pure Bending Stresses

The relationship between the ratios $\tau_c/\tau_c^{\,\circ}$ and $\sigma_{1c}/\sigma_{1c}^{\,\circ}$ is indicated in Fig. 207 by two interaction curves for $\alpha = \frac{1}{2}$ and $\alpha = 1$ which have been derived from Timoshenko's solution of this problem.[1] These curves lie close together and may be replaced without substantial error by the dashed curve in Fig. 207, which is part of a circle represented by the equation

$$\left(\frac{\sigma_{1c}}{\sigma_{1c}^{\,\circ}}\right)^2 + \left(\frac{\tau_c}{\tau_c^{\,\circ}}\right)^2 = 1 \quad (762)$$

This simple relationship can be used to develop a formula of design in a manner similar to that applied in the previous articles.

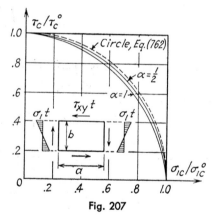

Fig. 207

Introducing the ratio $\beta = \sigma_1/\tau_{xy} = \sigma_{1c}/\tau_c$, Eq. (762) assumes the form

$$\left(\frac{\tau_c}{\tau_c^{\,\circ}}\right)^2 \left[1 + \beta^2 \left(\frac{\tau_c^{\,\circ}}{\sigma_{1c}^{\,\circ}}\right)^2\right] - 1 = 0$$

With $\kappa = \tau_c^{\,\circ}/\sigma_{1c}^{\,\circ}$ this equation yields the positive root

$$\tau_c = \kappa \sigma_{1c}^{\,\circ} \sqrt{\frac{1}{1 + \beta^2 \kappa^2}} \quad (763)$$

[1] Timoshenko, S., Stability of the Webs of Plate Girders, *Engineering*, Vol. 238, p. 207, 1935.

Inspection of Table 34 shows that the smallest value of k for pure bending, $\sigma_1 = -\sigma_2$, is 23.9, and it is assumed that $\sigma_{1c}{}^\circ$ for all aspect ratios $\alpha \geq \frac{1}{2}$ can be expressed with sufficient accuracy by

$$\sigma_{1c}{}^\circ = \frac{24\pi^2 E}{12(1 - \nu^2)} \left(\frac{t}{b}\right)^2 \tag{764}$$

Furthermore we have

$$\left. \begin{array}{ll} \text{For } \alpha \leq 1: & \tau_c{}^\circ = \dfrac{\pi^2 E}{12(1 - \nu^2)} \left(\dfrac{t}{b}\right)^2 \left(4 + \dfrac{5.34}{\alpha^2}\right) \\[3mm] \text{For } \alpha \geq 1: & \tau_c{}^\circ = \dfrac{\pi^2 E}{12(1 - \nu^2)} \left(\dfrac{t}{b}\right)^2 \left(5.34 + \dfrac{4}{\alpha^2}\right) \end{array} \right\} \tag{765}$$

from which the following values of κ are derived:

$$\left. \begin{array}{ll} \text{For } \dfrac{1}{2} < \alpha \leq 1: & \kappa = \dfrac{4 + 5.34/\alpha^2}{24} = \dfrac{1}{6} + \dfrac{2}{9\alpha^2} \\[3mm] \text{For } \alpha \geq 1: & \kappa = \dfrac{5.34 + 4/\alpha^2}{24} = \dfrac{2}{9} + \dfrac{1}{6\alpha^2} \end{array} \right\} \tag{766}$$

Substituting the value of $\sigma_{1c}{}^\circ$ from Eq. (764) into Eq. (763) we obtain finally

$$\left. \begin{array}{l} \tau_c = \dfrac{\pi^2 E}{12(1 - \nu^2)} \left(\dfrac{t}{b}\right)^2 24\kappa \sqrt{\dfrac{1}{1 + \beta^2\kappa^2}} \\[3mm] \sigma_c = \beta\tau_c \end{array} \right\} \tag{767}$$

Critical Stress in the Inelastic Range. Reasoning in the same manner as in the previously discussed cases we arrive at the following equation for the stress σ_i:

$$\frac{\sigma_i}{\sqrt{\tau}} = \frac{\pi^2 E}{12(1 - \nu^2)} \left(\frac{t}{b}\right)^2 24\kappa \sqrt{\beta^2 + 3} \sqrt{\frac{1}{1 + \beta^2\kappa^2}} \tag{768}$$

Having determined σ_i, the critical stresses τ_c and σ_{1c} are

$$\tau_c = \frac{\sigma_i}{\sqrt{\beta^2 + 3}} \quad \text{and} \quad \sigma_{1c} = \frac{\beta\sigma_i}{\sqrt{\beta^2 + 3}} \tag{769}$$

109. Summary of Design Formulas for Web Plates of Plate Girders

The results obtained in Arts. 105 to 108 are summarized in Table 36 in a manner convenient for routine design. For reasons of simplicity it was assumed that the web panels are simply supported by the chords and stiffeners, neglecting the favorable influence of the restraining effect of these members.

This table contains formulas for the computation of the critical stress σ_{1c} and τ_c. The application of these formulas to actual design requires the selection of an appropriate safety factor, and the reader is referred to the discussion concerning this factor in Art. 113.

When applying Table 36 determine the plate factor k from the table and compute

$$\frac{\sigma_i}{\sqrt{\tau}} = \frac{\pi^2 E}{12(1 - \nu^2)} \left(\frac{t}{b}\right)^2 k \qquad (770)$$

For steel this equation can be written

$$\frac{\sigma_i}{\sqrt{\tau}} = 26{,}750 \left(\frac{t}{b}\right)^2 k \ \text{(kips/in.}^2\text{)} \qquad (770a)$$

If the value $\sigma_i/\sqrt{\tau}$ is below the proportional limit, we have $\tau = 1$ and $\sigma_c = \sigma_i/\sqrt{\tau}$, but if this value is above this limit, the stress intensity σ_i can be taken for steel from Tables 27 and 28 on pages 343 and 344, which give the stresses σ as function of $\sigma/\sqrt{\tau}$. The stress intensity σ_i being found, the last column of Table 36 indicates simple formulas for the values of the critical stresses σ_{1c} and τ_c.

To obtain the critical stresses for longitudinal stress distributions having ratios σ_1/σ_2 not shown in the table, the plate factor k may be computed by linear interpolation.

110. Transversely Stiffened Web Plates in Shear

Equation (733) in Art. 105 indicates that the critical stress of a plate in shear depends on the ratio b/t, i.e., the ratio of the smaller dimension of the plate to its thickness t. Subdividing a simply supported plate of length a by sufficiently rigid, transverse stiffeners of spacing d as indicated in Fig. 208, smaller panels are formed which may be considered approximately as simply supported. Thus, the decisive width-to-thickness ratio, d/t, can be considerably reduced, and the critical stress, being inversely proportional to the square of this ratio, substantially increased.

An approximate analysis for stiffened plates in shear in the elastic range was developed first by Timoshenko. It reveals features similar to those which characterized the theory of plates with longitudinal stiffeners in compression discussed in Chap. X. Again, there exists a limiting value I_0 of the moment of inertia of the stiffeners which ensures straight nodal lines at these stiffeners. If I is smaller than I_0, the stiffeners buckle and deflect together with the plate. With increasing flexural rigidity the buckling strength of the stiffened plate increases until an upper limit is reached when $I = I_0$. A further increase of the moment of inertia I does not add to the buckling strength of the stiffened plate. When reinforced by stiffeners having the moment of inertia I_0, each plate panel can be considered as a simply supported plate in shear, and the critical stress τ_c reaches the maximum possible value. Introducing the ratio b/d the

TABLE 36.   Plates in Shear and/or Uniform or Linearly Distributed Longitudinal Compression

Loading condition	Plate factor k in Eqs. (770) and (770a)	Critical stresses τ_c and σ_{1c}
Uniform compression, $\sigma_2/\sigma_1 = 1$ $\alpha = a/b$	$\alpha \geq 1: \quad k = 4$ $\alpha \leq 1: \quad k = \left(\alpha + \dfrac{1}{\alpha}\right)^2$	$\sigma_{1c} = \sigma_i$
Longitudinal compression, $\sigma_2/\sigma_1 = 0$ $\alpha = a/b$	$\alpha \geq 1: \quad k = 7.7$ $\alpha \leq 1: \quad k = 7.7 + 33(1 - \alpha)^3$	$\sigma_{1c} = \sigma_i$

Longitudinal compression, $\sigma_2/\sigma_1 = -1$

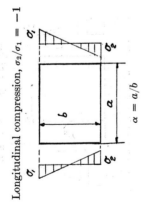

$\alpha = a/b$

$\alpha \geq \tfrac{2}{3}$: $\quad k = 24$

$\alpha < \tfrac{2}{3}$: $\quad k = 24 + 73(\tfrac{2}{3} - \alpha)^2$

$\sigma_{1c} = \sigma_i$

Pure shear

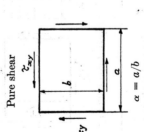

$\alpha = a/b$

$\alpha \geq 1$: $\quad k = \sqrt{3}\left(5.34 + \dfrac{4}{\alpha^2}\right)$

$\alpha \leq 1$: $\quad k = \sqrt{3}\left(4 + \dfrac{5.34}{\alpha^2}\right)$

$\tau_c = \dfrac{\sigma_i}{\sqrt{3}}$

TABLE 36. Plates in Shear and/or Uniform or Linearly Distributed Longitudinal Compression. (Continued)

Loading condition	Plate factor k in Eqs. (770) and (770a)	Critical stresses τ_c and σ_{1c}
Shear and longitudinal compression, $\sigma_2/\sigma_1 = 1$ $\alpha = a/b, \quad \beta = \sigma_1/\tau_{xy}$	$\alpha \geq 1:$ $$k = 2\kappa^2\beta\sqrt{\beta^2+3}\left[-1+\sqrt{1+\frac{4}{\beta^2\kappa^2}}\right]$$ where $\quad \kappa = \frac{4}{3}+\frac{1}{\alpha^2}$ $\tfrac{1}{2} \leq \alpha \leq 1:$ $$k = \frac{1}{2}\kappa^2\left(\alpha+\frac{1}{\alpha}\right)^2\beta\sqrt{\beta^2+3}\left[-1+\sqrt{1+\frac{4}{\beta^2\kappa^2}}\right]$$ where $\quad \kappa = \frac{4\alpha^2+5.34}{(\alpha^2+1)^2}$	$\tau_c = \dfrac{\sigma_i}{\sqrt{\beta^2+3}}$ $\sigma_{1c} = \dfrac{\beta\sigma_i}{\sqrt{\beta^2+3}}$
Shear and longitudinal compression $\sigma_2/\sigma_1 = 0$ $\alpha = a/b, \quad \beta = \sigma_1/\tau_{xy}$	$\alpha \geq 1:$ $$k = 3.85\kappa^2\beta\sqrt{\beta^2+3}\left[-1+\sqrt{1+\frac{4}{\beta^2\kappa^2}}\right]$$ where $\quad \kappa = \frac{5.34+4/\alpha^2}{7.7}$ $\tfrac{1}{2} \leq \alpha \leq 1:$ $$k = 3.85\kappa^2\beta\sqrt{\beta^2+3}\left[-1+\sqrt{1+\frac{4}{\beta^2\kappa^2}}\right]$$ where $\quad \kappa = \frac{4+5.34/\alpha^2}{7.7+33(1-\alpha)^3}$	$\tau_c = \dfrac{\sigma_i}{\sqrt{\beta^2+3}}$ $\sigma_{1c} = \dfrac{\beta\sigma_i}{\sqrt{\beta^2+3}}$

Shear and longitudinal compression, $\sigma_2/\sigma_1 = -1$

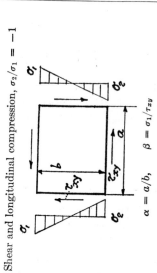

$\alpha = a/b, \quad \beta = \sigma_1/\tau_{xy}$

$\alpha \geq 1$:

$$k = 24\kappa\sqrt{\beta^2+3}\,\sqrt{\frac{1}{1+\beta^2\kappa^2}}$$

where

$$\kappa = \frac{2}{9}+\frac{1}{6\alpha^2}$$

$\tfrac{1}{2} \leq \alpha \leq 1$:

$$k = 24\kappa\sqrt{\beta^2+3}\,\sqrt{\frac{1}{1+\beta^2\kappa^2}}$$

where

$$\kappa = \frac{1}{6}+\frac{2}{9\alpha^2}$$

$$\tau_c = \frac{\sigma_i}{\sqrt{\beta^2+3}}$$

$$\sigma_{1c} = \frac{\beta\sigma_i}{\sqrt{\beta^2+3}}$$

value of this stress in the elastic range can be found for pure shear from Table 36 for $\alpha = d/b \leq 1$:

$$\tau_c = \frac{\pi^2 E}{12(1 - \nu^2)} \left(\frac{t}{b}\right)^2 k \tag{771}$$

where

$$k = 4 + \frac{5.34}{(d/b)^2} \quad \text{if} \left(\frac{d}{b} \leq 1\right) \tag{772}$$

Plates Having One or Two Stiffeners. Timoshenko[1] solved the problem of transversely stiffened plates in shear approximately by means of the energy method for plates with one and two stiffeners (Figs. 208

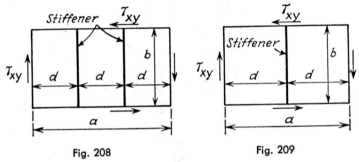

Fig. 208   Fig. 209

and 209). The stability condition is obtained in a manner similar to the one in Art. 105 for the plate without stiffeners. Under the assumption that the stiffeners have no torsional stiffness, the expression for the potential energy of the plate stiffener system now includes an additional term for the bending energy V_s of each stiffener, namely,

$$V_s = \frac{EI}{2} \int_0^b \left(\frac{d^2w}{dy^2}\right)^2 dy \tag{773}$$

Introducing the two-dimensional expansion Eq. (726) into the expression $V + V_s + U_w$ for the potential energy, the critical shear stress τ_c can be determined from the theorem of stationary potential energy.

Using the nondimensional parameter

$$\gamma = \frac{EI}{Dd} = \frac{12(1 - \nu^2)I}{t^3 d} \tag{774}$$

Timoshenko has determined the values γ_0 of the parameter γ which are required to ensure the critical shear stresses τ_c given by Eq. (771). Fourth-order determinants were used for the computations, the results of which are shown in Tables 37 and 38.

[1] Timoshenko, S., Stability of Rectangular Plates with Stiffeners, *Mem. Inst. Engrs. Ways of Commun.*, Vol. 89, p. 23, 1915 (in Russian); Über die Stabilität versteifter Platten, *Der Eisenbau*, Vol. 12, p. 147, 1921.

Wang[1] extended Timoshenko's theory to plates reinforced by any number of transverse stiffeners and gave diagrams for plates with three and four stiffeners and for infinitely long plates.

TABLE 37. Data for Required Moment of Inertia I_0 for Plates in Shear Having **One** Stiffener, Fig. 209

d/b	0.5	0.625	0.75	1.00
$\gamma_0 = EI_0/Dd$	30.0	12.6	5.8	1.66

TABLE 38. Data for Required Moment of Inertia I_0 for Plates in Shear Having **Two** Stiffeners, Fig. 208

d/b	0.4	0.5	0.667	0.833	1.00
$\gamma_0 = EI_0/Dd$	67.8	32.1	10.6	4.11	1.92

A recent investigation of infinitely long plates by Stein and Fralich, reported on below, indicates that the numerical results obtained by Timoshenko and Wang for stiffened plates in shear may be considerably in error, because the expansion (726) is not suitable to express the deformation of the stiffened plate with a limited number of terms.

Infinitely Long Plates Reinforced by Equidistant Stiffeners. A more exact solution for simply supported, infinitely long plates, reinforced by equally spaced transverse stiffeners,

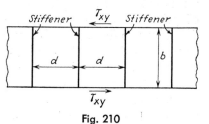

Fig. 210

was recently published by Stein and Fralich.[2] The solution was obtained by means of the Lagrangian multiplier method,[3] and numerical results were given for three stiffener spacings $b/d = 1$, 2, and 5 (Fig. 210).

Figures 211 and 212 show diagrams for $b/d = 1$ and 2, in which the plate factor k in Eq. (771) is plotted versus the ratio γ defined in Eq. (774).

The curves start at $\gamma = 0$ with the value 5.34 for the unstiffened infinitely long plate, have points of discontinuity A due to changes in buckle pattern, and approach asymptotically maximum values of k for $\gamma = \infty$. Theoretically, there are no limiting values γ_0 associated

---

[1] Wang, T. K., Buckling of Transverse Stiffened Plates under Shear, *Jour. Applied Mechanics*, Vol. 14, p. A-269, 1947.

[2] Stein and Fralich, *loc. cit.* on p. 389.

[3] See Art. 26, Chap. II.

with finite values of I_0 as in the previously discussed theory. However, for practical purposes the points A indicate such limiting values for I, since an increase of I above these values has only a slight effect on the critical stress τ_c. The k-curves on the right-hand side of the points A are nearly horizontal lines.

Figures 211 and 212 indicate in dashed lines the values k obtained by Wang using Timoshenko's approximate analysis. Above a certain value

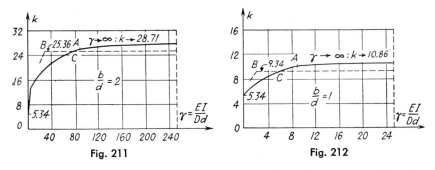

Fig. 211   Fig. 212

of γ the plate factor k is constant, as indicated by the horizontal lines at the right of points B. For large values of γ the more exact theory gives somewhat larger values k, which is not very important, but in the vicinity of points B the discrepancy between the two curves is considerable. According to Wang a value $\gamma_0 = 2$ is required for the ratio $b/d = 1$ to ensure that the plate buckles as simply supported plate, while the more accurate theory requires the much larger value $\gamma_0 = 6$ (see point C in Fig. 211). The exact theory requires very much heavier stiffeners. Similar conditions exist for the ratio $b/d = 2$ (Fig. 212). While no accurate results for plates with two and three stiffeners are available, it must be expected that similar discrepancies would be found, and it is believed that the values in Tables 37 and 38 are not reliable and their use would lead to unsafe designs.

Comparison of the theoretical results obtained by Stein and Fralich with data observed in laboratory tests conducted on 20 specimens with various sizes of stiffeners indicates, as these authors state, fair agreement between theory and experiments. However, the tests do not cover the whole range of γ-values, and for a conclusive check additional tests are required.

The solution of the stability problem for the infinitely long stiffened plate just discussed is applicable to the design of the end portion of a girder web where the longitudinal stresses are small and can be neglected. The three curves obtained by Stein and Fralich make it possible to interpolate an approximate equation for the plate factor k, showing it as a function of the stiffness ratio γ and of the aspect ratio of the panel,

This approximate formula is

$$k = 5.34 + (5.5\beta^2 - 0.6) \sqrt[3]{\frac{\gamma}{4(7\beta^2 - 5)}} \qquad (775)$$

valid for $1 \leq \beta \leq 5$ and $0 \leq \gamma/(7\beta^2 - 5) \leq 4$.

Equation (775) is not applicable when $\gamma > 4(7\beta^2 - 5)$. In this case the plate factor is practically independent of γ and can be computed from

$$k = 4.74 + 5.5\beta^2 \qquad (776)$$

This equation defines the largest plate factor, and therefore the largest shear stress, which can be obtained for the aspect ratio $\beta = b/d$. To obtain these values of k the ratio γ must be larger than the limiting ratio

$$\gamma_0 = 4(7\beta^2 - 5) \qquad (777)$$

Equation (775) furnishes the value k when the moment of inertia I of the stiffener is given and the buckling strength τ_c of the plate is sought. When in turn the required moment of inertia I of the stiffener is to be determined, such that a desired buckling strength τ_c is obtained, Eq. (775) can be solved for the value γ:

$$\gamma = (k - 5.34)^3 \frac{4(7\beta^2 - 5)}{(5.5\beta^2 - 0.6)^3} \qquad (778)$$

where k must be computed for the given τ_c by means of Eq. (771). Formula (778) applies for $k > 5.34$; if $k < 5.34$, no stiffener is necessary. On the other hand, when γ computed from Eq. (778) becomes larger than the limiting value γ_0 according to Eq. (777), the spacing d of the stiffeners must be reduced.

Design Formulas for the Inelastic Range. In order to adapt the results found to the inelastic range it is essential to realize that in a stiffened plate in shear the stiffeners remain fully elastic even when the stresses in the plate are above the elastic limit.

The critical stress τ_c for the rectangular panel in shear in the inelastic range was determined in Art. 105, Eqs. (738) and (739):

$$\tau_c = \frac{\sigma_i}{\sqrt{3}} \qquad (779)$$

and

$$\frac{\sigma_i}{\sqrt{\tau}} = \frac{\pi^2 \sqrt{3}E}{12(1 - \nu^2)} \left(\frac{t}{b}\right)^2 k \qquad (780)$$

The value of the plate factor k is given by Eq. (772). Equations (779) and (780) are to be used wherever Eq. (771) would be applied in the elastic range. The term $\sqrt{\tau}$ in Eq. (780) is the plasticity factor, discussed in detail in Art. 105.

Provided the plate factor k is determined from Eqs. (779) and (780), the formulas (775) to (778) inclusive remain fully applicable in the inelastic range. The stiffness ratio γ, defined in the elastic range by Eq. (774), must, however, be corrected to allow for the smaller effective modulus of elasticity in the plate. This leads to

$$\gamma = \frac{EI}{D \sqrt{\tau}\, d} = \frac{12(1 - \nu^2)I}{\sqrt{\tau}\, t^3 d} \tag{781}$$

To determine the required moment of inertia I so that the plate can sustain a desired critical stress τ_c, one proceeds as follows: Determine the equivalent stress σ_i from Eq. (779), and if σ_i lies above the proportional limit, $\sigma_i/\sqrt{\tau}$ can be read from Tables 27 and 28 on pages 343 and 344. This furnishes also the value of $\sqrt{\tau}$ required later. The plate factor k and the stiffness ratio γ can now be determined from Eqs. (780) and (778), respectively. The value γ must be smaller than γ_0 from Eq. (777); if $\gamma > \gamma_0$, the stiffener distance d is too large and must be reduced. Finally I can be computed from Eq. (781), using the value of the plasticity factor $\sqrt{\tau}$ found earlier.

111. Longitudinally Stiffened Web Plates in Longitudinal Compression

In deep plate girders it is often economical to stiffen the web plate by longitudinal stiffeners in locations where the longitudinal compressive stresses due to bending are high. Two positions of the stiffener will be considered: (1) The stiffener is located at the longitudinal center line of the web, i.e., at the neutral axis (Fig. 213). In this case the stiffener itself does not carry compressive stresses. (2) The stiffener is located in the compressive region at a distance m from the edge of the plate (Fig. 214).

Stiffener at the Center Line. The critical stress σ_{1c} of the stiffened plate panel was computed by Hampl[1] by means of the Ritz method. The effect of a stiffener along the neutral axis for small ratios of $\alpha = a/b$ is very small but becomes more marked when $\alpha > \frac{2}{3}$. The critical stress σ_{1c} of an unstiffened plate panel having the same stress distribution is, according to Eq. (746),

$$\sigma_{1c} = \frac{\pi^2 E}{12(1 - \nu^2)} \left(\frac{t}{b}\right)^2 k$$

where k can be taken from the first line of Table 34. The critical stresses of the stiffened plate can be expressed in the form

$$\sigma_{1c} = \frac{\pi^2 E}{12(1 - \nu^2)} \left(\frac{t}{b}\right)^2 \kappa k \tag{782}$$

[1] Hampl, M., Ein Beitrag zur Stabilität des horizontal ausgesteiften Stegbleches, Der Stahlbau, Vol. 10, p. 16, 1937.

where the coefficient κ is a function of the stiffness ratio

$$\gamma = \frac{EI}{Db} = \frac{12(1 - \nu^2)I}{bt^3} \tag{783}$$

For plates with aspect ratios $\alpha \geq \frac{2}{3}$, the coefficient κ is practically independent of α and its values are given in Table 39.

TABLE 39. Values of Coefficient κ in Eq. (782), valid for $\alpha \geq \frac{2}{3}$

γ.............	0	1	5	10	∞
κ.............	1.0	1.25	1.46	1.49	1.52

The maximum value of the critical stress is reached when $\gamma = \infty$, *i.e.*, when the stiffener is perfectly rigid. But κ approaches the limiting value 1.52 rapidly, and a stiffener whose flexural rigidity corresponds to $\gamma = 10$ is practically as effective as a rigid stiffener. Thus, the largest practically useful value I_0 of the moment of inertia of the stiffener is

$$I_0 = \frac{10}{12(1 - \nu^2)} t^3 b = 0.92t^3 b \tag{784}$$

To determine the critical stress σ_{1c} which will be reached if a stiffener according to Eq. (784) is used we find $\kappa = 1.49$ for $\gamma = 10$ from Table 39.

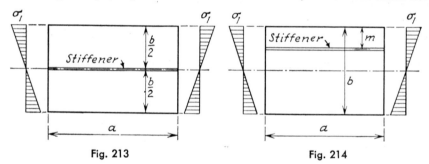

Fig. 213   Fig. 214

Furthermore, from Table 34 we find that for $\alpha \leq \frac{2}{3}$ the plate factor k is nearly constant, and using the smallest value $k = 23.9$, we have $\kappa k = 1.49 \times 23.9 = 35.6$. Equation (782) gives

$$\sigma_{1c} = 35.6 \frac{\pi^2 E}{12(1 - \nu^2)} \left(\frac{t}{b}\right)^2 \tag{785}$$

which is valid for $\alpha \geq \frac{2}{3}$.

Formulas for the Inelastic Range. Equations (784) and (785) apply in the elastic range only but can be adapted for the inelastic range as follows: The critical stress in the inelastic range is given approximately by

$$\frac{\sigma_{1c}}{\sqrt{\tau}} = 35.6 \frac{\pi^2 E}{12(1 - \nu^2)} \left(\frac{t}{b}\right)^2 \tag{786}$$

provided the moment of inertia I_0 of the stiffener is computed according to the formula

$$I_0 = 0.92 \sqrt{\tau} t^3 b \qquad (787)$$

The term $\sqrt{\tau}$ in this equation is due to the fact that the stiffener remains elastic, and the stiffness ratio for inelastic buckling is therefore

$$\gamma = \frac{EI}{\sqrt{\tau} \, Db} = \frac{12(1 - \nu^2)I}{\sqrt{\tau} bt^3} \qquad (788)$$

Equations (786) to (788) are approximations but give conservative results. They are based on the assumption that the plasticity factor $\sqrt{\tau}$ is the same for the entire web and is a function of the largest stress σ_{1c}.

Stiffeners Located between Compression Edge and Neutral Axis. The increase of buckling strength which can be obtained by a stiffener at the center line of the web amounts to only 50% of the strength of the unstiffened plate in the elastic range and is even smaller in the inelastic range. Stiffeners at the center line are therefore not very effective in improving the stability of web plates in case of pure bending stresses.

A larger effect is obtained when the stiffener is placed between the compression flange and the neutral axis (Fig. 214). The problem was studied by Chwalla,[1] who gave the numerical results for a plate of aspect ratio $\alpha = 0.8$, reinforced by a stiffener at the quarter point of the web, $m = b/4$. The problem was discussed in more detail by Massonnet,[2] who extended Timoshenko's analysis for the unstiffened plate presented in Art. 106 by including the bending energy V_s of the stiffener in the expression for the potential energy of the system. With

$$\gamma = \frac{EI}{Db}, \qquad \delta = \frac{A}{bt}, \qquad \xi = 2 \text{ (pure bending)} \qquad (789)$$

the system of Eqs. (745) assumes the extended form

$$(1 + i^2\alpha^2)^2 f_i + (2\gamma - k\alpha^2\delta) \sin\frac{i\pi}{4} \sum_{p=1}^{n} f_p \sin\frac{p\pi}{4} - \frac{16k\alpha^2}{\pi^2} \sum_{j=1}^{n} f_j \frac{ij}{(i^2 - j^2)} = 0$$

$$(i = 1, 2, 3, \ldots, n) \qquad (790)$$

By limiting i to the numbers 1, 2, 3, 4 Massonnet obtained four equations, leading to an equation of the fourth degree in k. The smallest root k defines the critical stress σ_{1c}. Massonnet determined curves representing

---

[1] Chwalla, E., Beitrag zur Stabilitätstheorie des Stegbleches vollwandiger Träger, *Der Stahlbau*, Vol. 9, p. 161, 1936.

[2] Massonnet, C., La stabilité de l'âme de poutres munies de raidisseurs horizontaux et sollicitées par flexion pure, *Pubs. Intern. Assoc. Bridge and Structural Eng.*, Vol. 6, p. 233, 1940–1941.

the plate factor k as a function of α for various values of γ and δ. These curves are shown as curves A in Fig. 215 for $\gamma = 2$, 5, 10, and 20 and $\delta = 0.1$.

For a given plate there exists a limiting value $\gamma = \gamma_0$ defining the flexural rigidity EI_0 of stiffeners which just guarantee straight nodal

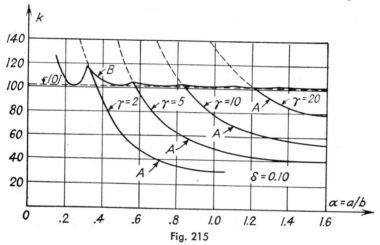

Fig. 215

lines of the buckled plate along the stiffeners (Fig. 216). This value of γ_0 is associated with the highest possible value of the critical stress σ_{1c} which the stiffened plate can carry. To determine the plate factor k for this highest value of σ_{1c} the analysis outlined in Art. 106 for the unstiffened plate can again be used. It is, however, necessary to consider, in addition to the extremum conditions $\partial(V + U_w)/\partial f_i = 0$ which lead to the system of equations (745), a further condition of constraint

$$[w]_{y=\frac{b}{4}} = \sum_{p=1}^{n} f_p \sin \frac{p\pi}{4} = 0 \qquad (791)$$

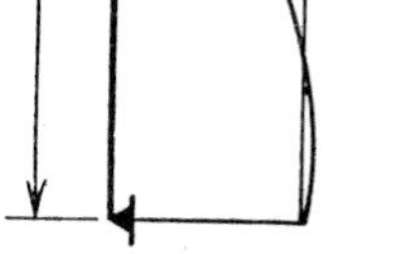

This equation expresses the condition that the deflection w along the stiffener must vanish. Thus, another system of equations, different from the system (790), is obtained from which k as a function of α is derived (curve B in Fig. 215). It is seen from this figure that for values of $\alpha > 0.4$ the plate factor k rapidly approaches the value $k = 101$. The highest values σ_{1c} of the critical stress can be expressed approximately

Fig. 216

$$\sigma_{1c} = \frac{\pi^2 E}{12(1 - \nu^2)} \left(\frac{t}{b}\right)^2 101 \qquad (\alpha \geq 0.4) \qquad (792)$$

The point of intersection of the horizontal line $k = 101$ and of the curve A in Fig. 215, associated with the given properties γ and δ of the stiffener, determines an aspect ratio α which the plate must have to develop the critical stress σ_{1c} defined by Eq. (792). For design purposes Massonnet expressed the relationship between α, δ, and γ_0 in a diagram (Fig. 217) showing the values of γ_0 as functions of α, for values $\delta = 0.05$, 0.10, and 0.20.

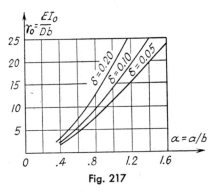

Fig. 217

From these curves the approximate expression

$$\gamma_0 = (12.6 + 50\delta)\alpha^2 - 3.4\alpha^3$$
$$(\alpha \leq 1.6) \quad (793)$$

was derived by the author. If a stiffener is provided such that $\gamma \geq \gamma_0$ the critical stress σ_{1c} according to Eq. (792) is assured.

Comparison of the results obtained above for a stiffener at the center line of the plate with the results just obtained for a plate stiffened in the compression region shows that the reinforcement in the latter case is much more effective.

The problem of the buckling of the web plate due to pure bending was also discussed by Dubas,[1] who derived charts by means of a method of

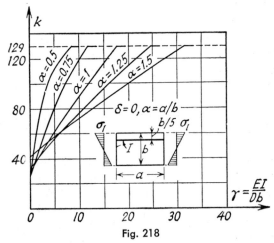

Fig. 218

successive approximations. Numerical results were obtained for plates reinforced by a longitudinal stiffener located at a distance $m = b/5$ from the compression edge of the plate. Figures 218 and 219 show the plate

[1] Dubas, C., Contribution à l'étude du voilement des tôles raidies, *Prelim. Rept.* 3d *Congr. Intern. Assoc. Bridge and Structural Eng.*, Liège, 1948, p. 129.

factor k plotted against the stiffness ratio γ for various values of the aspect ratio $\alpha = a/b$. The largest value of the buckling strength σ_{1c} of the plate stiffener system corresponds to $k = 129$ and is larger than in the case of a stiffener located at the distance $b/4$ from the compression edge. The numerical results were obtained only for $\delta = 0$ and 0.10 and are unfortunately not sufficient to derive a formula similar to Eq. (793).

Formulas for the Inelastic Range. Equation (792) applies in the elastic range only but can easily be adapted for the inelastic range. The

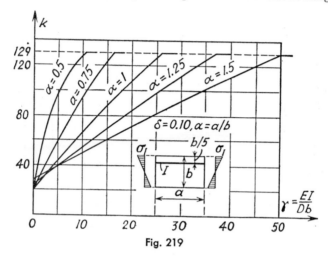

Fig. 219

critical stress for the case of a stiffener at the distance $m = b/4$ from the compression chord is

$$\frac{\sigma_{1c}}{\sqrt{\tau}} = \frac{\pi^2 E}{12(1 - \nu^2)} \left(\frac{t}{b}\right)^2 101 \tag{794}$$

provided the stiffness ratio γ is equal to or larger than the value γ_0 according to Eq. (793). However, the relations (789) defining γ and δ must be adapted for the inelastic range and become

$$\gamma = \frac{EI}{\sqrt{\tau}\,Db} = \frac{12(1 - \nu^2)I}{\sqrt{\tau}\,bt^3} \quad \text{and} \quad \delta = \frac{A}{\sqrt{\tau}\,bt} \tag{795}$$

To determine the required moment of inertia I one proceeds as follows: Compute $\sigma_{1c}/\sqrt{\tau}$ from Eq. (794), and read the value σ_{1c} from Table 27 or 28. This furnishes the value $\sqrt{\tau}$ required to find δ from the second Eq. (795). γ_0 can now be computed from Eq. (793), and the first Eq. (795) finally gives the required moment of inertia

$$I_0 = \frac{\sqrt{\tau}\,bt^3}{12(1 - \nu^2)}\,\gamma_0 \tag{796}$$

112. Stiffened Plates in Combined Shear and Longitudinal Compression

The complex problem of plates in combined shear and longitudinal compression reinforced by transverse and longitudinal stiffeners is of importance in the design of deep web plates of bridge girders and was recently considered by Milosavljevitch.[1] This author presents the solution of the buckling problem for a rectangular plate reinforced by two transverse stiffeners and one longitudinal stiffener as shown in Fig. 220,

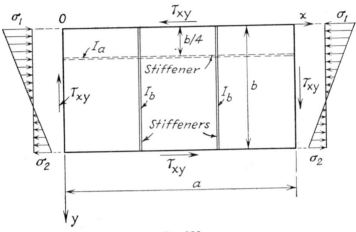

Fig. 220

loaded by linearly distributed longitudinal stresses and uniform shearing stresses along the edges.   The analysis is based on the differential equation of the plate under the action of longitudinal stresses $\sigma = \sigma_1(1 - \xi y/b)$ [see Eq. (740)], shear stresses τ_{xy}, and lateral forces q.   The forces q are the reactions of the stiffeners supporting the plate; these forces are line loads acting at the center lines of the stiffeners.   The differential equation reads

$$D\left(\frac{\partial^4 w}{\partial x^4} + 2\,\frac{\partial^4 w}{\partial x^2\,\partial y^2} + \frac{\partial^4 w}{\partial y^4}\right) = -q - \sigma_1 t\left(1 - \xi\frac{y}{b}\right)\frac{\partial^2 w}{\partial x^2} - 2\tau_{xy}t\,\frac{\partial^2 w}{\partial x\,\partial y} \quad (797)$$

The solution is obtained by means of a series method.   In the paper the author discusses the numerical solution for plates with two transverse stiffeners at the third points and a longitudinal stiffener at the distance of $b/4$ from the compression edge.   Tables are given for routine calculations of plates in pure bending and plates in combined shear and pure bending.

[1] Milosavljevitch, M., Sur la stabilité des plaques rectangulaires reinforcées par des raidisseurs et sollicitées à la flexion et au cisaillement, *Pubs. Intern. Assoc. Bridge and Structural Eng.*, Vol. 8, p. 141, 1947.

113. Ultimate Strength of Plates in Shear

The ultimate strength of plates in compression was discussed in Art. 103 and will be studied extensively in Chap. XII. It is obvious that plates in shear or in combined shear and compression show a similar behavior when stressed above the buckling load. Theoretical investigations and experiments on plate girders show that there is a distinct margin between the load at which buckling begins and the ultimate, actual failure load. After appearance of the first buckling waves, redistribution of stresses takes place in such a manner that, as the load is increased above the buckling load, one part of the load is still balanced by shearing stresses while another part is carried by diagonal tension along the buckles and by compression in the transverse stiffeners. Thus, a kind of truss effect comes into play which permits a substantial increase of the actual load-carrying capacity of the web until the yield point in the highest stressed fibers is reached.

The margin between critical load and ultimate load increases with decreasing critical stress τ_c, i.e., as the controlling width-thickness ratio of the web becomes greater. For small width-thickness ratios, associated with critical stresses above the proportional limit, the difference between critical load and ultimate load decreases and becomes zero when τ_c approaches the yield point.

The problem of the ultimate strength of thin plates in shear was first studied by Wagner,[1] who discussed theoretically the load-carrying capacity of thin webs, neglecting its flexural rigidity. His results are known as the diagonal tension field theory. The general solution, taking into account membrane and bending stresses, was presented by Kromm and Marguerre.[2] The problem was further studied by Levy, Fienup, and Wooley,[3] who studied web plates of girders having transverse stiffeners forming square panels. All these analytical investigations have been carried out with special regard to the requirements of the aircraft designer and have not much bearing on the problems encountered in the design of the types of plate girders which are common in heavy steel structures.

The design of girder webs in such structures is based on the principle that under the worst loading condition buckling should be avoided by a sufficient margin, despite the fact that the occurrence of buckling waves

[1] Wagner, H., Ebene Blechträger mit sehr dünnem Stegblech, *Zeitschrift für Flugtechnik und Motorluftschiffahrt*, Vol. 20, 1929, p. 220.

[2] Kromm, A., and K. Marguerre, Verhalten eines von Schub und Druckkräften beanspruchten Plattenstreifens oberhalb der Beulgrenze, *Luftfahrt-Forschung*, Vol. 17, p. 62, 1937.

[3] Levy, S., K. L. Fienup, and R. M. Wooley, Analysis of Square Shear Web above Buckling Load, *NACA Tech. Note* 962, 1945.

in the web in itself does not imperil the safety of the structure. After passing the critical load a new state of stable equilibrium with redistributed stresses occurs, and the failure load is larger than the buckling load. The amount of additional load which can be carried will depend on the strength of the web in tension and on the strength of the stiffeners in compression. In conventional steel construction, as opposed to aircraft design, the stiffeners are not capable of carrying a very large percentage of the buckling load, and the ultimate load will be only a limited percentage higher than the buckling load. A deliberate increase in stiffener area would not be economical, as it would be better to increase the number of stiffeners and prevent buckling altogether.

The implication from this reasoning is that the factor of safety used in the design of web plates with regard to buckling can be chosen with a view to a more economic utilization of the web. Unlike columns, where local failure causes a reduction of the effective area of the column, the web plates and stiffeners have an additional margin of strength, and therefore it seems logical to use a lower factor of safety against buckling of web plates than that used in column design. A factor of safety $\nu = 1.4$ to 1.6 is proposed in German specifications, and $\nu = 1.5$ is recommended by Timoshenko.[1] The factor of safety viewed in the light of experience resulting from tests is discussed comprehensively by Bergman and Wästlund.[2]

114. Experimental Research

Corroboration between Theory and Experiment. Only a limited number of tests have been made with the primary purpose of checking the theoretical findings. One of the test series which may be mentioned here was made to provide an experimental check on the validity of the parabolic interaction curve for the elastic buckling of rectangular plates in combined shear and uniform longitudinal compression.[3] The tests were made with four plates forming a square tube, and in interpreting the test results account was taken of the effect of the mutual restraint of the four walls of the tube. The test results indicate that the interaction formula (749) may be considered suitable for design purposes.

Two other groups of experiments were concerned with the study of the behavior of plates reinforced by transverse stiffeners.[4] The aspect ratios

[1] Timoshenko, S., "Theory of Elastic Stability," p. 415, McGraw-Hill Book Company, Inc., New York, 1936.

[2] Wästlund and Bergman, *loc. cit.* on p. 389.

[3] Peters, R. G., Buckling Tests of Flat Rectangular Plates under Combined Shear and Longitudinal Compression, *NACA Tech. Note* 1750, 1948.

[4] Levin, L. R., and C. W. Sandlin, Jr., Strength Analysis of Stiffened Thick Beam Webs, *NACA Tech. Note* 1820, 1949. Sandlin, C. W., Jr., Strength Tests of Shear Webs with Uprights Not Connected to the Flanges, *NACA Tech. Note* 1635, 1948.

b/d of the panels investigated were 1.4, 2.4, and 4.8. The slenderness ratios c/t of the webs were 70, 125, and 250. These tests, as has already been mentioned in Art. 110, showed fair agreement with the theoretical results derived from the theory of the infinitely long stiffened plate by Stein and Fralich. Figure 221 shows the test results and three curves derived from the design formula (775) for the aspect ratios $\beta = 1.4$, 2.4, and 4.8.

Critical Stress and Ultimate Strength in Girder Webs. In order to clarify the behavior of web plates in welded steel girders extensive tests have been made by Wästlund and Bergmann.[1] The tests were made on

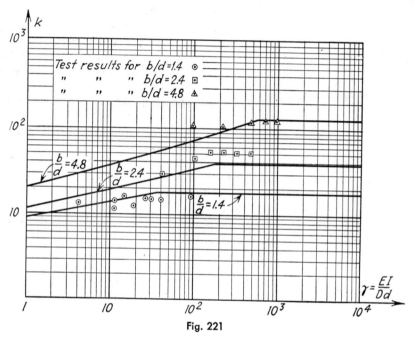

Fig. 221

web plates welded to the flanges of the test girders under various loading conditions, including tests on plates subjected to pure shear or pure bending stresses or a combination of both. The aspect ratio of the panels investigated was between 1 and 3.43, and the width-thickness ratio varied between 175 and 285.

It was found that the webs underwent lateral deflections as soon as the load was applied, indicating initial deviations from flatness. In most cases the rate of increase of the deflection was nearly constant from zero load up to the load that caused yielding. Accordingly, no proper buckling phenomena could be observed, except in two cases in which, at loads

[1] Wästlund and Bergman, *loc. cit.* on p. 389.

10 and 20% above the critical load computed under the assumption of simply supported edges, a rather rapid increase of the deflection was observed, indicating that a stability limit was reached. The rate of increase in deflection in these two cases, however, slowed down when the load was further increased, and the ultimate loads were far beyond the theoretical critical load. The ultimate loads as observed in all tests were 2 to 4.2 times as great as the critical loads.

Strain gauge measurements on the flanges indicated that the shearing stresses were not uniformly distributed along the edges of the web but varied considerably.

Additional References

Ban, S., Knickung der rechteckigen Platte bei veränderlicher Randbelastung, *Pubs. Intern. Assoc. Bridge and Structural Eng.*, Vol. 3, p. 1, 1935.

Trefftz, E., and F. A. Willers, Die Bestimmung der Schubbeanspruchung beim Ausbeulen rechteckiger Platten, *Zeitschrift angewandte Mathematik und Mechanik*, Vol. 16, p. 336, 1936.

Schleicher, F., and R. Barbré, Stabilität versteifter Rechteckplatten mit anfänglicher Ausbiegung, *Der Bauingenieur*, Vol. 18, p. 665, 1937.

Fröhlich, H., Stabilität der gleichmässig gedrückten Rechteckplatte mit Streben Kreuz, *Der Bauingenieur*, Vol. 18, p. 673, 1937.

Burchard, W., Beulspannungen der quadratischen Platte mit Schrägsteife unter Druck bzw. Schub, *Ingenieur-Archiv*, Vol. 8, p. 332, 1937.

Bergman, S. G. A., "Behaviour of Buckled Rectangular Plates under the Action of Shearing Forces," Kungl. Tekniska Hogskola, Stockholm, 1948.

Schunk, T. E., Die quadratische Platte bei Schubbelastung oberhalb der Beulgrenze, *Ingenieur-Archiv*, Vol. 17, p. 117, 1949.

CHAPTER XII

SPECIAL PROBLEMS IN THE DESIGN OF SHIP PLATING

115. Introduction

In Chap. IX we considered the basic problem of the stability of rectangular plates and developed a method of analysis applicable to elastic and inelastic buckling. This method was then applied to the problem of local buckling of the plate elements of columns. In Chaps. X and XI the buckling of longitudinally stiffened plates and of web plates of girders was studied. In this chapter we are going to consider a series of special problems encountered in the design of ship plating.

Ships are essentially structures composed of rectangular plates supported by floors and longitudinals. Bottom, strength deck, and side plating are plates extending continuously in the longitudinal and transverse directions over a great number of supporting elements. The effect of the continuity on the buckling strength of plating should in certain cases be taken into account because this continuity may have considerable influence on the stability of the plates. Articles 116 to 118 of this chapter will therefore be devoted to problems of continuous and restrained plates.

The effect of restraint against rotation of the loaded edges of plates in compression was not considered in Chap. IX. In the case of transversely framed vessels where the plates have small aspect ratios, $\alpha < 1$, this effect is considerable and must be taken into account to obtain economical designs. This problem will be treated in Art. 116.

While plate panels which can be considered clamped on all four edges occur rarely, it is still of interest to have information on clamped plates. The theory of such plates will be discussed and numerical results given in Art. 117.

Single bottoms in longitudinally framed vessels are chiefly designed as plate-stiffener combinations, and the buckling problems of this type of structure were dealt with comprehensively in Chap. X. Double and triple bottoms are plate assemblies of a cellular type, and local instability of such structures will be investigated in Art. 118, where a general theory of plate assemblies of tubular and cellular cross section will be presented.

429

This theory also provides the means of discussing the effect of continuity of plating in cases where unequal panels join.

Article 119 is devoted to the stiffening effect of lapped joints on the buckling strength of plates.

The fact that redistribution of the compressive stresses, originally uniformly distributed, takes place after the critical load of a plate is reached and the plate distorts constitutes a new aspect of the buckling problem concerning the behavior of plates above the critical stress. Theory and experimental research show that the ultimate load, *i.e.*, the load which can be carried until actual failure occurs, is often substantially higher than the load computed from the buckling stress. Investigation of this phase no longer can be based upon the linear strength theory developed in the previous chapters. The remaining articles of this chapter are devoted to a study of this problem, based on the theory of plates with large deflections, and to a study of the related problem of plates in longitudinal compression under normal pressure. The latter problem is of prime importance for the design of hull plating.

Much controversy has arisen as to the effect on the buckling strength of normal loads, like hydrostatic pressure, acting on the hull plating in addition to the compressive stresses in the plane of the plate. A theoretical approach toward solving this problem and a report on a series of laboratory tests supporting the theoretical results were published recently. A brief account of this work and a conclusive answer to this problem, which is of considerable importance in the design of ships, will be given in the final article of this chapter.

116. Rectangular Plates in Longitudinal Compression, Elastically Restrained at the Loaded Edges, Simply Supported at the Unloaded Edges

It was pointed out in Chap. IX that any restraint at the edges where the compressive stress σ_x is applied has no noticeable effect on the buckling strength of plates of large aspect ratio α, *i.e.*, of plates the length of which in the direction of the compressive forces is many times larger than the width b. However, when the ratio α approaches unity or becomes less than unity, the effect of restraint at the edges where the compressive loads act becomes significant. Since plates of aspect ratios $\alpha < 1$ occur in transversely framed vessels, it is necessary to discuss the stability problem of this type of plate.

The case of fixed, loaded edges was investigated by Schleicher,[1] who

---

[1] Schleicher, F., Die Knickspannungen von eingespannten rechteckigen Platten, *Mitteilungen aus den Forschungsanstalten des Gutehoffnungshütte-Koncerns*, Vol. 1, 1931. See also *Final Rept. 1st Congr. Intern. Assoc. Bridge and Structural Eng.*, Paris, 1932, p. 123.

presented a table of the values of the plate factor k for various ratios α. Inasmuch as the elastic restraint of plating in ships is supplied by the torsional rigidity of the transverse framing, the loaded edges cannot be considered as rigidly built in. Instead, a finite degree of restraint, based on the resistance against rotation of the supporting structural elements, must be considered effective.

In order to obtain a solution of the problem, valid in the elastic and inelastic range of buckling, the subsequent analysis will be based on the differential equation (604) of Chap. IX (Roš-Brunner theory). In this case it is permissible to base the analysis on this equation rather than on the more accurate but more complicated Eq. (601), because the results for small aspect ratios, $\alpha < 1$, differ very little. See the discussion concerning this point in Chap. IX, page 324.

Figure 222a shows a short plate elastically restrained against rotation at the long edges and uniformly loaded at these two edges by the compressive forces $\sigma_x t$ per unit length.

With the nondimensional coordinates $\xi = x/b$, $\eta = y/b$, the differential equation (604) becomes

$$\frac{\partial^4 w}{\partial \xi^4} + 2 \frac{\partial^4 w}{\partial \xi^2 \partial \eta^2} + \frac{\partial^4 w}{\partial \eta^4} + \frac{\sigma_x t b^2}{D\tau} \frac{\partial^2 w}{\partial \xi^2} = 0 \qquad (798)$$

The critical stress $\sigma_x = \sigma_c$ can be expressed by a plate factor k:

$$\sigma_c = \frac{\pi^2 E \tau}{12(1 - \nu^2)} \left(\frac{t}{b}\right)^2 k \qquad (799)$$

Substituting this expression and $D = Et^3/12(1 - \nu^2)$ into Eq. (798) gives

$$\frac{\partial^4 w}{\partial \xi^4} + 2 \frac{\partial^4 w}{\partial \xi^2 \partial \eta^2} + \frac{\partial^4 w}{\partial \eta^4} + \pi^2 k \frac{\partial^2 w}{\partial \xi^2} = 0 \qquad (800)$$

The smallest value of the critical stress σ_c is connected with a deflection of the plate in one half wave in the direction parallel to the y-axis, as indicated in Fig. 222b. The expression

$$w = X \sin \pi \eta \qquad (801)$$

is therefore a suitable solution of Eq. (800), where X is a function of the coordinate ξ. Substitution of Eq. (801) into Eq. (800) leads to a differential equation for the function X:

$$\frac{d^4 X}{d\xi^4} - 2(\pi^2 - k) \frac{d^2 X}{d\xi^2} + \pi^4 X = 0 \qquad (802)$$

This ordinary differential equation of the fourth order is of a well-known type and has the general solution

$$X = C_1 \cos \kappa_1 \xi + C_2 \cos \kappa_2 \xi + C_3 \sin \kappa_1 \xi + C_4 \sin \kappa_2 \xi \qquad (803)$$

where κ_1 and κ_2 are parameters yet to be determined. Substituting $X = \cos \kappa_1 \xi$ into Eq. (802) gives

$$[\kappa^4 + (2 - k)\pi^2\kappa^2 + \pi^4] \cos \kappa\xi = 0 \qquad (804)$$

This equation is satisfied for all values of ξ when the expression within

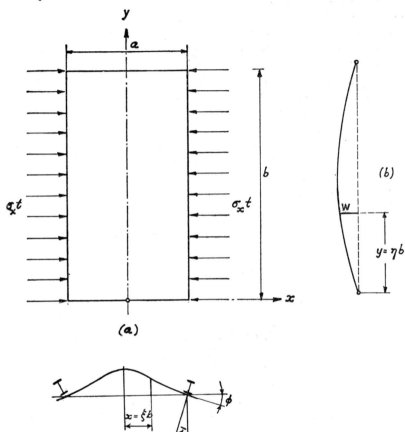

(a)

(b)

(c)

Fig. 222

the brackets vanishes. Therefore,

$$(\kappa^2 + \pi^2)^2 - \pi^2\kappa^2 k = 0$$

or

$$\kappa^2 - \pi \sqrt{k}\,\kappa + \pi^2 = 0 \qquad (805)$$

This quadratic equation yields two roots:

$$\kappa_{1,2} = \frac{\pi}{2} (\sqrt{k} \pm \sqrt{k - 4}) \qquad (806)$$

Substitution of the other terms of Eq. (803) leads to the same values κ_1 and κ_2. The solution (801) therefore becomes

$$w = \sin \pi\eta(C_1 \cos \kappa_1\xi + C_2 \cos \kappa_2\xi + C_3 \sin \kappa_1\xi + C_4 \sin \kappa_2\xi) \quad (807)$$

The critical buckling load is associated with symmetric deformations as shown in Fig. 222c. The terms with C_3 and C_4 in Eq. (807) represent antisymmetric deflections, and the desired symmetric deflection w can therefore be expressed by the terms C_1 and C_2 alone:

$$w = \sin \pi\eta(C_1 \cos \kappa_1\xi + C_2 \cos \kappa_2\xi) \quad (808)$$

The constants C_1 and C_2 will be determined from the boundary conditions requiring that at the loaded edges the deflection $w = 0$ and that the angle of rotation φ of the tangent to the deflection curve at these edges must equal the angle of rotation $\bar{\varphi}$ of the supporting structure (Fig. 222c).

Using the same reasoning as for the derivation of the condition of continuity at the elastically restrained unloaded edges of a rectangular plate, Eq. (628) in Chap. IX, the condition $\varphi = \bar{\varphi}$ for the edge $\xi = \alpha/2$ takes the form

$$\left[\frac{\partial w}{\partial \xi} + \frac{D}{\bar{\zeta} b}\frac{\partial^2 w}{\partial \xi^2}\right]_{\xi=\frac{\alpha}{2}} = 0 \quad (809)$$

The factor of proportionality $\bar{\zeta}$ depends on the torsional rigidity of the restraining structure and can be found in the following way: In deriving Eq. (809) it was assumed that the bending moment M_x per unit length which acts at the edges is proportional to the angle of rotation $\bar{\varphi}$ of the restraining structure,

$$M_x = -\bar{\zeta}\bar{\varphi} \quad (810)$$

where $\bar{\varphi}$ is positive as shown in Fig. 222.

Another relationship between M_x and $\bar{\varphi}$ is given by the differential equation of the twisted supporting member:[1]

[1] This equation can be derived by means of the theorem of stationary potential energy as follows: The supporting member is a bar forced to rotate around its line of attachment to the plate. Equation (266) gives the potential energy for a compressed bar with an enforced axis of rotation. Omitting in this equation the term with σ, which represents the potential energy of the external force, and using $\beta = \bar{\varphi}$ and $\tau = 1$, because the supporting member is elastic, we obtain

$$V = \frac{1}{2}\int[E(a^2 I_y + \Gamma)\bar{\varphi}''^2 + GK\bar{\varphi}'^2]\,dz$$

We need further the potential energy of the external load, which is the distributed moment M_x. The direction of positive moments M_x is defined by Eq. (602), and it will be found that this direction is opposed to the direction of positive angles $\bar{\varphi}$

$$E\Gamma^* \frac{d^4\bar{\varphi}}{dy^4} - GK \frac{d^2\bar{\varphi}}{dy^2} = -M_x \tag{811}$$

According to Eq. (805) the deflection w and therefore the moment M_x are sinusoidally distributed along the loaded edges. The moment M_x is therefore,

$$M_x = C \sin \frac{\pi y}{b}$$

where C is an arbitrary constant. Substituting this expression into Eq. (811), one can find the solution of this equation:

$$\bar{\varphi} = \frac{-b^2}{\pi^2 \left(\frac{\pi^2}{b^2} E\Gamma^* + GK\right)} C \sin \frac{\pi y}{b} = \frac{-b^2}{\pi^2 \left(\frac{\pi^2}{b^2} E\Gamma^* + GK\right)} M_x \tag{812}$$

Comparison of Eqs. (810) and (812) finally yields

$$\bar{\zeta} = \frac{\pi^2}{b^2} \left(\frac{\pi^2}{b^2} E\Gamma^* + GK\right) \tag{813}$$

Equation (809) can finally be written in the form

$$\left[\frac{\partial w}{\partial \xi} + \alpha \zeta \frac{\partial^2 w}{\partial \xi^2}\right]_{\xi = \frac{\alpha}{2}} = 0 \tag{814}$$

where the nondimensional coefficient of restraint ζ is defined by

$$\zeta = \frac{1}{\pi^2} \frac{Db^2}{a \left(\frac{\pi^2}{b^2} E\Gamma^* + GK\right)} = \frac{1}{\pi^2} \frac{t^3 b^2}{12(1 - \nu^2)} \frac{E}{a \left(\frac{\pi^2}{b^2} E\Gamma^* + GK\right)} \tag{815}$$

ζ decreases with increasing torsional rigidity, $(\pi^2/b^2)E\Gamma^* + GK$. The coefficient ζ becomes zero when this rigidity becomes infinite resulting in clamped edges. For simply supported edges, $\zeta = \infty$.

In the majority of cases the supporting member is of T- or I-section and Γ^* can be replaced with sufficient accuracy by Id^2, where d is the

---

shown in Fig. 222c. The potential energy of the load is therefore

$$U_w = \int M_x \bar{\varphi} \, dz$$

The condition $V + U_w = $ stationary leads to the Eulerian equation (see Art. 30)

$$E(a^2 I_y + \Gamma)\bar{\varphi}^{IV} - GK\bar{\varphi}'' = -M_x$$

As defined in Art. 43, a in this equation is the distance from the center of shear to the center of rotation. To avoid confusion with the distance a in Fig. 211, we denote $\Gamma^* = a^2 I_y + \Gamma$ and obtain Eq. (811). The constants K and Γ are defined for important sections in Art. 38.

depth of the stiffening member and I the moment of inertia of the upper flange of this member with respect to the axis $n\text{-}n$ (Fig. 223). Equation (815) therefore becomes

$$\zeta = \frac{1}{\pi^2} \frac{t^3 b^2}{12(1 - \nu^2)} \frac{1}{a\left[\dfrac{\pi^2}{b^2} I d^2 + \dfrac{K}{2(1 + \nu)} \right]} = \frac{t^3 b^2}{107.8a\left(\dfrac{\pi^2 I d^2}{b^2} + \dfrac{K}{2.6} \right)} \tag{816}$$

where $G/E = 1/2(1 + \nu) = 1/2.6$

The value ζ given by Eq. (816) was derived for an individual plate supported along the loaded edges. For continuous plating as illustrated

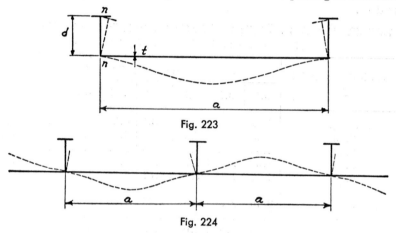

Fig. 223

Fig. 224

by Fig. 224, the coefficient of restraint is twice the value given by Eq. (816). Therefore

$$\zeta_{\text{cont}} = \frac{t^3 b^2}{53.9a\left(\dfrac{\pi^2 I d^2}{b^2} + \dfrac{K}{2.6} \right)} \tag{817}$$

We now introduce the value of w from Eq. (808) into the boundary condition $w = 0$ and into Eq. (814), obtaining the two homogeneous equations

$$C_1 \cos \frac{\alpha \kappa_1}{2} + C_2 \cos \frac{\alpha \kappa_2}{2} = 0$$

$$C_1 \kappa_1 \sin \frac{\alpha \kappa_1}{2} + C_2 \kappa_2 \sin \frac{\alpha \kappa_2}{2} + \alpha \zeta \left(C_1 \kappa_1^2 \cos \frac{\alpha \kappa_1}{2} + C_2 \kappa_2^2 \cos \frac{\alpha \kappa_2}{2} \right) = 0$$

The determinant of the coefficients of these equations must vanish, furnishing the stability condition

$$\kappa_1 \tan \frac{\alpha \kappa_1}{2} - \kappa_2 \tan \frac{\alpha \kappa_2}{2} + \alpha \zeta (\kappa_1^2 - \kappa_2^2) = 0 \tag{818}$$

κ_1 and κ_2 are functions of the plate factor k [see Eq. (806)], and k can be computed from Eq. (818). The critical stress σ_c can then be found from Eq. (799). However, in the case of short plates it is convenient to replace the ratio t/b in Eq. (799) by the ratio t/a and introduce a plate factor $\bar{k} = \alpha^2 k$. The critical stress σ_c is then

$$\frac{\sigma_c}{\tau} = \frac{\pi^2 E}{12(1 - \nu^2)} \left(\frac{t}{a}\right)^2 \bar{k} \tag{819}$$

In order to facilitate routine computation of σ_c Table 40 contains the values of $\bar{k}$ for values of α between 0.1 and 1.0 and for values of ζ between 0 and ∞.

TABLE 40.   Plate Factors $\bar{k}$ in Eq. (819) for Short Plates in Compression, Elastically Restrained at the Loaded Edges, Fig. 222

Coefficient of restraint ζ	Aspect ratio $\alpha = a/b$							
	0.1	0.2	0.3	0.4	0.5	0.6	0.8	1.0
0, clamped	4.02	4.08	4.19	4.34	4.55	4.82	5.59	6.74
0.05	3.35	3.40	3.51	3.63	3.88	4.15	4.94	6.18
0.10	2.88	2.93	3.04	3.18	3.42	3.70	4.51	5.78
0.15	2.56	2.62	2.72	2.86	3.10	3.38	4.21	5.48
0.20	2.32	2.38	2.49	2.62	2.86	3.15	3.98	5.26
0.25	2.15	2.21	2.32	2.45	2.68	2.97	3.80	5.09
0.30	2.01	2.07	2.18	2.32	2.55	2.84	3.67	4.98
0.35	1.90	1.96	2.08	2.22	2.44	2.73	3.57	4.89
0.40	1.81	1.88	1.99	2.13	2.35	2.65	3.48	4.80
0.45	1.74	1.81	1.91	2.06	2.28	2.58	3.41	4.73
0.50	1.69	1.75	1.85	2.00	2.23	2.52	3.35	4.68
1.00	1.39	1.46	1.55	1.71	1.92	2.22	3.06	4.37
2.00	1.22	1.27	1.38	1.55	1.76	2.04	2.89	4.19
∞, simply supported.....	1.02	1.08	1.19	1.35	1.56	1.85	2.69	4.00

In deriving Eq. (815), which defines the degree of restraint, it was tacitly assumed that buckling of the plate occurs in the elastic region. If the critical stress lies above the elastic limit, the term D in Eq. (815) should be replaced by $D\tau$ and the coefficient of restraint would become $\zeta\tau$, the parameter τ depending on the unknown critical stress σ_c. This requires computation by trial and error. Since k can be taken from Table 40, a sufficiently accurate value of ζ could be found in two or three steps. For practical computation it is, however, not necessary to use this procedure, as the effect of the use of the correction on the critical stress σ_c is very small and is always on the side of safety.

The computation of the critical stress σ_c is therefore extremely simple.

After computing ζ from Eq. (816) or (817), read $\bar{k}$ from Table 40, and compute σ_c/τ from Eq. (819). σ_c can be found from Tables 41 or 42[1] giving σ_c as function of σ_c/τ.

117. Buckling of Rectangular Plates Clamped on All Four Edges

It is not possible to obtain finite expressions in terms of elementary functions for the stability conditions of plates having four clamped edges, as is the case when only two opposite edges are elastically restrained or clamped, where the buckling modes can be expressed by a combination of circular and hyperbolic functions [Eq. (624) of Chap. IX].

Approximate solutions can be obtained by the Ritz method. Such solutions satisfy the boundary conditions but do not satisfy the differential equation of the buckling problem. Another method for solving this problem approximately was used by Sazawa,[2] who derived an analytical expression which actually satisfies the differential equation (600) but does not comply exactly with the condition at the edges except at the middle of the edges and at the corners. Numerical results were given for square plates under edge compression σ_A and σ_B in the directions of the x- and y-axes, respectively, for various values of σ_B/σ_A. Sazawa and Watanabe[3] improved the theory subsequently by expanding the solution of the differential equation in trigonometric series, arriving in this way at solutions which satisfy all the boundary conditions. Numerical values for the plate coefficient k for rectangular plates in longitudinal compression were obtained for the ratios $\alpha = a/b = 1$, 1.5, and 2.

A rigorous solution of the buckling problem of clamped rectangular plates was published by Taylor,[4] who gave the numerical results for the square plate in equal compression in both directions, $\sigma_A = \sigma_B$.

Faxén[5] discussed the problem under consideration in an extensive mathematical study, confirming Taylor's result for the square plate, and gave values of the plate coefficient k for several aspect ratios between 0.75 and 2, assuming $\sigma_B = 0$.

Maulbetsch[6] used Faxén's analysis and extended the numerical investi-

---

[1] Tables 41 and 42 apply for the same types of steel as Tables 27 and 28. See the footnote on p. 344.

[2] Sazawa, K., Das Ausknicken von allseitig befestigten und gedrückten rechteckigen Platten, *Zeitschrift für angewandte Mathematik und Mechanik*, Vol. 12, p. 227, 1932.

[3] Sazawa, K., and W. Watanabe, Buckling of a Rectangular Plate with Four Clamped Edges Re-examined with Improved Theory, *Repts. Tokyo Imp. Univ. Aeronaut. Research Inst.*, Vol. 11, No. 143, 1936.

[4] Taylor, G. I., The Buckling Load for a Rectangular Plate with Four Clamped Edges, *Zeitschrift für angewande Mathematik und Mechanik*, Vol. 13, p. 147, 1933.

[5] Faxén, O. H., Die Knickfestigkeit rechteckiger Platten, *Zeitschrift für angewandte Mathematik und Mechanik*, Vol. 15, p. 268, 1935.

[6] Maulbetsch, J. L., Buckling of Compressed Rectangular Plates with Built-in Edges, *Trans. ASME*, APM Vol. 4, p. A59, 1937.

TABLE 41.   Determination of the Critical Stress σ_c for Steel, Kips/In.^{2}
($\sigma_p = 25$ kips/in.^{2}, $\sigma_y = 33$ kips/in.^{2})

σ_c/τ	σ_c	σ_c/τ	σ_c	σ_c/τ	σ_c
25.0	25.00	35.0	27.29	120.0	31.33
25.5	25.17	36.0	27.45	140.0	31.57
26.0	25.32	37.0	27.60	160.0	31.74
26.5	25.46	38.0	27.74	180.0	31.88
27.0	25.60	39.0	27.87	200.0	32.00
27.5	25.73	40.0	28.00	250.0	32.20
28.0	25.86	45.0	28.54	300.0	32.32
28.5	25.98	50.0	29.00	400.0	32.48
29.0	26.10	55.0	29.36	500.0	32.60
29.5	26.22	60.0	29.67		
30.0	26.33	70.0	30.14		
31.0	26.54	80.0	30.50		
32.0	26.74	90.0	30.78		
33.0	26.94	100.0	31.00		
34.0	27.12				

TABLE 42.   Determination of the Critical Stress σ_c for Steel, Kips/In.^{2}
($\sigma_p = 34$ kips/in.^{2}, $\sigma_y = 45$ kips/in.^{2})

σ_c/τ	σ_c	σ_c/τ	σ_c	σ_c/τ	σ_c
34.0	34.00	46.0	36.87	100.0	41.26
34.5	34.17	47.0	37.02	110.0	41.60
35.0	34.31	48.0	37.20	120.0	41.88
35.5	34.46	49.0	37.37	130.0	42.11
36.0	34.60	50.0	37.52	140.0	42.32
36.5	34.74				
		52.0	37.81	150.0	42.50
37.0	34.89	54.0	38.08	200.0	43.12
27.5	35.02	56.0	38.32	250.0	43.50
38.0	35.15	58.0	38.55	300.0	43.75
38.50	35.27	60.0	38.77		
39.0	35.40			400.0	44.06
39.5	35.52	65.0	39.24	500.0	44.24
		70.0	39.65	600.0	44.37
40.0	35.64	75.0	40.01		
41.0	35.87	80.0	40.32		
42.0	36.09	85.0	40.60		
43.0	36.30	90.0	40.85		
44.0	36.50	95.0	41.06		
45.0	36.69				

gation to rectangular plates up to the aspect ratio $\alpha = 4$, assuming $\sigma_B = 0$. He also gave a solution based on the Ritz method. Maulbetsch approximates the displacement form of the plate by the normal modes of vibration of a bar clamped on both ends, using in the direction of the compressive force a six-term expansion and a three-term expression in the other direction. This investigation yielded values of k which were 3 to 10% larger than those obtained from his exact method.

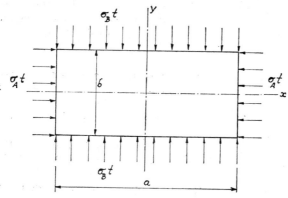

Fig. 225

Further progress was made by Levy,[1] who obtained rigorous solutions in the form of infinite series by expressing the deflection w and the moments along the edges by Fourier series. The significance of Levy's investigation lies in the fact that the series are rapidly converging, thus reducing the numerical work in determining the k-values. The buckling loads were computed for rectangular plates in longitudinal compression for 14 aspect ratios ranging from $\alpha = a/b = 0.75$ to 4.00. The possible error of the results is of the order of 0.1%.

The critical stress σ_c of a rectangular plate rigidly clamped on all four sides can be expressed

$$\sigma_c = \frac{\pi^2 E}{12(1 - \nu^2)} \left(\frac{t}{b}\right)^2 k \tag{820}$$

where the plate factor k depends on the aspect ratio $\alpha = a/b$ and upon the ratio σ_B/σ_A of the compressive stresses (Fig. 225). Equation (820) is valid only when σ_c is equal to or smaller than the proportional limit. A similar formula for the inelastic range is discussed at the end of this article.

Square Plates in Equal Compression in Both Directions. Taylor and Faxén found

$$k = 5.31 \tag{821}$$

[1] Levy, S., Buckling of Rectangular Plates with Built-in Edges, *Trans. ASME*, Vol. 64, p. A171, 1942.

Square Plates in Unequal Compression, σ_A in x-direction and σ_B in y-direction. The values of the plate factor k found by Sazawa by an approximate method are given in Table 43. These values of k introduced into Eq. (820) give the critical values of σ_A.

The exact value of k for $\sigma_B/\sigma_A = 0$ is 10.07 (see Table 44), and the exact value for $\sigma_B/\sigma_A = 1$ is $k = 5.31$ [Eq. (821)]. The difference in these two limiting cases between Sazawa's approximate values and the exact values is about 6%. It can be assumed that the other k-values found by Sazawa are also approximately 6% too high. The last line of Table 43 gives the corrected values of k which may be used for design purposes.

TABLE 43.   Plate Factors k in Eq. (820) for Square Plates in Compression in Both Directions

σ_B/σ_A...............	0	¼	⅓	½	¾	1
k (Sazawa).............	10.65	8.80	8.40	7.48	6.41	5.61
k (corrected)..........	10.07	8.27	7.90	7.04	6.02	5.31

Rectangular Plates, Longitudinal Compression σ_A Only (Fig. 226). Levy obtained the k-values listed in Table 44.

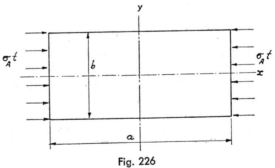

Fig. 226

TABLE 44.   Plate Factors k in Eq. (820) for Rectangular Plates in Longitudinal Compression, Fig. 226

$\alpha = a/b$......	0.75	1.00	1.25	1.50	1.75	2.00	2.25
k.............	11.66	10.07	9.25	8.33	8.11	7.88	7.63
$\alpha = a/b$......	2.50	2.75	3.00	3.25	3.50	3.75	4.00
k.............	7.59	7.44	7.37	7.35	7.27	7.24	7.23

Buckling in the Inelastic Range. The investigations mentioned above are all based on the theory of elastic buckling, and no analysis on the basis of the differential equation (601) which applies in the inelastic range is available. From analogy with the theory of buckling of long plates in Chap. IX we can conclude that the plate factors k determined in the elastic range will remain valid approximately if the critical stress is computed from

$$\frac{\sigma_c}{\sqrt{\tau}} = \frac{\pi^2 E}{12(1 - \nu^2)} \left(\frac{t}{b}\right)^2 k \tag{822}$$

where $\sqrt{\tau} = \sqrt{E_t/E}$ is the plasticity factor. Equation (822), however, cannot be valid for very short plates, and it is recommended only if the aspect ratio is $\alpha \geq \frac{2}{3}$.

Short plates, $\alpha < \frac{2}{3}$, behave rather similarly to columns, and the relation

$$\frac{\sigma_c}{\tau} = \frac{\pi^2 E}{12(1 - \nu^2)} \left(\frac{t}{b}\right)^2 k \tag{823}$$

is recommended. This equation is similar to Eq. (799) used in Art. 116.

In case of a square plate equally compressed in the x- and y-directions (Table 43, $\sigma_A/\sigma_B = 1$), Eq. (823) should be used instead of Eq. (822), because in this case the plate will act isotropically and the effective plasticity factor is $\tau = E_t/E$.

To find the critical stresses σ_c, the applicable Eq. (822) or (823) is to be used in conjunction with the plate factors k in Tables 43 and 44. The computed value $\sigma_c/\sqrt{\tau}$ or σ_c/τ can be used to find σ_c from Tables 27 and 28 on pages 343 and 344, or Tables 41 and 42 respectively.

118. Stability of Compression Members Having Cellular Cross Sections

One of the special problems in the design of the hulls of ships is the question of the buckling strength of bottoms of cellular cross sections. Figures 227a and 227b show the simplest types of double and triple bottoms having evenly spaced longitudinals. In general, the thickness of the plates which form the cellular structure varies from skin to skin. Frequently the longitudinals or the inner skins are reinforced by stiffeners as indicated in Figs. 227c to 227e.

For the simplest case of a cellular cross section, namely, the rectangular tube section with two axes of symmetry, a sufficiently accurate approximate method for the determination of the mutual restraining effect of one plate element upon the others has been presented in Chap. IX. In the much more complicated compression members under discussion here the interaction between the plates forming the structure becomes far more complex and a more refined mathematical analysis is required to obtain dependable results for these structures.

In the following, a theory of stability of tubular or cellular structures composed of thin plates is outlined. The method is applicable in the elastic and inelastic range. It is based upon an extension of the method of four-moment equations discussed in Chap. VI. The basic idea is as follows: The plates of a cellular structure in longitudinal compression buckle in half waves of a certain length λ which, however, is not known beforehand.   For any assumed wavelength λ it is possible to determine a plate coefficient k and, therefore, a corresponding critical compressive stress σ_c of the structure by deriving a system of homogeneous linear equations the determinant of the coefficients of which must vanish. Under all possible values of k computed in this way the smallest value finally determines the actual critical stress σ_c of the system.[1]   The follow-

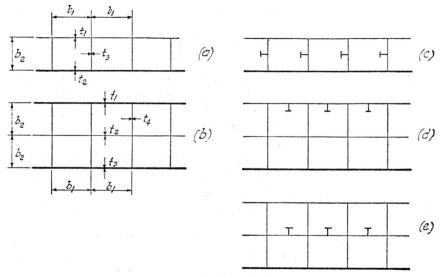

Fig. 227

ing analysis is restricted to closed sections of tubular or cellular shape, but the concept can also be applied to find the critical stress of open sections with outstanding flanges.

Derivation of the Four-moment Equations.   The analysis is based upon the following two fundamental assumptions:

1. The plates are rigidly joined along the edges. This implies that all the plates which meet at one edge rotate through the same angle when the cross section distorts.

2. The edges are considered straight, which implies the assumption that primary failure of the entire structure does not occur before local buckling sets in.

Each individual plate of the structure therefore may be regarded as a plate supported on both unloaded edges and elastically restrained by the

[1] This method is an original contribution of the author.

adjacent plates. When a plate deflects in its unstable state of equilibrium, moments $\bar{M}^r$ and $\bar{M}^l$ per unit length act along the unloaded edges as illustrated by Fig. 228. Between two nodal lines which are the distance λ apart, the moments $\bar{M}^r$ and $\bar{M}^l$ are sinusoidally distributed.[1] We therefore have

$$\bar{M}^r = M^r \sin \frac{\pi x}{\lambda} \quad \text{and} \quad \bar{M}^l = M^l \sin \frac{\pi x}{\lambda} \tag{824}$$

where M^r and M^l are the largest values of the moments at the edges.

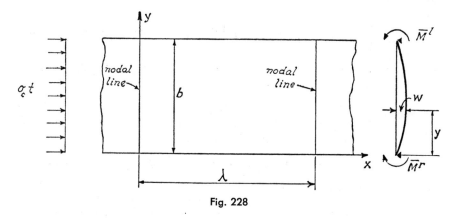

Fig. 228

As a preparatory step for deriving the four-moment equations, we determine the deflection w of a plate due to an uniformly distributed longitudinal force $\sigma_c t$ and edge moments $\bar{M}^r$ and $\bar{M}^l$. It is convenient to assume first $\bar{M}^r = 0$, the corresponding deflection being denoted by w_1. From the expression for w_1 the deflection w_2 due to $\bar{M}^r$ alone can be easily derived and the total deflection $w = w_1 + w_2$ determined.

We base this analysis on the general differential equation (601), which is applicable in the elastic and inelastic range. The general solution for the deflection w_1 is again given by Eq. (624):

$$w_1 = \sin \frac{\pi x}{\lambda} \left(C_1 \cosh \kappa_1 y + C_2 \sinh \kappa_1 y + C_3 \cos \kappa_2 y + C_4 \sin \kappa_2 y \right) \tag{825}$$

κ_1 and κ_2 are defined by Eqs. (631), which, using $n = 1$ and $\alpha = \lambda/b$, take the form

$$\kappa_1 = \frac{\pi}{\lambda'} \sqrt{\mu + 1}, \quad \kappa_2 = \frac{\pi}{\lambda'} \sqrt{\mu - 1}, \quad \lambda' = \frac{\lambda}{\sqrt[4]{\tau}} \tag{826}$$

[1] The theory of stability of rectangular plates discussed in Chap. IX indicates that the deflection w has the form $w = \sin (\pi x/\lambda) Y$, where Y is a function of y [see Eq. (618)]. Since $\bar{M}^r$ and $\bar{M}^l$ are proportional to $\dfrac{d^2 w}{dy^2} = \sin \dfrac{\pi x}{\lambda} \left(\dfrac{d^2 Y}{dy^2} \right)$, it follows that these moments vary sinusoidally.

The constants C_1 to C_4 are to be determined by the boundary conditions

$$[w_1]_{y=0} = 0 \quad \text{and} \quad [w_1]_{y=b} = 0 \tag{827}$$
$$[M_y]_{y=0} = 0 \quad \text{and} \quad [M_y]_{y=b} = \bar{M}^l \tag{828}$$

According to Eq. (602) we have

$$M_y = -D\left(\frac{\partial^2 w_1}{\partial y^2} + \nu \sqrt{\tau} \frac{\partial^2 w_1}{\partial x^2}\right)$$

and since $\dfrac{\partial^2 w_1}{\partial x^2} = 0$ at the edges, the conditions (828) assume the form

$$\left[\frac{\partial^2 w_1}{\partial y^2}\right]_{y=0} = 0 \quad \text{and} \quad -D\left[\frac{\partial^2 w_1}{\partial y^2}\right]_{y=b} = \bar{M}^l = M^l \sin\frac{\pi x}{\lambda} \tag{829}$$

Introducing the expression (825) into Eqs. (827) and (829) leads to the four equations for the constants C

$$C_1 + C_3 = 0$$
$$C_1\kappa_1{}^2 - C_3\kappa_2{}^2 = 0$$
$$C_1 \cosh \kappa_1 b + C_2 \sinh \kappa_1 b + C_3 \cos \kappa_2 b + C_4 \sin \kappa_2 b = 0$$
$$\kappa_1{}^2(C_1 \cosh \kappa_1 b + C_2 \sinh \kappa_1 b) - \kappa_2{}^2(C_3 \cos \kappa_2 b + C_4 \sin \kappa_2 b) = -\frac{M^l}{D}$$

Solving for the constants C we obtain

$$C_1 = 0 \quad \text{and} \quad C_2 = -\frac{M^l}{D}\frac{1}{(\kappa_1{}^2 + \kappa_2{}^2)\sinh \kappa_1 b}$$

$$C_3 = 0 \quad \text{and} \quad C_4 = \frac{M^l}{D}\frac{1}{(\kappa_1{}^2 + \kappa_2{}^2)\sin \kappa_2 b}$$

The deflection w_1 is therefore

$$w_1 = \frac{M^l \sin \pi x/\lambda}{D(\kappa_1{}^2 + \kappa_2{}^2)}\left(\frac{\sin \kappa_2 y}{\sin \kappa_2 b} - \frac{\sinh \kappa_1 y}{\sinh \kappa_1 b}\right) \tag{830}$$

Because of symmetry, an expression for w_2 can be obtained by replacing M^l by M^r and y by $b - y$,

$$w_2 = \frac{M^r \sin \pi x/\lambda}{D(\kappa_1{}^2 + \kappa_2{}^2)}\left[\frac{\sin k_2(b - y)}{\sin \kappa_2 b} - \frac{\sinh \kappa_1(b - y)}{\sinh \kappa_1 b}\right] \tag{831}$$

and the entire deflection w is

$$w = \frac{\sin \pi x/\lambda}{D(\kappa_1{}^2 + \kappa_2{}^2)}\left\{ M^r\left[\frac{\sin \kappa_2(b - y)}{\sin \kappa_2 b} - \frac{\sinh \kappa_1(b - y)}{\sinh \kappa_1 b}\right] \right.$$
$$\left. + M^l\left(\frac{\sin \kappa_2 y}{\sin \kappa_2 b} - \frac{\sinh \kappa_1 y}{\sinh \kappa_1 b}\right)\right\} \tag{832}$$

Let us now consider two adjacent plates $i - 1$, i and i, $i + 1$ which meet along the edge i. In general, other plates may also join at this edge as indicated in Fig. 229a by the dashed lines. The widths of the plates are b_i and b_{i+1}, and their thicknesses t_i and t_{i+1}, respectively. Figure 229b shows the two plates in the distorted state acted on by edge moments $\bar{M}_{i-1}{}^r$, $\bar{M}_i{}^l$ and $\bar{M}_i{}^r$, $\bar{M}_{i+1}{}^l$. Since the two plates are rigidly joined, the two elements rotate through the same angle φ, and the condi-

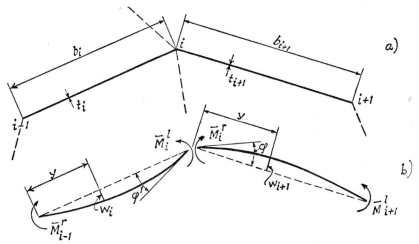

Fig. 229

tion of continuity is (Fig. 229b)

$$\left[\frac{\partial w_i}{\partial y}\right]_{y=b_i} = \left[\frac{\partial w_{i+1}}{\partial y}\right]_{y=0} \tag{833}$$

Applying Eq. (832) we have, for the plate $i - 1$, i,

$$\left[\frac{\partial w_i}{\partial y}\right]_{y=b} = \frac{\sin \pi x/\lambda}{D_i(\kappa_{1,i}{}^2 + \kappa_{2,i}{}^2)}\left[M_{i-1}{}^r\left(-\frac{\kappa_{2,i}}{\sin \kappa_{2,i}b_i} + \frac{\kappa_{1,i}}{\sin \kappa_{1,i}b_i}\right)\right.$$
$$\left. + M_i{}^l(\kappa_{2,i} \cot \kappa_{2,i}b_i - \kappa_{1,i} \coth \kappa_{1,i}b_i)\right] \tag{834}$$

and for the plate i, $i + 1$,

$$\left[\frac{\partial w_{i+1}}{\partial y}\right]_{y=0} = \frac{\sin \pi x/\lambda}{D_{i+1}(\kappa_{1,i+1}{}^2 + \kappa_{2,i+1}{}^2)}\left[M_i{}^r(-\kappa_{2,i+1} \cot \kappa_{2,i+1}b_{i+1}\right.$$
$$\left. + \kappa_{1,i+1} \coth \kappa_{1,i+1}b_{i+1}) + M_{i+1}{}^l\left(\frac{\kappa_{2,i+1}}{\sin \kappa_{2,i+1}b_{i+1}} - \frac{\kappa_{1,i+1}}{\sin \kappa_{1,i+1}b_{i+1}}\right)\right] \tag{835}$$

We compute from Eqs. (826)

$$\kappa_1{}^2 + \kappa_2{}^2 = 2\frac{\pi^2}{\lambda'^2}\mu$$

Introducing $D_i = \dfrac{Et_i{}^3}{12(1 - \nu^2)}$ and $D_{i+1} = \dfrac{Et_{i+1}{}^3}{12(1 - \nu^2)}$, the factors before the brackets in the two equations above become

$$\frac{6(1 - \nu^2)\lambda'^2}{\pi^2\mu_i t_i^3} \sin\frac{\pi x}{\lambda} \quad \text{and} \quad \frac{6(1 - \nu^2)\lambda'^2}{\pi^2\mu_{i+1}t_{i+1}^3} \sin\frac{\pi x}{\lambda} \qquad (836)$$

respectively. μ^2 is defined by Eq. (619), and introducing $n = 1$, $a = \lambda$ and the above values for D, we have

$$\mu_i^2 = 12(1 - \nu^2)\frac{\sigma_c}{\tau E t_i^2}\frac{\lambda^2}{\pi^2} \quad \text{and} \quad \mu_{i+1}^2 = 12(1 - \nu^2)\frac{\sigma_c}{\tau E t_{i+1}^2}\frac{\lambda^2}{\pi^2}$$

Observing that σ_c/τ has the same value in all plates of the structure, the relation

$$\mu_i t_i = \mu_{i+1}t_{i+1} \qquad (837)$$

can be derived. The two terms (836) therefore may be given the form

$$\frac{6(1 - \nu^2)\lambda'^2}{\pi^2\mu_i t_i}\frac{\sin \pi x/\lambda}{t_i^2} \quad \text{and} \quad \frac{6(1 - \nu^2)\lambda'^2}{\pi^2\mu_i t_i}\frac{\sin \pi x/\lambda}{t_{i+1}^2}$$

Introducing the expressions (834) and (835) into Eq. (833) and dividing by

$$\frac{6(1 - \nu^2)\lambda'^2}{\pi^2\mu_i t_i} \sin\frac{\pi x}{\lambda}$$

leads to the equation

$$\frac{1}{t_i^2 b_i}(M_{i-1}{}^r\Psi_i + M_i{}^l\Phi_i) + \frac{1}{t_{i+1}^2 b_{i+1}}(M_i{}^r\Phi_{i+1} + M_{i+1}{}^l\Psi_{i+1}) = 0 \qquad (838)$$

where

$$\left.\begin{array}{l}\Psi = -\dfrac{\kappa_2 b}{\sin \kappa_2 b} + \dfrac{\kappa_1 b}{\sinh \kappa_1 b} \\[2mm] \Phi = \kappa_2 b \cot \kappa_2 b - \kappa_1 b \coth \kappa_1 b\end{array}\right\} \qquad (839)$$

$\sqrt{\tau}$ does not appear in Eq. (838), which is therefore valid in the elastic and inelastic range of buckling. This is an important fact, because it permits using precalculated tables of the coefficients Ψ and Φ which apply regardless of whether the finally determined critical stress σ_c lies below or above the proportional limit. Equation (838) is a relation between the four moments at the longitudinal edges of two adjacent plates and will be referred to as the four-moment equation of the stability problem of plate structures.

In deriving Eq. (838) it was assumed that other plates also join at the edge i. If this is not the case, $M_i{}^l = M_i{}^r = M_i$ and the equation becomes a three-moment equation.

If the plate i, $i + 1$ is rigidly clamped at edge i, the restraint at i can be considered due to an infinitely rigid panel $i - 1$, i to the left of i. In

this case the four-moment equation (838) for the plate i, $i + 1$ becomes a two-moment equation:

$$M_i{}^r\Phi_{i+1} + M_{i+1}{}^l\Psi_{i+1} = 0$$

The Stability Condition. Consider a tubular structure as shown in the cross section in Fig. 230 representing a closed circuit of n plates. For each edge where two plates join, a four-moment equation (838) can be obtained, and there are altogether n equations which determine the n unknown moments. Splitting the single circuit of plates into a double circuit by adding a plate (see the dashed line in Fig. 230) results in two more unknown edge moments, but also in two additional independent four-moment equations. When this process is repeated, all sorts of cellular structures representing double or triple bottoms can be obtained, but the number of four-moment equations will always remain equal to the number of unknown edge moments.

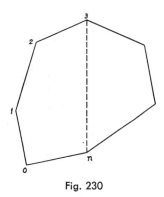

Fig. 230

In setting up the four-moment equations all the edge moments may be considered positive,[1] except those pertaining to plates which are common to two cells, for which the moments are considered positive in one and negative in the other circuit. In the latter case an adjustment of signs in Eq. (838) is required.

The four-moment equations form a complete system of linear, homogeneous equations in the unknown moments; nonzero solutions exist only if the determinant Δ of its coefficients vanishes, $\Delta = 0$. The stability condition is a function of the n ratios $\alpha_i' = \lambda'/b_i$ and of the n coefficients μ_i. If we select one plate as a reference plate, we can express the ratios α_i' and coefficients μ_i by the values α and μ for this plate: $\alpha_i' = \alpha'b/b_i$, and from Eq. (837), $\mu_i = \mu t/t_i$ where b and t are the values for the reference plate. The stability condition is therefore only a function of the two independent variables α' and μ. Assuming a certain value of α', the parameter μ can be computed from the transcendental stability equation by numerical methods. In this way several values of μ can be determined, and the corresponding values of k are computed from[2]

$$k = \frac{\mu^2 b^2}{\lambda'^2} = \frac{\mu^2}{\alpha'^2} \tag{840}$$

[1] Positive moments are those which tend to bend the plate toward the interior of the circuit.

[2] This relation follows from a comparison of Eqs. (621) and (841).

These values k can be plotted as a function of α', and the minimum value $k_{\min}$ and the corresponding value α' can be determined (Fig. 231). The critical stress σ_c at which the entire structure will buckle finally is given by

$$\frac{\sigma_c}{\sqrt{\tau}} = \frac{\pi^2 E}{12(1 - \nu^2)} \left(\frac{t}{b}\right)^2 k_{\min} \tag{841}$$

where b and t are the dimensions of the plate to which the selected independent parameter μ belongs.

The coefficients Ψ and Φ in Eq. (838) are functions of $\alpha' = \lambda'/b$ and μ. Typical Ψ and Φ curves, for $\alpha = 0.5$, are shown in Fig. 232. The com-

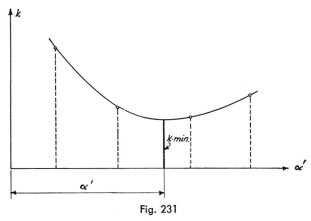

Fig. 231

plete curves show an infinite number of singularities dividing each of the two curves into individual branches. In order to facilitate the application of the method it is convenient to have the functions $\Psi(\mu)$ and $\Phi(\mu)$ tabulated for various values of α. However, such tables would not be too convenient for use because of the difficulty of interpolation in the neighborhood of those μ-values for which Ψ or Φ becomes infinite. This difficulty may be overcome by tabulating also the reciprocals $1/\Psi$ and $1/\Phi$, which are smooth curves.[1]

In the case of double or triple bottoms of ships with equally spaced vertical plates, the four-moment equation method leads to two or, in some cases, to three linear equations the determinant of which can easily be evaluated. The procedure will be explained on a few simple problems.

Problem 1: Determine the critical stress of a rectangular tube having side lengths b_1 and b_2 and plate thicknesses t_1 and t_2, respectively (Fig. 233a). Because of the symmetry the moments M at the four edges are identical, and one four-moment equation suffices to determine the plate factor $k_{\min}$ in Eq. (841). Considering the plates 1, 2 and 2, 3 which join

[1] Such tables were prepared by the author but are not included in this volume.

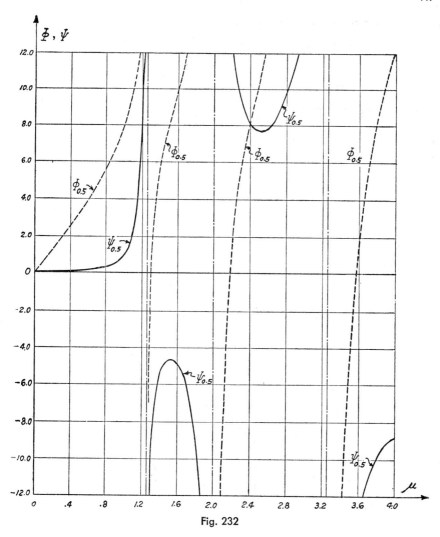

Fig. 232

at the edge 2 (Fig. 233b), Eq. (838) becomes

$$\frac{1}{t_1^2 b_1} (M_1 \Psi_1 + M_2 \Phi_1) + \frac{1}{t_2^2 b_2} (M_2 \Phi_2 + M_3 \Psi_3) = 0$$

and since $M_1 = M_2 = M_3$, we obtain the stability condition in the form

$$\frac{\Psi_1 + \Phi_1}{t_1^2 b_1} + \frac{\Phi_2 + \Psi_2}{t_2^2 b_2} = 0$$

This equation has been solved with the aid of the above-mentioned tables by trial and error for $b_2/b_1 = 0.5$ and 0.833 and for thickness ratios

$t_2/t_1 = 1$ and **2**. The results are shown in Table 45. For comparison the table contains in parentheses the k-values read from the diagram (Fig. 169) representing values of k derived by Lundquist. The values of

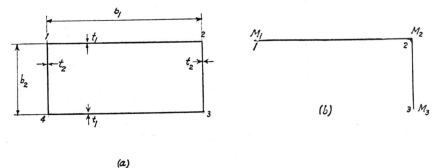

(a)

(b)

Fig. 233

k in Table 45 are to be used in Eq. (841) in connection with the ratio $b/t = b_1/t_1$.

TABLE 45.   Plate Coefficients k_{min} for Box Section, Fig. 233a

b_2/b_1	$t_2/t_1 = 1$	$t_2/t_1 = 2$
0.5	5.15 (5.13)	6.51 (6.51)
0.833	4.56 (4.56)	4.51 (4.51)

Problem 2: Continuous plating of unequal widths (Fig. 234). Consider a plate panel of width b_2 joined on both sides by narrower plates of width b_1. The plate thickness t is the same in all panels. The buckling

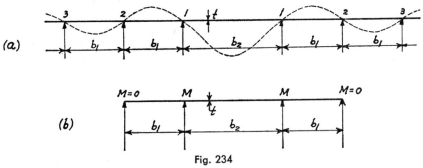

(a)

(b)

Fig. 234

configuration is shown in Fig. 234a, and it can be assumed without great error that points of inflection will lie very close to the supports 2. Therefore, an approximate solution may be obtained by assuming that the plates are hinged at the supports 2. Considering only three panels having simply supported edges at both ends (Fig. 234b), the problem can be

solved by one four-moment equation.   On account of the symmetry and
of $M_2 = 0$ at the ends we obtain

$$\frac{1}{t_1^2 b_1} M_1 \Phi_1 + \frac{1}{t_2^2 b_2} (M_1 \Phi_2 + M_1 \Psi_2) = 0$$

The stability condition is finally

$$\frac{\Phi_1}{t_1^2 b_1} + \frac{\Phi_2 + \Psi_2}{t_2^2 b} = 0$$

This equation has been solved for various values of b_2/b_1 between 0.5
and 2.   The k-values are plotted versus the ratio b_2/b_1 in Fig. 235.

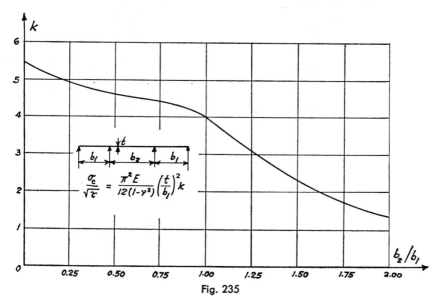

Fig. 235

Problem 3: Double bottom as shown in Fig. 236a.   It is assumed that
the bottom extends on both sides without limit.   Due to the symmetry
of geometry and loading of the individual cells, two four-moment equations suffice to solve the problem.   Denoting the edge moments of the
inner bottom and the hull plating by M_1 and M_2, respectively, the edge
moments of the vertical plates follow directly from a consideration of the
equilibrium at the edges where the plates join.   Figure 236b needs no
further explanation.   Let us consider one cell of the structure composed
of four plates.   Proceeding from left to right as viewed from the interior
of the cell, the edges are numbered, 1, 2, 3, 4.   According to the number
of plates which compose the cell, four four-moment equations could be
written, but because of the symmetry only two are required, namely,

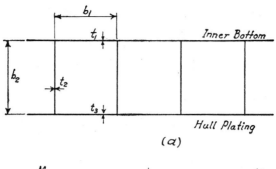

(a)

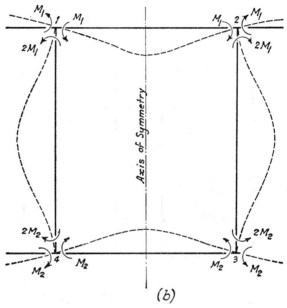

(b)

Fig. 236

Plates 1, 2 *and* 2, 3:

$$\frac{1}{t_1^2 b} M_1(\Psi_1 + \Phi_1) + \frac{1}{t_2^2 b_2} (2M_1\Phi_2 + 2M_2\Psi_2) = 0$$

Plates 2, 3 *and* 3, 4:

$$\frac{1}{t_2^2 b_2} (2M_1\Psi_2 + 2M_2\Phi_2) + \frac{1}{t_3^2 b_1} (M_2\Phi_3 + M_2\Psi_3) = 0$$

Rearranging, we arrive at two equations:

$$[c_1(\Psi_1 + \Phi_1) + 2c_2\Phi_2]M_1 + 2c_2\Psi_2 M_2 = 0$$
$$2c_2\Psi_2 M_1 + [2c_2\Phi_2 + c_3(\Phi_3 + \Psi_3)]M_2 = 0$$

where the abbreviations

$$c_1 = \frac{1}{t_1{}^2 b_1}, \qquad c_2 = \frac{1}{t_2{}^2 b_2}, \qquad c_3 = \frac{1}{t_3{}^2 b_1}$$

are used. The determinant of the above system furnishes the stability condition

$$[c_1(\Psi_1 + \Phi_1) + 2c_2\Phi_2][2c_2\Phi_2 + c_3(\Phi_3 + \Psi_3)] - 4c_2{}^2\Psi_2{}^2 = 0$$

119. Effect of Lapped Joints on Buckling Strength of Plates

A special feature in the design of ships is the use of lapped joints between the supports of a plate panel as shown in Fig. 237. The plate apparently is stiffened by the lapped joints, and this stiffening effect is

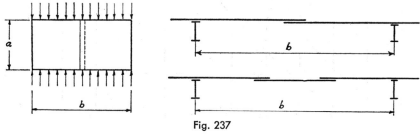

Fig. 237

quite considerable. Plates with lapped joints were investigated by Schnadel,[1] who used the energy method in his attempt to approach the stability problem of such plates in compression. The theory of longitudinally stiffened plates developed in Chap. X provides the means for treating the problem of plates with lapped joints in a comparatively simple manner. In the subsequent discussion the cases of one lap in the middle of the plate, two laps located at the third points, and one eccentrically located lap at the third point will be considered.

Plates with One Lapped Joint on the Center Line. Plates having one stiffener on the center line were treated in Art. 98. The stability condition for symmetric buckling where the stiffener deflects with the plate [Eq. (685)] becomes, for $n = 1$,

$$\left(\frac{1}{\kappa_1} \tanh \frac{\kappa_1 b}{2} - \frac{1}{\kappa_2} \tan \frac{\kappa_2 b}{2}\right)\Phi' - 2(\kappa_1{}^2 + \kappa_2{}^2) = 0 \qquad (842)$$

where

$$\kappa_1 b = \frac{\pi}{\alpha} \sqrt{\mu + 1} \qquad \text{and} \qquad \kappa_2 b = \frac{\pi}{\alpha} \sqrt{\mu - 1} \qquad (843)$$

$$\Phi' = \frac{\gamma}{b^3}\left(\frac{\pi}{\alpha}\right)^4 - \delta \frac{\sigma_c t}{Db\tau}\left(\frac{\pi}{\alpha}\right)^2 \qquad (844)$$

$$\gamma = \frac{EI}{bD} \qquad \text{and} \qquad \delta = \frac{A}{bt} \qquad (845)$$

[1] Schnadel. G., Knickung von Schiffsplatten, *Werft-Reederei-Hafen*, 1930, p. 461.

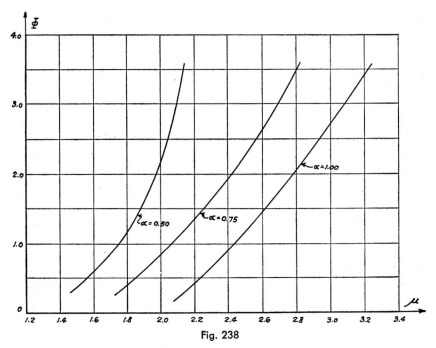

Fig. 238

With $n = 1$ and $a = \alpha b$, Eq. (621) furnishes the expression

$$\sigma_c = \frac{1}{b^2} \left(\frac{\pi}{\alpha} \right)^2 \frac{D\tau}{t} \mu^2 \qquad (846)$$

Substituting this value into Eq. (844) we obtain

$$\Phi' = \left(\frac{\pi}{\alpha} \right)^4 \frac{1}{b^3} (\gamma - \mu^2 \delta) = \left(\frac{\pi}{\alpha} \right)^4 \frac{1}{b^3} \Phi \qquad (847)$$

where $\Phi = \gamma - \mu^2 \delta$. Using Eqs. (843) and (847) the stability condition (842) can be written

$$\left(\frac{1}{\sqrt{\mu + 1}} \tanh \frac{\pi}{2\alpha} \sqrt{\mu + 1} - \frac{1}{\sqrt{\mu - 1}} \tan \frac{\pi}{2\alpha} \sqrt{\mu - 1} \right) \Phi - \frac{4\mu\alpha}{\pi} = 0 \qquad (848)$$

For any given value of Φ, which expresses the relative rigidity of the stiffener as compared with the flexural rigidity of the plate, Eq. (848) could be solved for μ. However, it is more convenient to express Φ as a function of μ, namely,

$$\Phi = \frac{4\mu\alpha/\pi}{\dfrac{1}{\sqrt{\mu + 1}} \tanh \dfrac{\pi}{2\alpha} \sqrt{\mu + 1} - \dfrac{1}{\sqrt{\mu - 1}} \tan \dfrac{\pi}{2\alpha} \sqrt{\mu - 1}} \qquad (849)$$

In Fig. 238 Φ is plotted versus μ for the aspect ratios $\alpha = 0.5, 0.75$, and 1.0. This diagram can be used to determine the value of μ for any given value of Φ. The plate factor k_s of the stiffened plate is a function of μ:

$$k_s = \frac{\mu^2}{\alpha^2} \tag{850}$$

and the critical stress of the stiffened plate can be found from

$$\frac{\sigma_c}{\sqrt{\tau}} = \frac{\pi^2 E}{12(1 - \nu^2)} \left(\frac{t}{b}\right)^2 k_s \tag{851}$$

A difficulty arises in estimating the proper value of the moment of inertia I which is to be introduced in Eq. (845) for γ. There is no doubt that a certain portion of the plate adjacent to the lapped joint contributes to the bending resistance of the lapped joint. Accordingly, we assume a section of width b_e to be effec-

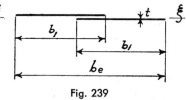

Fig. 239

tive (see Fig. 239). This figure shows the stiffener which consists of two strips of plate of width b_1. Computing the moment of inertia with respect to the axis ξ-ξ we have

$$I = b_1 \frac{(2t)^3}{12}$$

and

$$\gamma = \frac{EI}{bD} = 8 \frac{b_1}{b} (1 - \nu^2) \tag{852}$$

The effective width b_e, first of all, depends on the span a of the plate. This was shown by a theoretical investigation of plates reinforced by a

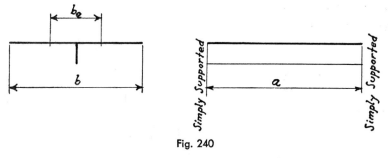

Fig. 240

rib in the middle and acting as simple beams of span a (see Fig. 240). In the special case of a sinusoidal deflection, which actually occurs in a buckled plate, it was found that the effective width is $b_e = 0.363a$ if the width b of the plate is infinite.[1] This value decreases only slightly when b is finite and about equal to a. Since long plates buckle in half waves of length b, it follows that the effective width b_e in such cases can be assumed to be somewhat less than $0.363b$. To fix finally the value of b_1 with sufficient margin against the previously discussed limits. we assume $b_1 = 0.25a$ or $b_1 = 0.25b$ whichever is smaller. Substituting these values into Eq. (852) and using $\prime = 0.3$, the simple relation

$$\gamma = 1.8\alpha < 1.8$$

is obtained.

In order to obtain $\Phi = \gamma - \delta\mu^2$ the term $\delta\mu^2$ has to be subtracted from γ. Comparative computations show that in practical cases $\delta\mu^2$ does not exceed $\gamma/3$. For the sake of simplicity we assume $\delta\mu^2 = \gamma/3$, resulting in a low and conservative value for Φ. By this reasoning one arrives finally at

$$\left. \begin{array}{ll} \text{For } \alpha > 1\text{:} & \Phi = 1.2 \\ \text{For } \alpha < 1\text{:} & \Phi = 1.2\alpha \end{array} \right\} \tag{853}$$

The value of Φ is independent of the ratio b/t.

The diagrams in Fig. 238 furnish for $\Phi = 1.2\alpha$ the values of the plate factor k_s shown in Table 46. These values may be compared with the values of k for the unstiffened plate given in the last line of this table.

TABLE 46.   Plate Factors k_s in Eq. (851) for Plates with Lapped Joint at Center, Fig. 237

$\alpha = a/b$....................	0.5	0.75	1.00
Lapped plate, k_s..............	10.21	7.33	6.33
Unstiffened plate, k..........	6.25	4.34	4.00

Plates Lapped at the Third Points. The stability condition for symmetric buckling when the two stiffeners deflect together with the plate is[2]

$$3 \left(\frac{\pi}{3\alpha} \right)^4 \Phi \left[\frac{\sinh \bar{\kappa}_1}{\bar{\kappa}_1 (2 \cosh \bar{\kappa}_1 - 1)} - \frac{\sin \bar{\kappa}_2}{\bar{\kappa}_2 (2 \cos \bar{\kappa}_2 - 1)} \right]$$
$$- (\bar{\kappa}_1{}^2 + \bar{\kappa}_2{}^2) = 0 \tag{854}$$

where

$$\bar{\kappa}_1 = \frac{\pi}{3\alpha} \sqrt{\mu + 1} \quad \text{and} \quad \bar{\kappa}_2 = \frac{\pi}{3\alpha} \sqrt{\mu - 1} \tag{855}$$

$$\Phi = \gamma - \delta\mu^2 \tag{856}$$

Introducing

$$\bar{\kappa}_1{}^2 + \bar{\kappa}_2{}^2 = \left(\frac{\pi}{3\alpha} \right)^2 2\mu$$

[1] Chwalla, E., Die Formeln zur Berechnung der "voll mittragenden Breite" dünner Gurt und Rippenplatten, *Der Stahlbau*, Vol. 9, p. 73, 1936.

[2] Barbré, R., Beulspannungen in Rechteckplatten mit Längssteifen bei gleichmässiger Druckbeanspruchung, *Der Bauingenieur*, Vol. 17, p. 268. 1936.

into Eq. (854) leads to the following expression for Φ:

$$\Phi = \frac{(3\alpha/\pi)^2(2\mu/3)}{\dfrac{\sinh \bar{\kappa}_1}{\bar{\kappa}_1(\cosh \bar{\kappa}_1 - 1)} - \dfrac{\sin \bar{\kappa}_2}{\bar{\kappa}_2(\cos \bar{\kappa}_2 - 1)}} \tag{857}$$

This equation was used to obtain the diagram shown in Fig. 241, where Φ is plotted versus μ for the values $\alpha = 0.5$, 0.75, and 1.00.

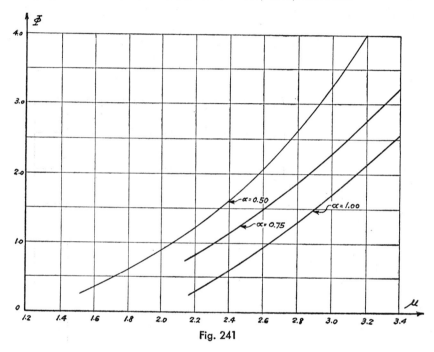

Fig. 241

Using Eqs. (850) and (853), which are again applicable, values of the plate factor k_s in Table 47 were determined from Fig. 241. For comparison, the values of k for the unstiffened plate are also given.

TABLE 47. Plate Factors k_s in Eq. (851) for Plates with Two Lapped Joints at the Third Points

$\alpha = a/b$	0.5	0.75	1.00
Lapped plate, k_s	13.10	9.06	7.57
Unstiffened plate, k	6.25	4.34	4.00

Plates Having One Lapped Joint at a Third Point. The stability condition (703) in Art. 100 is applicable, and with $r = 3$ and $n = 1$, this equation takes the form

$$27 \left(\frac{\alpha}{\pi}\right)^4 (\bar{\kappa}_1^2 + \bar{\kappa}_2^2) - \Phi \left(\frac{\sinh \bar{\kappa}_1 \sinh 2\bar{\kappa}_1}{\bar{\kappa}_1 \sinh 3\bar{\kappa}_1} - \frac{\sin \bar{\kappa}_2 \sin 2\bar{\kappa}_2}{\bar{\kappa}_2 \sin 3\bar{\kappa}_2}\right) = 0 \quad (858)$$

where

$$\bar{\kappa}_1 = \frac{\pi}{3\alpha} \sqrt{\mu + 1} \quad \text{and} \quad \bar{\kappa}_2 = \frac{\pi}{3\alpha} \sqrt{\mu - 1} \quad (859)$$

$$\Phi = \gamma - \delta\mu^2 \quad (860)$$

Solving Eq. (858) for the value Φ, we obtain

$$\Phi = \frac{6\mu(\alpha/\pi)^2}{\dfrac{\sinh \bar{\kappa}_1 \sinh 2\bar{\kappa}_1}{\bar{\kappa}_1 \sinh 3\bar{\kappa}_1} - \dfrac{\sin \bar{\kappa}_2 \sin 2\bar{\kappa}_2}{\bar{\kappa}_2 \sin 3\bar{\kappa}_2}} \quad (861)$$

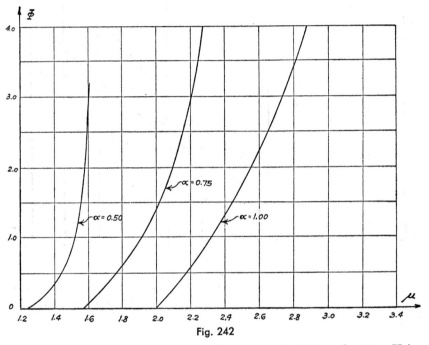

Fig. 242

Figure 242 shows Φ as function of μ for $\alpha = 0.5$, 0.75, and 1.00. Using Eqs. (850) and (853) the values of the plate factor k_s in Table 48 were determined from Fig. 242.

TABLE 48.   Plate Factors k_s in Eq. (851) for Plates with One Lapped Joint at a Third Point

$\alpha = a/b$	0.5	0.75	1.00
Lapped plate, k_s	8.60	6.30	5.63
Unstiffened plate, k	6.25	4.34	4.00

120. Ultimate Strength of Rectangular Plates under Compressive and Normal Loading. Introduction

In Chap. I it was demonstrated that the actual failure load of a column is practically identical with the critical load at which the ideal straight column begins to deflect. The investigation of column behavior when the critical load is exceeded shows that no appreciable reserve of strength remains after the buckling load is reached and that a slight increase of this load suffices to produce such a distortion that actual collapse of the column takes place. The phenomenon of buckling of a plate is fundamentally different from that of the buckling of a column.

The plate starts to buckle when the critical load is reached, but as the load is increased above this critical load, the rate of increase of the deflections decreases. When the applied load exceeds the critical load, the supported edges parallel to the acting load supply the plate with an additional element of strength which comes into play when the middle part of the plate buckles. Thus a redistribution of stresses takes place which, together with the occurrence of stabilizing membrane stresses, enables the plate to regain its stability in the distorted shape. Finally, under steadily increasing load the highest stressed parts of the plate will yield, and the ultimate load, as distinguished from the critical load, is reached.

The margin between buckling strength and ultimate strength increases with decreasing critical stress σ_c and becomes considerable when σ_c lies below the proportional limit. On the other hand the margin approaches zero when σ_c nears the yield point. For plates having very high slenderness ratios b/t, as used, for instance, in the sheet stringer panels of aircraft structures, the ultimate strength can be as much as thirty times the critical stress. In structural engineering and in the design of ships the increase of the actual load-carrying capacity is less impressive because the slenderness ratio b/t rarely reaches the value of 100. The ultimate stress is, therefore, less than twice the critical stress.

To understand the behavior of a thin flat plate after the critical stress is exceeded, it is necessary to consider what occurs in a plate which has reached a state of deformation, where the deflections are comparable to the thickness of the plate but small compared with its width. In deriving the linear differential equation (599) in Chap. IX it was assumed that the compressive stresses which act in the plane of the plate do not change when the plate deflects, and the stresses σ_x, σ_y, τ_{xy} in this equation are constant. But this assumption is no longer permissible when the deflections become large. The membrane effect is negligible when the transverse deflections are very small but becomes more and more prominent as the distortion of the plate under increasing load becomes larger and larger. This membrane effect is caused by the stretching of the middle surface which is due to the curvature of the plate and is characterized by the occurrence of membrane stresses necessary to maintain equilibrium and to comply with the conditions regarding the compatibility of the deformations at the edges. These membrane stresses vary over the surface of the plate but, like the initial load stresses, do not vary in a direction perpendicular to the plane of the plate. The fibers of the plate behave as if they were anchored at the supported edges, and in some regions of the plate tensile stresses, due to elongation of the curved fibers, impede the increase of the deflection caused by the compressive loading. Thus, the membrane stresses exert a stabilizing effect on the plate.

The discussion of the buckling problems of plates in the previous chapters was based upon a linear differential equation derived under the assumption that the deflections of the plates are small in comparison with its thickness. Therefore the solution of this differential equation applies only to the incipient state of buckling at which an infinitely small distortion of the plate is implied and consequently gives only the critical load at which the elastic equilibrium of the plate becomes unstable. It is obvious that the linear theory of plates no longer applies when the behavior of the plate above the buckling load is to be investigated, since finite deflections of the order of magnitude of the plate thickness must be considered. The problem becomes a nonlinear stress problem and requires a new basic theory.

The nonlinearity of the differential equation has its origin in the fact that, in the case of large deflections, there is an interaction between the membrane stresses and the curvature of the plate, and this interaction leads to nonlinear terms in the equations of equilibrium of the plate element.

Föppl[1] was the first to develop a large deflection theory of thin plates, assuming that the bending stresses are small in comparison with the membrane stresses and therefore negligible. The complete differential equations of the problem were formulated by Kármán,[2] who added the terms depending on the flexural rigidity of the plate. Timoshenko[3] and Marguerre and Trefftz[4] derived the expressions for the strain energy of plates with large deflection.

The earliest paper in the field of compressed rectangular plates with

[1] Föppl, A., "Vorlesungen über technische Mechanik," Vol. 5, p. 132, Leipzig, 1907.

[2] v. Kármán, T., "Encyclopädie der mathematischen Wissenschaften," Vol. 15/4, p. 349, 1910.

[3] Timoshenko, S., "Theory of Elastic Stability," p. 390, McGraw-Hill Book Company, Inc., New York, 1936.

[4] Marguerre, K., and E. Trefftz, Über die Tragfähigkeit eines längsbelasteten Plattenstreifens nach Überschreiten der Beullast, Zeitschrift für angewandte Mathematik und Mechanik, Vol. 17, p. 85, 1937.

large deflections above the buckling load was presented by Schnadel,[1] who gave an approximate solution for the simply supported plate loaded on two opposite edges. Using the energy method, he assumed that the wave form of the deflected plate after exceeding the stability limit remains the same as in the state of incipient buckling. He extended his investigation by including the effect of elastic restraint against rotation along the unloaded edges and showed how the results can be improved by using two terms in the assumed expression for the deflections. Schnadel's results have been confirmed by subsequent investigators.

Timoshenko[2] presented another approximate solution for the simply supported plate compressed in one direction in its plane. The investigation is based on the energy method, using the same wave form as Schnadel. Timoshenko introduces in his analysis an arbitrarily chosen form of the displacement functions which describe the displacements u and v in the middle surface of the plate. The distribution of stresses found by Timoshenko deviates considerably from that found by Schnadel and by subsequent investigators who applied more accurate methods.

In a paper published in 1935, Cox[3] also utilizes the energy method, but the results of the investigation, partly based on arbitrary assumptions, are not in good agreement with results obtained by other authors and do not agree with the results of his own tests.

A more accurate solution of the problem of large deflections was given by Marguerre.[4] His analysis of simply supported rectangular plates in compression avoids a number of arbitrary assumptions made by his predecessors, thus eliminating possible sources of error. The only assumption made concerns the shape of the buckled plate. Marguerre uses the energy method to determine in a rational manner the free parameters in the assumed expression for the deflections. Marguerre's analysis will be presented in Arts. 122 to 125.

The problem of rectangular plates carrying longitudinal compression and normal pressure is of prime importance in the design of the hull plating of ships. This problem is closely related to the question of ultimate strength of buckled plates and will therefore also be considered in this chapter in Arts. 127 to 129. An attempt to approach the large deflection problem of rectangular plates under combined bending and

[1] Schnadel, G, Die Überschreitung der Knickgrenze bei dünnen Platten, *Proc. 3d Intern. Congr. Applied Mechanics*, Stockholm, 1930, p. 73; Knickung von Schiffsplatten, *Werft-Reederei-Hafen*, 1930, p. 461.

[2] Timoshenko, *op. cit.* on p. 460.

[3] Cox, H. L., Buckling of Thin Plates in Compression, *R. & M.*, No. 1554, London, 1933.

[4] Marguerre, K., Die mittragende Breite der gedrückten Platte, *Luftfahrt-Forschung*, Vol. 14, p. 121, 1937. Translated in *NACA Tech. Note* 833, 1937.

longitudinal compression was made by Bengston,[1] whose studies include plates with simply supported and clamped edges. Approximate solutions were derived by the Ritz method. However, Bengston introduces in the course of the analysis certain arbitrary assumptions which in part contradict each other, and it is very doubtful whether the results of his analysis can be considered as sufficiently correct.

In a series of papers Levy *et al.* gave solutions of theoretically exact nature for rectangular plates with large deflections. The theories developed include simply supported and clamped plates. The authors obtained general solutions of Kármán's differential equation for plates with large deflections by expressing deflections and normal pressure in the form of Fourier series.[2] Numerical solutions were obtained for various cases of loading and of support. The analysis is highly involved, and the numerical work for obtaining special solutions is very laborious. However, these investigations are important because they afford the possibility of checking the accuracy of simpler approximate methods. Furthermore, these detailed analytical solutions provide the means to investigate the effect of normal pressure on the buckling of edge compressed plates (see Art. 130).

Experimental work has been done in the field of thin plates for the purpose of determining the ultimate load directly from tests and with the aim of corroborating the theory by tests. These tests will be reported in Art. 126.

121. The Basic Equations of the Large Deflection Theory of Thin Plates

The following notation will be used (Fig. 243):

a, b = the dimensions of the rectangular plate

t = the thickness of the plate

σ_A = uniformly distributed compressive load at the edges acting in the direction of the x-axis

p = the uniformly distributed normal load

u and v = the displacements of the reference point x,y of the middle surface of the plate in the x- and y-directions, respectively

[1] Bengston, H. W., Ship Plating under Compression and Hydrostatic Pressure, *Trans. Soc. Naval Architects Marine Engrs.*, Vol. 47, p. 80, 1939.

[2] Levy, S., Bending of Rectangular Plates with Large Deflections *NACA Tech. Note* 846, 1942, and *NACA Tech. Rept.* 737, 1942, p. 139; Square Plate with Clamped Edges under Normal Pressure Producing Large Deflections, *NACA Tech. Note* 847, 1942, and *NACA Tech. Rept.* 740, 1942, p. 209. Levy, S., and S. Greenman, Bending with Large Deflection of a Clamped Rectangular Plate with Length-Width Ratio of 1.5 under Normal Pressure, *NACA Tech. Note* 853, 1942. Levy, S., D. Goldenberg, and G. Zibritosky, Simply Supported Long Rectangular Plate under Combined Axial Load and Normal Pressure, *NACA Tech. Note* 949, 1944. Corrick, J. N., and S. Levy, Clamped Long Rectangular Plates under Combined Axial Load and Normal Pressure, *NACA Tech. Note* 1047, 1946.

w = the lateral displacement of the reference point

$\bar{\sigma}_x, \bar{\sigma}_y, \bar{\tau}_{xy}$ = the median fiber stresses (membrane stresses); σ assumed positive in case of compression

$\epsilon_x, \epsilon_y, \gamma_{xy}$ = the median fiber strains (membrane strains); ϵ assumed positive in case of compression

ν = Poisson's ratio

$D = Et^3/12(1 - \nu^2)$ flexural rigidity of plate

The following relations exist between the displacements u, v, w and the strains $\epsilon_x, \epsilon_y, \gamma_{xy}$:

$$\left.\begin{array}{c} -\epsilon_x = \dfrac{\partial u}{\partial x} + \dfrac{1}{2}\left(\dfrac{\partial w}{\partial x}\right)^2 \\[2mm] -\epsilon_y = \dfrac{\partial v}{\partial y} + \dfrac{1}{2}\left(\dfrac{\partial w}{\partial y}\right)^2 \\[2mm] \gamma_{xy} = \dfrac{\partial u}{\partial y} + \dfrac{\partial v}{\partial x} + \dfrac{\partial w}{\partial x}\dfrac{\partial w}{\partial y} \end{array}\right\} \tag{862}$$

The median fiber stresses, therefore, can be written as follows:

$$\left.\begin{array}{c} -\bar{\sigma}_x = \dfrac{E}{1 - \nu^2}\left\{\left(\dfrac{\partial u}{\partial x} + \nu\dfrac{\partial v}{\partial y}\right) + \dfrac{1}{2}\left[\left(\dfrac{\partial w}{\partial x}\right)^2 + \nu\left(\dfrac{\partial w}{\partial y}\right)^2\right]\right\} \\[3mm] -\bar{\sigma}_y = \dfrac{E}{1 - \nu^2}\left\{\left(\dfrac{\partial v}{\partial y} + \nu\dfrac{\partial u}{\partial x}\right) + \dfrac{1}{2}\left[\left(\dfrac{\partial w}{\partial y}\right)^2 + \nu\left(\dfrac{\partial w}{\partial x}\right)^2\right]\right\} \\[3mm] \bar{\tau}_{xy} = \dfrac{E}{2(1 + \nu)}\left(\dfrac{\partial u}{\partial y} + \dfrac{\partial v}{\partial x} + \dfrac{\partial w}{\partial x}\dfrac{\partial w}{\partial y}\right) \end{array}\right\} \tag{863}$$

The theory of thin flat plates with large deflections is governed by the following fundamental partial differential equations:[1]

$$\frac{\partial^4 F}{\partial x^4} + 2\frac{\partial^4 F}{\partial x^2\,\partial y^2} + \frac{\partial^4 F}{\partial y^4} = E\left[\left(\frac{\partial^2 w}{\partial x\,\partial y}\right)^2 - \frac{\partial^2 w}{\partial x^2}\frac{\partial^2 w}{\partial y^2}\right] \tag{864}$$

$$\frac{\partial^4 w}{\partial x^4} + 2\frac{\partial^4 w}{\partial x^2\,\partial y^2} + \frac{\partial^4 w}{\partial y^4}$$
$$= \frac{p}{D} + \frac{t}{D}\left(\frac{\partial^2 F}{\partial x^2}\frac{\partial^2 w}{\partial y^2} + \frac{\partial^2 F}{\partial y^2}\frac{\partial^2 w}{\partial x^2} - 2\frac{\partial^2 F}{\partial x\,\partial y}\frac{\partial^2 w}{\partial x\,\partial y}\right) \tag{865}$$

Equations (864) and (865) were derived by Kármán under the assumption that lines normal to the middle surface before deformation remain normal to the middle surface after deformation and that the deflection w is of the order of magnitude of the plate thickness but is small in comparison with the plate dimensions. F is a stress function defining the median fiber stresses of the plate:

$$-\bar{\sigma}_x = \frac{\partial^2 F}{\partial y^2}, \qquad -\bar{\sigma}_y = \frac{\partial^2 F}{\partial x^2}, \qquad \bar{\tau}_{xy} = -\frac{\partial^2 F}{\partial x\,\partial y} \tag{866}$$

[1] For derivation of these equations see Timoshenko, "Theory of Elastic Stability," p. 321.

The strain energy of the deflected plate consists of two parts: the strain energy V_S due to the membrane stresses and the strain energy V_B due to bending.[1] V_S is given by

$$V_S = \frac{Et}{2(1 - \nu^2)} \int_{-\frac{a}{2}}^{\frac{a}{2}} \int_{-\frac{b}{2}}^{\frac{b}{2}} \left(\epsilon_x^2 + \epsilon_y^2 + 2\nu\epsilon_x\epsilon_y + \frac{1 - \nu}{2} \gamma_{xy}^2 \right) dx \, dy \quad (867)$$

and V_B by

$$V_B = \frac{D}{2} \int_{-\frac{a}{2}}^{\frac{a}{2}} \int_{-\frac{b}{2}}^{\frac{b}{2}} \left\{ \left(\frac{\partial^2 w}{\partial x^2} + \frac{\partial^2 w}{\partial y^2} \right)^2 \right.$$
$$\left. - 2(1 - \nu) \left[\frac{\partial^2 w}{\partial x^2} \frac{\partial^2 w}{\partial y^2} - \left(\frac{\partial^2 w}{\partial x \, \partial y} \right)^2 \right] \right\} dx \, dy \quad (868)$$

For certain conditions of support along the edges, including the cases of simply supported or clamped edges, the integral

$$\int_{-\frac{a}{2}}^{\frac{a}{2}} \int_{-\frac{b}{2}}^{\frac{b}{2}} \left[\frac{\partial^2 w}{\partial x^2} \frac{\partial^2 w}{\partial y^2} - \left(\frac{\partial^2 w}{\partial x \, \partial y} \right)^2 \right] dx \, dy$$

is zero, and Eq. (868) becomes

$$V_B = \frac{D}{2} \int_{-\frac{a}{2}}^{\frac{a}{2}} \int_{-\frac{b}{2}}^{\frac{b}{2}} \left(\frac{\partial^2 w}{\partial x^2} + \frac{\partial^2 w}{\partial y^2} \right)^2 dx \, dy \quad (869)$$

Using the stress function F, Marguerre[2] used the expression (867) for the strain energy V_S in the following form:

$$V_S = \frac{t}{2E} \int_{-\frac{a}{2}}^{\frac{a}{2}} \int_{-\frac{b}{2}}^{\frac{b}{2}} \left\{ \left(\frac{\partial^2 F}{\partial x^2} + \frac{\partial^2 F}{\partial y^2} \right)^2 \right.$$
$$\left. - 2(1 + \nu) \left[\frac{\partial^2 F}{\partial x^2} \frac{\partial^2 F}{\partial y^2} - \left(\frac{\partial^2 F}{\partial x \, \partial y} \right)^2 \right] \right\} dx \, dy \quad (870)$$

122. Marguerre's Large Deflection Theory of Rectangular Plates in Longitudinal Compression

The theory discussed hereafter deals with rectangular plates free to rotate about the supported edges and moving freely along the supports. It is assumed that the edges remain straight and the plate retains its rectangular outline as shown in Fig. 244 when the plate deforms.

[1] *Ibid.*, pp. 305, 391.
[2] Marguerre, *loc. cit.* on p. 461

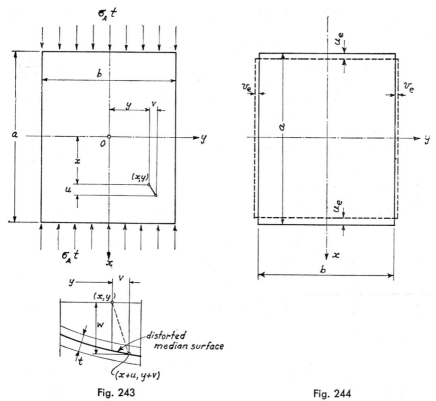

Fig. 243   Fig. 244

We define the mean value p_1 of the membrane stresses $\bar{\sigma}_x$ by the equation

$$p_1 = \frac{1}{b} \int_{-\frac{b}{2}}^{\frac{b}{2}} \bar{\sigma}_x \, dy = \sigma_A \tag{871}$$

and the mean value of the membrane stresses $\bar{\sigma}_y$ by

$$p_2 = \frac{1}{a} \int_{-\frac{a}{2}}^{\frac{a}{2}} \bar{\sigma}_y \, dx \tag{872}$$

It is obvious that the mean value p_1 is identical with the external load σ_A. We introduce furthermore the mean strain ϵ_1 by the definition

$$u_e = \frac{\epsilon_1 a}{2} \tag{873}$$

and the mean strain ϵ_2 by

$$v_e = \frac{\epsilon_2 b}{2} \tag{874}$$

in which u_e and v_e designate the displacements of the edges (Fig. 244).

In accordance with the definition of the strains, u_e and v_e are positive if the plate shortens.

The expression "mean strain" needs some explanation. The displacements of the edges u_e and v_e consist of two parts: the change in length of chord due to the deflection and the change in length due to the variable fiber strain in the deflected plate. According to the above definition ϵ_1 and ϵ_2 represent the mean values of the entire change in length u_e or v_e per unit length, and for the sake of simplicity are referred to as mean strains. Before buckling, the axial compression p_1 is uniformly distributed and proportionality[1] exists between the strain ϵ_1 and the compressive stress p_1, namely, $p_1 = E\epsilon_1$. Above the critical value of $\epsilon_1 = \epsilon_c$, the plate deflects more in the middle than near the restrained sides, resulting in a nonuniform distribution of the compressive stresses $\bar{\sigma}_x$ as illustrated by Fig. 245. The problem to be solved is the determination of the deflected form of the plate, magnitude and distribution of the membrane stresses, and in particular establishment of the relation between the mean value p_1 and the mean strain ϵ_1, in other words, the stress-strain relationship $p_1 = f(\epsilon_1)$.

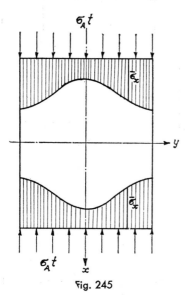

Fig. 245

The method of approach in solving the large deflection problem is as follows: Marguerre assumes a suitable expression for the deflection w, having a number of free parameters, and determines the stress function F from the differential equation (864). Then he introduces F together with the chosen expression for w into the expression for the potential energy of the distorted plate and determines finally the free parameters in w from the condition that the potential energy is stationary. Marguerre develops his analysis for two different assumptions as to the form of the deflected surface of the plate. In the first part of the paper it is assumed that the expression for w contains one free parameter only. This theory applies with sufficient accuracy to plates where the ultimate load is less than about five times the critical load. The analysis in the second part of the paper is based on an expression for w having three free parameters applying to very thin plates. For the heavy plating used in ship construction the simpler of the two theories presented by Marguerre is of interest. This

---

[1] Marguerre assumes unlimited validity of Hooke's law.

part of Marguerre's paper will be discussed in the following, while the refined theory is considered in Art. 125.

The simplest expression for the deflection w having only one free parameter is obtained if we assume that the buckling form of the simply supported rectangular plate is preserved even when the buckling load is exceeded:

$$w = f \cos \frac{\pi x}{a} \cos \frac{\pi y}{b} \tag{875}$$

Introducing this expression into the differential equation (864) gives

$$\frac{\partial^4 F}{\partial x^4} + 2 \frac{\partial^4 F}{\partial x^2\, \partial y^2} + \frac{\partial^4 F}{\partial y^4} = -E \frac{\pi^4 f^2}{2a^2 b^2} \left(\cos \frac{2\pi x}{a} + \cos \frac{2\pi y}{b} \right) \tag{876}$$

To obtain a solution of this differential equation it is necessary to specify boundary conditions for the stress function F. Two boundary conditions were obtained by Marguerre from the assumption that the edges of the plate remain straight (Fig. 244). This leads to two relations between the displacements u_e, v_e and the mean strains:

$$u_e = \mp \frac{\epsilon_1 a}{2} \quad \text{and} \quad v_e = \mp \frac{\epsilon_2 b}{2} \tag{877}$$

Two other boundary conditions are obtained from the fact that the shearing stresses $\bar{\tau}_{xy}$ at the edges of the plate vanish. Using the third Eq. (863), this leads to

$$\left. \begin{array}{ll} \text{For } x = \pm \dfrac{a}{2}: & \dfrac{\partial v}{\partial x} = 0 \\[2mm] \text{For } y = \pm \dfrac{b}{2}: & \dfrac{\partial u}{\partial y} = 0 \end{array} \right\} \tag{878}$$

Marguerre now determines u and v from Eqs. (863) as a function of F, and substituting the result into Eqs. (877) and (878), he obtains boundary conditions for the differential equation (876). He finally derives in this manner

$$F = -\frac{Ef^2}{32} \left[\left(\frac{a}{b} \right)^2 \cos \frac{2\pi x}{a} + \left(\frac{b}{a} \right)^2 \cos \frac{2\pi y}{b} \right] - \frac{1}{2} p_1 y^2 - \frac{1}{2} p_2 x^2 \tag{879}$$

where p_1, and p_2 are constants, which will be found to be equal to the mean membrane pressures in the x- and y-directions [Eqs. (871) and (872)].

From Eq. (879) we derive the expressions for the membrane stresses

$$\left. \begin{array}{l} \bar{\sigma}_x = -\dfrac{\partial^2 F}{\partial y^2} = p_1 - \dfrac{E\pi^2 f^2}{8a^2} \cos \dfrac{2\pi y}{b} \\[3mm] \bar{\sigma}_y = -\dfrac{\partial^2 F}{\partial x^2} = p_2 - \dfrac{E\pi^2 f^2}{8b^2} \cos \dfrac{2\pi x}{a} \\[3mm] \bar{\tau}_{xy} = -\dfrac{\partial^2 F}{\partial x\, \partial y} = 0 \end{array} \right\} \tag{880}$$

$\bar{\sigma}_x$ and $\bar{\sigma}_y$ are counted positive when compression. Substitution of these values of $\bar{\sigma}_x$ and $\bar{\sigma}_y$ into Eqs. (871) and (872) confirms the statement that the constants p_1 and p_2 in Eq. (879) are the mean values of the membrane stresses.

Solving the first two Eqs. (863) for $\dfrac{\partial u}{\partial x}$ and $\dfrac{\partial v}{\partial y}$ gives

$$
\left.
\begin{aligned}
E \frac{\partial u}{\partial x} &= -(\bar{\sigma}_x - \nu \bar{\sigma}_y) - \frac{E}{2}\left(\frac{\partial w}{\partial x}\right)^2 \\
E \frac{\partial v}{\partial y} &= -(\bar{\sigma}_y - \nu \bar{\sigma}_x) - \frac{E}{2}\left(\frac{\partial w}{\partial y}\right)^2
\end{aligned}
\right\}
\tag{881}
$$

Equations (877) can be written

$$
u_e = \int_0^{\frac{a}{2}} \frac{\partial u}{\partial x}\, dx = -\frac{\epsilon_1 a}{2}
\qquad \text{and} \qquad
v_e = \int_0^{\frac{b}{2}} \frac{\partial v}{\partial y}\, dy = -\frac{\epsilon_2 b}{2}
$$

Applying Eqs. (875), (880), and (881) we derive

$$
\left.
\begin{aligned}
E\epsilon_1 &= p_1 - \nu p_2 + E\frac{\pi^2 f^2}{8a^2} \\
E\epsilon_2 &= p_2 - \nu p_1 + E\frac{\pi^2 f^2}{8b^2}
\end{aligned}
\right\}
\tag{882}
$$

which permits the determination of the values of the constants p_1 and p_2 expressed as functions of the mean strains ϵ_1 and ϵ_2

$$
\left.
\begin{aligned}
p_1 &= \frac{E}{1 - \nu^2}\left[\epsilon_1 + \nu\epsilon_2 - \frac{\pi^2 f^2}{8}\left(\frac{1}{a^2} + \frac{\nu}{b^2}\right)\right] \\
p_2 &= \frac{E}{1 - \nu^2}\left[\epsilon_2 + \nu\epsilon_1 - \frac{\pi^2 f^2}{8}\left(\frac{1}{b^2} + \frac{\nu}{a^2}\right)\right]
\end{aligned}
\right]
\tag{883}
$$

The value of the deflection f can now be determined from the theorem of stationary potential energy.[1] For this purpose the potential energy must be expressed as function of f, and the condition

$$
\frac{\partial U}{\partial f} = 0
\tag{884}
$$

will furnish an equation for f.

The total potential energy U will consist of the strain energy V_S of the membrane stresses, the strain energy V_B due to bending, and the potential energy U_w of the external loads $\sigma_A \cdot V_S$ and V_B are given by Eqs. (869) and (870), and $V = V_B + V_S$ can be expressed as function of the mean strains ϵ_1, ϵ_2, and f [see Eq. (887) below]. The potential energy U_w of the

[1] See Art. 23.

external forces, on the other hand, does not depend on f at all, but only on the mean strain ϵ_1:

$$U_w = -\sigma_A tab\epsilon_1 \qquad (885)$$

As a result $\dfrac{\partial U_w}{\partial f} = 0$, and Eq. (884) becomes simply

$$\frac{\partial V}{\partial f} = 0 \qquad (886)$$

Introducing Eqs. (874) and (879) into Eqs. (869) and (870), we obtain the strain energy V as function of the mean values p_1 and p_2 of the membrane stresses:

$$V = V_s + V_B = \frac{abt}{2}\left[\frac{\pi^4 E}{128}f^4\left(\frac{1}{a^4}+\frac{1}{b^4}\right)+\frac{1}{E}(p_1+p_2)^2-\frac{2(1+\nu)}{E}p_1p_2\right]$$
$$+\frac{\pi^4 Eabt^3}{96(1-\nu^2)}f^2\left(\frac{1}{a^2}+\frac{1}{b^2}\right)^2$$

Introducing the values of p_1 and p_2 from Eqs. (883) the potential energy becomes a function of the values ϵ_1 and ϵ_2 and of the parameter f:

$$V = \frac{Eabt}{1-\nu^2}\left\{\frac{\epsilon_1{}^2+\epsilon_2{}^2}{2}+\nu\epsilon_1\epsilon_2-\frac{\pi^2 f^2}{8b^2}\left[\epsilon_1\left(\frac{b^2}{a^2}+\nu\right)+\epsilon_2\left(1+\nu\frac{b^2}{a^2}\right)\right]\right.$$
$$\left.+\frac{\pi^4 f^4}{256b^4}\left[(3-\nu^2)\left(1+\frac{b^4}{a^4}\right)+4\nu\frac{b^2}{a^2}\right]+\frac{\pi^4 t^2 f^2}{96b^4}\left(1+\frac{b^2}{a^2}\right)^2\right\} \qquad (887)$$

Equation (886) now furnishes the relation

$$\epsilon_1\left(\nu+\frac{b^2}{a^2}\right)+\epsilon_2\left(1+\nu\frac{b^2}{a^2}\right)=\frac{\pi^2 t^2}{12b^2}\left(1+\frac{b^2}{a^2}\right)^2$$
$$+\frac{\pi^2 f^2}{16b^2}\left[(3-\nu^2)\left(1+\frac{b^4}{a^4}\right)+4\nu\frac{b^2}{a^2}\right] \qquad (888)$$

which determines f as function of the mean strains ϵ_1 and ϵ_2.

123. Results of Marguerre's Theory for Square Plates

It is simpler to discuss the behavior of the plate with large deflections in the case of a square plate, without impairing the general validity of certain conclusions which can be drawn from the analytical results.

The analysis simplifies considerably when $a = b$. Equation (888) becomes

$$\frac{\pi^2 f^2}{8b^2} = \frac{1}{3-\nu}\left(\epsilon_1+\epsilon_2-\frac{1}{1+\nu}\frac{\pi^2 t^2}{3b^2}\right) \qquad (889)$$

The critical stress of a square plate having side length b and thickness t in compression in the x-direction is

$$\sigma_c = \frac{\pi^2 E t^2}{3(1-\nu^2)b^2} \qquad (890)$$

and Eq. (890) can therefore be written

$$\frac{\pi^2 f^2}{8b^2} = \frac{1}{3-\nu}\left[\epsilon_1 + \epsilon_2 - (1-\nu)\frac{\sigma_c}{E}\right] \tag{891}$$

Substituting the values of ϵ_1 and ϵ_2 from Eq. (882) into Eq. (891) we obtain

$$\frac{E\pi^2 f^2}{8b^2} = p_1 + p_2 - \sigma_c \tag{892}$$

This expression can now be substituted in Eqs. (880), and noting $a = b$, the membrane stresses are

$$\left.\begin{aligned}
\bar{\sigma}_x &= p_1 - (p_1 + p_2 - \sigma_c)\cos\frac{2\pi y}{b} \\
\bar{\sigma}_y &= p_2 - (p_1 + p_2 - \sigma_c)\cos\frac{2\pi x}{b}
\end{aligned}\right\} \tag{893}$$

The maximum stress occurs at the longitudinal edges

$$\text{Max } \bar{\sigma}_x = \bar{\sigma}_e = 2p_1 + p_2 - \sigma_c \tag{894}$$

and the minimum stress at the center

$$\text{Min } \bar{\sigma}_x = \bar{\sigma}_m = -p_2 + \sigma_c \tag{895}$$

We have so far avoided defining the conditions of support of the plate on the unloaded edges. Two limiting cases will now be considered: Case 1, where the longitudinal edges are free to move transversely, so that $p_2 = 0$, and Case 2, where the longitudinal edges cannot move transversely, $\epsilon_2 = 0$.

Case 1: Using $p_2 = 0$, Eq. (892) becomes

$$\frac{\pi^2 f^2}{8b^2} = \frac{1}{E}(p_1 - \sigma_c) \tag{896}$$

indicating that the deflection f is proportional to the square root of the excess of the actual load over the critical load.

The membrane stresses are

$$\left.\begin{aligned}
\bar{\sigma}_x &= p_1 - (p_1 - \sigma_c)\cos\frac{2\pi y}{b} \\
\bar{\sigma}_y &= (p_1 - \sigma_c)\cos\frac{2\pi x}{b}
\end{aligned}\right\} \tag{897}$$

Substituting $p_2 = 0$ and the value of f^2 from Eq. (891) into the second Eq. (883) gives

$$\epsilon_2 = \frac{1-\nu}{2}\epsilon_1 - \frac{1}{2}(1+\nu)\frac{\sigma_c}{E}$$

Introduction of this expression into Eq. (891) leads to

$$\frac{\pi^2 f^2}{8b^2} = \frac{1}{2}\left(\epsilon_1 - \frac{\sigma_c}{E}\right) = \frac{1}{2}(\epsilon_1 - \epsilon_c) \qquad (898)$$

where ϵ_c is the compressive strain corresponding to the critical stress σ_c. Comparison of Eqs. (896) and (898) furnishes the stress-strain relation

$$p_1 - \sigma_c = \frac{E}{2}(\epsilon_1 - \epsilon_c) \qquad (899)$$

Above the critical stress, the additional mean strain $\epsilon_1 - \epsilon_c$ is proportional to the excess of the stress $p_1 - \sigma_c$. The apparent modulus of elasticity is $E/2$. This surprisingly simple relationship is, of course, a

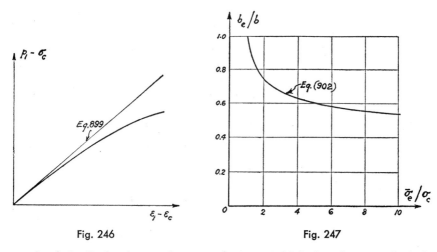

Fig. 246   Fig. 247

result of the limitation to the wave form on which the above analysis is based. As a matter of fact, Eq. (899) is valid only in the very first instant after the buckling load is exceeded. The straight line in Fig. 246 which depicts Eq. (899) is the tangent to the actual stress-strain curve, which, starting from this tangent, deflects downward. For not too large values of ϵ_1/ϵ_c the deviation, however, is so small that the stress-strain relationship (899) may be considered sufficiently accurate for practical purposes.

It is conventional to express the load capacity of a plate when the buckling load is exceeded by defining the maximum stress at the edges by an effective width b_e of the plate:

$$b_e \bar{\sigma}_e = b p_1 \qquad (900)$$

where $\bar{\sigma}_e$ is the stress along the longitudinal edges. Since $p_2 = 0$, Eq. (894) yields

$$\bar{\sigma}_e = 2p_1 - \sigma_c \qquad (901)$$

Introducing $p_1 = (\bar{\sigma}_e + \sigma_c)/2$ into Eq. (900) we have

$$\frac{b_e}{b} = \frac{1}{2}\left(1 + \frac{\sigma_c}{\bar{\sigma}_e}\right) \tag{902}$$

In Fig. 247 b_e/b is plotted versus $\bar{\sigma}_e/\sigma_c$ the curve having a horizontal asymptote at $b_e/b = \frac{1}{2}$. Although its validity is limited to values of $\bar{\sigma}_e/\sigma_c < 5$,* it is sufficiently accurate for ship plating, where $\bar{\sigma}_e/\sigma_c$ seldom exceeds the value of 3.

For practical calculations in the design of ships, in which the effective width is used, it is more convenient to have b_e/b expressed by the compressive load p_1 of the plate. Substitution of Eq. (901) into (900) and noting $p_1 = \sigma_A$ lead to

$$\frac{b_e}{b} = \frac{1}{2 - \sigma_c/\sigma_A} \tag{903}$$

Assuming that the ultimate strength is reached when $\bar{\sigma}_e$ approaches the yield point, we obtain from Eq. (902) the design formula

$$\frac{b_e}{b} = 0.5 + \frac{0.5\sigma_c}{\sigma_y} \tag{904}$$

and from Eq. (901) an expression for the ultimate strength

$$p_1 = \sigma_{\text{ult}} = 0.5\sigma_y + 0.5\sigma_c \tag{905}$$

Case 2: Using $\epsilon_2 = 0$ Eq. (891) becomes

$$\frac{\pi^2 f^2}{8b^2} = \frac{1}{3 - \nu}\left[\epsilon_1 - (1 - \nu)\frac{\sigma_c}{E}\right] \tag{906}$$

The first Eq. (883) can be used to express ϵ_1 in terms of p_1:

$$\epsilon_1 = \frac{1 - \nu^2}{E}p_1 + (1 + \nu)\frac{\pi^2 f^2}{8b^2}$$

and substitution into Eq. (906) leads to

$$\frac{E\pi^2 f^2}{8b^2} = \frac{1 + \nu}{2}\left(p_1 - \frac{\sigma_c}{1 + \nu}\right) \tag{907}$$

For $f = 0$ this equation indicates the stress at which the deflection starts:

$$p_1 = \sigma_c^* = \frac{\sigma_c}{1 + \nu} \tag{908}$$

The value σ_c^* is the critical stress of a plate compressed in both directions $\sigma_A = \sigma_c$, $\sigma_B = \nu\sigma_c$.[1] This is only logical, because the restraint $\epsilon_2 = 0$ produces stresses $\sigma_B = \nu\sigma_A$.

---

* See the discussion of Fig. 248 on p. 475.
[1] See Timoshenko, "Theory of Elastic Stability," p. 333.

For $f = 0$ Eq. (906) gives the strain ϵ_c^* at the instant of buckling:

$$\epsilon_c^* = \frac{(1 - \nu)\sigma_c}{E}$$

Comparison of Eqs. (906) and (907) yields

$$\frac{1 + \nu}{2} (p_1 - \sigma_c^*) = \frac{E}{3 - \nu} (\epsilon_1 - \epsilon_c^*)$$

This equation can be written

$$p_1 - \sigma_c^* = \frac{2(1 - \nu)}{3 - \nu} \frac{E}{1 - \nu^2} (\epsilon_1 - \epsilon_c^*) \tag{909}$$

Comparing this relation with the one valid below the critical load

$$p_1 = \frac{E}{1 - \nu^2} \epsilon_1$$

we find that Eq. (909) is still linear but the coefficient $2(1 - \nu)/(3 - \nu)$ occurs. The value of this coefficient for $\nu = 0.3$ is 0.52. The apparent modulus of elasticity above the critical load is therefore approximately one-half of the value $E/(1 - \nu^2)$ before buckling.

Reasoning in a similar manner as in Case 1, the ratio b_e/b assumes the value

$$\frac{b_e}{b} = \frac{2}{3 + \nu} + \frac{1 + \nu}{3 + \nu} \frac{\sigma_c^*}{\bar{\sigma}_e} \tag{910}$$

and substituting $\nu = 0.3$,

$$\frac{b_e}{b} = 0.604 + 0.394 \frac{\sigma_c^*}{\bar{\sigma}_e} \tag{911}$$

The ultimate strength is

$$\sigma_{\text{ult}} = 0.604\sigma_y + 0.394\sigma_c^* \tag{912}$$

The actual boundary conditions in ship plating are not exactly known and may lie anywhere between the two limiting cases discussed. Since σ_c, as far as ship plating is concerned, lies in most cases above the proportional limit, it will be found that the difference between the values of σ_{ult} computed from Eqs. (905) and (912) is moderate. It is therefore advisable to employ the more conservative formula derived for Case 1, the use of which will not impair the economy of any design materially.

124. Results of Marguerre's Theory for Rectangular Plates

It will be recalled that a long plate in longitudinal compression buckles in half waves the lengths of which are approximately equal to the width of the plate. The results found in the previous article, in particular Eqs. (902) to (905), apply therefore to long plates as used in longitudinally framed vessels.

In order to obtain corresponding results for the plates used in transversely framed ships where the ratio $\beta = b/a > 1$, we must apply the general Eqs. (880) to (888). Assuming that the unloaded edges are free to move laterally, $p_2 = 0$, the maximum stresses are obtained as follows:

Introducing $p_2 = 0$, Eqs. (882) become

$$\left. \begin{array}{c} E\epsilon_1 = p_1 + E\dfrac{\pi^2 f^2}{8b^2}\beta^2 \\[2mm] E\epsilon_2 = -\nu p_1 + E\dfrac{\pi^2 f^2}{8b^2} \end{array} \right\} \tag{913}$$

where $\beta = b/a$.

Substitution of these expressions into Eq. (888) leads to a relationship between $\pi^2 f^2 / 8b^2$ and the mean compressive stress p_1:

$$\frac{\pi^2 f^2}{8b^2} = \frac{2p_1\beta^2}{E(1+\beta^4)} - \frac{2\dfrac{\pi^2 t^2}{12b^2}(1+\beta^2)^2}{(1-\nu^2)(1+\beta^4)} \tag{914}$$

The critical compressive stress σ_c for a plate of aspect ratio

$$\alpha = \frac{a}{b} = \frac{1}{\beta}$$

is given by Eq. (634). In the elastic range $\tau = 1$, and we obtain, using $n = 1$,

$$\sigma_c = \frac{\pi^2 E}{12(1-\nu^2)}\left(\frac{t}{b}\right)^2\left(\beta + \frac{1}{\beta}\right)^2 \tag{915}$$

The numerator of the second term on the right-hand side of Eq. (914) can be written

$$2\frac{\sigma_c}{E}(1-\nu^2)\beta^2$$

and Eq. (914) becomes simply

$$\frac{\pi^2 f^2}{8b^2} = \frac{2\beta^2(p_1 - \sigma_c)}{E(1+\beta^4)} \tag{916}$$

The stress $\bar{\sigma}_e$ follows from Eqs. (880) for $y = \pm b/2$

$$\bar{\sigma}_e = p_1 + \frac{E\pi^2 f^2}{8b^2}\beta^2$$

and substituting Eq. (916) we obtain

$$\bar{\sigma}_e = \frac{(1+3\beta^2)p_1 - 2\beta^4\sigma_c}{1+\beta^4} \tag{917}$$

Referring to Eq. (900) we find the effective width

$$\frac{b_e}{b} = \frac{p_1}{\bar{\sigma}_e} = \frac{1+\beta^4}{1+3\beta^4} + \frac{2\beta^4}{1+3\beta^4}\frac{\sigma_c}{\bar{\sigma}_e}$$

and, finally, the ultimate stress based on the yield point,

$$\sigma_{\text{ult}} = \frac{1 + \beta^4}{1 + 3\beta^4} \sigma_y + \frac{2\beta^4}{1 + 3\beta^4} \sigma_c \tag{918}$$

Expressing b_e/b as a function of the compressive stress $p_1 = \sigma_A$, the following formula for the effective width can be obtained:

$$\frac{b_e}{b} = \frac{1 + \beta^4}{1 + 3\beta^4 - 2\beta^4 \sigma_c/\sigma_A} \tag{919}$$

Equations (916) to (919) apply for $\beta = b/a > 1$. If $\beta \lessgtr 1$, Eqs. (902) and (905) apply,

125. Marguerre's Theory for Very Thin Plates

In the second part of the paper Marguerre[1] discusses the stress distribution in thin plates when the load capacity exceeds the buckling load more than five times. In such cases the two strips adjacent to the edges carry nearly the entire load while the middle of the plate takes little more than the buckling stress. A secondary wave formation will appear near the edges, since the edge strips, now carrying the main portion of the load, buckle into square panels, somewhat like a long plate of width $b_e/2$. This wave formation is superimposed upon the primary buckling wave, and Marguerre therefore assumes the following expression for the displacement w of a square plate:

$$w = f_1 \cos \frac{\pi x}{b} \cos \frac{\pi y}{b} - f_3 \cos \frac{3\pi x}{b} \left(\cos \frac{\pi y}{b} - \eta \cos \frac{3\pi y}{b} \right) \tag{920}$$

This expression is suitable to depict the aforementioned wave formation. The values of the three parameters f_1, f_3, and η are determined from the theorem of stationary potential energy. The appearance of the secondary buckles in the vicinity of the longitudinal edges has been actually observed in tests on thin plates.

The mathematical procedure is essentially the same as previously demonstrated, but the analysis becomes highly involved. The result of Marguerre's investigation for square places is given in Fig. 248 showing the ratio b_e/b plotted versus the ratio $\bar{\sigma}_e/\sigma_c$. The dashed curve is identical with the diagram in Fig. 247, and it can be seen that the two curves in Fig. 248 agree quite well between $\bar{\sigma}_e/\sigma_c = 1$ and 5 and that in this range the results of the simplified theory presented in Art. 123 are sufficiently accurate.

In closing the discussion of Marguerre's theory the fact must be stressed that the theory assumes unlimited validity of Hooke's law until the yield point is reached. The stress-strain diagram which underlies

---

[1] Marguerre, *op. cit.* on p. 461.

the analysis is shown in the insert of Fig. 249, and the critical stress σ_c used in the mathematical development of the theory is that value of σ_c which would be obtained if the plate were perfectly elastic until σ_c reaches the yield point. When σ_c exceeds the yield point, this calculated value of σ_c has to be replaced by σ_y. To illustrate this the ultimate stress

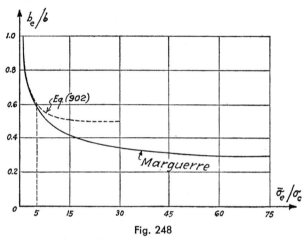

Fig. 248

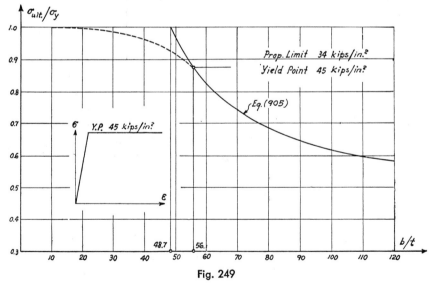

Fig. 249

of a square plate of H.T. steel is plotted in Fig. 249 versus the ratio b/t. The nondimensional ratios σ_{ult}/σ_y have been computed from Eq. (905). For $b/t = 48.7$, σ_c reaches the yield strength σ_y, and σ_{ult}/σ_y assumes the limiting value which applies for all plates having a ratio $b/t < 48.7$.

In reality, however, Hooke's law is valid only below the proportional

limit, and the solid curve in Fig. 249, therefore, applies only for ratios $b/t > 56.1$, where σ_c equals the proportional limit. The remaining part of the $\sigma_{\text{ult}}/\sigma_y$ diagram ought to be replaced by a more accurate curve which takes into account the fact that the value σ_c and also the value σ_{ult} are different in the inelastic range, where the actual stress-strain diagram differs from the simplified diagram in Fig. 249.

Let us assume that the distortion of the plate, after the buckling stress σ_c is exceeded, is controlled by the same effective modulus E_e which determines the value of σ_c. This assumption is far from being correct but is obviously closer to the actual conditions than the assumption of the unlimited validity of the modulus of elasticity E. Accordingly, the modulus E in the previous analysis can be replaced by the modulus E_e. This means that the formulas for the membrane stresses $\bar{\sigma}_x$ and $\bar{\sigma}_y$ and for the effective width or ultimate strength developed above apply also in the inelastic range provided that the value of σ_c in these equations be determined as the actual critical stress in the inelastic range of buckling. In this manner, computing σ_c from the formula

$$\sigma_c = \frac{\pi^2 E \sqrt{\tau}}{3(1 - \nu^2)} \left(\frac{t}{b}\right)^2$$

the dashed curve in Fig. 249 was found, giving in the inelastic region somewhat smaller values for σ_{ult} than Marguerre's original equation.

It should not be concealed that, in spite of this correction, Marguerre's theory gives too large values for the ultimate stresses. Tests[1] on steel plates having ratios $b/t = 30 - 100$, important in ship design, indicate that the actual ultimate stresses are 10 to 20% smaller than the theoretical results. It is likely that these differences are largely due to the smaller effective modulus of elasticity in the highly stressed regions near the edges of the plates.

It is interesting to consider the margin between ultimate strength and buckling strength in the case just discussed in order to obtain insight into the order of magnitude of the reserve of strength in plates. Table 49 gives

TABLE 49. Ratios $\sigma_{\text{ult}}/\sigma_c$ for Square Plates

b/t.............	30	40	50	60	70	80	90	100	120
$\sigma_{\text{ult}}/\sigma_c$............	1.01	1.06	1.10	1.26	1.53	1.84	2.13	2.60	3.54

the ratio $\sigma_{\text{ult}}/\sigma_c$ for ratios $b/t = 30$ to 120. These ratios change somewhat when material with other properties is used; they go up when the yield point goes up.

[1] Frankland. J. M., The Strength of Ship Plating under Edge Compression, U.S. Experimental Model Basin, *Rept.* 469, 1940.

It was deemed necessary to discuss the behavior of plates having a buckling strength which lies between the proportional limit and the yield point, since the plates used in the construction of ships usually fall into this category.

126. Tests on the Ultimate Strength of Plates

The earliest tests with the purpose of determining experimentally the ultimate strength of plates were made by Schuman and Back,[1] who observed that for wide, thin plates the ultimate strength was as much as thirty times the critical load and that in the case of narrow, thick plates the failure load did not exceed materially the critical load. For wide, thin plates the ultimate load became nearly independent of the width of the plate. The question of the ultimate strength of thin sheet, particularly of stiffened sheet, was at this time a vitally important question in aeronautical engineering (see Art. 103). Based on these tests, empirical methods were proposed,[2] until Kármán[3] developed a semiempirical formula for the ultimate strength of a simply supported plate. It is based on the assumption that, at the moment of collapse, two strips adjacent to the supports are stressed to the yield point and carry the total load whereas the heavily distorted middle portion of the plate may be considered as unstressed (Fig. 250). The formula for the width $2c$ of the load carrying strips is

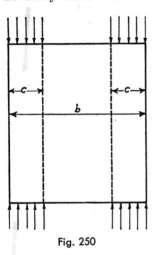

Fig. 250

$$2c = \frac{2\pi t}{\sqrt{12(1 - \nu^2)}} \sqrt{\frac{E}{\sigma_y}} = Ct \sqrt{\frac{E}{\sigma_y}} \tag{921}$$

where $C = 1.9$ and σ_y is the yield strength. Hence, the ultimate strength is

$$\sigma_{\text{ult}} = \frac{2c}{b} \sigma_y = C \frac{t}{b} \sqrt{E\sigma_y} \tag{922}$$

To check the validity of Kármán's hypothesis a series of tests was made

[1] Schuman, L., and G. Back, Strength of Rectangular Flat Plates under Edge Compression, *NACA Tech. Rept.* 356, 1930.

[2] Newell, J. S., Data on the Strength of Aircraft Materials, *Aviation Eng.*, 1932.

[3] v. Kármán, T., E. E. Sechler, and L. H. Donnell, The Strength of Thin Plates in Compression, *Trans. ASME*, Vol. 54, APM 54-5, p. 53, 1932.

by Sechler.[1] These experiments revealed that the factor $C = 1.9$ does not remain constant but varies with $\sqrt{E/\sigma_y}\, t/b$, decreasing with increasing values of this parameter. C approaches 1.9 only for wide and thin plates.

In a recent paper Winter[2] published the results of an extensive investigation of U-shaped sections of thin steel. The tests were made in order to study the behavior of thin, wide flanges in compression. Equation (921) for the effective width was found valid also for stresses s below the yield point:

$$b_e = Ct\sqrt{\frac{E}{s}} \tag{923}$$

where the value of the coefficient C

$$C = 1.9\left(1 - 0.475\frac{t}{b}\sqrt{\frac{E}{s}}\right) \tag{924}$$

was established experimentally.

Numerous other tests made and design formulas developed for the needs of aeronautical engineers do not cover the problem in the range of interest in ship design and are therefore not reported. Of prime interest to the naval architect are the extensive tests conducted by the U.S. Experimental Model Basin intended to determine the ultimate strength of flat rectangular steel plates under edge compression.[3] The first group of tests was made on plates 30 in. long and 0.109 in. thick, the width varying between 5 and 30 in. It was observed that, for large b/t ratios, $b/t > 100$, the ultimate load was affected only in a minor degree by the width of the plate, in accordance with Kármán's formula. The 30-in.-wide plates proved, for example, only a little stronger than the 10-in. plates.

In a second series of tests the specimens had constant length and width, $a = 30$ in., $b = 15$ in., but varied in thickness between 0.05 and 0.109 in. The load at failure was found approximately proportional to the thickness as predicted by Eq. (922). In another group of experiments an attempt was made to determine the effect of length upon ultimate strength. Tests with 15-in.-long plates showed that such plates carried slightly higher loads than the 30-in. plates of the first series of tests. The fact is of considerable interest that these tests showed again that the ultimate

[1] Sechler, E. E., The Ultimate Strength of Thin Flat Sheets in Compression, *Guggenheim Aeronaut. Lab. Pub.* 27, California Institute of Technology, Pasadena, 1933.

[2] Winter, G., Performance of Thin Steel Compression Flanges, *Prelim. Pub. 3d Congr. Intern. Assoc. Bridge and Structural Eng.*, Liège, 1948, p. 137.

[3] Sweeney, R. J., The Strength of Hull Plating under Compression, U.S. Experimental Model Basin, *Progress Repts.* 1 and 2, 1933.

stress can be expressed[1] as a function of the nondimensional parameter $\sqrt{E/\sigma_y}\, t/b$; this is in essential agreement with Sechler's tests.

The aforementioned experiments were made on individual plate panels. In addition, plates were tested which were divided into two panels by a longitudinal stiffener at the center line. The strength of these plates was approximately twice the strength of a single plate, the specimens showing two opposite half waves after buckling.

127. Extension of Marguerre's Theory to Plates under Longitudinal Compression and Normal Loading

Marguerre considered in his paper only the effect of longitudinal compression acting in the plane of the plate. However, his method can be extended to include also the effect of normal loads p uniformly distributed over the plate. This will be done in this article, reusing as far as possible the analytical results of Arts. 121 and 122. More accurate solutions required for the analysis of very thin plates occurring in aeronautical engineering were given by Levy[2] and by Wang.[3]

The problem of plates in longitudinal compression carrying also normal loads occurs in the design of outer hull plating. The theoretical results derived in this article will be used in the following article to draw important conclusions on the limits of validity of a simplified method of analysis proposed for the design of outer hull plating of vessels.

We assume that the deflection w of the plate under the equally distributed normal load p and simultaneous longitudinal compression σ_A can again be expressed with sufficient accuracy by the expression (875):

$$w = f \cos \frac{\pi x}{a} \cos \frac{\pi y}{b} \qquad (925)$$

Equation (879), which gives an expression for the stress function F satisfying the differential equation (864) of the large deflection problem, is not affected by the presence of a lateral load p and remains valid. Therefore, Eqs. (880) to (883), being derived from Eq. (879), remain true. The deflection f occurring in these equations can be determined from the theorem of stationary potential energy. The strain energy V is given by Eq. (887), the potential energy U_w of the external loads p is

$$U_w = - \int_{-\frac{a}{2}}^{\frac{a}{2}} \int_{-\frac{b}{2}}^{\frac{b}{2}} pw \, dx \, dy$$

[1] Frankland, *op. cit.* on p. 477.

[2] Levy, *loc. cit.* on p. 482.

[3] Wang, C. T., Nonlinear Large-deflection Boundary-value Problems of Rectangular Plates, *NACA Tech. Note* 1425, 1948.

and upon introducing Eq. (925) we find

$$U_w = -\frac{4pab}{\pi^2} f \tag{926}$$

The condition

$$\frac{\partial(V + U_w)}{\partial f} = 0 \tag{927}$$

leads to the following equation for f:

$$\frac{Eabt}{1 - \nu^2} \left\{ -\frac{\pi^2 f}{4b^2} \left[\epsilon_1 \left(\frac{b^2}{a^2} + \nu \right) + \epsilon_2 \left(1 + \nu \frac{b^2}{a^2} \right) \right] \right.$$
$$\left. + \frac{\pi^4 f^3}{64b^4} \left[(3 - \nu^2) \left(1 + \frac{b^4}{a^4} \right) + 4\nu \frac{b^2}{a^2} \right] + \frac{\pi^4 t^2 f}{48b^4} \left(1 + \frac{b^2}{a^2} \right)^2 \right\} = \frac{4pab}{\pi^2} \tag{928}$$

Assuming that the side ratio $b/a > 0.7$, the plate buckles in one half wave, $n = 1$, and Eq. (634) gives the critical stress σ_c of the plate in longitudinal compression in the direction of x:

$$\sigma_c = \frac{\pi^2 E}{12(1 - \nu^2)} \left(\frac{t}{b} \right)^2 \left(\frac{a}{b} + \frac{b}{a} \right)^2 \tag{929}$$

The last term on the left-hand side of Eq. (928) can therefore be replaced by

$$(1 - \nu^2) \frac{\pi^2}{4b^2} \frac{\sigma_c}{E} \beta^2 f$$

and denoting $\beta = b/a$, we obtain

$$\frac{\pi^2 f^3}{16b^2} \left[(3 - \nu^2)(1 + \beta^4) + 4\nu\beta^2 \right]$$
$$- f \left[\epsilon_1 (\nu + \beta^2) + \epsilon_2 (1 + \nu\beta^2) - (1 - \nu^2)\beta^2 \frac{\sigma_c}{E} \right] = \frac{16(1 - \nu^2)b^2}{\pi^4 Et} p \tag{930}$$

Introducing $p_1 = \sigma_A$ and $p_2 = 0$ into Eqs. (882), we compute

$$\epsilon_1(\beta^2 + \nu) + \epsilon_2(1 + \nu\beta^2) = \frac{\sigma_A}{E} \beta^2(1 - \nu^2) + \frac{\pi^2 f^2}{8b^2} (\beta^4 + 2\nu\beta^2 + 1) \tag{931}$$

and Eq. (930) becomes

$$\frac{\pi^2 f^3}{16b^2} (1 + \beta^4) - \frac{f\beta^2}{E} (\sigma_A - \sigma_c) = \frac{16b^2 p}{\pi^4 Et}$$

It is convenient to write this equation in a nondimensional manner:

$$\left(\frac{f}{t} \right)^3 - \frac{16}{\pi^2} \frac{\beta^2}{1 + \beta^4} \left(\frac{\sigma_A}{\sigma_c} - 1 \right) \frac{\sigma_c}{E} \frac{b^2}{t^2} \left(\frac{f}{t} \right) - \frac{256}{\pi^6} \frac{1}{1 + \beta^4} \frac{pb^4}{Et^4} = 0 \tag{932}$$

Using Eq. (929) we compute

$$\frac{\sigma_c}{E} \frac{b^2}{t^2} = \frac{\pi^2}{12(1 - \nu^2)} \left(\beta + \frac{1}{\beta} \right)^2$$

Substituting this expression into the second term of Eq. (932), we obtain finally

$$\left(\frac{f}{t}\right)^3 - \frac{4}{3(1-\nu^2)}\frac{(1+\beta^2)^2}{1+\beta^4}\left(\frac{\sigma_A}{\sigma_c}-1\right)\left(\frac{f}{t}\right) - \frac{256}{\pi^6}\frac{1}{1+\beta^4}\frac{pb^4}{Et^4} = 0 \quad (933)$$

valid for $\beta = b/a > 0.7$. This equation is of the third degree in f/t and has one, and only one, real positive root which can be found for

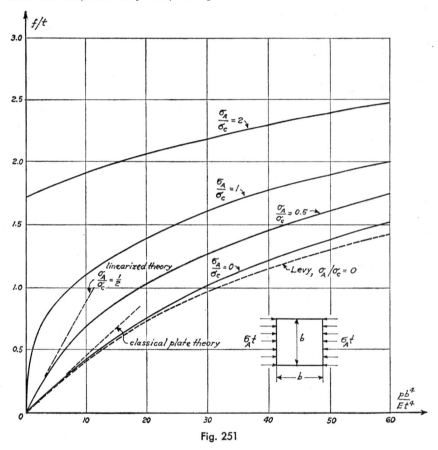

Fig. 251

given values of the ratios β, σ_A/σ_c, and pb^4/Et^4 by any of the conventional methods for solving equations of the third degree.

Equation (933) has been solved for square plates, $\beta = 1$, for $\sigma_A = 0$ and various values of pb^4/Et^4. Figure 251 shows the ratio f/t plotted versus pb^4/Et^4. For comparison the diagram computed by Levy[1] from his rigorous theory is represented by the dashed curve. The two curves for

[1] Levy, S., Bending of Rectangular Plates with Large Deflections, *NACA Tech. Note* 846, 1942, and *NACA Tech. Rept.* 737, 1942, p. 139.

$\sigma_A = 0$ deviate but slightly, indicating that Eq. (933) is sufficiently accurate if $pb^4/Et^4 < 60$, which is the case for hull plating. To illustrate the effect of longitudinal compression σ_A on normally loaded plates, further f/t-curves, computed for $\sigma_A/\sigma_c = 0.5$, 1, and 2, are also shown in Fig. 251.

Having found the numerical value of f, the membrane stresses $\bar{\sigma}_x$ and $\bar{\sigma}_y$ can be determined from Eqs. (880):

$$\left.\begin{aligned} \bar{\sigma}_x &= \sigma_A - \frac{E\pi^2 f^2}{8a^2} \cos\frac{2\pi y}{b} \\ \bar{\sigma}_y &= - \frac{E\pi^2 f^2}{8b^2} \cos\frac{2\pi x}{a} \end{aligned}\right\} \tag{934}$$

Positive values of $\bar{\sigma}_x$ and $\bar{\sigma}_y$ indicate compression. Maximum values $\bar{\sigma}_x$ and $\bar{\sigma}_y$ occur at the edges $x = \pm a/2$ and $y = \pm b/2$, respectively.

The membrane stresses given by the above equations are uniformly distributed over the thickness t of a strip of plate of unit width. In addition we have to superimpose the bending stresses caused by the curvature of the plate. These stresses vary linearly with the distance z of the fiber from the median surface of the plate, and the external fiber stresses σ_{xB} and σ_{yB} are given by

$$\begin{aligned} \sigma_{xB} &= \frac{6}{t^2} M_x = -\frac{6D}{t^2}\left(\frac{\partial^2 w}{\partial x^2} + \nu\frac{\partial^2 w}{\partial y^2}\right) \\ \sigma_{yB} &= \frac{6}{t^2} M_y = -\frac{6D}{t^2}\left(\frac{\partial^2 w}{\partial y^2} + \nu\frac{\partial^2 w}{\partial x^2}\right) \end{aligned}$$

Using Eq. (925) we obtain

$$\left.\begin{aligned} \sigma_{xB} &= \frac{\pi^2 E t f}{2(1-\nu^2)a^2}\left(1 + \nu\frac{a^2}{b^2}\right)\cos\frac{\pi x}{a}\cos\frac{\pi y}{b} \\ \sigma_{yB} &= \frac{\pi^2 E t f}{2(1-\nu^2)b^2}\left(1 + \nu\frac{b^2}{a^2}\right)\cos\frac{\pi x}{a}\cos\frac{\pi y}{b} \end{aligned}\right\} \tag{935}$$

The maximum bending stresses will occur at the center of the plate where $\cos\pi x/a = 1$ and $\cos\pi y/b = 1$.

Clamped Plates. The first large deflection theory for clamped rectangular plates under normal pressure was given by Way,[1] who applied the Ritz method using polynomials as expansion functions. The problem of the square plate under normal pressure was treated recently by Levy,[2]

---

[1] Way, S., Uniformly Loaded, Clamped, Rectangular Plates with Large Deflection, *Proc. 5th Intern. Congr. Applied Mechanics*, Cambridge, Mass., 1938, p. 123.

[2] Levy, S., Square Plate with Clamped Edges under Normal Pressure Producing Large Deflections, *NACA Tech. Note 847*, 1942, and *NACA Tech. Rept. 740*, 1942, p. 209.

who used a Fourier series method to solve the differential equations of the large deflection problem. Deflection and membrane stresses derived from Way's and Levy's analyses, respectively, agree very well. In another paper by Levy and Greenman[1] the series method was applied to plates of length-width ratio 1.5:1. Clamped plates under simultaneous longitudinal compression and normal pressure were discussed by Bengston.[2] As mentioned previosuly Bengston based his analysis in part on arbitrary assumptions, and the reliability of the results is questionable.

We will find in the next article that the conditions prevailing in hull plating are such that the deflections of clamped panels do not reach values requiring the use of the large deflection theory. This theory is therefore not required by the naval architect, whose needs can be satisfied by the much simpler theory discussed in the following article. This eliminates the necessity for detailed consideration of large deflection theories for clamped plates.

128. Design of Outer Hull Plating

The outer hull consists of rectangular panels of plate loaded by normal pressure from the surrounding water; in addition, the plates near the bottom of the vessel may be in longitudinal compression due to bending of the hull.

In the preceding article we have considered a large deflection theory for rectangular plates in longitudinal compression and under normal pressure, a theory that would appear applicable to the problem of hull plating. However, it is appropriate to consider whether a large deflection theory really need be used at all or the conditions are such that simpler theories, not assuming large deflections, are sufficient. It should be remembered that hull plating under normal pressure alone is usually analyzed by the conventional plate theory,[3] which does not assume large deflections; on the other hand, the much more complicated large deflection theory was found necessary for the study of the behavior of plates in longitudinal compression above the critical load. To decide just what type of theory should be used for the design of outer hull plating, we have to consider certain fundamental facts.

When analyzing the stresses in any structure, successive stages of theory can be used; depending on the accuracy required, these theories differ in the assumptions on the magnitude of the deflections. For our present purpose we divide the theories in three groups:

[1] Levy, S., and S. Greenman, Bending with Large Deflection of a Clamped Rectangular Plate with Length-Width Ratio of 1.5 under Normal Pressure, *NACA Tech. Note* 853, 1942.

[2] Bengston, *loc. cit.* on p. 462).

[3] Schade, H. A., Design Curves for Cross-stiffened Plating under Uniform Bending Load, *Proc. Soc. Naval Architects Marine Engrs.*, 1941.

Group 1: The theories assume that the deflections of the structure are so small that higher powers of the deflection can be neglected in the analysis and that the deflections have no effect whatsoever on the stresses. The classical theory of thin plates belongs in this group. The principle of superposition is applicable.

Group 2: While it is still assumed that the deflections are small enough to neglect their higher powers, for some types of structures an effect of the deformations on the stresses can be taken into account by retaining products of external loads and deflections in the analysis. We call such theories "linearized," because they are linear in the deflections. In such theories the deformations are not proportional to the external loads, and the principle of superposition is not valid.[1]

Group 3: Theories in this group consider at least the first two powers of the deflections in the analysis. The principle of superposition is, of course, not valid.

Considering for the moment hull plating under normal pressure but without longitudinal compression, the classical theory of plates in bending due to normal loads belongs to Group 1. We have already encountered the large deflection theory, Group 3, leading to the differential equations (864) and (865). For this particular problem no theory belonging to Group 2 exists, because for small values of w and F Eq. (865) becomes the classical differential equation of the plate. We have already mentioned that hull plates under normal pressure alone are analyzed by the classical plate theory, and the question arises as to the limit for the validity of this theory. The answer can be obtained from Fig. 251, in which the curve marked $\sigma_A/\sigma_c = 0$ shows the deflection f of a square plate according to the large deflection theory. The deflection according to the classical plate theory is represented by a straight line, which must be tangent to the above curve at the origin, because the two theories agree for very small values of the deflection and load. It is apparent that the difference between the curve and its tangent is not of practical importance as long as $f/t \leq 0.5$. This indicates that the classical theory may be used for design purposes up to deflections f equal to one-half the plate thickness but that for larger deflections the classical theory will give deflections and stresses which are 10% or more in excess of the actual values.

Now consider the case of normal load and simultaneous longitudinal

---

[1] An elementary example is the problem of a bar in compression P under simultaneous transverse loads p. The differential equation of the problem is

$$EIy^{IV} + Py'' = p$$

The term Py'' would be neglected in a theory of Group 1 and is the reason for the deformations not being proportional to the loads.

compression. Figure 251 shows a curve for $\sigma_A/\sigma_c = \frac{1}{2}$ derived from the large deflection theory. If we apply a theory of Group 1 to this problem, we have again the classical plate theory. Because of the law of superposition the longitudinal compression produces stresses σ_A but no deflection, and this theory gives the same deflections as if no longitudinal stresses were present. Figure 251 shows very clearly that the classical and the large deflection theories give very different results even for small deflections. However, it is possible to obtain an approximation to the large deflection theory by replacing the curve $\sigma_A/\sigma_c = \frac{1}{2}$ in Fig. 251 by its tangent at the origin. This line represents a "linearized" theory belonging to Group 2. We can obtain the linearized theory from the large deflection theory by suppressing higher powers of f in the final Eq. (933). In this way we obtain

$$\frac{4}{3(1 - \nu^2)} \frac{(1 + \beta^2)^2}{1 + \beta^4} \left(1 - \frac{\sigma_A}{\sigma_c}\right)\frac{f}{t} = \frac{256}{\pi^6 (1 + \beta^4)} \frac{pb^4}{Et^4} \tag{936}$$

The result is shown for $\sigma_A/\sigma_c = \frac{1}{2}$ in Fig. 251, indicating that the linearized theory gives sufficiently accurate results as long as $f/t \leq \frac{1}{2}$. While Fig. 251 indicates only the deflections of square plates, the finding that the linearized theory can be used for $f/t \leq \frac{1}{2}$ is valid for other side ratios too as long as $\sigma_A < \sigma_c$. The linearized theory is of little use if σ_A is close to σ_c but could be used again if $\sigma_A > \sigma_c$. This, however, is of no importance for the design of hull plating, where σ_A will always be less than σ_c.

Equation (936), which represents the linearized relationship between the deflection f and the loads σ_A and p, is capable of a far-reaching and extremely useful interpretation. We can apply Eq. (936) to plates without longitudinal compression by substituting $\sigma_A = 0$. Denoting the deflection for this case by f_1, we have

$$\frac{4}{3(1 - \nu^2)} \frac{(1 + \beta^2)^2 f_1}{1 + \beta^4} \frac{f_1}{t} = \frac{256}{\pi^6 (1 + \beta^4)} \frac{pb^4}{Et^4} \tag{937}$$

The right-hand sides of Eqs. (936) and (937) being alike, the left-hand sides must also be alike, and after cancellations we obtain

$$f = \frac{f_1}{1 - \sigma_A/\sigma_c} \tag{938}$$

This equation is of extreme practical usefulness. It states that the deflection f of a plate under normal load and simultaneous longitudinal compression can be found from the deflection f_1 of the same plate under normal load alone. The deflection f_1 need not be determined from the linearized theory but can be taken from the classical plate theory, the results of which are known and easily available. To find the deflection

f we have to multiply the deflection f_1 according to the plate theory by a "magnification factor" m which indicates the effect of the longitudinal force. The bending stresses being proportional to the deflections, the same factor m applies to the bending stresses also. The value of this magnification factor is

$$m = \frac{1}{1 - (\sigma_A/\sigma_c)} \tag{939}$$

All equations used so far in this article applied to simply supported plates and were derived in a rather roundabout way from the large deflection theory. We shall derive similar linearized equations in the next article in a more direct manner applicable also to clamped plates. Before approaching this question, we shall examine whether the linearized theory can be expected to be valid for hull plating of conventional thickness.

We have concluded from Fig. 251 that the linearized theory for simply supported plates is sufficiently accurate if $f/t \leq \frac{1}{2}$. It may be recalled that the cubic term in Eq. (933), which indicates the effect of large deflections, is due to membrane stresses in the plane of the plate. The magnitude of these membrane stresses being essentially a function of the deflection f at the center of the plate, we can conclude that the membrane stresses even for a clamped plate will have little effect if $f/t \leq \frac{1}{2}$. This conclusion can be confirmed from Bengston's theory for clamped plates.[1]

The largest deflections f which need be considered are the ones at which yielding of the material of the plates occurs. These maximum deflections, at which yielding just occurs, were determined from Schade's diagrams[2] for rectangular plates under normal loads and are shown in Table 50. The largest possible f/t ratios are functions of σ_y/E and of the ratios a/t or b/t, whichever is smaller.

The last column of Table 50 gives the deflection ratios f/t for the thinnest plates of H.T. steel which are likely to occur. For the clamped plates f/t is less than $\frac{1}{2}$, but not for the simply supported plates, where f/t may reach unity. The results in Table 50 apply to plates without longitudinal compression; if we consider that the presence of longitudinal stresses of, say, $\sigma_A = \sigma_y/4$ or $\sigma_A = \sigma_y/2$ reduces the permissible bending stress and therefore reduces these ratios to $\frac{3}{4}$ or $\frac{1}{2}$ of above values, we can conclude that in most cases f/t will be less than $\frac{1}{2}$ but that occasional values up to $f/t = 0.8$ might occur.

To summarize, we have found that the linearized theory will always be valid for clamped rectangular plates, while simply supported panels

[1] Bengston, *loc. cit.* on p. 462.
[2] Schade, *loc. cit.* on p. 484.

may have too large deflections for its use. In the case of simply supported panels where $f/t > 0.5$, the linearized theory gives too large values of deflections and moments. It will be seen in the next article that the linearized theory can still be utilized in the range $0.5 < f/t \leq 0.8$ if an appropriate correction factor is used.

TABLE 50. Maximum Values of f/t for Rectangular Plates under Normal Loads

All four sides are—	Ratio a/b	Value of f/t for any material	Value of f/t for H.T. steel	
			$\sigma_y = 45$ kips/in.^{2}, $E = 29{,}600$ kips/in.^{2}	$a/t = 60$ or $b/t = 60$
Simply supported	$\frac{1}{3}$	$0.186\ (a/t)^2\ \sigma_y/E$	$2.83 \times 10^{-4}\ (a/t)^2$	1.01^*
	1	$0.154\ (b/t)^2\ \sigma_y/E$	$2.34 \times 10^{-4}\ (b/t)^2$	$0.84\dagger$
	3	$0.186\ (b/t)^2\ \sigma_y/E$	$2.83 \times 10^{-4}\ (b/t)^2$	$1.01\dagger$
Clamped	$\frac{1}{3}$	$0.056\ (a/t)^2\ \sigma_y/E$	$0.94 \times 10^{-4}\ (a/t)^2$	0.34^*
	1	$0.042\ (b/t)^2\ \sigma_y/E$	$0.64 \times 10^{-4}\ (b/t)^2$	$0.23\dagger$
	3	$0.056\ (b/t)^2\ \sigma_y/E$	$0.94 \times 10^{-4}\ (b/t)^2$	$0.34\dagger$

* $a/t = 60$.
† $b/t = 60$.

129. Linearized Theory for the Design of Outer Hull Plating

In the preceding article we concluded that the linearized theory is sufficient for the design of hull plating, except in rather rare cases of simply supported panels where f/t may exceed $\frac{1}{2}$. In this article we shall consider the well-known linearized theory and simplify it for design purposes by introducing the concept of the magnification factor encountered in the preceding article.

The differential equation of the linearized theory is[1]

$$\frac{\partial^4 w}{\partial x^4} + 2\frac{\partial^4 w}{\partial x^2\,\partial y^2} + \frac{\partial^4 w}{\partial y^4} + \frac{t}{D}\sigma_x\frac{\partial^2 w}{\partial x^2} = \frac{p}{D} \tag{940}$$

This equation is the differential equation of elastic buckling [Eq. (600)] to which the load term p/D has been added. It is linear in w and its derivatives but contains a product of load and deflection which causes a nonlinear relationship between the loads and deflections.

Equation (940) has been solved for simply supported rectangular plates by series,[2] but the results are not available in tabulated form or diagrams suitable for routine design. Solutions for clamped plates have not been derived and are not available. Approximate solutions of

[1] Timoshenko, S., "Theory of Plates and Shells," p. 301, McGraw-Hill Book Company, Inc., New York, 1940.
[2] *Ibid.*, pp. 302, 308.

the problem for various types of support will be derived here by the energy method, and we shall see in the following how the magnification factor appears in these derivations.

We consider the rectangular plate (Fig. 252) under the action of normal pressure p and longitudinal loads σ_A in the x-direction.   In order to obtain the expression for the potential energy of the system in the simplest manner, we elect to compute the changes of potential energy with reference to a state in which the plate carries the longitudinal loads σ_A, but no normal load.   If we now add the normal loads p, the plate will deflect, and the change in the strain energy of bending of the plate will be given by Eq. (869).   In a general case we should also have a change of strain energy due to membrane stresses in the

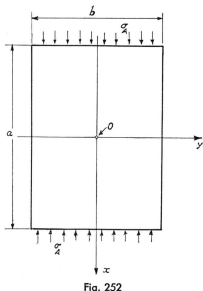

Fig. 252

plane of the plate, but because we do not change σ_A and neglect higher powers of w, the change in the membrane strain energy is zero, and we have

$$V = \frac{D}{2} \int_{-\frac{a}{2}}^{\frac{a}{2}} \int_{-\frac{b}{2}}^{\frac{b}{2}} \left(\frac{\partial^2 w}{\partial x^2} + \frac{\partial^2 w}{\partial y^2} \right)^2 dx\, dy \qquad (941)$$

The change of the potential energy U_w of the external loads p and σ_A is

$$U_w = - \int_{-\frac{a}{2}}^{\frac{a}{2}} \int_{-\frac{b}{2}}^{\frac{b}{2}} \left[pw + \frac{\sigma_A}{2} \left(\frac{\partial w}{\partial x} \right)^2 \right] dx\, dy \qquad (942)$$

The first term in this equation represents the change of the potential energy of the loads p; the second term is the change in the potential energy of the longitudinal loads σ_A, which is solely due to the shortening of the plate because of the deflection.

The potential energy U is therefore

$$U = \int_{-\frac{a}{2}}^{\frac{a}{2}} \int_{-\frac{b}{2}}^{\frac{b}{2}} \left[\frac{D}{2} \left(\frac{\partial^2 w}{\partial x^2} + \frac{\partial^2 w}{\partial y^2} \right)^2 - \frac{\sigma_A}{2} \left(\frac{\partial w}{\partial x} \right)^2 - pw \right] dx\, dy \quad (943)$$

Assuming a series expression for w, the deflection of the plate can be determined by the Ritz method.   Using only the first term of such a series,

$$w = c\varphi(x,y) \tag{944}$$

where c is an unknown constant and $\varphi(x,y)$ a function of x and y satisfying the boundary conditions, we can determine the deflection by Timoshenko's method[1] from Eq. (93). Because the external work W in Eq. (93) is equal[2] to U_w, we can write this equation simply as

$$U = 0 \tag{945}$$

Substituting Eq. (944) into (943) we determine in this manner the unknown coefficient c:

$$c = \frac{p\iint\varphi\,dx\,dy}{\dfrac{D}{2}\iint\left(\dfrac{\partial^2\varphi}{\partial x^2} + \dfrac{\partial^2\varphi}{\partial y^2}\right)^2 dx\,dy - \dfrac{\sigma_A}{2}\iint\left(\dfrac{\partial\varphi}{\partial x}\right)^2 dx\,dy} \tag{946}$$

where the limits of the integrals have been omitted for brevity. We can apply Eq. (946) also to the case of a plate without longitudinal compression σ_A. Denoting the deflection in this case by w_1 and the value of c by c_1, we have

$$w_1 = c_1\varphi(x,y) \tag{947}$$

$$c_1 = \frac{p\iint\varphi\,dx\,dy}{\dfrac{D}{2}\iint\left(\dfrac{\partial^2\varphi}{\partial x^2} + \dfrac{\partial^2\varphi}{\partial y^2}\right)^2 dx\,dy} \tag{948}$$

Dividing Eq. (946) by Eq. (948) we obtain a relation

$$c = mc_1 \tag{949}$$

where the magnification factor m is defined as

$$m = \frac{1}{1 - \dfrac{\sigma_A}{D}\dfrac{\iint\left(\dfrac{\partial\varphi}{\partial x}\right)^2 dx\,dy}{\iint\left(\dfrac{\partial^2\varphi}{\partial x^2} + \dfrac{\partial^2\varphi}{\partial y^2}\right)^2 dx\,dy}} \tag{950}$$

From Eq. (944), (947), and (949) we conclude that

$$w = mw_1 \tag{951}$$

which means that the deflections w can be obtained from the deflections w_1 of a plate under normal loads alone. The bending stresses in the plate being proportional to the second derivatives of w_1, the magnification factor can also be applied to these stresses. Denoting the maximum fiber stresses in the x- and y-directions in the plate due to normal load combined with longitudinal compression by σ_x and σ_y, respectively, and

[1] See p. 75.
[2] See the footnote on p. 76.

the corresponding bending stresses in a plate under normal loads alone by σ_{xB} and σ_{yB}, we obtain

$$\left.\begin{array}{l} \sigma_x = \sigma_A + m\sigma_{xB} \\ \sigma_y = m\sigma_{yB} \end{array}\right\} \tag{952}$$

The relations (951) and (952) are based on the assumption that one coordinate function φ is sufficient to represent the deflection. If more than one coordinate function is used, more complicated expressions ensue, but due to the fact that the first coordinate function, if suitably chosen, is of paramount importance, Eqs. (951) and (952) are very good approximations within certain limits stated below.

There is no reason to compute the deflection w_1 and the stresses σ_{xb} and σ_{yB} in a plate under normal loads alone by the energy method, as these deflections and stresses can be conveniently obtained from Schade's diagrams.[1] To be able to apply Eqs. (951) and (952) in conjunction

TABLE 51

	Coordinate function φ	k
Case 1, Fig. 253.......	$(1 + \cos 2\pi x/a)(1 + \cos 2\pi y/b)$	$4a^2/b^2 + \frac{8}{3} + 4b^2/a^2$
Case 2, Fig. 254.......	$(\cos \pi x/a)(\cos \pi y/b)$	$a^2/b^2 + 2 + b^2/a^2$
Case 3, Fig. 255.......	$(1 + \cos 2\pi x/a) \cos \pi y/b$	$3a^2/4b^2 + 1 + 4b^2/a^2$
Case 4, Fig. 256.......	$(\cos \pi x/a)(1 + \cos 2\pi y/b)$	$16a^2/3b^2 + \frac{8}{3} + b^2/a^2$

with these diagrams we must evaluate the general expression (950) for the magnification factor for various boundary conditions. The magnification factor can be expressed in the general form

$$m = \cfrac{1}{1 - \cfrac{\sigma_A}{\cfrac{\pi^2 E}{12(1 - \nu^2)}\left(\cfrac{t}{b}\right)^2 k}} \tag{953}$$

For steel this equation becomes

$$m = \cfrac{1}{1 - \cfrac{\sigma_A}{26{,}750(t/b)^2 k}} \tag{954}$$

where σ_A is in kips per square inch. Table 51 shows the coordinate functions assumed and the expressions for the coefficient k obtained for four conditions of support of the plate:

Case 1. All edges clamped (Fig. 253).
Case 2. All edges simply supported (Fig. 254).

[1] Schade, *loc. cit.* on p. 484.

Case 3. Loaded edges clamped, longitudinal edges simply supported (Fig. 255).

Case 4. Loaded edges simply supported, longitudinal edges clamped Fig. (256).

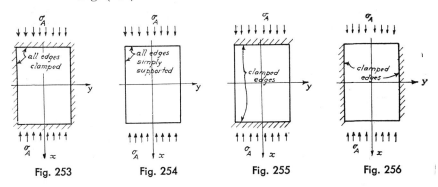

Fig. 253   Fig. 254   Fig. 255   Fig. 256

The numerical values of k for various aspect ratios a/b are shown in Table 52. It should be mentioned that the expression $26{,}750\,(t/b)^2 k$ in Eq. (954) has the dimension of a stress and is in certain cases equal to or

TABLE 52. Values of k in Eqs. (953) and (954)

a/b	Case 1, Fig. 253	Case 2, Fig. 254	Case 3, Fig. 255	Case 4, Fig. 256
0.4	28.31	8.41	26.12	9.77
0.6	15.22	5.14	12.39	7.37
0.8	11.48	4.20	7.72	7.64
1.0	10.67	4.00	5.75	9.00
1.2	11.21	4.13	4.84	11.04
1.4	12.55	4.47	4.51	13.63
1.6	14.47	4.95	4.48	16.71
1.8	16.86	5.55	4.67	20.26
2.0	19.67	6.25	5.00	24.25
2.2	22.86	7.05	5.47	28.69
2.4	26.40	7.93	6.00	33.56
2.6	30.30	8.91	6.67	38.87
2.8	34.54	9.97	7.40	44.61
3.0	39.11	11.11	8.19	50.78
3.2	44.02	12.34	9.08	57.38
3.4	49.26	13.65	10.03	64.41
3.6	54.82	15.04	11.04	71.87
3.8	60.71	16.51	12.11	79.73
4.0	66.92	18.06	13.25	88.06

approximately equal to the critical stress of the plate, and the factor k is equal to the plate factor for buckling.   This is, however, not always the case; if the plates are not square, k in Table 52 may differ substantially from the factor k for buckling.

Limits for Use of Magnification Factor m.   Equations (951) to (954) are applicable only if the following three conditions are satisfied:

1. The maximum deflection f computed by means of Eq. (951) must be less than $t/2$, where t is the thickness of the plate.
2. The longitudinal compressive stress σ_A must be less than the proportional limit of the material.
3. The longitudinal compressive stress σ_A must be less than the critical buckling load σ_c of the plate.

The reasons for the first condition have been discussed at length in the preceding article.   In order to appreciate the error to be expected if the theory were applied in the range $0.5 < f/t < 0.8$ which may occur in simply supported plate panels, Fig. 257 illustrates the error resulting from the use of the linearized theory. The figure shows the reduction of the deflections if the more accurate Eq. (933) is used instead of the linearized theory.   The reduction is plotted versus the f/t ratio according to the linearized theory, and curves for $b/a = 1$ and 3 are shown.   It appears

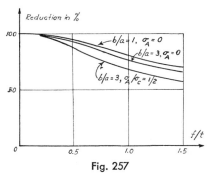

Fig. 257

from Fig. 257 that, for the range $0.6 < f/t < 0.8$, the error in the linearized theory could be reduced somewhat by using a magnification factor of $0.9m$ instead of m.

The second condition is necessary because we have assumed fully elastic behavior of the plate.   This condition will usually be satisfied, because if σ_A were above the elastic limit, the plate could carry only very little additional normal load.

The third condition is necessary because the magnification concept is based on the assumption that the one coordinate function listed in Table 51 is sufficient to express the deflection; in most cases this is no longer true if $\sigma_A \geq \sigma_c$, and Eqs. (952) would give stresses much too low.   In the design of hull plating the case $\sigma_A \geq \sigma_c$ cannot possibly occur in any actual design, because, according to Table 49, plates having a side-to-thickness ratio $a/t < 60$ or $b/t < 60$ have an ultimate strength which lies less than 25% above the buckling strength.   Such plates obviously would not be able to carry any appreciable normal load p in addition to longitudinal compression $\sigma_A \geq \sigma_c$.

Table 52 contains the coefficient k for the computation of the magnification factors for plates with freely supported or clamped edges. Actually, hull plating is usually continuous over many spans. If the spans are equal and the load p constant, it is apparent from Fig. 258 that each individual panel can be considered for purposes of stress analysis as clamped at the edges. The question arises whether it is permissible to make the same assumption when computing the critical buckling stress σ_c which must be done to ensure that Condition 3 is satisfied. A continuous plate without normal load will buckle in waves alternatively to the inside and to the outside, as shown in Fig. 259. If the normal pressure is small enough, it cannot be assumed that the pressure p can prevent

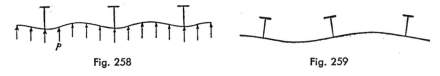

Fig. 258   Fig. 259

buckling according to Fig. 259; if the normal pressure is large, it might conceivably force the plate to buckle like a clamped plate. This important problem will be considered in detail in the next article.

The stress analysis of plates under normal pressure and longitudinal compression by the linearized theory presented in this article is simple and easy to apply. It should be repeated, however, that it is necessary to ascertain in every individual case that the three conditions listed above are satisfied. Condition 3, requiring $\sigma_A < \sigma_c$, is of particular importance, and therefore the critical stress σ_c of the plating must always be computed.

130. Effect of Normal Pressure on the Buckling Strength of Rectangular Plates

The fact that eccentricity of the axial load or additional lateral loads may have a disastrous effect on the buckling strength of a straight column gave rise to the question whether normal pressure applied to a plate supported on all four edges also reduces, to a more or less considerable extent, the critical load of a plate. In the previous article it was pointed out that a plate, after reaching the stability limit, behaves in a manner which is fundamentally different from a straight column and that the actual failure load of the plate occurs under a compressive load which may exceed many times the critical load. Hence, there is some reason to assume that the peculiar mechanism in the plate which operates to stabilize the equilibrium beyond the buckling load may also work to help stabilize the equilibrium between external and internal forces of a normally loaded plate in longitudinal compression, with the result of actually delaying the incipient state of buckling of the plate.

To investigate the stability condition of a plate under the aforementioned loading, it is necessary to base the analysis upon a sufficiently rigorous solution of the basic nonlinear differential equations (864) and (865) of the large deflection theory and to study the successively changing displacement forms under varying loading conditions.

In a recently published paper Levy, Goldenberg, and Zibritosky[1] reported on the results of an extensive theoretical investigation into the

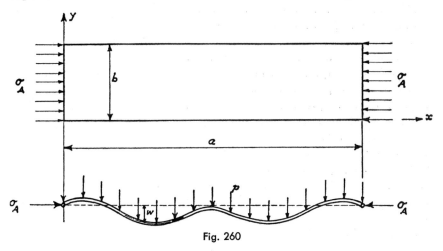

Fig. 260

behavior of very thin simply supported rectangular plates of length-width ratio 4 to 1 under combined normal pressure and longitudinal compression (Fig. 260). The mathematical analysis is based on the general solution outlined in Levy's paper on plates with large deflections.[2] Approximating the deflection w by a symmetric Fourier expansion with four indeterminate constants c_i,

$$w = c_1 \sin \frac{\pi x}{a} \sin \frac{\pi y}{b} + c_3 \sin \frac{3\pi x}{a} \sin \frac{\pi y}{b} + c_5 \sin \frac{5\pi x}{a} \sin \frac{\pi y}{b}$$
$$+ c_7 \sin \frac{7\pi x}{a} \sin \frac{\pi y}{b} \quad (955)$$

the authors arrive at a system of four simultaneous equations of the third degree which determine the relationship between the axial and normal loads and the deflection coefficients c_i. Solution of these equations by a

[1] Levy, S., D. Goldenberg, and G. Zibritosky, Simply Supported Long Rectangular Plate under Combined Axial Load and Normal Pressure, *NACA Tech. Note* 949, 1944.

[2] Levy, *loc. cit.* on p. 482.

specially devised method furnishes the deflections and the average longitudinal strain of the loaded plate. The analysis is based on the assumption of elastic behavior of the plate.

The laborious numerical investigations yield the following results which are of fundamental significance:

"The buckling load is considerably increased by normal pressure. For the highest pressure considered, the theoretical buckling load is 3.1 times the buckling load for zero normal pressure. Normal pressure causes a decrease in effective width at strains below the normal buckling strain and an increase in effective width for strains somewhat greater than the normal buckling strain. If the buckling load is considerably exceeded, however, normal pressure causes less than 1 per cent increase in effective width. For some combinations of normal pressure and axial load the plate can be in equilibrium in more than one position. Under such circumstances it is possible for the plate to be either unbuckled or buckled, depending on the previous history of loading.

"The axial load at which buckling occurs is $\sigma_A = 3.84Et^3/b$ when $p = 0$; $\sigma_A = 4.05Et^3/b$ when $p = 2.40Et^4/b^4$; $\sigma_A = 8.56Et^3/b$ when $p = 12.02Et^4/b^4$, and $\sigma_A = 11.84Et^3/b$ when $p = 24.03Et^4/b^4$."

In another paper the behavior of plates clamped on all four sides was investigated.[1] The following results were found again for plates having a length-width ratio 4 to 1. The axial load p at which buckling first occurs is $\sigma_A = 6.4Et^3/b$ when $p = 0$; $\sigma_A = 6.8Et^3/b$ when $p = 15.02Et^4/b^4$, and $\sigma_A = 8.3Et^3/b$ when $p = 37.55Et^4/b^4$. The buckling load at the highest normal pressure was 1.3 times the buckling load for $p = 0$. Normal pressure causes a much smaller increase in buckling load of a plate with fixed edges than of a plate with simply supported edges. The authors conclude:

"For low axial stresses the displacement form of the plate is a single long bulge which gradually builds up to a regular buckle pattern at increasing values of the compressive stress. The initial general downward deflection of the plate due to normal pressure p tends to disappear at high axial loads."

The effect of lateral load upon the buckling strength of plates was experimentally studied, and at least qualitative agreement with the theoretical predictions has been found.[2] The theoretically assumed conditions of support at the edges could not be actually realized. The tests showed that in the case of larger width-thickness ratios b/t the conditions of fixed edges were approximately fulfilled whereas in the case of

[1] Corrick, J. N., and S. Levy, Clamped Long Rectangular Plates under Combined Axial Load and Normal Pressure, *NACA Tech. Note* 1047, 1946.

[2] McPherson, A. E., S. Levy, and G. Zibritosky, Effect of Normal Pressure on Strength of Axially Loaded Sheet-stringer Panels, *NACA Tech. Note* 1041, 1946.

smaller ratios b/t the degree of restraint at the edges deviated considerably from the condition of clamped edges.

The theoretical studies quoted above indicate that the buckling load
of rectangular plates increases considerably when sufficiently large normal
loads are present.   It appears also that simply supported plates are more
affected than clamped plates.   The question arises whether the normal
loads in the case of bottom plating are sufficiently large to produce a
noticeable effect on the buckling load or not.   This question can be
decided by considering the magnitude of the deflections of the plate.   The
increase in buckling strength is essentially due to the tensile membrane

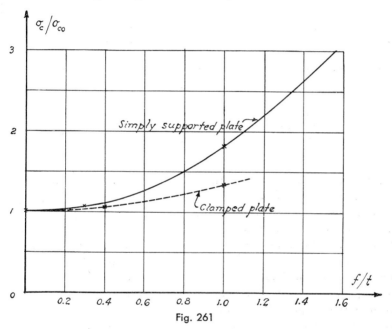

Fig. 261

stresses which are caused by the deflection of the plate under normal load,
and we expect therefore that the magnitude of these deflections is related
to the increase in buckling strength.   This is borne out by Fig. 261,
which shows for the two plates considered above the ratio of the buckling
stress σ_c to the buckling stress σ_{c0} for $p = 0$.   The ratios are plotted as a
function of the ratio f/t.   Hull plating is continuous and acts, under
normal load, like a clamped plate; it was shown in Art. 128 that the deflection of such plating in ships' hulls cannot exceed $f/t = 0.4$.   This deflection is so small that, according to Fig. 261, the increase of buckling
strength is insignificant and of no practical importance.

The above reasoning also contains the clue to the problem, mentioned
at the end of the preceding article, whether continuous bottom plating

carrying normal load will buckle as clamped or as simply supported. A continuous plate under normal load will deflect as shown in Fig. 258. If additional longitudinal compression due to bending of the hull occurs, the possibility of buckling exists. The question is whether the normal load can prevent the lowest buckling deformation as shown in Fig. 259 and can force the plate to buckle like a clamped plate.

This problem is really quite similar to the one of the buckling of a plate of length-width ratio 4 to 1 discussed above. Under normal loads alone a one-wave deformation occurs in this plate, indicated in Fig. 262, which shows the longitudinal profile of the deflected surface. If longitudinal

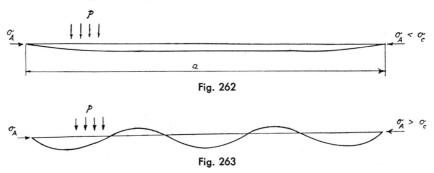

Fig. 262

Fig. 263

compression is added, the deformation will remain of the one-wave type until the buckling load is reached. Above the buckling load the deflection is in five waves, as shown in Fig. 263, the type of deformation changing rapidly in the vicinity of the buckling load. The normal load does not prevent the appearance of the usual buckle pattern, but delays it by raising the critical load. Similarly, it may be expected that the normal pressure on a continuous plate will delay, but not prevent, the usual buckle pattern according to Fig. 259. Knowing that the deflection of the continuous hull plating shown in Fig. 258 cannot exceed $f/t = 0.4$, we can conclude that the membrane stresses will again be small and the critical load will only be slightly higher than in a plate without normal pressure.

It is therefore recommended to compute the critical load of outer hull plating as if the normal pressure were not present. This conclusion applies also to plating forming part of double or triple bottoms. The stability of such plating should be analyzed by the method given in Art. 118 without regard to normal pressure.

AUTHOR INDEX

SUBJECT INDEX

A

Analytical stability criterion for plane frameworks, 196–209
  modification of, 210–213
Angles, outstanding legs of, 342–343, 347
Approximate method, of finite differences, 87–91
  Ritz (*see* Ritz method)
  successive approximation, 81–87
  Timoshenko (*see* Timoshenko's energy method)
Axis, of rotation, enforced, 138–142, 163–164

B

Bars, bent and twisted, potential energy of, 107–113
  elastically supported (*see* Elastically supported bars)
Batten plates, 175, 183
Battened columns, 175–179
Beams, lateral buckling of (*see* Lateral buckling of beams)
Bending moments, effect on buckling strength of frames, 222–231, 266–267
Bleich's method in stability of frameworks, 196–213
Box sections, 333–337, 346
Buckling, as characteristic value problem, 62–64
  lateral (*see* Lateral buckling of beams)
  local (*see* Local buckling)
  mathematical treatment of, 61–103
Built-up columns, 167–169
  battened, 175–179
  laced, 169–175, 182–186
  secondary stresses in, 183–186
  local failure of, 179–182
  of varying moment of inertia, 186–191

C

Calculus of variations, boundary conditions, 99–103

Calculus of variations, integrals, containing a function of one independent variable, 93–96
  containing a function of two independent variables, 97–99
  containing several functions of one independent variable, 97
  introduction to, 91–93
Cellular cross sections, hull plates of ships with, 441–453
Centrally loaded columns, where center of shear coincides with centroid, 128–132
  with one axis of symmetry, 132–138
  potential energy of, 123–127
  torsion and flexure in, 104–107
Channel-sections, outstanding flanges of, 339–340, 347
  web plates in, 337–339, 347
Chords, of pony trusses, effect of torsion on, 294–300
  stability of, as elastically supported bars, 268–301
Clamped plates, 437–441
Coefficient of restraint, plate buckling, 318, 331–343
Column curve, 21–23
Column formula, 54
Columns, battened, 175–179
  buckling loads of, effect of shear stresses, 23–25
  built-up (*see* Built-up columns)
  centrally loaded (*see* Centrally loaded columns)
  design of, 51–54
  safety in, 54–56
  eccentrically loaded (*see* Eccentrically loaded columns)
  laced, 169–175, 182–186
  plate elements of (*see* Plates)
  straight, buckling of, elastic, 4–8
  of varying moment of inertia, 186–191
  inelastic, 8–21

503